TEST BANK FOR

FOR STARR AND TAGGART'S
BIOLOGY
the unity and diversity of life

TENTH EDITION

Larry G. Sellers
Louisiana Tech University

Allen Reich
Harvard University

Kendall Corbin
University of Minnesota

Jane B. Taylor
Northern Virginia Community College

John Jackson
North Hennepin Community College

Tommy E. Wynn
North Carolina State University

D1501365

THOMSON
™
BROOKS/COLE

Australia • Canada • Mexico • Singapore • Spain • United Kingdom • United States

Printed in the United States of America
1 2 3 4 5 6 7 07 06 05 04 03

Printer: Victor Graphics, Inc.

0-534-39755-7

For more information about our products, contact us at:
Thomson Learning Academic Resource Center
1-800-423-0563

For permission to use material from this text,
contact us by:
Phone: 1-800-730-2214
Fax: 1-800-731-2215
Web: http://www.thomsonrights.com

Asia
Thomson Learning
5 Shenton Way #01-01
UIC Building
Singapore 068808

Australia/New Zealand
Thomson Learning
102 Dodds Street
Southbank, Victoria 3006
Australia

Canada
Nelson
1120 Birchmount Road
Toronto, Ontario M1K 5G4
Canada

Europe/Middle East/South Africa
Thomson Learning
High Holborn House
50/51 Bedford Row
London WC1R 4LR
United Kingdom

Latin America
Thomson Learning
Seneca, 53
Colonia Polanco
11560 Mexico D.F.
Mexico

Spain/Portugal
Paraninfo
Calle/Magallanes, 25
28015 Madrid, Spain

Test Bank Contents

Preface

This book contains more than 4,500 test bank questions to accompany Starr and Taggart's *Biology: The Unity and Diversity of Life,* Tenth Edition. The test bank questions are available on disk through the Faculty Support Department of Brooks/Cole or your local Brooks/Cole representative.

We hope you find these questions useful, and we welcome any comments that will help to improve them.

Several instructors contributed to the test bank, including three who have extensive experience writing questions for the Educational Testing Service. Eight reviewers also have contributed valuable suggestions to help eliminate inadvertent ambiguity and to check for possible errors. The test bank represents a consensus of the kind of questions that are most suitable for students.

All questions are ranked according to level of difficulty (E = Easy, M = Moderate, and D = Difficult). (On the disk version of the test bank, because of the requirements of the test-generator program, 1 = Easy, 3 = Moderate, and 5 = Difficult.) Each rank is represented by about a third of the total questions. The test bank includes the following categories:

1. Multiple-choice questions.
2. Matching questions.
3. Classification questions, which use the same group of answers for a series of questions.
4. Select the Exception questions, which require the student to select the exception from four or five given answers.
5. Problems, which appear only in two of the genetics chapters.

CHAPTER 1
CONCEPTS AND METHODS IN BIOLOGY

Multiple-Choice Questions

E 1. Which of the following would NOT be a key characteristic of "life"?
  a. organization into cells
  b. response to environmental change
  c. reproduction
  * d. inability to change
  e. using energy

E 2. Life
  a. is difficult to define.
  b. is viewed differently by different people.
  c. may be characterized, but not fully understood.
  d. has a history of several billion years.
  * e. all of these

M 3. The study of biology is important because
  * a. it provides an understanding of life.
  b. it is essential for humans to understand how organisms survive.
  c. it is the most difficult and comprehensive of the sciences.
  d. it explains the nature of the universe.

DNA, ENERGY, AND LIFE

M 4. Nonliving entities would NOT possess
  a. energetic interactions.
  * b. DNA.
  c. atoms.
  d. elements.
  e. any of these

M 5. The DNA molecule is most similar functionally to a
  a. pair of scissors.
  b. flashlight battery.
  * c. computer memory chip.
  d. ballpoint pen.
  e. craft kit of ceramic tiles.

E 6. Which is the smallest unit of life that can exist as a separate entity?
  * a. a cell
  b. a molecule
  c. an organ
  d. a population
  e. an ecosystem

E 7. Living organisms are different from inanimate objects because they
  a. react to environmental stimuli.
  b. exhibit massive complexity.
  c. possess molecules of deoxyribonucleic acid.
  d. exhibit multiple levels of organization.
  * e. all of these

D 8. Living organisms are members of all of the levels listed below; however, rocks are components of
  a. the community.
  b. the population.
  c. the ecosystem.
  d. the biosphere.
  * e. both the ecosystem and the biosphere.

E 9. The flow of energy among living organisms is best characterized as a
  a. circle.
  b. ladder.
  c. lattice.
  * d. web.
  e. funnel.

E 10. During metabolism, ATP (adenosine triphosphate) is an energy source for which of the following processes?
  I.   reproduction
  II. growth
  III. development
  a. I and II
  b. I and III
  c. II only
  d. II and III
  * e. I, II, and III

E 11. The ability to acquire, store, transfer, or utilize energy is called
  a. biochemistry.
  b. photosynthesis.
  * c. metabolism.
  d. respiration.
  e. phosphorylation.

D 12. Energy transfers take place at what organizational level?
  * a. molecule
  b. organelle
  c. cell
  d. organ
  e. organism

E 13. Homeostasis provides what kind of environment?
   a. positive
 * b. constant
   c. limiting
   d. changing
   e. chemical and physical

D 14. Which of the following phrases would most likely be used in a discussion of homeostasis?
   a. respond to environmental stimuli
 * b. limited range of variation
   c. rapid energy turnover
   d. cycle of elements
   e. structural and functional units of life

M 15. The conversion of solar energy to chemical energy is known as
   a. metabolism.
 * b. photosynthesis.
   c. chemosynthesis.
   d. catabolism.
   e. anabolism.

D 16. Metabolic reactions would most likely be described during a discussion of
 * a. energy transduction.
   b. cellular organization.
   c. responses to environmental stimuli.
   d. perpetuation of the species.
   e. none of the above

E 17. Each cell is able to maintain a constant internal environment. This is called
   a. metabolism.
 * b. homeostasis.
   c. physiology.
   d. adaptation.
   e. evolution.

M 18. About twelve to twenty-four hours after the previous meal, a person's blood-sugar level normally varies from 60 to 90 milligrams per 100 milliliters of blood, though it may rise to 130 mg/100 ml after meals high in carbohydrates. That the blood-sugar level is maintained within a fairly narrow range despite uneven intake of sugar is due to the body's ability to carry out
   a. adaptation.
   b. inheritance.
   c. metabolism.
 * d. homeostasis.
   e. all of these

D 19. For a cell to take up sugar from the bloodstream,
 * a. receptors for insulin on the cells must be activated.
   b. a person must have had a meal with sugar within the last twenty-four hours.
   c. homeostatic mechanisms must activate the blood-brain barrier.
   d. glycogen must be broken down to provide a supply of glucose.
   e. the pancreas must supply the appropriate enzymes to make sugar available.

E 20. A fertilized moth egg passes through which stages of development before becoming an adult?
   I.   larval
   II. pupal
   III. reproductive
   a. I only
   b. II only
 * c. I and II
   d. I and III
   e. II and III

M 21. A new life cycle begins with
   a. death.
   b. pupation.
   c. formation of a larva.
 * d. fertilization of an egg.
   e. hatching of an egg.

ENERGY AND LIFE'S ORGANIZATION

M 22. All organisms are alike in
   a. their requirements for energy.
   b. their participation in one or more nutrient cycles.
   c. their ultimate dependence on the sun.
   d. their interaction with other forms of life.
 * e. all of these

M 23. Which of the following do not depend directly on sunlight for energy?
   I.   producers
   II. consumers
   III. decomposers
   a. I only
 * b. II and III only
   c. II only
   d. III only
   e. I and III

D 24. Which of the following would NOT be characteristic of living organisms?
   a. complex structural organization
   b. dependence on other organisms for energy and resources
   c. reproductive capacity
 * d. uniformity of size and form
   e. capacity to evolve

IF SO MUCH UNITY, WHY SO MANY SPECIES?

E 25. A scientific name consists of which of the following?
   I.   family name
   II. genus name
   III. species name
   a. I only
   b. II only
   c. III only
   d. I and II
 * e. II and III

E   26. The plural for genus is
        a. genus.
        b. geni.
     * c. genera.
        d. genuses.
        e. genae.

M   27. The least inclusive of the taxonomic categories listed
         here is
        a. family.
        b. phylum.
        c. class.
        d. order.
     * e. genus.

E   28. Which group includes all of the other groups?
     * a. phylum
        b. order
        c. family
        d. genus
        e. species

D   29. The hierarchical system of nomenclature
        a. allows diversity to be catalogued.
        b. shows the evolutionary relationships among
            organisms.
        c. permits organisms to be identified.
        d. clarifies confusion produced by tremendous
            variation.
     * e. all of these

E   30. Members of what kingdom are single cells of
         considerable internal complexity?
        a. Animalia
     * b. Protista
        c. Fungi
        d. Plantae
        e. Eubacteria

E   31. Members of what kingdom are all anaerobic?
        a. Animalia
        b. Protista
        c. Fungi
        d. Plantae
     * e. Archaebacteria

E   32. Members of what kingdom are multicellular
         producers?
        a. Animalia
        b. Protista
        c. Fungi
     * d. Plantae
        e. Monera

E   33. Which of the following are decomposers?
        a. Plantae
     * b. Fungi
        c. Animalia
        d. Monera
        e. Protista

E   34. Which of the following is NOT a eukaryote?
        a. fungi
     * b. bacteria
        c. plants
        d. animals
        e. protistans

AN EVOLUTIONARY VIEW OF DIVERSITY

M   35. Hereditary instructions must
        a. be unchanging most of the time.
        b. pass from one generation to the next.
        c. control a large number of different characteristics.
        d. provide for the rare change in instructions.
     * e. all of these

E   36. A mutation is a change in
        a. homeostasis.
        b. the developmental pattern in an organism.
        c. metabolism.
     * d. hereditary instructions.
        e. the life cycle of an organism.

D   37. A color mutation in a moth from light to dark
        a. is an advantage in industrial environments.
        b. may be beneficial under changing environmental
            conditions.
        c. produces a form of moth that will have a better
            chance for survival in some environments.
        d. may be easily spotted by predators in some
            environments.
     * e. all of these

M   38. Evolution occurs at what level of organization?
        a. organism
        b. molecule
        c. organ
     * d. population
        e. ecosystem

D   39. Which of the following statements is NOT true?
        a. Diversity is the result of evolution.
        b. The characteristics of any living organism are
            under the control of a chemical.
     * c. The diversity of living organisms makes life
            unpredictable, even using scientific methods.
        d. All organisms are alike in that their structure,
            organization, and interactions arise from matter
            and energy.
        e. The behavior of individual organisms is dependent
            upon their evolutionary history.

D   40. The diversity of structure, function, and behavior in
         living organisms is primarily the result of
        a. reproduction.
        b. heredity.
     * c. evolution.
        d. chance variations in living organisms.

D 41. Which of the following ultimately accounts for variation in genetic traits?
   a. replication of DNA molecules
   * b. genetic mutation
   c. asexual reproduction
   d. ecological succession
   e. homeostatic mechanisms

D 42. An adaptive trait is a trait that has
   a. mutated.
   * b. survival value.
   c. decreased in frequency in a population.
   d. deleterious biological effects.
   e. the potential to produce variation.

E 43. The animals used by Darwin to show variation in domesticated forms were
   * a. pigeons.
   b. chickens.
   c. pigs.
   d. dogs.
   e. cats.

M 44. The principal point of Darwin's theory of evolution by natural selection was that
   a. long-term heritable changes in organisms are caused by use and disuse.
   b. mutations that adapt an organism to a given environment always arise in the greatest frequency in the organisms that occupy that environment.
   c. mutations are caused by all sorts of environmental influences.
   * d. survival of characteristics in a population depends on competition between organisms, especially between members of the same species.

M 45. Which premise used by Darwin in his theory is INCORRECTLY stated below?
   a. More offspring are produced than can survive to reproduce.
   b. Members of populations show heritable variation.
   c. Some varieties have a better chance to survive and reproduce.
   * d. Organisms that possess advantageous traits have a decreased chance of producing offspring.
   e. Some traits become more common because their bearers contribute more offspring to the next generation.

M 46. The explanation for the diversity seen in nature is
   a. sexual dimorphism; that is, different characteristics are based upon sexual differences.
   b. divine creation of the many different forms of life.
   c. found in the science of taxonomy.
   * d. natural selection.

D 47. In the example in the text, the change in moth populations from predominantly white- to black-winged forms was the result of
   a. environmental changes.
   b. natural selection.
   c. food choices by predators.
   d. the ability of birds to find the prey.
   * e. all of these

D 48. Which of the following statements is NOT true?
   a. Natural selection is based upon differential reproduction and survival.
   b. For evolution to occur in a population, there must be some variation.
   * c. All variations found in a population are heritable.
   d. A population undergoes evolution when the frequency of its genes change.
   e. Over time, some genetic traits are more adaptive than others.

THE NATURE OF BIOLOGICAL INQUIRY

M 49. Of the following, which is the first explanation of a problem? (It is sometimes called an "educated guess.")
   a. principle
   b. law
   c. theory
   d. fact
   * e. hypothesis

E 50. Hypotheses are
   a. often in the form of a statement.
   b. often expressed negatively.
   c. sometimes crude attempts to offer a possible explanation for observations.
   d. testable predictions.
   * e. all of these

E 51. In order to arrive at a solution to a problem, a scientist usually conducts one or more
   a. laws.
   b. theories.
   * c. experiments.
   d. principles.
   e. facts.

M 52. Which represents the lowest degree of certainty?
   * a. hypothesis
   b. conclusion
   c. fact
   d. principle
   e. theory

M 53. Which represents the highest degree of certainty?
   a. hypothesis
   b. fact
   c. principle
   * d. law
   e. theory

M 54. The control in an experiment
   a. makes the experiment valid.
   b. is an additional replicate for statistical purposes.
   c. reduces the experimental errors.
   d. minimizes experimental inaccuracy.
   * e. allows a standard of comparison for the experimental group.

M 55. As a result of experimentation,
   a. more hypotheses may be developed.
   b. more questions may be asked.
   c. a new biological principle could emerge.
   d. entire theories may be modified or discarded.
  * e. all of these

M 56. In an experiment, the control group
   a. is not subjected to experimental error.
   b. is exposed to experimental treatments.
   c. is maintained under strict laboratory conditions.
  * d. is treated exactly the same as the experimental group, except for the one independent variable.
   e. is statistically the most important part of the experiment.

E 57. The choice of whether a particular organism belongs to the experimental group or the control group should be based on
   a. age.
   b. size.
  * c. chance.
   d. designation by the experimenter.
   e. sex.

THE LIMITS OF SCIENCE

E 58. Science is based on
   a. faith.
   b. authority.
  * c. evidence.
   d. force.
   e. consensus.

E 59. Which of the following can be changed based on new evidence?
   a. hypothesis
   b. theory
   c. prediction
   d. experiment
  * e. all of these

M 60. Which of the following is NOT used in the development of science?
   a. evaluation of data
  * b. personal conviction
   c. prediction
   d. systematic observation

E 61. All of the following will strengthen a theory EXCEPT
   a. repetitions of experiments.
   b. increased observations.
   c. time.
  * d. faith.
   e. confirmation by many scientists.

E 62. The validity of scientific discoveries cannot be based on
   a. morality.
   b. aesthetics.
   c. philosophy.
   d. economics.
  * e. any of these

Classification Questions

Answer questions 63–66 by matching the descriptions to the most appropriate function, process, or trait listed below.
   a. metabolism
   b. reproduction
   c. photosynthesis
   d. growth
   e. homeostasis

M 63. A process found only in plants and some bacteria

E 64. Most organisms exhibit this characteristic that tends to buffer the effects of environmental change.

M 65. The capacity to acquire, store, and use energy

E 66. Process in which one generation replaces another

Answers: 63. c 64. e 65. a 66. b

Answer questions 67–73 by matching the descriptions with the most appropriate kingdom listed below.
   a. Eubacteria
   b. Protista
   c. Plantae
   d. Fungi
   e. Animalia

E 67. Multicellular producers

E 68. Prokaryotic

M 69. Unicellular organisms of considerable internal complexity

M 70. Multicellular consumers

E 71. Oldest living organisms

M 72. Unicellular producers

M 73. Multicellular decomposers

Answers: 67. c 68. a 69. b 70. e
         71. a 72. b 73. d

Selecting the Exception

E   74. Four of the five answers listed below are necessary characteristics to the life of an individual. Select the exception.
  a. metabolism
  b. homeostasis
  c. development
  d. heredity
  * e. diversity

M   75. Four of the five answers listed below are characteristics of life. Select the exception.
  * a. ionization
  b. metabolism
  c. reproduction
  d. growth
  e. cellular organization

E   76. Four of the five answers listed below are aspects of the scientific method. Select the exception.
  a. observation
  b. hypothesis
  c. experimentation
  * d. philosophy
  e. conclusion

M   77. Four of the five answers listed below are terms associated with the scientific method. Select the exception.
  * a. faith
  b. theory
  c. experiment
  d. prediction
  e. hypothesis

M   78. Four of the five answers listed below are taxonomic categories. Select the exception.
  a. family
  * b. kind
  c. species
  d. order
  e. genus

D   79. Four of the five answers listed below are deductions made by Charles Darwin. Select the exception.
  a. Natural selection is a result of differential reproduction.
  b. Much of biological variation is heritable.
  c. More offspring are produced than can survive.
  * d. Mutations produce changes in inheritance.
  e. Some variations of heritable traits improve chances of survival.

M   80. Four of the five answers listed below are names of kingdoms. Select the exception.
  a. Animalia
  b. Protista
  * c. Bacteria
  d. Fungi
  e. Plantae

CHAPTER 2
CHEMICAL FOUNDATIONS FOR CELLS

Multiple-Choice Questions

REGARDING THE ATOMS

M   1.   Which is NOT an element?
*   a.   water
       b.   oxygen
       c.   carbon
       d.   chlorine
       e.   hydrogen

M   2.   Which is the smallest portion of a substance that retains the properties of an element?
*   a.   atom
       b.   compound
       c.   ion
       d.   molecule
       e.   mixture

E   3.   The atom that represents the greatest weight in the human body is
       a.   hydrogen.
       b.   carbon.
       c.   nitrogen.
*   d.   oxygen.
       e.   phosphorus.

E   4.   The atomic number refers to the
       a.   mass of an atom.
*   b.   number of protons in an atom.
       c.   number of both protons and neutrons in an atom.
       d.   number of neutrons in an atom.
       e.   number of electrons in an atom.

M   5.   Radioactive isotopes
       a.   are electrically unbalanced.
       b.   behave the same chemically and physically but differ biologically from other isotopes.
       c.   are the same physically and biologically but differ from other isotopes chemically.
*   d.   have an excess number of neutrons.
       e.   are produced when substances are exposed to radiation.

E   6.   Which is NOT a compound?
       a.   salt
       b.   a carbohydrate
*   c.   carbon
       d.   a nucleotide
       e.   methane

E   7.   The negative subatomic particle is the
       a.   neutron.
       b.   proton.
*   c.   electron.
       d.   both the neutron and proton.
       e.   both the proton and electron.

E   8.   The positive subatomic particle is the
       a.   neutron.
*   b.   proton.
       c   electron.
       d.   both the neutron and proton.
       e.   both the proton and electron.

E   9.   The neutral subatomic particle is the
*   a.   neutron.
       b.   proton.
       c.   electron.
       d.   both the neutron and proton.
       e.   both the proton and electron.

E   10.   The nucleus of an atom contains
*   a.   neutrons and protons.
       b.   neutrons and electrons.
       c.   protons and electrons.
       d.   protons only.
       e.   neutrons only.

E   11.   Which components of an atom are negatively charged?
           I.   electrons
           II.   protons
           III. neutrons
*   a.   I only
       b.   II only
       c.   III only
       d.   I and II
       e.   II and III

E   12.   Which components of an atom do not have a charge?
           I.   electrons
           II.   protons
           III. neutrons
       a.   I only
       b.   II only
*   c.   III only
       d.   I and II
       e.   II and III

M   13.   The atomic weight (or mass) of an atom is determined by the weight of
*   a.   neutrons and protons.
       b.   neutrons and electrons.
       c.   protons and electrons.
       d.   protons only.
       e.   neutrons only.

E   14.   The atomic number is determined by the number of
           a. neutrons and protons.
           b. neutrons and electrons.
           c. protons and electrons.
      *   d. protons only.
           e. neutrons only.

D   15.   If the atomic weight of carbon is 12 and the atomic
           weight of oxygen is 16, the molecular weight of
           glucose ($C_6H_{12}O_6$) is
           a. 24 grams.
           b. 28 grams.
           c. 52 grams.
           d. 168 grams.
      *   e. 180 grams.

E   16.   All atoms of an element have the same number of
           a. ions.
      *   b. protons.
           c. neutrons.
           d. electrons.
           e. protons and neutrons.

D   17.   Trace elements
           a. are used in minute amounts in plants.
      *   b. can be monitored through biochemical reactions.
           c. must be radioactive.
           d. have an unbalanced electrical charge.

D   18.   Which of the following statements is NOT true?
           a. All isotopes of an element have the same number
              of electrons.
           b. All isotopes of an element have the same number
              of protons.
      *   c. All isotopes of an element have the same number
              of neutrons.
           d. All radioactive isotopes are unstable.

M   19.   Radioactive isotopes have
           a. excess electrons.
           b. excess protons.
      *   c. excess neutrons.
           d. insufficient neutrons.
           e. insufficient protons.

M   20.   In the chemical shorthand ^{14}C, the fourteen represents
           the number of
           a. excess neutrons.
      *   b. protons plus neutrons.
           c. electrons.
           d. protons plus electrons.
           e. radioactive particles.

E   21.   In a chemical equation, the chemicals to the left of the
           arrow are
           a. products.
           b. in greater abundance.
           c. at higher energy levels.
      *   d. reactants.
           e. all of these

FOCUS ON SCIENCE: USING RADIOISOTOPES TO
TRACK CHEMICALS AND SAVE LIVES

E   22.   Radioactive iodine tends to concentrate in the
           a. heart.
           b. lungs.
           c. gonads.
           d. bones.
      *   e. thyroid glands.

M   23.   Which statement concerning radioisotope ^{14}C is
           LEAST accurate?
           a. It will substitute for ^{12}C in glucose.
      *   b. It will kill cells in which it occurs.
           c. It has more neutrons than ^{12}C.
           d. It behaves the same chemically as ^{12}C.
           e. It has six carbons and eight neutrons.

M   24.   When carbon 14 undergoes radioactive decay,
           _____ is produced.
           a. carbon 12
           b. carbon 13
           c. carbon 14
      *   d. nitrogen 14
           e. oxygen 14

WHAT HAPPENS WHEN ATOM BONDS WITH ATOM?

M   25.   By analogy, the orbitals and atomic nucleus may be
           said to most resemble a
           a. merry-go-round.
           b. sundial.
      *   c. solar system.
           d. nest of mixing bowls.
           e. wave of water currents.

M   26.   Magnesium has 12 protons. How many electrons are in
           its third energy level?
      *   a. 2
           b. 4
           c. 6
           d. 8
           e. 10

M   27.   Magnesium has 12 protons. How many electrons are in
           its first energy level?
      *   a. 2
           b. 4
           c. 6
           d. 8
           e. 10

M   28.   Magnesium has 12 protons. How many electrons are in
           its second energy level?
           a. 2
           b. 4
           c. 6
      *   d. 8
           e. 10

D 29. Nitrogen has an atomic number of 7. How many hydrogen atoms are necessary to join with the nitrogen to form a stable compound?
    a. 1
    b. 2
*   c. 3
    d. 4
    e. 5

D 30. Oxygen, with an atomic number of 8, has _____ electrons in the first energy level and _____ electrons in the second energy level.
    a. 1, 7
*   b. 2, 6
    c. 3, 5
    d. 4, 4
    e. 5, 3

M 31. Which statement is NOT true?
    a. Electrons closest to the nucleus are at the lowest energy level.
    b. No more than two electrons can occupy a single orbital.
*   c. Electrons are unable to move out of the assigned orbital space.
    d. The innermost orbital holds two electrons.
    e. At the second energy level there are four possible orbitals with a total of eight electrons.

E 32. Water is an example of a(n)
    a. atom.
    b. ion.
*   c. compound.
    d. mixture.
    e. element.

E 33. Which includes the other four?
    a. atoms
*   b. molecules
    c. electrons
    d. elements
    e. protons

M 34. Which statement is false?
    a. A molecule is made of at least two atoms.
    b. Compounds are made of elements.
    c. Two atoms of oxygen make a molecule of oxygen.
*   d. Proportions of elements in compounds vary according to their source in nature.
    e. Elements are found in compounds and molecules.

M 35. A molecule is
*   a. a combination of two or more atoms.
    b. less stable than its constituent atoms separated.
    c. electrically charged.
    d. a carrier of one or more extra neutrons.
    e. none of these

IMPORTANT BONDS IN BIOLOGICAL MOLECULES

E 36. What is formed when an atom loses or gains an electron?
    a. mole
*   b. ion
    c. molecule
    d. bond
    e. reaction

D 37. Which of the following is NOT accurate concerning ionization?
    a. When one atom loses an electron, another must gain.
*   b. When an atom loses an electron, it becomes negatively charged.
    c. Ionic bonds form between ionized atoms.
    d. In the compound NaCl, Na loses an electron to become positive.
    e. In an ion, the number of protons and electrons is unequal.

M 38. The bond in table salt (NaCl) is
    a. polar.
*   b. ionic.
    c. covalent.
    d. double.
    e. nonpolar.

D 39. In _____ bonds, both atoms exert the same pull on shared electrons.
*   a. nonpolar covalent
    b. polar covalent
    c. double covalent
    d. triple covalent

M 40. Which of these statements is false concerning covalent bonds?
    a. Atoms share electrons.
    b. Proteins possess many covalent bonds.
    c. Water contains polar covalent bonds.
    d. Covalent bonds may be "double bonds."
*   e. Polar covalent bonds share electrons equally.

E 41. Electrons are shared in bonds called
    a. covalent.
    b. polar.
    c. nonpolar.
*   d. all of these

D 42. The shape (or tertiary form) of large molecules is often controlled by what kind of bonds?
*   a. hydrogen
    b. ionic
    c. covalent
    d. inert
    e. single

D 43. A hydrogen bond is
    a. a sharing of a pair of electrons between a hydrogen and an oxygen nucleus.
    b. a sharing of a pair of electrons between a hydrogen nucleus and either an oxygen or a nitrogen nucleus.
*   c. an attractive force that involves a hydrogen atom and an oxygen or a nitrogen atom that are either in two different molecules or within the same molecule.
    d. none of these
    e. all of these

D 44. Which of the following is NOT true of hydrogen bonds?
    a. They are quite weak.
    b. The hydrogen is slightly positive.
    c. They are common in macromolecules.
*   d. They form in salts such as NaCl.
    e. They always involve hydrogen.

PROPERTIES OF WATER

M 45. Water is important to the interactions of biological molecules because
    a. water molecules are attracted to the charged regions of molecules such as proteins.
    b. it forms a cushion around the macromolecules.
    c. it helps disperse the macromolecules for reactivity..
    d. it prevents settling of the molecules in places where they would be unavailable.
*   e. all of these

M 46. Hydrophobic molecules are _____ water.
    a. attracted to
    b. absorbed by
*   c. repelled by
    d. mixed with
    e. polarized by

D 47. Which of the following is true of water?
    a. The oxygen end is slightly electropositive.
*   b. Hydrogen bonds hold water molecules together.
    c. Water covers about one-half of the earth's surface.
    d. Hydrophobic interactions attract water molecules.
    e. Solvent properties are greatest with nonpolar molecules.

D 48. Water is an excellent solvent because
    a. it forms spheres of hydration around charged substances and can form hydrogen bonds with many substances.
    b. it has a high heat-containing property.
    c. of its cohesive properties.
    d. it is a liquid at room temperature.
*   e. all of these

D 49. In a lipid bilayer, the _____ phospholipid tails point inward and form a region that excludes water.
    a. acidic
    b. basic
    c. hydrophilic
*   d. hydrophobic
    e. none of these

D 50. Glucose dissolves in water because it
    a. ionizes.
    b. is a polysaccharide.
*   c. is polar and forms many hydrogen bonds with the water molecules.
    d. has a very reactive primary structure.
    e. none of these

D 51. Water has the ability to retard heat gain and loss due to its
    a. hydrophilic interactions.
    b. evaporation.
*   c. hydrogen bonds.
    d. crystal structure.
    e. liquidity.

M 52. The column of water extending in tubes from plant roots to leaves is due mostly to
*   a. cohesion.
    b. evaporation.
    c. ionization.
    d. hydrophobic interactions.
    e. all of these

D 53. Sodium chloride (NaCl) in water could be described by any of the following EXCEPT:
    a. Na^+ and Cl^- form
    b. a solute
    c. ionized
*   d. forms spheres of hydration
    e. dissolved

ACIDS, BASES, AND BUFFERS

M 54. A salt will dissolve in water to form
    a. acids.
    b. gases.
*   c. ions.
    d. bases.
    e. polar solvents.

M 55. A reaction of an acid and a base will produce water and
    a. a buffer.
*   b. a salt.
    c. gas.
    d. solid precipitate.
    e. solute.

M 56. Which of the following is a naked proton?
*   a. hydrogen ion
    b. acid
    c. base
    d. hydroxyl ion
    e. acceptor

M 57. Which of the following would NOT be used in connection with the word *acid*?
    a. excess hydrogen ions
    b. contents of the stomach
*   c. magnesium hydroxide
    d. HCl
    e. pH less than 7

D 58. A pH of 10 is how many times as basic as a pH of 7?
    a. 2
    b. 3
    c. 10
    d. 100
*   e. 1,000

D 59. A solution with a pH of 8 has how many times fewer hydrogen ions than a solution with a pH of 6?
    a. 2
    b. 4
    c. 10
*   d. 100
    e. 1,000

D 60. Which of the following is NOT true?
    a. Acids release hydrogen ions.
    b. In a neutral solution, the amounts of hydrogen and hydroxyl ions are almost equal.
*   c. Salts precipitate out of solution and have no function in cells.
    d. Polar water molecules are attracted to water.
    e. Hydrogen bonding between water molecules gives water its temperature-stabilizing and cohesive properties.

M 61. Cellular pH is kept near a value of 7 because of
    a. salts.
*   b. buffers.
    c. acids.
    d. bases.
    e. water.

Classification Questions

The various energy levels in an atom of magnesium have different numbers of electrons. Use the following numbers to answer questions 62–64.
    a. 1
    b. 2
    c. 3
    d. 6
    e. 8

D 62. Number of electrons in the first energy level

D 63. Number of electrons in the second energy level

D 64. Number of electrons in the third energy level

Answers   62. b   63. e   64. b

The following are types of chemical bonds. Answer questions 65–69 by matching the descriptions with the most appropriate bond type.
    a. hydrogen
    b. ionic
    c. covalent
    d. disulfide
    e. peptide

M 65. The bond between the atoms of table salt

M 66. The bond type holding several molecules of water together

M 67. The bond between the oxygen atoms of gaseous oxygen

M 68. The bond that breaks when salts dissolve in water

M 69. Atoms connected by this kind of bond share electrons.

Answers   65. b   66. a   67. c
              68. b   69. c

Selecting the Exception

D 70. Four of the five answers listed below possess electrons in the third energy level. Select the exception.
    a. sodium
    b. magnesium
    c. chlorine
*   d. nitrogen
    e. sulfur

D 71. Four of the five answers listed below are related by a unifying characteristic. Select the exception.
    a. ionic bond
    b. covalent bond
    c. polar bond
    d. hydrogen bond
*   e. cluster of nonpolar groups

M 72. Four of the five answers listed below are alkaline (pH above 7). Select the exception.
   a. milk of magnesia
   b. household ammonia
   c. Tums
   d. phosphate detergent
   * e. wine

M 73. Four of the five answers listed below are acidic (pH below 7). Select the exception.
   a. vinegar
   b. soft drink
   * c. soap
   d. lemon juice
   e. beer

M 74. Four of the five answers listed below are positively charged ions. Select the exception.
   a. potassium ion
   b. hydrogen ion
   c. calcium ion
   d. magnesium ion
   * e. chlorine ion

D 75. Four of the five answers listed below are characteristics of water. Select the exception.
   a. stabilizes temperature
   b. is a common solvent
   c. has cohesion and surface tension
   * d. produces salts
   e. changes shape of hydrophilic and hydrophobic substances

CHAPTER 3
CARBON COMPOUNDS IN CELLS

Multiple-Choice Questions

THE MOLECULES OF LIFE—FROM STRUCTURE TO FUNCTION

E   **1.**   The three most common atoms in your body are
    *   a.   hydrogen, oxygen, and carbon.
        b.   carbon, hydrogen, and nitrogen.
        c.   carbon, nitrogen, and oxygen.
        d.   nitrogen, hydrogen, and oxygen.
        e.   carbon, oxygen, and sulfur.

M   **2.**   Carbon usually forms how many bonds with other atoms?
        a.   2
        b.   3
    *   c.   4
        d.   5
        e.   6

E   **3.**   The atom diagnostically associated with organic compounds is
    *   a.   carbon.
        b.   oxygen.
        c.   nitrogen.
        d.   sulfur.
        e.   hydrogen.

D   **4.**   Carbon has an atomic number of 6 and oxygen has an atomic number of 8. Which combination of carbon and oxygen atoms is most stable?
    *   a.   1 carbon, 2 oxygen
        b.   1 carbon, 3 oxygen
        c.   2 carbon, 1 oxygen
        d.   2 carbon, 2 oxygen
        e.   3 carbon, 1 oxygen

D   **5.**   Although carbon dioxide contains carbon, it is not considered an "organic" compound because
        a.   it is not found in the earth.
        b.   it is not present in living cells.
        c.   no hydrogen is present.
    *   d.   the carbons are not in chains or rings.
        e.   it is too small.

D   **6.**   Which compound is hydrophobic?
        a.   ethyl alcohol
        b.   simple sugar
    *   c.   hydrocarbon
        d.   glycerol
        e.   amino acid

OVERVIEW OF FUNCTIONAL GROUPS

M   **7.**   An —OH group is a(n) _____ group.
        a.   carboxyl
    *   b.   hydroxyl
        c.   amino
        d.   methyl
        e.   ketone

M   **8.**   A —CH_3 group is a(n) _____ group.
        a.   carboxyl
        b.   hydroxyl
        c.   amino
    *   d.   methyl
        e.   ketone

M   **9.**   An —NH_2 group is a(n) _____ group.
        a.   carboxyl
        b.   hydroxyl
    *   c.   amino
        d.   methyl
        e.   ketone

M   **10.**   A —COOH group is a(n) _____ group.
    *   a.   carboxyl
        b.   hydroxyl
        c.   amino
        d.   methyl
        e.   ketone

HOW DO CELLS BUILD ORGANIC COMPOUNDS?

M   **11**   Which are NOT macromolecules?
        a.   proteins
        b.   polysaccharides
    *   c.   nucleotides
        d.   lipids
        e.   nucleic acids

D   **12**   Which of the following would NOT be classified as a polymer?
        a.   starch
        b.   nucleic acid
    *   c.   triglyceride
        d.   protein
        e.   polysaccharide

M   **13.**   The formation of large molecules from small repeating units is known as what kind of reaction?
        a.   oxidation
        b.   reduction
    *   c.   condensation
        d.   hydrolysis
        e.   decarboxylation

E 14 The breakdown of large molecules by the enzymatic addition of water is an example of what kind of reaction?
- a. oxidation
- b. reduction
- c. condensation
- * d. hydrolysis
- e. decarboxylation

E 15. A condensation reaction typically produces
- a. monomers.
- b. salts.
- * c. polymers.
- d. simple sugars.
- e. amino acids.

D 16. Which of the following demonstrates a condensation reaction?
- a. photosynthesis
- b. digestion
- c. lipid synthesis
- * d. photosynthesis and lipid synthesis
- e. photosynthesis, digestion, and lipid synthesis

M 17. Which reaction results in the breakdown of a chemical into simpler substances?
- a. synthesis
- * b. cleavage
- c. condensation
- d. polymerization
- e. both cleavage and condensation

D 18. Condensation and hydrolysis are accomplished in cells by
- a. bonding attraction.
- * b. the action of enzymes.
- c. spontaneous action.
- d. functional group interactions.
- e. all of these

M 19. The relatively unimportant by-product(s) of many condensation reactions is (are)
- a. carbon dioxide.
- b. aldehyde groups.
- c. enzymes.
- d. alcohols.
- * e. water.

CARBOHYDRATES—THE MOST ABUNDANT MOLECULES OF LIFE

E 20. Which is a monomer of carbohydrates?
- a. glycogen
- b. nucleotide
- c. simple sugar
- d. monosaccharide
- * e. both simple sugar and monosaccharide

E 21. Which substance is the most common in cells?
- * a. carbohydrates
- b. salts and minerals
- c. proteins
- d. fats
- e. nucleic acids

E 22. A macromolecule is composed of smaller units called
- a. polymers.
- b. isomers.
- * c. monomers.
- d. isotopes.
- e. dimers.

M 23. Which of the following is composed of a 1:2:1 ratio of carbon to hydrogen to oxygen?
- * a. carbohydrate
- b. protein
- c. lipid
- d. nucleic acid
- e. steroid

D 24. Monosaccharides are characterized by all EXCEPT which of the following?
- a. a carboxyl group
- b. carbon, hydrogen, and oxygen in a 1:2:1 ratio
- c. a molecule of three to seven carbon atoms
- d. possession of one or more hydroxyl groups
- * e. the presence of glycerol and fatty acids

M 25. Fructose and glucose are
- a. isotopes.
- b. monosaccharides.
- c. disaccharides.
- d. six-carbon sugars.
- * e. both monosaccharides and six-carbon sugars.

M 26. The primary carbohydrate used in the transport of food from the leaves to the root is
- a. glucose.
- * b. sucrose.
- c. fructose.
- d. maltose.
- e. lactose.

D 27. Oligosaccharides are used as
- a. transport molecules in plants.
- b. storage compounds in both plants and animals.
- c. as side chains on proteins.
- d. as monomers to form polysaccharides.
- * e. both transport molecules in plants and as side chains on proteins.

D 28. Glucose and fructose are different
- a. in the number of carbons they possess.
- b. in their relationship to the sucrose molecules.
- * c. in the way that their atoms are arranged.
- d. in the number of double bonds they possess.
- e. both in the way that their atoms are arranged and in the number of double bonds they possess.

D 29. Glucose and fructose
- a. form rings with the same number of carbon atoms.
- b. both have an oxygen atom as part of their ring structure.
- c. are alike in that both are aldehydes.
- * d. contain the same number of hydrogens and hydroxyl groups.
- e. are disaccharides.

M 30. Fructose and glucose are
    a. hexoses.
    b. structurally different.
    c. monosaccharides.
    d. simple sugars.
*   e. all of these

M 31. Glucose and ribose
    a. have the same number of carbon atoms.
    b. have the same structural formulas.
    c. are the two components of sucrose.
*   d. are monosaccharides.
    e. are molecules whose atoms are arranged the same way.

M 32. Sucrose is composed of
    a. two molecules of fructose.
    b. two molecules of glucose.
*   c. a molecule of fructose and a molecule of glucose.
    d. a molecule of fructose and a molecule of galactose.
    e. two molecules of fructose.

M 33. The combination of glucose and galactose forms
    a. fructose.
    b. maltose.
*   c. lactose.
    d. sucrose.
    e. mannose.

M 34. Sugar dissolves in water because
    a. it is a nonpolar molecule.
*   b. water can form hydrogen bonds with hydroxyl groups.
    c. it forms rings when it gets wet.
    d. it is a nonpolar molecule and water can form hydrogen bonds with hydroxyl groups.
    e. it is a nonpolar molecule; water can form hydrogen bonds with hydroxyl groups; and it forms rings when it gets wet.

D 35. Sugars are characterized by all but which one of the following functional groups?
    a. hydroxyl
    b. carboxyl
    c. ketone
    d. aldehyde
*   e. methyl

E 36. Plants store their excess carbohydrates in the form of
*   a. starch.
    b. glycogen.
    c. glucose.
    d. cellulose.
    e. fats.

M 37. Glycogen is a polysaccharide used for energy storage by
*   a. animals.
    b. plants.
    c. protistans.
    d. monerans.
    e. both animals and protistans.

M 38. Cellulose is
*   a. a material found in cell walls.
    b. a component of cell membranes.
    c. a plant protein.
    d. formed by photosynthesis.
    e. the most complex of the organic compounds.

D 39. Which of these components of a tossed salad will pass through the human digestive tract with the least digestion?
    a. sugar (in the dressing)
    b. oil (lipid)
    c. starch (in the croutons)
*   d. cellulose (lettuce leaves)
    e. protein (in bacon bits)

M 40. Which is NOT a monosaccharide?
    a. glucose
    b. fructose
    c. deoxyribose
*   d. starch
    e. ribose

M 41. Which of the following includes all the others?
    a. sucrose
    b. glucose
    c. cellulose
    d. glycogen
*   e. carbohydrate

M 42. Which of the following cannot be used to describe some aspect of polysaccharides?
    a. energy storage
    b. straight or branched chain
    c. glucose subunits
*   d. insoluble in water

M 43. A polysaccharide
    a. is composed of many monosaccharides that have been linked together.
    b. may be straight and unbranched or highly branched.
    c. is most likely made of glucose molecules if it is one of the natural polysaccharides.
    d. may be insoluble because of its large size and structure.
*   e. all of these

D 44. Chitin is a polysaccharide with _____ atoms attached to the glucose backbone.
    a. magnesium
    b. phosphorus
    c. potassium
*   d. nitrogen
    e. sulfur

GREASY, OILY-MUST BE LIPIDS

M **45.** Which of the following is more soluble in a nonpolar solvent (such as acetone) than in water?
  - a. lipids
  - b. polysaccharides
  - c. fats
  - d. sterols
  - * e. all of these except polysaccharides

M **46.** Triglycerides are
  - a. carbohydrates.
  - b. nucleotides.
  - c. proteins.
  - * d. neutral fats.
  - e. amino acids.

M **47.** Oils are
  - a. liquid at room temperatures.
  - b. unsaturated fats.
  - c. found only in animals.
  - d. complex carbohydrates.
  - * e. both liquid at room temperature and unsaturated fats.

E **48.** Which of the following are lipids?
  - a. sterols
  - b. triglycerides
  - c. oils
  - d. waxes
  - * e. all of these

D **49.** Sterols
  - a. are used in the synthesis of amino acids.
  - b. consist of four rings.
  - c. may have different numbers, types, and positions of functional groups attached to them.
  - d. are a specialized type of lipid.
  - * e. All of the choices are true except "are used in the synthesis of amino acids."

D **50.** Sterols
  - a. contribute to atherosclerosis.
  - b. are not found in plants.
  - c. are fats characterized by fatty-acid tails.
  - d. are needed to produce sexual development and maturity.
  - * e. both contribute to atherosclerosis and are needed to produce sexual development and maturity.

D **51.** Cholesterol
  - a. is synthesized in the large intestine.
  - b. floats free in the bloodstream.
  - * c. is used in the construction of biomembranes.
  - d. levels in the bloodstream can be increased by eating plant fats.
  - e. is much greater in the bloodstream of rats than humans.

M **52.** Which of the following is secreted by specific glands?
  - * a. waxes
  - b. triglycerides
  - c. bone and cartilage
  - d. hemoglobin
  - e. keratin

D **53.** Long-chain fatty acids attached to long-chain alcohols is characteristic of
  - a. triglycerides.
  - b. phospholipids.
  - c. sterols.
  - * d. waxes.
  - e. glycoproteins.

M **54.** Polyunsaturated fats
  - * a. have fewer hydrogens than saturated fats.
  - b. are more characteristic of animal fats than plant fats.
  - c. contribute to the possibility of arteriosclerosis.
  - d. have no double bonds.
  - e. are solid at room temperature.

D **55.** If the cuticle were removed from an apple while leaving the skin intact,
  - * a. the apple would lose water and dehydrate.
  - b. the apple would undergo fungal decomposition.
  - c. nothing would happen.
  - d. the apple would begin to swell as it absorbs moisture from the air.
  - e. all of these

M **56.** An example of a saturated fat is
  - a. olive oil.
  - b. corn oil.
  - * c. butter.
  - d. oleo.
  - e. soybean oil.

M **57.** Lipids
  - * a. serve as food reserves in many organisms.
  - b. include cartilage and chitin.
  - c. include fats consisting of one fatty acid molecule and three glycerol molecules.
  - d. are composed of monosaccharides.
  - e. none of these

E **58.** Plasma membranes are characterized by the presence of
  - a. triglycerides.
  - * b. phospholipids.
  - c. unsaturated fats.
  - d. steroids.
  - e. fatty acids.

D **59.** All sterols have
  - a. the same number of double bonds.
  - b. double bonds in the same positions.
  - * c. four rings of carbon to which are attached other atoms.
  - d. the same functional groups.
  - e. the same number and positions of double bonds.

M **60.** Sterols are
  - a. compounds that are related to lipids.
  - b. sex hormones.
  - c. components of membranes.
  - d. troublesome on artery walls.
  - * e. all of these

A STRING OF AMINO ACIDS: PROTEIN PRIMARY STRUCTURE

D **61.** Primary protein structure is dependent on
    a. hydrophobic interactions.
    b. hydrogen bonds.
  * c. bonds between carbon and hydrogen.
    d. covalent linkages between carbon and oxygen.
    e. all of these

M **62.** Proteins may function as
    a. structural units.
    b. hormones.
    c. storage molecules.
    d. transport molecules.
  * e. all of these

D **63.** Which amino acid possesses the least extensive R group?
    a. proline
    b. serine
    c. tryptophan
    d. cysteine
  * e. glycine

D **64.** Which of the following is structurally the simplest of the amino acids?
    a. proline
    b. serine
    c. tryptophan
    d. cysteine
  * e. glycine

D **65.** The R group found in amino acids consists of
    a. an amine group.
    b. a hydroxyl group.
    c. a carboxyl group.
  * d. additional atoms.
    e. an amine group and a carboxyl group.

E **66.** Amino acids are the building blocks for
  * a. proteins.
    b. steroids.
    c. lipids.
    d. nucleic acids.
    e. carbohydrates.

E **67.** What kind of bond exists between two amino acids in a protein?
  * a. peptide
    b. ionic
    c. hydrogen
    d. amino
    e. sulfhydroxyl

M **68.** The sequence of amino acids is the _____ structure of proteins.
  * a. primary
    b. secondary
    c. tertiary
    d. quaternary
    e. stereo

E **69.** Amino acids are linked by what kind of bonds to form the primary structure of a protein?
    a. disulfide
    b. hydrogen
    c. ionic
  * d. peptide
    e. none of these

HOW DOES A PROTEIN'S FINAL STRUCTURE EMERGE?

M **70.** The secondary structure of proteins is
    a. helical.
    b. sheetlike.
    c. globular.
    d. the sequence of amino acids.
  * e. both helical and sheetlike.

M **71.** The interaction of four polypeptide chains in a hemoglobin molecule is _____ structure.
  * a. quaternary
    b. secondary
    c. primary
    d. tertiary
    e. quintinery

M **72.** Glycoproteins are NOT used for which of the following?
    a. outer cell membranes
    b. cell secretions
    c. blood proteins
  * d. transport of cholesterol
    e. cell identification

D **73.** Denaturation of proteins may result in all but one of the following. Which one is it?
    a. breakage of hydrogen bonds
    b. loss of three-dimensional structure
  * c. removal of R groups from amino acids
    d. alteration of enzyme activity
    e. endangerment of cell's life

WHY IS PROTEIN STUCTURE SO IMPORTANT?

E **74.** The sixth amino acid in normal hemoglobin is glutamate, but it is replaced by __?__ in sickle-cell anemia.
    a. histidine
    b. proline
    c. leucine
  * d. valine
    e. threonine

M **75** Which of the following is NOT a known dysfunction in the expression of sickle-cell anemia?
    a. loss of shape of red blood cells with insufficient oxygen
    b. rheumatism
    c. overactive bone marrow
  * d. excessive absorption of oxygen causing the cell to swell
    e. enlarged spleen

NUCLEOTIDES AND NUCLEIC ACIDS

E 76. Nucleotides are the building blocks for
    a. proteins.
    b. steroids.
    c. lipids.
  * d. ATP, NAD^+, and FAD.
    e. carbohydrates.

M 77. Which of the following is NOT found in every nucleic acid?
  * a. ribose
    b. phosphate group
    c. single-ring base
    d. double-ring base
    e. All of these are characteristic of every nucleotide.

D 78. The nucleotide associated with chemical messages is
  * a. cyclic AMP.
    b. FAD.
    c. NAD^+.
    d. ATP.
    e. all of these

D 79. Flavin adenine dinucleotide and nicotinamide adenine dinucleotide are examples of
    a. functional nucleotides.
  * b. transport nucleotides.
    c. structural nucleotides.
    d. nuclear proteins.
    e. chemical messengers.

M 80. The nucleotide most closely associated with energy is
    a. cyclic AMP.
    b. FAD.
    c. NAD^+.
  * d. ATP.
    e. all of these

E 81. Nucleotides contain what kind of sugars?
    a. three-carbon
    b. four-carbon
  * c. five-carbon
    d. six-carbon
    e. seven-carbon

M 82. DNA
    a. is one of the adenosine phosphates.
    b. is one of the nucleotide coenzymes.
  * c. contains protein-building instructions.
    d. translates protein-building instructions into actual protein structures.
    e. none of these

D 83. Which molecule is incorrectly matched with its component parts?
    a. fat: fatty acids
  * b. starch: riboses
    c. protein: amino acids
    d. glycogen: glucoses
    e. nucleic acids: nucleotides

Matching Questions

M 84. Matching. Choose the one most appropriate answer for each.

1. ___ enzymes
2. ___ glucose
3. ___ nucleotide coenzymes
4. ___ phospholipids

  A. a six-carbon sugar
  B. energy carriers such as NAD^+ and FAD
  C. principal components of cell membranes
  D. speed up metabolic reactions
  E. DNA and RNA

Answers: 1. D   2. A   3. B   4. C

Classification Questions

The following are chemical functional groups that may be part of a biologically active molecule. Answer questions 85–95 by matching the items with the most appropriate group.

  a. —COOH
  b. —CH_3
  c. —NH_2
  d. —OH

  e. $>C=O$

  f.
$$\begin{array}{c} O \\ \parallel \\ -P-O \\ | \\ O \end{array}$$

  g. —CHO

E 85. The amine group

E 86. The carboxyl group

M 87. The group that is acidic

M 88. The group that occurs repeatedly in sugars; composed of two elements

E 89. The methyl group

E 90. The hydroxyl group

E 91. The ketone group

M 92. The group on the amino-terminal end of proteins

M 93. The group on the carboxyl-terminal end of proteins

M 94. A group composed of three different elements; found in sugars

M 95. The group typical of energy carriers such as ATP

Answers   85. c   86. a   87. a   88. d
           89. b   90. d   91. e   92. c
           93. a   94. g   95. f

The following are basic building blocks of biopolymers. Answer questions 96–103 by matching the items with the most appropriate building block.

    a. amino acids
    b. glucose
    c. glycerol
    d. fatty acids
    e. nucleotides

E   96.   The basic unit of proteins

E   97.   The basic unit of DNA

E   98.   The basic unit of messenger RNA

E   99.   The basic unit of cellulose

E   100.   The basic unit of glycogen

E   101.   The basic unit of starch

M   102.   The monomeric unit of a polypeptide chain

M   103   Which two units combine in various ways to form lipids?
    a. a and b
    b. a and c
    c. b and c
    d. b and d
    e. c and d

Answers   96. a   97. e   98. e   99. b

          100. b   101. b   102 a   103 e

Selecting the Exception

M   104.   Four of the five answers listed below are related by a common chemical similarity. Select the exception.
    a. cellulose
   *   b. hydrochloric acid
    c. amino acid
    d. protein
    e. nucleic acid

M   105.   Four of the five answers listed below are related as members of the same group. Select the exception.
    a. glucose
    b. fructose
   *   c. cellulose
    d. ribose
    e. deoxyribose

D   106.   Four of the five answers listed below are related as members of the same group. Select the exception.
    a. lactose
    b. sucrose
    c. maltose
    d. table sugar
   *   e. fructose

D   107.   Four of the five answers listed below are carbohydrates. Select the exception.
   *   a. glycerol
    b. cellulose
    c. starch
    d. sucrose
    e. glycogen

D   108.   Four of the five answers listed below are polysaccharides. Select the exception.
    a. chitin
    b. cellulose
   *   c. collagen
    d. starch
    e. glycogen

M   109.   Four of the five answers listed below are lipids. Select the exception.
    a. triglyceride
    b. wax
    c. butter
   *   d. insulin
    e. steroid

M   110.   Three of the four answers listed below are saturated fats. Select the exception.
    a. butter
    b. bacon
   *   c. peanut oil
    d. animal fat

D   111.   Four of the five answers listed below are amino acids. Select the exception.
    a. glycine
   *   b. adenine
    c. phenylalanine
    d. valine
    e. tyrosine

D   112.   Four of the five answers listed below are functional groups. Select the exception.
   *   a. R group
    b. amino group
    c. carboxyl group
    d. hydroxyl group
    e. aldehyde group

CHAPTER 4
CELL STRUCTURE AND FUNCTION

Multiple-Choice Questions

E   1.   The first person to reportedly see living, moving cells using a microscope was
         a. Robert Hooke.
         b. Robert Brown.
         c. Theodor Schwann.
         d. Rudolf Virchow.
     *   e. Anton van Leeuwenhoek.

E   2.   The first cell seen by Robert Hooke using a microscope was a
     *   a. cork cell.
         b. blood cell.
         c. sperm cell.
         d. skin cell.
         e. root tip cell.

E   3.   Ten years before Schleiden's pronouncement of the cell theory, who had discovered the presence of nuclei in plant cells?
         a. Robert Hooke
     *   b. Robert Brown
         c. Theodor Schwann
         d. Rudolf Virchow
         e. Anton van Leeuwenhoek

E   4.   The cell theory was proposed by
         a. Robert Hooke.
         b. Robert Brown.
     *   c. Theodor Schwann.
         d. Rudolf Virchow.
         e. Anton van Leeuwenhoek.

E   5.   One of the generalizations of the cell theory is that
         a. all cells have a nucleus.
         b. all cells divide by meiosis.
     *   c. all living organisms are made up of cells.
         d. cells arise through spontaneous generation.
         e. growth is solely the result of cell division.

E   6.   The idea that all living cells came from preexisting living cells was proposed by
         a. Robert Hooke.
         b. Robert Brown.
         c. Theodor Schwann.
     *   d. Rudolf Virchow.
         e. Anton van Leeuwenhoek.

BASIC ASPECTS OF CELL STRUCTURE AND FUNCTION

M   7.   Which of these cell features is absent in a bacterial cell?
         a. plasma membrane
         b. nucleoid
         c. cytoplasm
     *   d. nucleus
         e. DNA

D   8.   If the volume of a cell increases, its surface area will
         a. decrease.
         b. remain the same.
         c. increase proportionately.
         d. increase to a greater degree.
     *   e. increase to a lesser degree.

D   9.   Volume increases by the _____ of the diameter, and surface area increases by the _____.
         a. square; doubling
         b. square; cube
     *   c. cube; square
         d. cube; cube
         e. none of these

M   10. Cells are of small size because of considerations of
         a. weight.
         b. complexity.
     *   c. diffusion.
         d. space.
         e. division.

D   11. Elephants are large animals because they
         a. have bigger cells.
         b. possess expandable cells.
     *   c. are made of a greater number of cells.
         d. have bigger cells and are made of a greater number of cells.
         e. have bigger cells that are expandable and of greater number.

FOCUS ON SCIENCE: MICROSCOPES–GATEWAYS CELLS

E   12. The maximum power of magnification of a light microscope is
         a. 500.
         b. 1,000.
     *   c. 2,000.
         d. 4,000.
         e. 10,000.

E 13. The highest magnification generally used to study cells is provided by the
* a. transmission electron microscope.
b. compound light microscope.
c. phase contrast microscope.
d. scanning electron microscope.
e. binocular dissecting microscope.

DEFINING FEATURES OF EUKARYOTIC CELLS

E 14. All cells except bacteria
a. are eukaryotes.
b. possess a nucleus.
c. use organelles for compartmentalization.
d. possess a nucleus and use organelles for compartmentalization.
* e. are eukaryotes, possess a nucleus, and use organelles for compartmentalization.

M 15. If a cell did not have ribosomes, it would be unable to
a. extract energy from glucose.
b. synthesize glucose.
c. store food in the form of fat.
* d. form proteins.

M 16. Which of the following organelles is correctly matched with its function?
a. nucleus: protein synthesis
b. ER: heredity
* c. Golgi bodies: packaging
d. mitochondria: digestion
e. chloroplasts: storage of lipids

D 17. The organelle that pinches off portions of its membrane to form a vesicle used for storage or transport is the
a. mitochondrion.
b. chloroplast.
c. nucleolus.
* d. Golgi body.

THE NUCLEUS

D 18. Which of the following is the primary advantage of the eukaryotic nuclear envelope?
a. providing residence for ribosomes
* b. allowing isolation of DNA from cytoplasmic machinery
c. providing pore entry places
d. enabling faster cell division
e. enabling larger cell size

E 19. An organelle found in the nucleus is a
a. plastid.
b. vacuole.
c. microvillus.
* d. nucleolus.
e. basal body.

M 20. Which of the following terms cannot be used to characterize eukaryotic chromosomes?
a. DNA plus proteins
b. duplicated
c. condensed
* d. bathed in cytoplasm
e. "colored bodies"

M 21. Which of the following is NOT a part of the endomembrane system?
* a. nucleus
b. endoplasmic reticulum
c. lysosomes
d. Golgi bodies
e. vesicles

M 22. The breakdown of a plasma or nuclear membrane would yield
a. cellulose.
b. suberin and cutin.
* c. phospholipids and proteins.
d. microtubules and microfilaments.

THE ENDOMEMBRANE SYSTEM

E 23. Organelles composed of a system of canals, tubes, and sacs that transport molecules inside the cytoplasm are
a. Golgi bodies.
b. ribosomes.
c. mitochondria.
d. lysosomes.
* e. endoplasmic reticula.

M 24. The endoplasmic reticulum
* a. serves as the internal transportation system of a cell.
b. is the inner membrane of the mitochondria.
c. is characterized by the presence of ribosomes throughout.
d. manufactures ATP.

E 25. Which of the following are sometimes referred to as rough or smooth, depending on the structure?
a. Golgi bodies
b. ribosomes
c. mitochondria
d. lysosomes
* e. endoplasmic reticula

M 26. Which of the following are the primary cellular assembly sites for the production of proteins?
a. Golgi bodies
* b. ribosomes
c. mitochondria
d. lysosomes
e. smooth endoplasmic reticula

M 27. Which of the following are the primary structures for the packaging of cellular secretions for export from the cell?
* a. Golgi bodies
  b. ribosomes
  c. mitochondria
  d. lysosomes
  e. endoplasmic reticula

E 28. Which of the following contain enzymes and are the main organelles of intracellular digestion?
  a. Golgi bodies
  b. ribosomes
  c. mitochondria
* d. lysosomes
  e. endoplasmic reticula

M 29. Which of the following cell organelles is responsible for disposal of hydrogen peroxide?
  a. Golgi bodies
  b. ribosomes
  c. mitochondria
  d. lysosomes
* e. peroxisomes

MITOCHONDRIA

M 30. Which of the following are the primary cellular sites for the recapture of energy from carbohydrates?
  a. Golgi bodies
  b. ribosomes
* c. mitochondria
  d. lysosomes
  e. endoplasmic reticula

M 31. Which of the following contain enzymes used in the breakdown of glucose and generation of ATP?
  a. Golgi bodies
  b. ribosomes
* c. mitochondria
  d. lysosomes
  e. endoplasmic reticula

D 32. Energy stored in which of the following molecules is converted by mitochondria to a form usable by the cell?
  a. water
* b. carbon compounds
  c. NAD^+
  d. ATP
  e. carbon dioxide

D 33. If a biologist said that the human body might be getting its power from "bacteria," he would be referring to
  a. energy cells that utilize bacteria by producing energy.
  b. bacteria in our intestinal tract that digest food to supply us with energy.
* c. the mitochondria in our cells that may have originated as endosymbiotic bacteria.
  d. the *E. coli* throughout the human body that produce ATP.

M 34. Which of the following is thought to be the descendant of engulfed ancient bacteria?
  a. nuclei
  b. Golgi bodies
  c. ER
* d. mitochondria
  e. lysosomes

D 35. Which of the following is NOT used as evidence that mitochondria and chloroplasts may have arisen according to the endosymbiotic relationship?
* a. They can live an independent existence when isolated from a cell.
  b. They possess their own type of DNA different from that found in the nucleus.
  c. They possess their own ribosomes.
  d. They have their own membranes and are the same size as bacteria.

D 36. In contrast to the membrane of the nucleus, the double membrane of a mitochondrion
  a. is riddled with holes.
  b. is not permeable.
* c. creates two compartments.
  d. separates DNA from cytoplasm.
  e. has two lipid bilayers.

SPECIALIZED PLANT ORGANELLES

M 37. Starch is stored in
* a. plastids.
  b. vacuoles.
  c. lysosomes.
  d. microvilli.
  e. any of the above

M 38. In which of the following is photosynthesis NOT possible?
  a. chloroplasts
  b. amyloplasts
  c. grana
  d. mitochondria
* e. both amyloplasts and mitochondria.

M 39. Fluid-filled sacs that may store food, ions, or water in cells are called
  a. plastids.
* b. vacuoles.
  c. microvilli.
  d. nucleoli.
  e. Golgi bodies.

D   40.   Which of the following are found in both plant and animal cells?
a.   nucleus, Golgi body, chloroplasts
* b.   ribosomes, mitochondria, plasma membranes
c.   centrioles, cell walls, nucleolus
d.   vacuoles, nucleolus, starch grains

M   41.   Organelles that dramatically increase the surface area of a membrane are
a.   plastids.
* b.   vacuoles.
c.   chloroplasts.
d.   nucleoli.
e.   microfilaments.

M   42.   Only plant cells possess
a.   a central vacuole.
b.   plastids.
c.   grana.
d.   stroma.
* e.   all of these

EVEN YOUR CELLS HAVE A SKELETON

M   43.   Structural features that contain the protein actin and help to control the shapes of cells are
a.   plastids.
b.   vacuoles.
c.   microvilli.
d.   nucleoli.
* e.   microfilaments.

E   44.   Cell components used to move chromosomes are the
a.   cilia.
b.   flagella.
* c.   microtubules.
d.   microfilaments.
e.   Golgi bodies.

HOW DO CELLS MOVE?

E   45.   The organelle that is compared to a whip is a
a.   microfilament.
b.   intermediate filament.
c.   microvillus.
* d.   flagellum.
e.   microtubule.

E   46.   A "9 + 2 array" refers to
a.   microtubules.
b.   Golgi bodies.
c.   ribosomes.
d.   cilia.
* e.   both microtubules and cilia.

D   47.   Microfilaments are commonly found in
a.   cilia.
b.   skeletal muscle cells.
c.   flagella.
d.   only cilia and flagella.
* e.   cilia, flagella, and skeletal muscle cells.

D   48.   The centrosome of a cell
a.   gives rise to the spindle microtubules.
b.   is a type of microtubule organizing center.
c.   is located near the nucleus.
d.   gives rise to the spindle microtubules and is a type of microtubule organizing center.
* e.   gives rise to the spindle microtubules, is a type of microtubule organizing center, and is located near the nucleus.

D   49.   Cilia and flagella
a.   are found only in motile cells.
b.   are found only in sex cells and unicellular organisms.
* c.   are fundamentally the same structurally.
d.   may also function as receptor sites for certain hormones.

CELL SURFACE SPECIALIZATIONS

M   50.   Which of the following is NOT found as a part of all cells?
a.   cell membrane
* b.   cell wall
c.   ribosomes
d.   DNA
e.   RNA

D   51.   The cell wall
* a.   provides skeletal support for plants.
b.   controls what enters and leaves a cell.
c.   replaces the plasma membrane of animal cells in plant cells.
d.   is found in all eukaryotes.

D   52.   Which of the following junctions permit(s) cytoplasmic interconnections between cells?
a.   gap junctions
b.   plasmodesmata
c.   adhering junctions
* d.   only gap junctions and plasmodesmata.
e.   gap junctions, plasmodesmata, and adhering junctions.

D   53.   Plasmodesmata are related to
a.   gap junctions in animal cells.
b.   tight junctions in bacteria.
* c.   wall junctions in plants.
d.   adhering junctions.
e.   both tight junctions in bacteria and adhering junctions.

PROKARYOTIC CELLS

E   54.   Which are examples of prokaryotes?
a.   protozoa
* b.   bacteria
c.   algae
d.   fungi
e.   mosses

E 55. Prokaryotic cells do NOT have
   a. ribosomes.
 * b. membrane-bound nuclei.
   c. cytoplasm.
   d. a plasma membrane.
   e. ribosomes or membrane-bound nuclei.

E 56. Prokaryotes
   a. have nucleoid regions.
   b. are unicellular.
   c. have cell walls.
   d. are monerans.
 * e. all of these

M 57. Which of the following are made of two subunits and are composed of RNA and protein?
   a. Golgi bodies
   b. mitochondria
   c. chloroplasts
 * d. ribosomes
   e. endoplasmic reticula

M 58. A mutant bacterial strain without ribosomes would be incapable of
   a. carbohydrate synthesis.
   b. respiration.
   c. DNA programming.
 * d. protein synthesis.
   e. diffusion.

Matching Questions

M 59. Matching. Choose the one most appropriate answer for each.
   1. ___ microtubules
   2. ___ chloroplasts
   3. ___ Golgi bodies
   4. ___ DNA molecules
   5. ___ RNA molecules
   6. ___ central vacuoles
   7. ___ lysosomes
   8. ___ mitochondria
   9. ___ nucleoli
   10. ___ ribosomes

A. contain enzymes for intracellular digestion
B. are primary cellular organelles where proteins are assembled
C. package cellular secretions for export
D. extract energy stored in carbohydrates; synthesize ATP; produce water and carbon dioxide
E. synthesize subunits that will be assembled into two-part ribosomes in the cytoplasm
F. transcribe, translate hereditary instructions into specific proteins
G. increase cell surface area; store substances
H. encode hereditary information
I. help distribute chromosomes to the new cells during cell division
J. convert light energy to chemical energy stored in the chemical bonds of glucose or starch

Answers: 1. I   2. J   3. C   4. H
         5. F   6. G   7. A   8. D
         9. E   10. B

Classification Questions

The following items are organelles found in animal cells. Answer questions 60–68 with reference to these organelles.
   a. ribosome
   b. mitochondrion
   c. lysosome
   d. Golgi body
   e. endoplasmic reticulum

E 60. This organelle is the site of polypeptide assembly.

M 61. The cellular digestion and disposal of biological molecules occurs inside this organelle.

M 62. Aerobic respiration occurs in and on this organelle.

M 63. RNA carries out the genetic code translation process in association with ribosomes on this organelle.

M 64. The packaging of secretory proteins occurs in association with this structure.

M 65. This organelle is involved in lipid production and protein transport.

D 66. The hemoglobin of mammals and birds is synthesized on this tiny, two-part organelle.

E 67. Sugar metabolism occurs in association with this organelle.

D 68. DNA synthesis occurs in the nucleus. Its breakdown can occur in this organelle.

Answers   60. a   61. c   62. b   63. e
          64. d   65. e   66. a   67. b
          68. c

Selecting the Exception

D   69. Four of the five answers listed below are related by a common observation. Select the exception.
   a. Hooke
 * b. Galileo
   c. Schwann
   d. Schleiden
   e. Virchow

M   70. Four of the five statements listed below are portions of a well-known theory. Select the exception.
   a. Cells are the structural and functional components of living things.
   b. Cells arise from preexisting cells.
   c. All organisms are composed of cells.
   d. Cells are the basic living unit of organization of living things.
 * e. All cells have a nucleus.

M   71. Four of the five answers listed below are familiar organelles in the cytoplasm. Select the exception.
 * a. nucleolus
   b. mitochondrion
   c. ribosome
   d. Golgi body
   e. chloroplast

M   72. Four of the five answers listed below are parts of an electron microscope. Select the exception.
   a. projector lens
 * b. mirror
   c. electron gun
   d. condensing lens
   e. fluorescent screen or photographic film

M   73. Four of the five answers listed below are organelles found in eukaryotic cells. Select the exception.
   a. mitochondrion
   b. Golgi body
 * c. nucleoid
   d. lysosome
   e. vacuole

D   74. Four of the five answers listed below are composed of membranes. Select the exception.
   a. endoplasmic reticulum
   b. granum
   c. plasma membrane
 * d. chromosome
   e. nuclear envelope

D   75. Four of the five answers listed below are chloroplast features. Select the exception.
   a. stroma
   b. granum
 * c. microbody
   d. pigment
   e. ATP

D   76. Four of the five answers listed below are features of plasma membrane extensions. Select the exception.
 * a. amyloplast
   b. centriole
   c. microtubule
   d. basal body
   e. 9 + 2 array

D   77. Four of the five answers listed below are types of intercellular connections. Select the exception.
   a. tight junctions
   b. gap junctions
   c. plasmodesmata
   d. adhering junctions
 * e. microvilli

M   78. Four of the five answers listed below are bound by membranes. Select the exception.
   a. mitochondrion
 * b. ribosome
   c. chromoplast
   d. vacuole
   e. lysosome

CHAPTER 5
A CLOSER LOOK AT CELL MEMBRANES

Multiple-Choice Questions

MEMBRANE STRUCTURE AND FUNCTION

E   **1.** The phospholipid molecules of most membranes have
    a. a hydrophobic head and a hydrophilic tail.
    b. a hydrophobic head and a hydrophobic tail.
    c. a hydrophobic head and two hydrophobic tails.
 *   d. a hydrophilic head and two hydrophobic tails.
    e. none of these

M   **2.** If a cell membrane is pierced with a very fine needle, the cell will
    a. explode.
 *   b. seal itself.
    c. collapse.
    d. absorb fluid from the outside and grow.
    e. none of these

E   **3.** Hydrophobic reactions of phospholipids can produce clusters of their fatty acid tails to form
 *   a. a lipid bilayer.
    b. hydrolysis of the fatty acids.
    c. a protein membrane.
    d. a cytoskeleton.
    e. a nonpolar membrane.

D   **4.** Which of the following statements is true?
    a. When lipids and water are mixed, it is the water molecules that isolate themselves into droplets.
    b. When lipids and water are mixed, the lipids dissolve and enter into a solution.
 *   c. Lipids are classified as nonpolar substances and will not mix with water.
    d. Polar substances are able to pass through a plasma membrane more readily than nonpolar substances.
    e. All portions of a phospholipid molecule found in a membrane are classified as nonpolar.

D   **5.** A hypothetical "microbullet" shot through a phospholipid bilayer would pass the components in which order?
    a. tail >>> tail >>> head >>> head
    b. head >>> tail >>> head >>> tail
    c. tail >>> head >>> head >>> tail
 *   d. head >>> tail >>> tail >>> head
    e. head >>> head >>> tail >>> tail

D   **6.** If a plasma membrane were compared to a sandwich, _____ would be considered the filling.
    a. cholesterol
    b. protein
    c. hydrophilic heads
 *   d. hydrophobic tails
    e. carbohydrates

M   **7.** Unsaturated tails of lipids
    a. are hydrophilic.
    b. are unstable and tend to break apart.
 *   c. have kinks in them and lessen the interaction between adjacent fat molecules.
    d. will break whenever exposed to phosphate ions.
    e. all of these

M   **8.** Unsaturated tails tend to _____ at the sites of their double bonds.
    a. dissolve
 *   b. kink or bend
    c. separate
    d. react with ions
    e. none of these

M   **9.** The relative impermeability of membranes to water-soluble molecules is a result of
    a. the nonpolar nature of water molecules.
    b. the presence of large proteins that extend through both sides of membranes.
    c. the presence of inorganic salt crystals scattered through some membranes.
    d. the presence of cellulose and chemicals such as cutin, lignin, pectin, and suberin in the membranes.
 *   e. the presence of phospholipids in the lipid bilayer.

D   **10.** Which statement is NOT true?
    a. Membranes are often perforated by proteins that extend through both sides of the membrane.
    b. Some membranes have proteins with channels or pores that allow for the passage of hydrophilic substances.
 *   c. Hydrophilic substances have an easier time passing through membranes than do hydrophobic substances.
    d. The current concept of a membrane can be best summarized by the fluid mosaic model.
    e. The lipid bilayer serves as a hydrophobic barrier between two fluid regions.

D   11.   Which of the following statements is NOT true?

a. A lipid bilayer is characteristic of all membranes.

b. Cellular organelles are associated with membranes.

c. In a plasma membrane, the hydrophilic portion is oriented to the outside of the cell.

d. Lipid molecules make the cell membrane relatively impermeable to water.

*   e. Even under extremely high magnification, an electron microscope cannot reveal the substructure of cell membranes.

D   12.   In an attempt to visualize the fluid mosaic model of a membrane, we could describe the _____ as floating in a sea of _____.

a. lipid; protein

b. phospholipids; carbohydrate

*   c. proteins; lipid

d. fats; water

e. glycolipids; sterols

M   13.   A membrane is more "fluid" than solid because

a. phospholipid tails prevent close packing.

b. proteins can shift positions.

c. water is the main component.

*   d. phospholipid tails prevent close packing and proteins can shift positions.

e. phospholipid tails prevent close packing, proteins can shift positions, and water is the main component.

D   14.   Which of the following statements is false?

a. The plasma membrane is more like a fluid than a solid.

*   b. The cell membrane is symmetrical, so it is impossible to identify which is the extracellular surface.

c. The glycoproteins have their sugar side chains on the outside of the cell membrane.

d. The plasma membrane is in constant movement, with proteins shifting positions.

e. There are functional differences between the two sides of the plasma membranes.

D   15.   Cholesterol

*   a. is not found in plant membranes.

b. makes a membrane more fluid (flexible) wherever it is found.

c. at high concentrations tends to make fatty-acid tails stick together.

d. renders membranes more fluid in cold temperature.

e. all of these

D   16.   Glycolipids differ from other membrane lipids in that they

a. have hydrophilic heads.

b. have hydrophobic heads.

*   c. have molecules of a monosaccharide associated with them.

d. have saturated and partially unsaturated tails.

e. are stationary molecules found scattered throughout the membrane.

A GALLERY OF MEMBRANE PROTEINS

M   17.   Which statement is true of plasma membranes?

*   a. They have molecules on their surfaces that identify them.

b. They are essentially impermeable.

c. They are basically static, nonchanging structures.

d. They are hydrophilic barriers between cells.

e. They function primarily through the activity of their carbohydrates.

D   18.   A transport protein is most analogous to a

a. water pipe.

*   b. subway train.

c. light switch.

d. voice identification device.

e. television receiver.

M   19.   Most of the functions of plasma membranes are carried out by

a. cholesterol.

*   b. proteins.

c. hydrophilic heads.

d. hydrophobic tails.

e. carbohydrates.

D   20.   A water-soluble hormone would most likely bind to which of the following membrane proteins?

a. carrier

b. recognition

*   c. receptor

d. channel

e. transport

D   21.   Which of the following proteins is not necessarily associated with the plasma membrane?

a. recognition protein

*   b. antibody protein

c. receptor protein

d. channel protein

e. adhesion protein

THINK DIFFUSION

D   22.   Which of the following affects the rate of diffusion through a semipermeable membrane?

I.   **steeper concentration gradients**

II.   **higher temperatures**

III.   **molecular size**

a. I only

b. II only

c. I and II

d. II and III

*   e. I, II, and III

D   23. The rate of diffusion through a semipermeable
          membrane will be lowest when which of the following
          is (are) true?
          I.   Concentration gradients are steep.
          II.   Temperatures are low.
          III.   Solutes are small molecules.
          a. I only
     *   b. II only
          c. I and III
          d. II and III
          e. I, II, and III

M   24. A concentration gradient ceases to exist when
          a. all the molecules have moved from high
              concentration to low.
          b. the membrane pores close.
          c. the temperature drops.
     *   d. there is no net movement.
          e. bulk flow intervenes.

E   25. In simple diffusion,
          a. the rate of movement of molecules is controlled by
              temperature and pressure.
          b. the movement of individual molecules is random.
          c. the movement of molecules of one substance is
              independent of the movement of any other
              substance.
          d. the net movement is away from the region of
              highest concentration.
     *   e. all of these

M   26. Oxygen, carbon dioxide, glucose, and other small
          molecules cross the plasma membrane through the
          process(es) of
          a. osmosis.
     *   b. diffusion.
          c. endocytosis and exocytosis.
          d. active transport.
          e. facilitated diffusion.

M   27. Which substance passes most readily into a cell?
          a. ions
          b. large molecules
          c. glucose
     *   d. ethanol
          e. polar molecules

D   28. Movement of matter or energy in nature may be the
          result of
          a. concentration gradients.
          b. differential pressures.
          c. differences in electrical charges.
          d. the existence of thermal differentials.
     *   e. all of these

TYPES OF CROSSING MECHANISMS

E   29. Movement of a molecule against a concentration
          gradient is
          a. simple diffusion.
          b. facilitated diffusion.
          c. osmosis.
     *   d. active transport.
          e. bulk flow.

M   30. The method of movement that requires the expenditure
          of ATP molecules is
          a. simple diffusion.
          b. facilitated diffusion.
          c. osmosis.
     *   d. active transport.
          e. bulk flow.

M   31. Which of the following does NOT require the
          participation of a membrane protein?
          a. active transport
          b. exocytosis
          c. facilitated diffusion
     *   d. simple diffusion
          e. all of these require a protein

HOW DO THE TRANSPORTERS WORK?

E   32. The sodium-potassium pump is an example of
          a. simple diffusion.
          b. facilitated diffusion.
          c. osmosis.
     *   d. active transport.
          e. bulk flow.

M   33. The carrier molecules used in active transport are
          a. calcium ions in the calcium pump.
     *   b. proteins.
          c. ATP molecules.
          d. carbohydrates.
          e. lipids.

WHICH WAY WILL WATER MOVE?

D   34. A single-celled freshwater organism, such as a
          protistan, is transferred to saltwater. Which of the
          following is likely to happen?
          a. The cell bursts.
          b. Salt is pumped out of the cell.
     *   c. The cell shrinks.
          d. Enzymes flow out of the cell.
          e. all of these

M   35. Which statement is true?
          a. A cell placed in an isotonic solution will swell.
     *   b. A cell placed in a hypotonic solution will swell.
          c. A cell placed in a hypotonic solution will shrink.
          d. A cell placed in a hypertonic solution will remain
              the same size.
          e. A cell placed in a hypotonic solution will remain
              the same size.

E   36. Distilled water refers to water that nearly is free of
     *   a. solutes.
          b. ions.
          c. gases.
          d. suspended solids.
          e. none of these

D   **37.** Which statement is true?
   * a. The movement of solvent occurs from a hypotonic solution to an isotonic solution.
      b. The net movement from an isotonic to a hypotonic solution involves the movement of solute molecules only.
      c. The concentration of the solute is greater in an isotonic solution than in a hypertonic solution.
      d. The concentration of the solvent is greater in a hypertonic solution than in an isotonic solution.
      e. Osmosis involves only hypertonic solutions.

D   **38.** The net direction that an ion or molecule moves is
      a. dependent upon the size of the molecule.
      b. unpredictable because movement is random.
      c. controlled by the temperature of the medium.
      d. controlled by the membranes in the vicinity.
   * e. the result of concentration differences.

E   **39** A red blood cell will lyse when placed in which of the following kinds of solution?
   * a. hypotonic
      b. hypertonic
      c. isotonic
      d. any of the above
      e. none of these

M **40.** If a plant cell is placed in a hypotonic solution,
      a. the entire cell will not swell or shrink.
      b. the entire cell will shrink.
      c. the turgor pressure will increase.
      d. the cell wall prevents the cell from exploding.
   * e. the turgor pressure will increase but the cell wall prevents the cell from exploding.

M **41** Wilting of a plant occurs
      a. if the plant is placed in an isotonic solution.
      b. if there is a rise in turgor pressure.
      c. as a result of facilitated diffusion.
   * d. when a plant with flexible cell walls is placed in a hypertonic solution.

M **42.** Wilting is counteracted by
   * a. turgor pressure.
      b. osmotic pressure.
      c. concentration gradients.
      d. diffusion.
      e. metabolic pressure within a cell.

M **43.** Which of the following is NOT a form of active transport?
      a. sodium-potassium pump
      b. endocytosis
      c. exocytosis
   * d. bulk flow
      e. none of these

D   **44.** Which statement is NOT true of bulk flow?
      a. It is faster than diffusion.
   * b. It explains massive movement on a microscopic scale, but movement over large distances in animals is more likely due to diffusion.
      c. It involves the movement of the molecules of different substances together.
      d. It accounts for the movement of sap in the vascular tissues of plants.
      e. When present, materials of different substances move in the same direction in response to pressure gradients.

M **45.** Bulk flow differs from osmosis in that bulk flow
   * a. involves molecules that are not all alike.
      b. goes against pressure gradients.
      c. is intracellular.
      d. is the reverse of osmosis.
      e. is used only by plants.

MEMBRANE TRAFFIC TO AND FROM THE CELL SURFACE

D   **46.** Which of the following is NOT a form of passive transport?
      a. osmosis
      b. facilitated diffusion
      c. bulk flow
   * d. exocytosis
      e. none of these

M **47.** White blood cells use _____ to get rid of foreign particles in the blood.
      a. simple diffusion
      b. bulk flow
      c. osmosis
   * d. phagocytosis
      e. facilitated diffusion

M **48.** The action of a white blood cell engulfing a bacterium is
      a. pinocytosis.
      b. phagocytosis.
      c. exocytosis.
      d. endocytosis.
   * e. phagocytosis and endocytosis.

M **49.** Exocytotic vesicles develop from the membranes of which of the following structures?
      a. mitochondria
   * b. Golgi bodies
      c. lysosomes
      d. vacuoles
      e. phagocytes

Classification Questions

Questions 50–54 ask about membrane permeability. Answer them in reference to the following five processes:

    a. simple diffusion
    b. bulk flow
    c. osmosis
    d. active transport
    e. endocytosis

E   **50.** This process is used by white blood cells to ingest bacteria.

E   **51.** This process specifically moves water molecules across a differentially permeable membrane.

E   **52.** This process explains the movement of any kind of molecule from areas of higher concentration to areas of lower concentration.

E   **53.** This process is the tendency of molecules to move more rapidly because they move together.

M   **54.** This process explains the movement of molecules against a concentration gradient.

Answers   50. e   51. c   52. a

              53. b   54. d

Selecting the Exception

M   **55.** Four of the five answers listed below are characteristics of the plasma membrane. Select the exception.
    a. phospholipid
    b. fluid mosaic
    c. lipid bilayer
*   d. inert and impermeable
    e. hydrophobic tails

M   **56.** Four of the five answers listed below are factors affecting simple diffusion. Select the exception.
    a. temperature
    b. pressure
*   c. characteristic of the membrane
    d. size of the molecules
    e. concentration gradient

M   **57.** Four of the five answers listed below result when a cell is placed in a hypertonic solution. Select the exception.
    a. wilting
    b. plasmolysis
*   c. turgidity
    d. limpness
    e. shriveling

D   **58.** Four of the five answers listed below are related by energy requirements. Select the exception.
    a. water potential
    b. osmosis
    c. bulk flow
*   d. active transport
    e. diffusion

D   **59.** Four of the five answers listed below are related by energy requirements. Select the exception.
    a. active transport
    b. endocytosis
*   c. facilitated diffusion
    d. exocytosis
    e. sodium-potassium pump

CHAPTER 6
GROUND RULES OF METABOLISM

Multiple-Choice Questions

ENERGY AND THE UNDERLYING ORGANIZATION OF LIFE

D **1.** Metabolism describes
    a. the cell's capacity to acquire energy.
    b. cellular processes used to store substances.
    c. reactions that break apart nutrients to release energy.
    d. the elimination of waste products.
    * e. all of these

M **2** Energy
    a. cannot be produced by fungi and heterotrophic organisms.
    b. involves ATP in living organisms.
    c. is the ability to do work.
    d. usage is governed by the laws of thermodynamics.
    * e. all of these

D **3.** According to the first law of thermodynamics,
    a. although energy in the universe is constant, energy in an earthly system may increase.
    b. the amount of energy in the universe is constant.
    c. chemical reactions do not create or destroy energy.
    d. energy can change from one form to another.
    * e. all of these

D **4.** The second law of thermodynamics holds that
    a. matter can be neither created nor destroyed.
    b. energy can be neither created nor destroyed.
    * c. energy of one form is converted to a less concentrated form whenever energy is transformed or transferred.
    d. entropy decreases with time.
    e. none of these

M **5.** The second law of thermodynamics states that
    a. energy can be transformed into matter and, because of this, we can get something for nothing.
    b. energy can be destroyed only during nuclear reactions, such as those that occur inside the sun.
    c. if energy is gained by one region of the universe, another place in the universe also must gain energy in order to maintain the balance of nature.
    * d. energy tends to become increasingly more disorganized.

D **6.** Which of the following statements is false?
    a. The universe has a certain amount of energy.
    b. One form of energy can be converted to other forms of energy.
    c. Whenever energy conversions occur, some energy is lost.
    * d. Once energy is utilized, it disappears.
    e. There are differences in the quality of energy.

E **7.** Essentially, the first law of thermodynamics says that
    a. one form of energy cannot be converted into another.
    b. entropy is increasing in the universe.
    * c. energy can be neither created nor destroyed.
    d. energy cannot be converted into matter or matter into energy.
    e. all of these

D **8.** Which of the following is an application of the first law of thermodynamics?
    a. The level of entropy increases as time passes.
    b. Living organisms represent an exception to the laws of energy.
    * c. Energy does not increase or decrease.
    d. Fungi and plants do not make their own energy but derive it from somewhere else.
    e. The amount of energy found in the compounds on one side of an equation is equal to that on the other side.

D **9.** Which statement is NOT true?
    a. Because living things maintain organization, entropy does not apply to living organisms.
    b. The amount of energy in the web of life is greatest among the plants that capture solar energy.
    * c. A state of maximum entropy will never occur.
    d. Entropy applies at the molecular level as well as at the organismal level.
    e. Entropy is a measure of the degree of disorder of a system.

D **10.** The energy used by living organisms
    a. is declining through time.
    * b. is derived by breaking bonds that hold the atoms in organic molecules together.
    c. involves ionic bonds more often than covalent bonds.
    d. is available only from glucose when it undergoes respiration.
    e. tends to accumulate in a food chain.

M **11.** Which of the following is NOT true?
    a. Cells lose some energy in the form of heat.
    b. Energy flows in one direction.
    c. The web of life refers to the flow of energy through an ecosystem.
    d. The primary source for energy on earth is the sun.
    * e. The most common and important form of energy available for living organisms is heat.

M   12.   The most common form of low-quality energy released in energy conversions is
      a.   metabolic.
   * b.   heat.
      c.   entropy.
      d.   exergonic emission.
      e.   oxidation.

ENERGY INPUTS, OUTPUTS, AND CELLULAR WORK

M   13.   Which reaction is NOT an exergonic reaction?
   * a.   protein synthesis
      b.   digestion
      c.   fire
      d.   respiration
      e.   movement

D   14.   Endergonic reactions
      a.   have more energy in the reactants than in the products.
   * b.   have more energy in the products than in the reactants.
      c.   are illustrated by the breakdown of glucose.
      d.   are the mechanisms used by animals to provide energy for biological reactions.
      e.   have more energy in the products than in the reactants and are illustrated by the breakdown of glucose.

D   15.   Which of the following statements about exergonic reactions is NOT true?
      a.   They release energy.
      b.   Glucose metabolism is an example.
   * c.   Their products have more energy than the reactants.
      d.   There is an energy loss.
      e.   Bonds are broken.

E   16.   ATP contains
      a.   alanine.
      b.   arginine.
   * c.   ribose.
      d.   tyrosine.
      e.   glucose.

E   17.   ATP contains
   * a.   adenine.
      b.   cytosine.
      c.   uracil.
      d.   thymine.
      e.   guanine.

D   18.   A "high-energy bond"
      a.   absorbs a large amount of free energy when the phosphate group is attached during hydrolysis.
      b.   is formed when ATP is hydrolyzed to ADP and one phosphate group.
      c.   is usually found in each glucose molecule; that is why glucose is chosen as the starting point for glycolysis.
   * d.   releases a large amount of usable energy when the phosphate group is split off during hydrolysis.
      e.   none of these

M   19.   A molecule that gives up an electron becomes
      I. ionized.   **II.   oxidized.**
      III. reduced.
      a.   I only
      b.   II only
      c.   III only
   * d.   I and II
      e.   I and III

M   20.   The removal of electrons from a compound is known as
      a.   dehydration.
   * b.   oxidation.
      c.   reduction.
      d.   phosphorylation.
      e.   a nonreversible chemical reaction.

M   21.   When NAD^+ combines with hydrogen, the NAD^+ is
   * a.   reduced.
      b.   oxidized.
      c.   phosphorylated.
      d.   denatured.
      e.   none of these

CELLS JUGGLE SUBSTANCES AS WELL AS ENERGY

M   22.   The "balancing" of chemical equations is dictated by
      a.   the laws of thermodynamics.
      b.   tradition.
      c.   chemistry teachers.
   * d.   the law of conservation of mass.
      e.   none of these

D   23.   Which of the following statements is true?
      a.   The products of a reaction can have less energy than the reactants.
      b.   The products of a reaction can have more energy than the reactants.
      c.   Reversible reactions tend to approach an equilibrium.
      d.   Most reactions are reversible.
   * e.   all of these

D   24.   Chemical equilibrium for a particular reaction will not be achieved if
      a.   more reactants are added.
      b.   products are removed.
      c.   additional enzyme is added.
      d.   more reactants are added and products are removed.
   * e.   more reactants are added, products are removed, and additional enzyme is added.

D   25.   Which of the following statements is NOT true?
         a.   At an equilibrium there are equal numbers of molecules on each side of a reaction.
         b.   Chemical equilibrium is controlled solely by the amount of the reactants available.
         c.   A chemical equilibrium is reached when the forward and reverse reactions occur at the same rate.
    *   d.   At an equilibrium there are equal numbers of molecules on each side of a reaction; and Chemical equilibrium is controlled solely by the amount of the reactants available.
         e.   At an equilibrium there are equal numbers of molecules on each side of a reaction; and Chemical equilibrium is controlled solely by the amount of the reactants available; and A chemical equilibrium is reached when the forward and reverse reactions occur at the same rate.

M   26.   Chemical reactions will reach an equilibrium under which of the following conditions?
         a.   There is sufficient time.
         b.   The reactions are reversible.
         c.   Product remains after it is formed.
         d.   There are sufficient reactants.
    *   e.   all of these

M   27.   A chemical equilibrium
         a.   means the concentration of reactants and products is the same.
    *   b.   means the rate of opposing reactions is equal.
         c.   means highly spontaneous reactions are less likely to occur than when the system is not at equilibrium.
         d.   means both reactions are typically proceeding against concentration gradients.
         e.   only occurs in endergonic reactions.

M   28.   A biosynthetic pathway can be characterized as
    *   a.   endergonic.
         b.   exergonic.
         c.   degradative.
         d.   releasing energy.
         e.   producing ATP.

E   29.   An orderly sequence of reactions with specific enzymes acting at each step is the definition of
         a.   energy carriers.
    *   b.   metabolic pathway.
         c.   induced-fit model.
         d.   intermediary compounds.
         e.   activation.

E   30.   Substances that enter a reaction are termed
         a.   intermediates.
         b.   enzymes.
         c.   energy carriers.
    *   d.   reactants.
         e.   none of these

ELECTRON TRANSFER CHAINS IN THE MAIN METABOLIC PATHWAYS

D   31   Which of the following substances would be unlikely to function as a coenzyme?
         a.   a water-soluble vitamin
         b.   an iron ion
    *   c.   glucose
         d. NAD^+
         e.   a magnesium ion

D   32 NAD^+ and FAD are
         a.   coenzymes.
         b.   electron acceptors.
         c.   reduced forms.
    *   d.   coenzymes and electron acceptors.
         e.   coenzymes, electron acceptors, and reduced forms.

M   33.   ATP and $NADP^+$ act as what type of agents between breakdown and synthesis pathways?
    *   a.   linkage
         b.   feedback
         c.   catalytic
         d.   allosteric
         e.   enzymatic

M   34.   Which of the following is most closely associated with photosynthesis?
         a.   FADH
         b.   FAD
         c. NAD^+
    *   d. $NADP^+$
         e. $NADH_2$

M   35   The molecule $NADP^+$ is
         I.   a coenzyme.
         II.   a prosthetic group.
         III. a nucleotide.
         a.   I only
         b.   I and II
    *   c.   I and III
         d.   III only
         e.   I, II, and III

ENZYMES HELP WITH ENERGY HILLS

D   36.   Which of the following may show enzymatic activity?
         I.   lipids   II.   proteins   III.   RNA
         a.   I only
         b.   II only
         c.   III only
         d.   I and II
    *   e.   II and III

E   37.   Which of the following is NOT true of enzyme behavior?
a.   Enzyme shape may change during catalysis.
b.   The active site of an enzyme orients its substrate molecules, thereby promoting interaction of their reactive parts.
c.   All enzymes have an active site where substrates are temporarily bound.
*   d.   Each enzyme can catalyze a wide variety of different reactions.

E   38.   Enzymes
a.   are very specific.
b.   act as catalysts.
c.   are organic molecules.
d.   have special shapes that control their activities.
*   e.   all of these

M   39.   Enzymes
a.   control the speed of a reaction.
b.   change shapes to facilitate certain reactions.
c.   may place physical stress on the bonds of the substrate.
d.   may require cofactors.
*   e.   all of these

D   40.   Which of the following statements is false?
a.   Enzymes catalyze reversible reactions in either direction.
b.   Enzymes are highly specific.
c.   Most enzymes are protein molecules.
*   d.   Enzymes allow some reactions to occur that would never occur without their help.
e.   Although enzymes may be modified during their involvement with the substrate, they revert to their original characteristics when the reaction is over.

M   41   For an enzyme to function, what kind of energy must be provided?
a.   combination
*   b.   activation
c.   thermal
d.   electrical
e.   solar

M   42   Activation energy
a.   is less when enzymes are present.
b.   allows greater interaction of substrate with the active site.
c.   is needed to begin a reaction.
d.   is less when enzymes are present and is needed to begin a reaction.
*   e.   is less when enzymes are present, allows greater interaction of substrate with the active site, and is needed to begin a reaction.

M   43.   Enzymes
*   a.   may be secreted by glands.
b.   are usually molecules of RNA.
c.   are nonspecific with regard to substrate.
d.   enable some reactions to occur that would never happen without the availability of enzymes.
e.   will mediate a reversible reaction in one direction only.

ENZYMES DON'T WORK IN A VACUUM

E   44.   During enzyme-catalyzed reactions, *substrate* is a synonym for
a.   end products.
b.   by-products.
c.   enzymes.
*   d.   reactants.
e.   none of these

D   45.   The active site of an enzyme
a.   is where the coenzyme is located.
b.   is a specific bulge or protuberance on an enzyme.
*   c.   is a groove or crevice in the structure of the enzyme.
d.   will react with only one substrate no matter how many molecules may resemble the shape of the substrate.
e.   rigidly resists any alteration of its shape.

M   46.   The inadequacy of the lock-and-key model of enzyme-substrate interaction was that
a.   there were more keys than locks.
b.   keys could change too easily.
c.   locks were too numerous for available keys.
*   d.   it was too inflexible.
e.   Emil Fischer did not know that enzymes were proteins.

D   47.   Which of the following is NOT a true statement?
a.   When an enzyme and a substrate fit together, they are in the "transition state."
*   b.   Most enzymes and substrates are exact fits, like a lock and key.
c.   Activation energy must be supplied before the "transition state" is reached.
d.   The idea for the lock-and-key theory was first proposed over 100 years ago.
e.   Enzymes have an active site where the substrate fits.

M   48.   Enzymatic reactions can be controlled by
a.   the amount of substrates available.
b.   the concentration of products.
c.   temperature.
d.   modification of reactive sites by substances that fit into the enzyme and, later, their reactive site.
*   e.   all of these

D   49.   Inhibitors of enzyme-catalyzed reactions act by
a.   forming clusters of reactants that are unable to break free.
b.   tying up ATP supplies.
*   c.   binding to the enzyme's active site.
d.   tying up ATP supplies, and binding to the enzyme's active site.
e.   forming clusters of reactants that are unable to break free, tying up ATP supplies, and binding to the enzyme's active site.

M 50. Enzymes may be controlled by
   a. hormones.
   b. pH.
   c. inhibitors.
   d. the presence of cofactors.
* e. all of these

E 51. Enzymes may be controlled by
   a. temperature.
   b. the presence of chemicals that fit into allosteric sites.
   c. feedback inhibition.
   d. current metabolic conditions in the cell.
* e. all of these

M 52. Which of the following statements is false?
   a. Enzymes are highly specific and act on chemicals called substrates.
   b. Enzymes act as catalysts and speed up chemical reactions within cells.
* c. Heavy metals such as cadmium and mercury function as coenzymes or activators of enzymes so they can function.
   d. Most enzymes are proteins.
   e. Enzymes can become denatured in high fevers.

M 53. Allosteric inhibition is generally a result of
   a. excess substrates.
* b. binding of regulatory molecules at another site.
   c. a change in the temperature of the system.
   d. a lack of coenzymes.
   e. pH inhibition.

D 54. An allosteric enzyme
* a. has an active site where substrate molecules bind and another site that binds with intermediate or end-product molecules.
   b. is an important energy-carrying nucleotide.
   c. carries out either oxidation reactions or reduction reactions but not both.
   d. raises the activation energy of the chemical reaction it catalyzes.
   e. all of these

Matching Questions

M 55. Matching. Choose the one most appropriate answer for each.

1. ___ active site
2. ___ allosteric enzyme
3. ___ adenosine triphosphate
4. ___ $NADP^+$
5. ___ catalyst
6. ___ cytochromes
7. ___ denaturation
8. ___ equilibrium
9. ___ feedback inhibition
10. ___ phosphorylation

A. rate of forward reaction equals rate of reverse reaction
B. transfer agent that carries hydrogen and electrons to sites where hydrogen-containing molecules are being assembled
C. attaching a phosphate group by a high-energy bond
D. an excess of end-product molecules alters the shape of the first enzyme in the pathway and shuts off that metabolic pathway
E. part of an enzyme that binds to the substrate
F. by binding a regulatory molecule, it changes the activity of a metabolic pathway
G. lowers the activation energy of a reaction
H. universal energy currency
I. carriers in a series that help transport electrons
J. a permanent loss of protein structure

Answers: 1. E   2. F   3. H   4. B

5. G   6. I   7. J   8. A

9. D   10. C

Classification Questions

Items a–c below are processes that occur during different stages of photosynthesis. Answer questions 56–59 by selecting one of these three processes.

- a. oxidation
- b. reduction
- c. phosphorylation

E **56.** This process leads to the formation of ATP from ADP plus inorganic phosphate.

M **57.** When an electron is passed to an electron acceptor molecule, such as $NADP^+$, this process occurs to the $NADP^+$.

D **58.** When a photon of light energy causes an electron to leave the chlorophyll molecule, this process is involved.

M **59.** When an electron transport molecule, such as ferrodoxin, gives up an electron, this process occurs to the ferrodoxin.

Answers   56. c   57. b   58. a   59. a

Selecting the Exception

E **60.** Four of the five answers listed below are related to the second law of thermodynamics. Select the exception.
- a. entropy
- * b. Energy can be neither created nor destroyed.
- c. The amount of available energy in a closed system declines with time.
- d. Energy is lost as it is transferred or transformed to another form.
- e. Spontaneous flow of energy from high- to low-quality forms occurs.

M **61.** Four of the five answers listed below apply to conditions in which energy is released. Select the exception.
- * a. endergonic reaction
- b. respiration
- c. entropy
- d. second law of thermodynamics
- e. exergonic reaction

M **62.** Four of the five answers listed below are related by their description of enzyme properties. Select the exception.
- a. cofactors
- b. active sites
- c. activation energy
- * d. substrate
- e. catalyst

D **63.** Four of the five answers listed below are cofactors or coenzymes. Select the exception.
- a. mineral
- b. water-soluble vitamin
- c. metallic ions
- d. NAD^+
- * e. protein

D **64.** Four of the five answers listed below affect the rate of an enzymatic reaction. Select the exception.
- a. pH
- b. temperature
- c. concentration
- d. built-up product
- * e. presence of hormones

D **65.** Four of the five answers listed below are metabolic processes. Select the exception.
- a. protein synthesis
- * b. growth
- c. digestion
- d. phosphorylation
- e. oxidation-reduction

D **66.** Three of the four answers listed below are parts of a common molecule. Select the exception.
- a. phosphate group
- b. adenine
- * c. deoxyribose
- d. ribose

CHAPTER 7
HOW CELLS ACQUIRE ENERGY

Multiple-Choice Questions

E 1. Plants need which of the following to carry on photosynthesis?
   a. H_2O
   b. CO_2
   c. O_2
   d. lipid
 * e. H_2O and CO_2

D 2. The text describes a long-lasting drought in the midwestern United States. The significance of this discussion is anchored in the concept that
   a. all organisms respond to environmental conditions.
   b. the balance of payments and the responding general economic conditions can be affected by a downturn in agriculture.
 * c. living organisms require food if they are going to survive.
   d. water is only one of a great number of environmental factors that affect living organisms.
   e. starvation is one of the common forms of death in foreign countries.

E 3. The ultimate source for food is
   a. the grocery store.
   b. the soil.
   c. certain green plants.
 * d. the sun.
   e. various metabolic pathways found in all living organisms.

E 4. The conversion of solar energy to chemical energy occurs during
   a. glycolysis.
 * b. photosynthesis.
   c. respiration.
   d. fermentation.
   e. chemosynthesis.

D 5. Chemosynthetic bacteria may use which element as a hydrogen donor instead of water?
   a. potassium dihydrogen phosphate
 * b. sulfur
   c. hydrogen sulfate
   d. hydrogen chloride
   e. hydrogen peroxide

D 6. Chemosynthetic forms of life
   a. derive energy from sunlight.
 * b. derive energy by stripping hydrogen from inorganic compounds such as sulfur compounds.
   c. are anaerobic forms that live in the dark.
   d. are one form of heterotrophic life.
   e. are unable to generate enough energy to synthesize complex food-storage molecules.

E 7. Organisms that derive their chemical energy from the process of chemosynthesis are classified as
 * a. autotrophs.
   b. parasites.
   c. heterotrophs.
   d. saprophytes.
   e. mutualists.

D 8. Heterotrophs are
   a. self-feeding.
   b. independent of other forms of life for sustenance.
   c. unable to participate in the web of life.
   d. animals only.
 * e. none of these

D 9. Animals obtain their energy and carbon from
   a. the sun and atmosphere directly.
 * b. chemical compounds formed by autotrophs.
   c. inorganic sources.
   d. chemical compounds formed by autotrophs and inorganic sources.
   e. the sun and atmosphere directly, chemical compounds formed by autotrophs, and inorganic sources.

PHOTOSYNTHESIS–AN OVERVIEW

E 10. The carbon source for organisms that derive their energy from photosynthesis is
   a. carbon monoxide.
 * b. carbon dioxide.
   c. hydrocarbons.
   d. methane.
   e. glucose.

M 11. Most carbon enters the web of life through
   a. chemosynthesis.
   b. aerobic respiration.
   c. anaerobic respiration.
 * d. photosynthesis.
   e. both chemosynthesis and aerobic respiration.

M 12. The oxygen released in photosynthesis comes from
   a. carbon dioxide.
   b. glucose.
   c. ribulose bisphosphate.
 * d. water.
   e. atmospheric oxygen.

M 13. The internal membrane system of the chloroplast is called a
* a. thylakoid.
   b. stroma.
   c. lamella.
   d. mitochondrion.
   e. tracheid.

M 14. Which of the following is NOT associated with the light-dependent reactions?
   a. ATP
   b. thylakoids
   c. chlorophyll
* d. stroma
   e. water

E 15. Thylakoid disks are stacked in groups called
* a. grana.
   b. stroma.
   c. lamellae.
   d. cristae.
   e. none of these

D 16. Actual assembly of sugars during photosynthesis
   a. occurs during light-independent reactions.
   b. takes place in the stroma.
   c. requires chlorophyll.
* d. occurs during light-independent reactions and takes place in the stroma.
   e. occurs during light-independent reactions, takes place in the stroma, and requires chlorophyll.

SUNLIGHT AS AN ENERGY SOURCE

M 17. Which of the following statements is NOT true?
   a. Photons are packages of solar energy.
* b. The longer the wavelength of light, the more energy it has.
   c. Chlorophyll absorbs energy from light.
   d. Photons with different energy levels produce different colors.
   e. Visible light is a very small portion of the electromagnetic spectrum.

D 18. Which of the following statements about the electromagnetic spectrum is true?
   a. Infrared energy is sufficient to produce ionization.
   b. Infrared radiation has more energy than red radiation.
   c. Visible light has more energy than ultraviolet radiation.
* d. Chlorophyll absorbs some visible wavelengths, but not all.
   e. Chloroplasts absorb all wavelengths of light equally.

E 19. Which of the following colors of light has the greatest energy?
   a. red
   b. yellow
   c. orange
* d. blue
   e. green

THE RAINBOW CATCHERS

M 20. When light excites chlorophyll, the chlorophyll molecule
   a. changes to carotene.
   b. becomes agitated and moves rapidly.
   c. becomes radioactive.
* d. absorbs the energy and moves an electron to a higher energy state.
   e. becomes ionized.

M 21. The first event of photosynthesis is the
   a. hydrolysis of water.
   b. synthesis of sugar.
* c. transfer of an electron from chlorophyll.
   d. manufacture of ATP.
   e. synthesis of NADPH.

M 22. When a molecule is excited by heat or light,
   a. it may lose an electron.
   b. it may gain an electron.
* c. an electron from an inner energy level may move to another level.
   d. an electron from an outer energy level may move to an inner level.
   e. an electron may be ejected from the nucleus of the atom.

M 23. The first event in photosynthesis is the
   a. formation of phosphoglyceric acid.
* b. donation of an electron from the photosystem to an acceptor.
   c. fixation of carbon dioxide.
   d. breakdown of the thylakoid membrane.
   e. formation of phosphoglyceraldehyde.

M 24. Chlorophyll reflects (does not absorb) which color of light?
   a. red
   b. yellow
   c. orange
* d. green
   e. blue

E 25. Carotenoid pigments reflect (do not absorb) which color of light?
   a. red
* b. yellow
   c. orange
   d. green
   e. blue

D 26. Which of the following choices is NOT true?
* a. Carotenoid pigments use yellow and red light to carry on photosynthesis.
   b. Carotenoids are accessory pigments that capture certain energy from light and transfer it into chlorophyll.
   c. The presence of carotenoid pigments in a leaf is masked by the presence of chlorophyll.
   d. Carotenoid pigments absorb blue and violet wavelengths and reflect red, orange, and yellow.

M 27. Where in a plant cell is chlorophyll found?
     a. on the outer chloroplast membrane
     b. inside the mitochondria
     c. in the stroma
   * d. in the thylakoids
     e. none of these

M 28. Photosystems are mainly
   * a. light-trapping molecules.
     b. enzymes for splitting water.
     c. clusters of ATP molecules.
     d. sugar assembly sites.

THE LIGHT-DEPENDENT REACTIONS

D 29. Which of the following is most descriptive of an electron transfer chain?
     a. It generates energy from nothing.
     b. It is a mechanism used by cells to dispose of unused electrons.
     c. It utilizes ATP in the synthesis of nutrients.
   * d. It transfers energy, stepwise, from one compound to another.
     e. It requires activation by sunlight.

D 30. The photosystem with P700 is designated "I" (Roman numeral one) because
     a. it is the first to react.
   * b. it is assumed to have evolved first.
     c. it is primary.
     d. a and b are correct
     e. b and c are correct

E 31. The cyclic pathway functions mainly to
     a. fix CO_2.
     b. produce O_2.
   * c. make ATP.
     d. reduce NADP.
     e. split H_2O.

M 32. In the cyclic pathway,
   * a. ATP alone forms.
     b. ATP and NADPH form.
     c. oxygen is a by-product.
     d. water participates in the process.
     e. two photosystems are involved.

E 33. The final hydrogen acceptor in the noncyclic pathway of ATP formation is
     a. FAD.
     b. PGA.
   * c. $NADP^+$.
     d. FMN.
     e. PEP.

M 34. The electrons that are passed to $NADP^+$ during the noncyclic pathway were obtained from
   * a. chlorophyll.
     b. CO_2.
     c. glucose.
     d. sunlight.
     e. ATP.

E 35. An important electron and hydrogen acceptor in the noncyclic pathway is
   * a. $NADP^+$.
     b. ADP.
     c. O_2.
     d. H_2O.
     e. none of these

M 36. Photolysis involves
     a. the cyclic pathway of ATP formation.
     b. photosystem I.
     c. carotenoid pigments.
   * d. the noncyclic pathway of ATP formation.
     e. both the cyclic pathway of ATP formation and photosystem I.

D 37. The products of the light-dependent reactions of photosynthesis
   * a. are used in the light-independent reactions.
     b. are complex carbohydrates and proteins.
     c. are stored in the vacuoles of the cell.
     d. are oxygen and glucose.
     e. are used in the light-independent reactions and are stored in the vacuoles of the cell.

D 38. The enzymes associated with the light-dependent reactions of photosynthesis are located
     a. on the outer membranes of the chloroplast.
     b. in the liquid portion of the chloroplast.
   * c. on the thylakoid membrane.
     d. throughout the cytoplasm.
     e. on the plasma membrane.

M 39. The light-dependent reactions of photosynthesis
   * a. involve photolysis of water.
     b. occur in mitochondria.
     c. consist of the fixation of carbon dioxide.
     d. produce phosphoglyceric acid as their first stable compound.
     e. none of these

M 40. The products of the light-dependent reactions in photosynthesis
     a. are complex carbohydrates.
     b. are not used in the light-independent reactions.
   * c. include ATP molecules and oxygen.
     d. are phosphoglyceraldehyde molecules that may be converted into glucose and/or ribulose bisphosphate.
     e. are complex carbohydrates and are phosphoglyceraldehyde molecules that may be converted into glucose and/or ribulose bisphosphate.

M 41. Plant cells produce one molecule of O_2
     a. by splitting carbon dioxide.
     b. during respiration.
     c. by splitting ribulose bisphosphate.
   * d. by splitting two molecules of water.
     e. by breaking down glucose.

D 42. In the noncyclic pathway of ATP formation, which event occurs last?
   a. excitation of P700
   b. photolysis of water
*   c. formation of NADPH
   d. ATP synthesis
   e. transfer of electron to P680

D 43. The transition of the early earth's atmosphere from one rich in hydrogen to one rich in oxygen may be attributed to
*   a. photolysis.
   b. photophosphorylation.
   c. cyclic AMP.
   d. chlorophyll breakdown.
   e. all of these

D 44. If P700 were replaced by a molecule that merely trapped electrons,
   a. photolysis would cease.
   b. NADPH synthesis would stop.
   c. ATP synthesis would continue.
   d. photolysis would cease and NADPH synthesis would stop.
*   e. NADPH synthesis would stop and ATP synthesis would continue.

D 45. In the noncyclic pathways,
   a. there is a one-way flow of electrons from photosystem I to photosystem II.
   b. ATP alone is produced.
*   c. hydrogen ions accumulate in the thylakoid compartments.
   d. only electrons are transferred to hydrogen acceptors.
   e. water is not involved in any of the reactions.

D 46. Which of the following is formed last in the transfer of solar energy?
   a. P680 molecules
   b. electron transfer system
   c. photosystem II
   d. photosystem I
*   e. NADPH

D 47. The chlorophyll molecules that give up electrons used in photosynthesis are
   a. the chlorophyll molecules that receive the energy in sunlight.
   b. the molecules that transfer energy from one chlorophyll molecule to another.
*   c. the chlorophyll molecules that respond to the longest wavelengths of light to which chlorophyll is sensitive.
   d. the chlorophyll molecules that are sensitive to the shortest, most energetic wavelengths of light.
   e. the chlorophyll acceptor molecules in the thylakoid membrane.

CASE STUDY: A CONTROLLED RELEASE OF ENERGY

D 48. Hydrogen ion flow in the thylakoid compartments
   a. occurs between photosystems I and II.
   b. is called the hydrogen transfer system.
*   c. provides energy to produce ATP molecules.
   d. causes excitation of chlorophyll molecules.
   e. requires the intermediary action of acceptor molecules.

M 49. ATP is formed when _____ the thylakoid compartment.
   a. hydrogen ions enter
   b. electrons leave
*   c. hydrogen ions leave
   d. electrons enter
   e. water is split in

D 50. The chemiosmotic model is based upon
   a. the use of two photosystems in photosynthesis.
*   b. the idea that concentration and hydrogen ion gradients drive ATP production.
   c. the cyclic pathway as the oldest method to produce ATP.
   d. the use of light to split water molecules in the noncyclic pathway.
   e. the polarity and high specific heat of water.

M 51. The concept that concentration differences in H^+ and electric gradients across a membrane are responsible for ATP formation is known as
*   a. the chemiosmotic model.
   b. the photosystem mechanism.
   c. the process of photolysis.
   d. the electron transfer system.
   e. the cyclic pathway.

THE LIGHT-INDEPENDENT REACTIONS

M 52. Which of the following is NOT one of the chemicals produced in the synthesis (light-independent) reactions?
*   a. NADPH
   b. phosphoglyceric acid (PGA)
   c. phosphoglyceraldehyde (PGAL)
   d. glucose
   e. ribulose bisphosphate

E 53. All but which condition must be present for light-independent reactions to occur?
   a. presence of carbon dioxide
*   b. exposure of the plant to light
   c. presence of ribulose bisphosphate
   d. presence of ATP and NADPH
   e. presence of required enzymes

E 54. The light-independent reactions were discovered by
   a. M. D. Hatch.
   b. Andrew Benson.
   c. Melvin Calvin.
   d. Robert Hill.
*   e. both Andrew Benson and Melvin Calvin.

E   55.   The first stable compound produced from CO_2 in the light-independent reaction is
*   a.   phosphoglycerate (PGA).
     b.   ribulose bisphosphate (RuBP).
     c.   phosphoglyceraldehyde (PGAL).
     d.   glucose.
     e.   phosphoenol pyruvate.

M   56.   The carbon dioxide acceptor in the Calvin-Benson cycle is
     a.   phosphoglycerate (PGA).
*   b.   ribulose bisphosphate (RuBP).
     c.   phosphoglyceraldehyde (PGAL).
     d.   glucose.
     e.   phosphoenol pyruvate.

M   57.   Which of the following chemicals has five carbon atoms?
     a.   phosphoglycerate (PGA)
*   b.   ribulose bisphosphate (RuBP)
     c.   phosphoglyceraldehyde (PGAL)
     d.   glucose
     e.   phosphoenol pyruvate

D   58.   The light-independent reactions of photosynthesis
*   a.   fix carbon dioxide.
     b.   involve the liberation of oxygen.
     c.   cannot occur in light.
     d.   are known as photolysis.
     e.   all of these

M   59.   For each six atoms of carbon dioxide fixed in the light-independent reaction, how many molecules of PGAL (phosphoglyceraldehyde) are produced?
     a.   2
     b.   3
     c.   6
*   d.   12
     e.   15

D   60.   How many molecules of PGAL (phosphoglyceraldehyde) are used to regenerate the six molecules of RuBP (ribulose bisphosphate)?
     a.   3
     b.   6
*   c.   10
     d.   12
     e.   18

D   61.   In the Calvin-Benson cycle, which of the following can donate phosphate?
     a.   NADPH
*   b.   ATP
     c.   RuBP
     d.   ATP and RuBP only
     e.   NADPH, ATP, and RuBP.

D   62.   Which of the following chemicals has six carbon atoms?
     a.   phosphoglycerate (PGA)
     b.   ribulose bisphosphate (RuBP)
     c.   phosphoglyceraldehyde (PGAL)
*   d.   glucose
     e.   oxaloacetate

M   63.   Which of the following chemicals has the most energy?
     a.   phosphoglycerate (PGA)
     b.   ribulose bisphosphate (RuBP)
     c.   phosphoglyceraldehyde (PGAL)
*   d.   glucose
     e.   oxaloacetate

E   64.   In most complex plants, the excess glucose is stored as
     a.   glucose.
*   b.   starch.
     c.   sucrose.
     d.   glycogen.
     e.   cellulose.

D   65.   Plants manufacture glucose
     a.   for exclusive use by animals.
*   b.   to function as the beginning of more complex molecules.
     c.   as a by-product produced as the plant manufactures oxygen.
     d.   during the process known as photorespiration.
     e.   via the tricarboxylic acid cycle.

FIXING CARBON—SO NEAR, YET SO FAR

M   66.   Which of the following chemicals has four carbon atoms?
     a.   phosphoglycerate (PGA)
     b.   ribulose bisphosphate (RuBP)
     c.   phosphoglyceraldehyde (PGAL)
     d.   glucose
*   e.   oxaloacetate

M   67.   Photosynthesis takes place in which of the following cells?
*   a.   mesophyll
     b.   epidermal
     c.   sclerenchyma
     d.   xylem
     e.   phloem

M   68.   Which is a C_4 plant?
     a.   corn
     b.   pine
     c.   sugarcane
     d.   crabgrass
*   e.   all except pine

M   69.   The C_4 pathway involves
     a.   RuBP.
     b.   FAD.
*   c.   oxaloacetate.
     d.   ATP.
     e.   water.

E 70. The process in which oxygen, not carbon dioxide, becomes attached to RuBP is
    a. the Calvin-Benson cycle.
    b. photolysis.
    c. photophosphorylation.
    d. chemiosmosis.
    * e. photorespiration.

M 71. Which of the following would NOT be true of CAM plants?
    a. fix carbon only once
    b. live in desert environments
    * c. fix carbon mostly during the day
    d. open stomata only at night
    e. grow slowly

E 72. Plants need which of the following to carry on photosynthesis?
    * a. carbon dioxide and water
    b. nitrogen and hydrogen
    c. oxygen and carbon dioxide
    d. water and oxygen
    e. ribose and carbon dioxide

Matching Questions

M 73. Matching. Choose the one most appropriate answer for each.
1. ___ cyclic pathway of ATP formation
2. ___ noncyclic pathway of ATP formation
3. ___ carbon dioxide fixation
4. ___ the PGA to PGAL conversion
5. ___ the formation of glucose

    A. uses ribulose bisphosphate; produces PGA
    B. uses ATP and NADPH
    C. detaches two phosphate groups
    D. produces ATP and NADPH
    E. uses an electron transfer chain to produce ATP

Answers: 1. E   2. D   3. A   4. B
        5. C

Classification Questions

The processes listed below represent major chemical pathways in the photosynthetic process. Answer questions 74–78 with reference to these five processes.
    a. light-dependent reactions
    b. chemosynthetic reactions
    c. carbon dioxide fixation
    d. Calvin-Benson cycle
    e. C_4 pathway

D 74. This leads to the formation of glucose-6-phosphate (sugar phosphate) from two molecules of phosphoglyceraldehyde.

M 75. In this process carbon dioxide is incorporated first into an unstable intermediate compound and then into phosphoglycerate.

E 76. This yields NADPH as well as ATP.

M 77. This is a carbon-fixing system that precedes the Calvin-Benson cycle in some plants.

M 78. PGAL molecules are formed from the reaction of PGA molecules with ATP and NADPH in this pathway.

Answers 74. d   75. c   76. a
        77. e   78. d

The five reactions listed below occur during the noncyclic pathway of ATP formation . Use them to answer questions 79–83.
    a. reduction of NADP
    b. phosphorylation of ADP
    c. photolysis of water
    d. oxidation of chlorophyll
    e. reduction of chlorophyll

D 79. This process releases electrons to fill "holes" in chlorophyll in noncyclic ATP formation.

D 80. When light energy is absorbed by a leaf, the first result will be this.

D 81. The final step that occurs during noncyclic ATP formation is this.

M 82. High-energy phosphate bonds are formed during this process.

D 83. Oxygen is produced by this process.

Answers 79. c   80. d   81. a
        82. b   83. c

Selecting the Exception

E 84. Four of the five answers listed below are heterotrophs. Select the exception.
    a. fungus
    * b. carrot
    c. earthworm
    d. lobster
    e. parasite

M 85. Four of the five answers listed below are autotrophic. Select the exception.
    a. self-nourishing organisms
    b. organisms whose carbon source is CO_2
    c. chemosynthetic organisms
    * d. most bacteria
    e. sulfur bacteria

D 86. Four of the five answers listed below are part of the light-independent reactions. Select the exception.
*   a. water
     b. carbon dioxide
     c. ribulose bisphosphate
     d. phosphoglyceraldehyde
     e. phosphoglycerate

D 87. Four of the five answers listed below are participants in photosynthesis. Select the exception.
     a. photosystem
     b. granum
*   c. mitochondrion
     d. chloroplast
     e. thylakoid

E 88. Four of the five answers listed below are wavelengths absorbed by chloroplast pigments. Select the exception.
     a. red
*   b. green
     c. blue
     d. violet
     e. yellow

D 89. Four of the five answers listed below are processes associated with light-dependent reactions. Select the exception.
     a. photolysis
     b. chemiosmosis
*   c. fixing carbon dioxide
     d. photosystem I and II
     e. noncyclic ATP formation

D 90. Four of the five answers listed below are processes associated with light-independent reactions. Select the exception.
     a. uses ATP and NADPH
     b. involves RuBP
     c. produces PGA
     d. is called the Calvin-Benson cycle
*   e. requires light

M 91. Three of the four answers listed below are C4 plants. Select the exception.
     a. corn
*   b. spinach
     c. sugarcane
     d. crabgrass

M 92. Three of the four answers listed below are sources of energy for chemosynthesis. Select the exception.
     a. ammonium ions
     b. iron compounds
*   c. sunlight
     d. sulfur compounds

CHAPTER 8
HOW CELLS RELEASE STORED ENERGY

Multiple-Choice Questions

M   1.   The minimum evidence of anything being "alive" is
    a.   breathing.
    b.   heartbeat.
*   c.   carbon dioxide production.
    d.   physical activity.
    e.   response to stimulus.

M   2.   All living organisms
    a.   generate ATP.
    b.   utilize oxygen.
    c.   have a well-defined nucleus.
    d.   produce carbon dioxide.
*   e.   generate ATP and produce carbon dioxide.

M   3.   When molecules are broken apart in respiration,
    a.   the heat produced is used to drive biological reactions.
    b.   the oxygen in the compounds that are broken apart is used as an energy source.
*   c.   the energy released in respiration is channeled into molecules of ATP.
    d.   ATP is converted into ADP.
    e.   ADP is released as a waste product.

D   4.   Cellular respiration
*   a.   is the mechanism that evolved to enable living organisms to utilize energy stored in glucose.
    b.   occurs only in animal cells because plants carry on photosynthesis.
    c.   utilizes fat as its primary energy source.
    d.   occurs at the same rate throughout all cells of the body.
    e.   is the only cellular mechanism that yields ATP.

D   5.   Cellular respiration
    a.   is the reverse of the process of photosynthesis.
    b.   involves the physical exchange of gases.
*   c.   is a mechanism of tapping the energy found in the bonds between atoms forming organic compounds.
    d.   can occur only if there is a supply of glucose available because no other compound is involved in cellular respiration.
    e.   occurs only in animal cells.

HOW DO CELLS MAKE ATP?

E   6.   ATP is
*   a.   the energy currency of a cell.
    b.   produced by the destruction of ADP.
    c.   expended in the process of photosynthesis.
    d.   produced during the phosphorylation of any organic compound.
    e.   none of these

M   7.   ATP is to the cell as _____ is (are) to the financial community.
*   a.   printed currency
    b.   checks
    c.   credit
    d.   gold reserves
    e.   automated tellers

M   8.   ATP
    a.   can be produced by photosynthesis.
    b.   is produced in the degradation of organic compounds such as glucose.
    c.   is generated in anaerobic respiration.
    d.   is released in aerobic respiration.
*   e.   all of these

D   9.   Plant cells are capable of
    a.   photosynthesis.
    b.   ATP production.
    c.   glucose breakdown.
    d.   aerobic respiration.
*   e.   all of these

M   10.   Aerobes use _____ as the final electron acceptor.
    a.   hydrogen
    b.   carbon
*   c.   oxygen
    d. H_2O
    e. NAD^+

M   11.   Most plants and animals use _____ as their final hydrogen acceptor in cellular respiration.
*   a.   oxygen
    b.   sulfur
    c.   nitrogen
    d.   magnesium
    e.   phosphorus

E   12.   Which of the following liberates the most energy in the form of ATP?
*   a.   aerobic respiration
    b.   anaerobic respiration
    c.   alcoholic fermentation
    d.   lactate fermentation
    e.   All liberate the same amount, but through different means.

M 13. Which of the following has the greatest total energy?
    a. cAMP
    b. ADP
    c. ATP
  * d. glucose
    e. NADPH

M 14. The correct operational sequence of the three processes listed below is:

    I. glycolysis   II. ETP   III. Krebs

    a. I >>> II >>> III
    b. II >>> I >>> III
    c. III >>> I >>> II
    d. II >>> III >>> I
  * e. I >>> III >>> II

GLYCOLYSIS: FIRST STAGE OF ENERGY-RELEASING PATHWAYS

M 15. Before a glucose molecule can be broken down to release energy,
    a. one ATP molecule must be added to glucose.
  * b. two phosphate groups must be attached to glucose.
    c. three ATP molecules must be added to glucose.
    d. one ATP molecule must be taken away from glucose.
    e. two ATP molecules must be taken away from glucose.

D 16. For glycolysis to begin,
    a. glucose must enter the mitochondria.
  * b. there must be an input of energy from ATP.
    c. oxygen must be available.
    d. some hydrogen acceptors must be available.
    e. none of these

M 17. Glycolysis depends upon a continuous supply of glucose and
    a. NADP.
    b. pyruvate.
  * c. NAD^+.
    d. NADH.
    e. H_2O.

M 18. Glycolysis
    a. occurs in the mitochondria.
    b. happens to glucose only.
    c. results in the production of pyruvate.
    d. occurs in the cytoplasm.
  * e. results in the production of pyruvate and occurs in the cytoplasm.

D 19. In the breakdown of glucose, a phosphorylated six-carbon compound is split into two three-carbon compounds., which are named
  * a. phosphoglyceraldehyde (PGAL).
    b. pyruvate.
    c. acetyl-CoA.
    d. lactate.
    e. acetaldehyde.

M 20. The conversion of PGAL to pyruvate is accompanied by
    a. anaerobic respiration.
    b. photophosphorylation.
    c. the electron transfer chain.
  * d. substrate-level phosphorylation.
    e. the Krebs cycle.

D 21. The use of two ATP molecules at the beginning of glycolysis is comparable to _____ in financial language.
    a. a dividend
    b. a credit
    c. a debt
  * d. an investment
    e. liquidity

M 22. How many ATP molecules (net yield) are produced per molecule of glucose degraded during glycolysis?
    a. 1
  * b. 2
    c. 4
    d. 36
    e. 38

D 23. Substrate-level phosphorylation
  * a. occurs during glycolysis.
    b. requires the presence of oxygen.
    c. is a precursor for the phosphorylation of glucose.
    d. is the source for the majority of the ATP produced in aerobic respiration.
    e. does not occur during fermentation.

D 24. Which of the following is the most unstable intermediate compound in respiration?
    a. pyruvate
    b. phosphoglycerate (PGA)
  * c. phosphoenol pyruvate (PEP)
    d. phosphoglyceraldehyde (PGAL)
    e. fructose bisphosphate

M 25. Which of the following molecules does NOT have three carbon atoms?
    a. PEP
    b. PGAL
  * c. oxaloacetate
    d. pyruvate
    e. phosphoglycerate (PGA)

M 26. The end product of glycolysis is
    a. acetyl-CoA.
    b. oxaloacetate.
  * c. pyruvate.
    d. citrate.
    e. both a and b

M 27. The process by which a small amount of the energy in a glucose molecule is released, as it is converted into two small organic acid molecules, is called
    a. photolysis.
  * b. glycolysis.
    c. oxidative phosphorylation.
    d. substrate-level phosphorylation.
    e. the Krebs cycle.

M 28. Pyruvate can be regarded as the end product of
   *   a. glycolysis.
       b. acetyl-CoA formation.
       c. fermentation.
       d. the Krebs cycle.
       e. the TCA cycle.

SECOND STAGE OF THE AEROBIC PATHWAY

E 29. The Krebs cycle takes place in the
       a. ribosomes.
       b. cytoplasm.
       c. nucleus.
   *   d. mitochondria.
       e. chloroplasts.

D 30. The chemical that enters the mitochondria to continue respiration is
       a. phosphoglyceraldehyde (PGAL).
       b. oxaloacetate.
       c. phosphoglycerate (PGA).
   *   d. pyruvate.
       e. citrate.

D 31. Which of the following compounds produces carbon dioxide during the breakdown of glucose in aerobic respiration?
       a. phosphoglycerate
   *   b. pyruvate
       c. oxaloacetate
       d. citrate
       e. fructose bisphosphate

D 32. Krebs cycle reactions and electron transfer phosphorylation are
       a. in the mitochondrion and ER, respectively.
   *   b. in separate parts of the mitochondrion.
       c. inside and outside the mitochondrion, respectively.
       d. in the same mitochondrial compartment.
       e. cytoplasmic reactions.

E 33. The breakdown of pyruvate in the Krebs cycle results in the release of
       a. energy.
       b. carbon dioxide.
       c. oxygen.
       d. hydrogen.
   *   e. all except oxygen.

D 34. During the Krebs cycle,
       a. substrate-level phosphorylation occurs.
       b. oxaloacetate is regenerated.
       c. electrons and H^+ are transferred to coenzymes NAD^+ and FAD.
       d. molecules of carbon dioxide are formed.
   *   e. all of these

D 35. During which phase of aerobic respiration is ATP produced directly by substrate-level phosphorylation?
       a. glucose formation
       b. ethanol production
       c. acetyl-CoA formation
   *   d. the Krebs cycle
       e. all of these

D 36. Which is capable of being reduced during either glycolysis or the Krebs cycle?
   *   a. NAD^+
       b. FAD^+
       c. ADP
       d. NADH
       e. $NADP^+$

D 37. Because _____ cells have a NAD^+ shuttle built into their mitochondria, they deliver 38 ATP molecules per glucose molecule.
       a. liver
       b. heart
       c. kidney
       d. liver and heart
   *   e. liver, heart, and kidney

D 38. To break down a glucose molecule completely, how many passes through the Krebs cycle are required?
   *   a. 2
       b. 3
       c. 4
       d. 6
       e. 12

M 39. The first intermediate produced after the entry of acetyl-CoA into the Krebs cycle is
       a. pyruvate.
       b. acetyl-CoA.
       c. fructose bisphosphate.
       d. oxaloacetate.
   *   e. citrate.

M 40. The last intermediate produced in the Krebs cycle before the entry of the next acetyl-CoA is
       a. pyruvate.
       b. acetyl-CoA.
       c. fructose bisphosphate.
   *   d. oxaloacetate.
       e. citrate.

M 41. Which of the following marks the transition from glycolysis to the Krebs cycle?
   *   a. acetyl-CoA formation
       b. conversion of PGAL to PGA
       c. regeneration of reduced NAD^+
       d. oxidative phosphorylation
       e. substrate-level phosphorylation

THIRD STAGE OF THE AEROBIC PATHWAY

M   **42.** When glucose is used as the energy source, the largest amount of ATP is produced in
     a. glycolysis.
     b. acetyl-CoA formation.
     c. the Krebs cycle.
     d. substrate-level phosphorylation.
 * e. electron transfer phosphorylation.

M   **43.** The greatest number of ATP molecules is produced in
     a. glycolysis.
     b. alcoholic fermentation.
     c. anaerobic electron transfer.
 * d. electron transfer phosphorylation.
     e. the Krebs cycle.

E   **44.** What is the name of the process by which reduced NAD^+ transfers electrons to oxygen?
     a. glycolysis
     b. acetyl-CoA formation
     c. the Krebs cycle
 * d. electron transfer phosphorylation
     e. substrate-level phosphorylation

D   **45.** The electron transfer chain of cellular respiration is located
 * a. on the inner membrane of the mitochondria.
     b. on the inner membrane of the chloroplasts.
     c. in the fluid part of the chloroplast.
     d. throughout the cytoplasm of the cell.
     e. on the plasma membrane.

M   **46.** The ultimate electron acceptor in aerobic respiration is
     a. NAD^+.
     b. CO_2.
     c. ADP.
     d. $NADP^+$.
 * e. O_2.

D   **47.** The most abundant acceptor for hydrogen released in the Krebs cycle is
     a. TPN.
     b. FMN.
 * c. NAD^+.
     d. FAD.
     e. cytochrome oxidase.

D   **48.** Which is NOT ordinarily capable of being reduced at any time?
     a. NAD^+
     b. FAD
     c. oxygen, O_2
 * d. water
     e. all of these

M   **49.** The energy used to generate most of the ATP formed in aerobic respiration is released when electrons are passed from NADH to
 * a. oxygen.
     b. acetyl CoA.
     c. FADH.
     d. CO_2.
     e. NADPH.

D   **50.** The generation of concentration gradients across the membranes of mitochondria is known as which theory of ATP production?
     a. glycolytic
     b. negative ion generator
     c. phosphate pump
 * d. chemiosmotic
     e. none of these

M   **51.** During electron transport phosphorylation, which ions accumulate in the outer compartment of the mitochondria?
     a. calcium
 * b. hydrogen
     c. oxygen
     d. phosphorus
     e. sodium

D   **52.** Which of the following statements is true?
     a. According to chemiosmotic theory, concentration and electric gradients drive the formation of ATP.
     b. Each time an electron is transferred down the electron transfer chain, it loses energy.
     c. There is a buildup of hydrogen in the outer compartment of the mitochondrion.
     d. ATP synthases are channels for the passage of hydrogen ions.
 * e. All of these statements are true.

D   **53.** The amount of energy released from a glucose molecule is dependent on what happens to
     a. carbon atoms.
     b. oxygen atoms.
 * c. hydrogen atoms.
     d. phosphorus atoms.
     e. water molecules.

M   **54.** Each NADH produced in the cytoplasm by glycolysis yields how many molecules of ATP if it is used in electron transfer phosphorylation in liver, heart, or kidney cells?
     a. 2
 * b. 3
     c. 4
     d. 6
     e. either 2 or 3

D   **55.** Because of its location in the electron transfer chain, delivery of electrons to each FAD results in _____ ATPs.
     a. 4
 * b. 2
     c. 3
     d. 32
     e. 0

M   **56.** The efficiency of the complete aerobic breakdown of a molecule of glucose is approximately
     a. 5 percent.
     b. 20 percent.
 * c. 40 percent.
     d. 60 percent.
     e. 80 percent.

ANAEROBIC ROUTES OF ATP FORMATION

D **57.** The bacteria that cause botulism and tetanus cannot live in the presence of
   a. carbon dioxide.
 * b. oxygen.
   c. glucose.
   d. alcohol.
   e. ATP.

D **58.** If fermentation follows glycolysis,
   a. CO_2 will be one of the products as pyruvate is converted to lactate.
 * b. the two NADH molecules produced during glycolysis will (depending on the organism) be used to reduce pyruvate to either lactate or ethanol and CO_2.
   c. ATP will be required to convert pyruvate to either lactate or ethanol and CO_2.
   d. oxidative phosphorylation occurs either on the plasma membrane or on derivatives of the plasma membrane.

D **59.** In the conversion of pyruvate to ethanol, which of the following is (are) produced?
   a. acetaldehyde
   b. carbon dioxide
   c. NADH
 * d. acetaldehyde and carbon dioxide only.
   e. acetaldehyde, carbon dioxide, and NADH.

M **60.** Under anaerobic conditions, muscle cells produce
   a. ethyl alcohol.
   b. acetaldehyde.
   c. pyruvate.
 * d. lactate.
   e. citrate.

D **61.** Fermentation
 * a. may occur in a muscle under anaerobic conditions.
   b. produces more ATP than is liberated in the hydrogen transfer series.
   c. breaks down glucose in reaction with oxygen.
   d. is restricted to yeasts.
   e. none of these

E **62.** Sour cream and sour milk are produced by bacteria that form
   a. ethyl alcohol.
   b. acetaldehyde.
   c. pyruvate.
 * d. lactate.
   e. citrate.

D **63.** If you were searching for anaerobic bacteria, you would NOT look for them in
   a. the guts of farm animals.
   b. swamps.
 * c. mountain streams.
   d. sediments of lakes and oceans.
   e. canned goods.

M **64.** Lactate production in muscle cells is
   a. temporary.
   b. due to oxygen deficiency.
   c. an NAD regenerator.
   d. temporary and due to oxygen deficiency.
 * e. temporary, due to oxygen deficiency, and an NAD regenerator.

D **65.** The bacteria that live in hot springs use _____ as their final hydrogen acceptor.
   a. oxygen
 * b. sulfate
   c. nitrogen
   d. magnesium
   e. phosphorus

M **66.** Sulfate-reducing bacteria transfer electrons to _____ in their environment.
   a. SO_2
   b. H_2
   c. H_2SO_4
   d. S
 * e. SO_4^{--}

M **67.** The first forms of life that produced ATP probably used pathways similar to
   a. photosynthesis.
   b. photophosphorylation.
 * c. glycolysis and fermentation.
   d. the Krebs cycle.
   e. aerobic respiration.

ALTERNATIVE ENERGY SOURCES IN THE HUMAN BODY

E **68.** The main source of energy in the human diet is
   a. fats.
 * b. carbohydrates.
   c. proteins.
   d. nucleotides.
   e. steroids.

D **69.** In glycolysis, approximately what percent of the total energy in glucose is released?
 * a. 2
   b. 6
   c. 10
   d. 15
   e. 20

M **70.** Molecules associated with glycolysis and the Krebs cycle provide
   a. sources of energy for ATP formation.
   b. intermediates in the formation of carbohydrates.
   c. intermediates in the formation of lipids.
   d. intermediates in the formation of proteins.
 * e. all of these

D 71. Which statement is false?
   a. High concentrations of ATP inhibit the formation of more ATP.
   b. When cells need large supplies of energy, the ATP concentration in these cells actually decreases at first.
* c. When ATP concentration declines, enzymatic activity that produces ATP declines.
   d. Cells constantly adjust their metabolic reactions to provide energy whenever it is needed.
   e. The activity of many different enzymes influences the supply of ATP in cells.

M 72. Which of the following statements is true?
   a. In aerobic respiration, ATP is released in the very first reaction.
   b. The process of fermentation is restricted to anaerobic organisms.
   c. Glucose has more energy than fructose bisphosphate.
   d. Glycolysis occurs free in the mitochondria.
* e. Enzymes lower the activation energy for each step in the chemical reactions in respiration.

E 73. Excess glucose in the human diet can result in accumulations of
   a. pyruvate.
   b. NADH.
* c. fat.
   d. lactate.
   e. ATP.

Matching Questions

M 74. Matching. Choose the one most appropriate answer for each.
   1. ___ glycolysis
   2. ___ fermentation
   3. ___ acetyl-CoA formation
   4. ___ the Krebs cycle
   5. ___ electron transfer phosphorylation

   A. produces NADH and CO_2; changes pyruvate
   B. produces ATP, NADH, and CO_2
   C. splits glucose into two pyruvate molecules
   D. regenerates NAD^+ as pyruvate; is converted to ethanol or lactate
   E. uses a membrane-bound system that contains cytochromes to produce ATP

Answers: 1. C   2. D   3. A
           4. B   5. E

Classification Questions

Use the five processes listed below for questions 75–79.
   a. glycolysis
   b. aerobic respiration
   c. anaerobic electron transfer
   d. alcoholic fermentation
   e. lactate fermentation

E 75. In this process the energy yield is equal to 2 molecules of ATP and the final product is ethanol.

E 76. In this process the final product is lactate.

M 77. This process yields the most energy.

D 78. This process involves electron transfer phosphorylation.

M 79. This process precedes the Krebs cycle.

Answers   75. d   76. e   77. b
            78. b   79. a

Use the five compounds listed below for questions 80–84.
   a. ethanol
   b. pyruvate
   c. lactate
   d. citrate
   e. acetaldehyde

M 80. This compound is utilized in alcoholic fermentation and lactate fermentation.

M 81. This compound is the most likely end product of a human runner experiencing an oxygen debt.

D 82. This compound is an intermediate product of alcoholic fermentation, but not lactate fermentation.

E 83. This compound is the end product of glycolysis.

M 84. This compound is an end product of anaerobic respiration in exercising muscle.

Answers   80. b   81. c   82. e
            83. b   84. c

Selecting the Exception

D 85. Four of the five answers listed below are hydrogen acceptors. Select the exception.
   a. oxygen
   b. cytochrome
* c. ATP
   d. NAD^+
   e. FAD

D   86.   Four of the five answers listed below are compounds associated with anaerobic respiration. Select the exception.
       a.   pyruvate
       b.   lactic acid
       c.   ethanol
 *   d.   oxaloacetic acid
       e.   phosphoglyceraldehyde

D   87.   Four of the five answers listed below are compounds in the glycolysis reactions. Select the exception.
       a.   fructose-1,6-bisphosphate
       b.   3-phosphoglycerate
       c.   pyruvate
       d.   phosphoenol pyruvate
 *   e.   isocitrate

D   88.   Four of the five answers listed below are intermediates in the Krebs cycle. Select the exception.
       a.   succinate
       b.   citrate
       c.   malate
       d.   fumarate
 *   e.   acetyl-CoA

D   89.   Four of the five answers listed below are compounds in the Krebs reactions. Select the exception.
       a.   oxaloacetate
       b.   isocitrate
       c.   alpha-ketoglutarate
 *   d.   pyruvate
       e.   succinyl-CoA

D   90.   Four of the five answers listed below are molecules that donate hydrogens to NAD^+. Select the exception.
       a.   pyruvate
       b.   alpha-ketoglutarate
       c.   isocitrate
 *   d.   succinate
       e.   malate

D   91.   Four of the five answers listed below are degradation processes for carbon compounds. Select the exception.
 *   a.   Calvin-Benson cycle
       b.   Krebs cycle
       c.   fermentation
       d.   respiration
       e.   glycolysis

CHAPTER 9
CELL DIVISION AND MITOSIS

Multiple-Choice Questions

DIVIDING CELLS: THE BRIDGE BETWEEN GENERATIONS

M 1. When a cell undergoes mitosis,
   a. the daughter cells have identical genes.
   b. the daughter cell has genes identical to those of the mother cell that produced it.
   c. the amount of cytoplasm in the mother cell and in each of the daughter cells is equal.
   d. there is an exact duplication and division of all of the organelles between daughter cells.
   * e. the daughter cells have identical genes and the daughter cell has genes identical to those of the mother cell that produced it.

D 2. When a eukaryotic cell divides, the daughter cells
   a. manufacture all the organelles from material in the cytoplasm.
   * b. receive enough of the organelles to start up the new cells and produce additional organelles as needed.
   c. produce individual organelles that attach to the spindle fibers and are distributed just like chromosomes.
   d. produce an equal number of organelles distributed to each cell.
   e. get cellular organelles by an unknown process.

D 3. Which of the following is NOT an example of a clone?
   a. a pair of identical twins
   b. a group of rooted plant cuttings from a single plant
   c. the cells produced by the asexual reproduction of a single-celled organism
   * d. the offspring produced by two parents

D 4. Which of the following statements is true?
   a. Once a person reaches maturity, cell division stops unless it is to repair a wound.
   b. Cell division in an adult signifies cancer.
   * c. Some specific cells throughout the body retain the ability to divide and replace themselves.
   d. Growth continues on throughout the life of an adult human.
   e. All cells retain the ability to divide even after the organism reaches maturity.

M 5. Strictly speaking, mitosis and meiosis are divisions of the
   a. nucleus.
   b. cytoplasm.
   c. chromosomes.
   * d. nucleus and chromosomes.
   e. nucleus, cytoplasm, and chromosomes.

M 6. Which of the following is NOT associated with meiosis?
   a. reduction of number of chromosomes
   * b. somatic cells
   c. sexual reproduction
   d. sperm and egg
   e. germ cells

M 7. Eukaryotic DNA molecules
   a. have no proteins.
   b. have small amounts of protein at each end of the DNA molecules.
   c. have large amounts of protein at each end of the DNA molecules.
   d. have small amounts of protein dispersed among the DNA molecules.
   * e. have large amounts of protein dispersed among the DNA molecules.

D 8. Which process is absolutely necessary for sexual reproduction to occur in a life cycle, but is not necessarily required for organisms that only reproduce asexually?
   a. prokaryotic fission
   b. mitosis
   * c. meiosis
   d. cytokinesis
   e. karyokinesis

E 9. Chromatids that are attached at the centromere are called what kind of chromatids?
   a. mother
   b. daughter
   * c. sister
   d. programmed
   e. either mother or daughter.

E 10. Proteins that resemble spools on which DNA molecules are wound are called
   a. kinetochores.
   b. centrioles.
   c. motor proteins.
   * d. histones.
   e. spindles.

M 11. A portion of a DNA molecules wound around a spool of histone protein is called a
   a. centromere.
   * b. nucleosome.
   c. spindle.
   d. furrow.
   e. cell cycle.

E 12. When chromosomes become visible during prophase of mitosis, it is the result of
   a. uncoiling.
   b. DNA synthesis.
*   c. condensation.
   d. chromatid duplication.
   e. addition of proteins to the DNA.

M 13. The number of DNA molecules present in a duplicated chromosome is
   a. 1.
   b. undetermined.
   c. half that of an unduplicated chromosome.
*   d. 2
   e. 4.

D 14. Which of these statements concerning the centromere is NOT true?
   a. It appears to join duplicated DNAs.
*   b. It anchors proteins to DNA.
   c. Its position along the chromosome varies.
   d. It is the attachment site for microtubules.
   e. It is temporary.

D 15. The number of chromosomes found in a eukaryotic cell
   a. indicates the phylogenetic position of the organism.
   b. is constant during the life cycle.
   c. is haploid among asexually reproducing forms and diploid if they reproduce sexually.
*   d. is doubled by fertilization and cut in half by meiosis.
   e. is dependent on the age of the tissue.

D 16. Which of the following statements is false?
   a. There are more than 1,000 chromosomes found in some organisms.
*   b. The more highly evolved a species is, the more chromosomes it possesses.
   c. The number of chromosomes remains constant throughout a life cycle.
   d. The number of chromosomes is the same for all members of a species.
   e. There are half as many chromosomes in germ cells as there are in somatic cells.

E 17. In mitosis, if a parent cell has 16 chromosomes, each daughter cell will have how many chromosomes?
   a. 64
   b. 32
*   c. 16
   d. 8
   e. 4

E 18. If a parent cell has 16 chromosomes, how many sister chromatids will be present after duplication of the chromosomes?
   a. 64
*   b. 32
   c. 16
   d. 8
   e. 4

D 19. Which statement is true of the behavior of chromosomes in mitosis?
   a. Each new cell receives half of the number of chromosomes in the original cell.
*   b. Each new cell receives copies of all the original chromosomes.
   c. If the original number of chromosomes was 46, each new cell will have 23..
   d. The sister chromosomes are not identical due to breakages in the DNA..
   e. All chromosomes are duplicated except the sex chromosomes.

E 20. Cells with two of each kind of chromosome are described by the term
   a. *polyploid.*
*   b. *diploid.*
   c. *triploid.*
   d. *haploid.*
   e. *tetraploid.*

THE CELL CYCLE

M 21. DNA replication occurs
*   a. between the gap phases of interphase.
   b. immediately before prophase of mitosis.
   c. during prophase of mitosis.
   d. during prophase of meiosis.
   e. at any time during cell division.

E 22. The chromosomes and genes are actually replicated during
   a. anaphase.
   b. metaphase.
*   c. interphase.
   d. prophase.
   e. telophase.

E 23. Chromosomes are duplicated during what portion of the cell cycle?
   a. M
   b. D
   c. G_1
   d. G_2
*   e. S

D 24. During the "gap" phases of the cell cycle, most of the activity is directed toward
   a. DNA replication.
   b. nuclear membrane synthesis.
   c. resting for the next step.
   d. sorting the chromosomes.
*   e. synthesizing cytoplasmic organelles.

M 25. The interval before the onset of DNA replication is
*   a. the G_1 stage.
   b. the G_2 stage.
   c. the M stage.
   d. the S stage.
   e. all stages.

M 26. Which of the following is NOT true of spindles?
* a. They are permanent cell structures.
   b. They interact with kinetochores.
   c. Some of their microtubules overlap at the cell equator.
   d. Tubulin is the main component.
   e. Their subunits continually change.

MITOSIS

E 27 The spindle apparatus is made of
   a. Golgi bodies.
* b. microtubules.
   c. endoplasmic reticulum.
   d. nucleoprotein.
   e. chromatids.

D 28 Which of the following is NOT necessary for spindle apparatus formation?
   a. microtubules
   b. proteins
* c. centrioles
   d. microtubule organizing centers
   e. tubulins

D 29. Which of the following statements is NOT true?
   a. When chromosomes are duplicated during interphase, the centromeres are not.
   b. The spindle fibers are attached to kinetochores.
   c. The spindle apparatus is composed of protein molecules of tubulin.
   d. The spindle fibers attach to kinetochores.
* e. All of these are true.

E 30. The spindle apparatus begins to become visible during
   a. anaphase.
   b. metaphase.
   c. interphase.
* d. prophase.
   e. telophase.

M 31. In eukaryotic cells, which can occur during the stages of mitosis?
   a. the duplication of chromatids
   b. the replication of DNA
   c. synapsis and crossing over
* d. fragmentation and disappearance of nuclear envelope and nucleolus
   e. all of these

D 32. Mitosis comes from the Greek word *mitos*, which means
   a. divide.
   b. grow.
   c. swell.
* d. thread.
   e. shrink.

E 33. The chromosomes are aligned at the spindle equator during
   a. anaphase.
* b. metaphase.
   c. interphase.
   d. prophase.
   e. telophase.

D 34. In which of the stages below does each chromosome consist of two DNA molecules?

   I.   **metaphase**   III. **prophase**
   II. **telophase**   IV.   **anaphase**

   a. III and IV
   b. I, III, and IV
* c. I and III
   d. I, II, and III
   e. I, II, III, and IV

M 35. The chromatids detach from one another and become visibly separate chromosomes during
* a. anaphase.
   b. metaphase.
   c. interphase.
   d. prophase.
   e. telophase.

D 36. The entire process of producing two cells from one cell
   a. starts with prophase.
   b. ends with cytokinesis.
   c. results in the equal distribution of organelles between cells.
   d. occurs only in multicellular organisms.
* e. starts with prophase and ends with cytokinesis.

E 37. The chromosomes are moving to opposite poles during
* a. anaphase.
   b. metaphase.
   c. interphase.
   d. prophase.
   e. telophase.

E 38. The chromosomes have arrived at opposite poles during
   a. anaphase.
   b. metaphase.
   c. interphase.
   d. prophase.
* e. telophase.

E 39. The nuclear membrane re-forms during
   a. anaphase.
   b. metaphase.
   c. interphase.
   d. prophase.
* e. telophase.

D 40. Which of the following statements is false?
   a. Homologous chromosomes do not pair during mitosis.
* b. Genes and chromosomes are duplicated during prophase.
   c. There is a specific number of chromosomes for each species.
   d. New nuclei are formed during telophase.

D   41. Which of the following statements is true?
     a. After the centromere divides, the chromatids are
         called chromosomes.
     b. Centromeres are separated during anaphase.
     c. During anaphase, some microtubules ratchet past
         each other while others shorten.
     d. Telophase is essentially the reverse of the events
         of prophase.
*   e. all of these

D   42. Which of the following is the proper sequence for
     mitosis?

     I.   metaphase   III.   prophase
     II.   telophase   IV.   anaphase

     a. I, III, IV, II
     b. I, II, III, IV
*   c. III, I, IV, II
     d. IV, I, III, II
     e. III, IV, I, II

DIVISION OF THE CYTOPLASM

M   43. Division of the cytoplasm (cytokinesis)
     a. in animal cells begins with various deposits of
         material associated with groups of microtubules at
         each pole of the nucleus.
     b. in animal cells occurs when the plasma membrane
         is pulled inward by a ring of microtubules that has
         become attached to the cell plate.
*   c. usually accompanies nuclear division.
     d. in plant cells begins with the deposition of a very
         rigid lipid bilayer, which is the major constituent
         of the cell wall.

M   44. The distribution of cytoplasm to daughter cells is
     accomplished during
     a. prokaryotic fission.
     b. mitosis.
     c. meiosis.
*   d. cytokinesis.
     e. karyokinesis.

M   45. The cell plate is composed of
     a. the nuclear membrane.
     b. the cytoplasmic membrane.
*   c. microtubule elements and cellulose.
     d. cellular organelles.
     e. the chitin and centrioles.

Matching Questions

E   46. Matching.
     1. ____ centriole
     2. ____ centromere
     3. ____ chromatid
     4. ____ cytokinesis
     5. ____ metaphase
     6. ____ microtubules
     7. ____ prophase
     8. ____ telophase
     9. ____ anaphase

     A. cytoplasm apportioned between the two
         daughter cells
     B. final phase of mitosis; daughter nuclei re-
         form
     C. two sister chromatids are joined here
     D. chromosomes condense and mitotic spindle
         begins to form
     E. chromosomes line up at spindle equator
     F. sister chromatids separate, move to opposite
         spindle poles now
     G. about 25 nm in diameter; form mitotic
         spindle
     H. half of a chromosome in prophase
     I. in pairs in some eukaryotic cells; move to
         poles during spindle formation

Answers: 1. I   2. C   3. H
              4. A   5. E   6. G
              7. D   8. B   9. F

Classification Questions

Answer questions 47–56 in reference to the eukaryotic cell cycle. Each question has only one BEST answer.

    a. G_2
    b. mitosis
    c. S
    d. G_1
    e. cytokinesis

E **47.** Period when DNA is duplicated

E **48.** Period when interphase ends in the parent cell

M **49.** Event that forms two daughter cytoplasmic masses

D **50.** Period of cell growth before DNA duplication

E **51.** Period after DNA is duplicated

M **52.** Period of nuclear division

E **53.** Period when interphase begins in a daughter cell

M **54.** Period commonly followed by cytokinesis

M **55.** The period in which metaphase occurs

D **56.** The period prior to mitosis

Answers   47. c   48. a   49. e

       50. d   51. a   52. b

       53. d   54. b   55. b

       56. a

The stages of mitosis plus interphase are listed under a–e below. Answer questions 57–67 with reference to these phases.

    a. interphase
    b. prophase
    c. metaphase
    d. anaphase
    e. telophase

E **57.** During this stage homologous pairs of chromosomes are lined up on the equatorial plate.

M **58.** Chromosomes replicate during this phase.

M **59.** Genes replicate during this phase.

E **60.** DNA replicates during this phase.

E **61.** Condensation and shortening of chromosomes occurs during this phase.

E **62.** Spindle fibers first appear during this stage.

M **63.** During this phase the centromeres break apart as the separated sister chromatids begin to move to opposite poles.

E **64.** The microtubular spindle develops during this phase.

E **65.** Sister chromatids joined at their centromeres are attached to spindle fibers during this phase.

M **66.** Cytokinesis occurs as this phase of mitosis proceeds.

E **67.** New daughter nuclear membranes form during this phase.

Answers   57. c   58. a   59. a

       60. a   61. b   62. b   63. d

       64. b   65. c   66. e   67. c

Selecting the Exception

E **68.** Four of the five answers listed below are stages of actual nuclear division. Select the exception.
    a. anaphase
    b. prophase
 * c. interphase
    d. telophase
    e. metaphase

D **69.** Four of the five answers listed below are related by a common phase of mitosis. Select the exception.
    a. beginning of microtubule assembly outside the nucleus
 * b. division of centromere
    c. disappearance of nucleolus
    d. disappearance of nuclear membrane
    e. shortening and condensation of chromosomes make them more visible

M **70.** Four of the five answers listed below are periods of the same cycle. Select the exception.
    a. G_1
    b. M
 * c. R
    d. S
    e. G_2

D **71.** Four of the five answers listed below are related by a common phase of mitosis. Select the exception.
    a. chromosomes decondense
    b. spindle microtubules disappear
    c. nucleolus reappears
 * d. chromosomes separate
    e. nuclear envelope re-forms

M **72.** Four of the five answers listed below are events occurring during mitosis. Select the exception.
 * a. chromosome replication
    b. division of centromere
    c. lining up of chromosomes at the cellular equator
    d. attachment of spindle microtubules to centromeres
    e. migration of chromosomes to opposite ends of the cell

D **73.** Four of the five answers listed below assist in chromosome movement. Select the exception.
    a. centromere
    b. spindle microtubules
    c. kinetochores
    d. centriole
 * e. nuclear envelope

D 74. Four of the five answers listed below are related by a common phase of mitosis. Select the exception.
* a. chromosomes align at the spindle equator
b. sister chromatids become individual chromosomes
c. centromeres divide
d. chromosomes move apart
e. spindle microtubules shorten, pulling chromosomes toward the poles

D 75. Four of the five answers listed below are related by a common division association. Select the exception.
a. mitochondria
* b. chromosomes
c. ribosomes
d. plastids
e. microbodies

CHAPTER 10
MEIOSIS

Multiple-Choice Questions

COMPARING SEXUAL WITH ASEXUAL REPRODUCTION

E   1.   Which is NOT a typical site for the occurrence of meiosis?
   a.   plant ovary
 * b.   plant root cells
   c.   human testis
   d.   human ovary
   e.   plant anther

D   2.   If meiosis did NOT occur in sexually reproducing organisms,
   a.   growth of the zygote would be halted.
   b.   mitosis would be sufficient.
   c.   gametes would be haploid.
 * d.   the chromosome number would double in each generation.
   e.   eggs would be haploid, but sperm would be diploid.

M   3.   Asexually produced daughter cells are
   a.   identical to each other.
   b.   identical to the parental cell.
   c.   different from parental cell.
   d.   different from each other.
 * e.   identical to each other and to the parental cell.

M   4.   Sexual reproduction
   a.   leads to uniform characteristics in a population.
 * b.   results in new combinations of genetic traits.
   c.   produces genetic clones.
   d.   requires less tissue differentiation than asexual reproduction.
   e.   produces genetic clones and requires less tissue differentiation than asexual reproduction.

D   5.   Which of the following statements is NOT true?
   a   In asexual reproduction, the parent passes a complete set of genes to its offspring.
   b.   In sexual reproduction, both meiosis and fertilization must occur during the life cycle.
   c.   In sexual reproduction, a human offspring receives two genes for every trait.
   d.   Sexual reproduction puts together new combinations of genes.
 * e.   Sexual reproduction produces clones.

M   6.   Through meiosis,
   a.   alternate forms of genes are shuffled.
   b.   parental DNA is divided and distributed to forming gametes.
   c.   the diploid chromosome number is reduced to haploid.
   d.   offspring are provided with new gene combinations.
 * e.   all of these

M   7.   Different, or alternative, forms of the same gene are called
   a.   genetomorphs.
 * b.   alleles.
   c.   mutants.
   d.   chromatids.
   e.   homologous.

HOW MEIOSIS HALVES THE CHROMOSOME NUMBER

M   8.   The essence of meiosis is that
   a.   gametes receive one copy of *each* member of *each* pair of homologous chromosomes.
   b.   gametes are formed that are diploid.
   c.   each gamete receives one member of *each* pair of homologous chromosomes.
   d.   gametes are formed that are haploid.
 * e.   each gamete receives one member of *each* pair of homologous chromosomes and gametes are formed that are haploid.

M   9.   Homologous chromosomes
   a.   may exchange parts during meiosis.
   b.   have alleles for the same characteristics even though the gene expression may not be the same.
   c.   are in pairs, one chromosome of each pair from the father and one from the mother.
   d.   pair up during meiosis.
 * e.   all of these

M   10.   Chromosomes of a pair of homologous chromosomes may differ from other chromosomes in terms of
   a.   size.
   b.   shape.
   c.   alleles they carry.
   d.   position of the centromere.
 * e.   all of these

E   11.   Copies of chromosomes linked together at their centromeres at the beginning of meiosis are appropriately called what kind of chromatids?
   a.   mother
   b.   daughter
 * c.   sister
   d   homologous

M 12. Chromatids are
a. attached at the centriole.
b. a pair of chromosomes, one from the mother and one from the father.
c. attached at their centromeres.
d. identical until crossing over occurs.
* e. attached at their centromeres and are identical until crossing over occurs.

M 13. Sister chromatids are separated from each other during
a. metaphase I.
b. anaphase I.
c. telophase II.
* d. anaphase II.
e. metaphase II.

A CLOSER LOOK AT KEY EVENTS OF MEIOSIS I

E 14. Synapsis and crossing over occur during
a. anaphase I.
b. metaphase II.
* c. prophase I.
d. prophase II.
e. telophase II.

D 15. Crossing over
a. generally results in synapsis and binary fission.
b. involves nucleoli.
c. involves breakages and exchanges between sister chromatids.
* d. alters the composition of chromosomes and results in new combinations of alleles being channeled into the daughter cells.
e. all of these

E 16. Under favorable conditions, during which phase of meiosis will the chromosomes appear as packets of four chromatids?
a. anaphase I
b. telophase II
c. anaphase II
* d. prophase I
e. metaphase II

D 17. Anaphase
a. involves the lining up of the chromosomes across the equatorial plate.
b. is the same in mitosis and meiosis I and II.
* c. is initiated when the newly divided centromeres begin to move apart.
d. results in an unequal distribution of chromosomes to the resulting cells.

D 18. Paired homologous chromosomes are found at the spindle equator during
* a. metaphase I.
b. telophase I.
c. prophase II.
d. metaphase II.
e. anaphase II.

D 19. Crossing over is one of the most important events in meiosis because
* a. it produces new arrays of alleles on chromosomes.
b. homologous chromosomes must be separated into different daughter cells.
c. the number of chromosomes allotted to each daughter cell must be halved.
d. homologous chromatids must be separated into different daughter cells.
e. all of these

M 20. Which of the following does NOT occur in prophase I of meiosis?
* a. cytokinesis
b. tetrad formation
c. synapsis
d. crossing over
e. condensation of chromatin

M 21. Chiasmata provide evidence of
a. meiosis.
* b. crossing over.
c. chromosomal aberration.
d. fertilization.
e. spindle fiber formation.

D 22. At the beginning of prophase I, there are _____ molecules of DNA in a developing human sperm cell.
* a. 92
b. 23
c. 46
d. half as many (as compared to somatic cells)
e. twice as many (as compared to mature sperm)

M 23. Which of the following events does NOT occur in prophase II, but does occur in prophase I?
a. crossing over
b. synapsis
c. spindle formation
* d. crossing over and synapsis only
e. crossing over, synapsis, and spindle formation.

D 24. Major gene reshuffling takes place during
* a. prophase I.
b. metaphase I.
c. anaphase I.
d. metaphase II.
e. anaphase II.

D 25. Crossing over
* a. increases variability in gametes.
b. results in only one exchange per homologue.
c. occurs between sister chromatids.
d. prevents genetic recombination.
e. is followed immediately by separation of each of the chromatids.

D	26.	If a child more strongly resembles one parent's physical traits than the other parent's, the explanation could be due to chromosome movements during
a. anaphase II.
b. metaphase II.
c. prophase II.
* d. anaphase I.
e. telophase I.

D	27.	At the end of telophase I in corn (20 chromosomes), which of the following is true?
a. Each cell has 10 chromosomes.
b. Each chromosome is duplicated.
c. Centromeres are undivided.
d. Each cell has 10 chromosomes; and Each chromosome is duplicated.
* e. Each cell has 10 chromosomes; Each chromosome is duplicated; and Centromeres are undivided.

D	28.	If a diploid organism has a genome consisting of 4 chromosomes, it can produce _____ different combinations of maternal and paternal chromosomes (disregarding crossing over).
a. 4
b. 8
c. 12
* d. 16
e. 32

D	29.	Independent assortment refers to which of the following statements?
a. The position where crossing over occurs is random.
b. The pole that any one chromosome moves toward is completely independent of the movement of the other 45 chromosomes in humans.
* c. A maternal chromosome may move toward either pole while the paternal homologue moves toward the other.
d. The sperm that fertilizes the egg is selected at random.
e. none of these

E	30.	The period that may occur between meiosis I and meiosis II is called
a. cytokinesis.
* b. interkinesis.
c. synapsis.
d. reduction division.
e. karyokinesis.

M	31.	During meiosis II,
a. cytokinesis results in the formation of a total of two cells.
* b. sister chromatids of each chromosome are separated from each other.
c. homologous chromosomes synapse.
d. homologous chromosomes separate.
e. sister chromatids exchange parts.

FROM GAMETES TO OFFSPRING

M	32.	Meiosis typically results in the production of
a. two diploid cells.
b. four diploid cells.
* c. four haploid cells.
d. two haploid cells.
e. one triploid cell.

D	33.	Which of the following is NOT true of human chromosomes?
a. The haploid number is 23.
b. The diploid number is 46.
c. There are 23 pairs of chromosomes.
* d. Human gametes end up with two of each type of 23 chromosomes.
e. Human gametes end up with one of each type of 23 chromosomes.

M	34.	Gametogenesis is
a. always the result of the process of meiosis.
b. the pairing of homologous chromosomes.
* c. the formation of sex cells.
d. the fusion of gametes.
e. a process that occurs only in asexually reproducing forms.

M	35.	Which of the following cells is NOT haploid?
a. secondary spermatocyte
b. sperm
* c. primary oocyte
d. spermatids
e. polar bodies

E	36.	Which of the following will NOT develop into a gamete?
a. spermatogonium
* b. polar bodies
c. oocyte
d. spermatid
e. secondary spermatocyte

D	37.	Polar bodies
a. are dumping places for excess genetic material.
b. have no known biological function.
c. are produced by meiosis.
d. will serve as the gametes if something happens to the egg.
* e. all of these are true except "will serve as the gametes if something happens to the egg"

E	38.	Sperm are formed from the direct maturation of
a. sperm mother cells.
* b. spermatids.
c. spermatogonial cells.
d. primary spermatocytes.
e. secondary spermatocytes.

M	39.	The mature ovum is produced by maturation of the
a. oogonium.
b. primary oocyte.
c. secondary polar body.
d. polar body I.
* e. none of these

D 40. In plants, which of the following cells is (are) diploid?
    a. egg
    b. sperm
    c. spore
  * d. leaf cell
    e. spore and leaf cell

M 41. A pine tree is called a sporophyte because it
    a. develops from a germinated spore.
  * b. produces spores by meiosis.
    c. is haploid.
    d. undergoes fertilization.
    e. reproduces by both sexual and asexual means.

M 42. Fertilization of plant gametes produces a
  * a. zygote.
    b. gametophyte.
    c. spore.
    d. meiospore.
    e. multicellular haploid plant.

MEIOSIS AND MITOSIS COMPARED

D 43. Which of the following does NOT produce variation?
    a. crossing over
    b. random alignment of chromosomes during meiosis
  * c. asexual reproduction
    d. genetic recombination of alleles
    e. sexual reproduction

D 44. In comparing mitosis and meiosis, which of the following statements is true?
    a. Meiosis I is more like mitosis than is meiosis II.
    b. Both processes result in four cells.
    c. Synapsis occurs in both.
    d. Chromatids are present only in mitosis.
  * e. Meiosis II resembles mitosis.

Classification Questions

With reference to the mammalian reproductive system, answer questions 45–47 by using the five items listed below.

    I. sperm
    II. mature ova
    III. primary oocytes
    IV. primary spermatocytes
    V. zygotes

E 45. During fertilization, which two items combine to form a fertilized egg?
  * a. I and II
    b. I and III
    c. I and IV
    d. II and IV
    e. III and IV

E 46. Which item or items are the same as a fertilized egg?
    a. II only
    b. III only
  * c. V only
    d. II and III
    e. III and V

D 47. Which is a normal sequence of development?
    a. I >>> II >>> III
    b. I >>> IV >>> V
    c. II >>> III >>> V
  * d. III >>> II + I >>> V
    e. I >>> IV + II >>> V

Answer questions 48–51 by using the five numbers below.

    a. 10
    b. 20
    c. 40
    d. 60
    e. 80

M 48. How many sperm would eventually be produced from 20 spermatids?

M 49. How many sperm would eventually be produced from 20 primary spermatocytes?

M 50. How many ova (eggs) would eventually result from 20 secondary oocytes?

M 51. How many ova (eggs) would eventually result from 20 primary oocytes?

Answers   48. b   49. e   50. b   51. b

Some of the stages of meiosis are listed under a–e below. Answer questions 52–59 with reference to these phases of meiosis.

    a. prophase I
    b. prophase II
    c. metaphase II
    d. anaphase I
    e. telophase I

E 52. The formation of tetrads by synapsis occurs during this stage.

E 53. Recombination via crossing over occurs during this stage.

D 54. By the end of this phase, the number of homologous chromosomes is reduced in half.

M 55. During this stage, the sister chromatids begin to separate.

D 56. Following this phase, each individual *cell* is haploid.

M 57. Chiasmata are present during this stage.

D 58. During this phase, the centromeres separate.

D 59. New genetic combinations, upon which natural selection can act, is present after this stage.

Answers   52. a   53. a   54. d

            55. c   56. e   57. a

            58. c   59. a

Selecting the Exception

M   60.   Four of the five answers listed below concern cells with two chromosome sets. Select the exception.
     a.   zygote
     b.   somatic cells
  *   c.   gamete
     d.   diploid
     e.   two full chromosome sets

M   61.   Four of the five answers listed below are related to pairing of chromosomes. Select the exception.
     a.   synapsis
     b.   crossing over
     c.   exchange of genes
     d.   pairing of homologues
  *   e.   interkinesis

D   62.   Four of the five answers listed below are related to the process of synapsis. Select the exception.
     a.   genetic recombination
     b.   increase in variability
     c.   exchange of genes
  *   d.   identical daughter cells
     e.   chiasmata

D   63.   Four of the five answers listed below are characteristic of meiosis. Select the exception.
     a.   involves two divisions
     b.   reduces the number of chromosomes
  *   c.   results in producing genetically identical cells
     d.   produces haploid cells
     e.   involves synapsis

M   64.   Four of the five answers listed below are terms describing haploid cells. Select the exception.
     a.   ovum
  *   b.   primary spermatocyte
     c.   spermatid
     d.   polar body
     e.   secondary spermatocyte

M   65.   Four of the five answers listed below are haploid. Select the exception.
  *   a.   zygote
     b.   meiospore
     c.   egg
     d.   sperm
     e.   gametophyte

CHAPTER 11
OBSERVABLE PATTERNS OF INHERITANCE

Multiple-Choice Questions

D   1. Which of the following is true of the textbook of example of inheritance of detached or attached earlobes?
    a. The genes an individual possesses are not as important as environment.
    * b. Earlobe attached is controlled by a single gene pair.
    c. If attached earlobes are detached surgically, that trait will be passed on to offspring.
    d. Detached earlobes are indicative of other genetic abnormalities.
    e. Most human traits are the result of single gene effects.

MENDEL'S INSIGHT INTO INHERITANCE PATTERNS

E   2. In Mendel's time, most people believed that
    a. all genetic traits bred true.
    b. only certain forms of domesticated plants and animals bred true.
    * c. the characteristics of parents were blended in the offspring.
    d. acquired characteristics were inherited.
    e. the inheritance of traits was controlled by blood.

E   3. Which of the following statements is true?
    * a. Darwin did not know which mechanisms were responsible for the variation he saw.
    b. The blending theory of inheritance provides excellent support for evolution.
    c. Darwin received Mendel's paper but did not understand its significance.
    d. The explanation for genetics had no implications for evolution.

M   4. The pea plant was an excellent choice for Mendel's experiments because
    a. true-breeding varieties were available.
    b. the plant can self-fertilize.
    c. it can be cross-fertilized.
    d. rue-breeding varieties were available and it can be cross-fertilized.
    * e. rue-breeding varieties were available, the plant can self-fertilize, and it can be cross-fertilized.

M   5. In his experiments with plants, Mendel removed which part of the plant to prevent unwanted fertilizations?
    a. flowers
    b. petals
    c. pistils
    * d. stamens
    e. stigmas

D   6. Which of the following is NOT a characteristic of the pea plants with which Mendel worked?
    a. They produced male and female parts.
    * b. They exhibited blending inheritance.
    c. They would normally self-fertilize.
    d. They had many different traits and exhibited some pure-breeding varieties.
    e. They could be easily cross-fertilized by human manipulation.

E   7. A locus is
    a. a recessive gene.
    b. an unmatched allele.
    c. a sex chromosome.
    * d. the location of an allele on a chromosome.
    e. a dominant gene.

E   8. Various forms of a gene at a given locus are called
    a. chiasmata.
    * b. alleles.
    c. autosomes.
    d. loci.
    e. chromatids.

M   9. Diploid organisms
    a. have corresponding alleles on homologous chromosomes.
    b. are usually the result of the fusion of two haploid gametes.
    c. have two sets of chromosomes.
    d. have pairs of homologous chromosomes.
    * e. all of these

E   10. Which of the following genotypes is homozygous?
    a. *AaBB*
    b. *aABB*
    * c. *aaBB*
    d. *aaBb*
    e. *AaBb*

M   11. The most accurate description of an organism with genotype *AaBb* is
    a. homozygous dominant.
    * b. heterozygous.
    c. heterozygous dominant.
    d. homozygous recessive.
    e. heterozygous recessive.

D   12. Gene *A* occurs on chromosome #5, gene *B* occurs on chromosome #21. Therefore, these two portions of the chromosomes CANNOT be
    a. genes.
    b. dominant.
    c. loci.
    * d. alleles.
    e. recessive.

E   13. Which organism did Mendel utilize to work out the laws of segregation and independent assortment?
    a. the fruit fly
    b. *Neurospora*
  * c. the garden pea
    d. the chicken
    e. *E. coli*

M   14. Mendel's study of genetics differed from his contemporaries' studies because he
    a. used only pure-breeding parents.
    b. examined several different traits at the same time.
  * c. kept careful records and analyzed the data statistically.
    d. worked on plants rather than animals.
    e. confirmed the blending theory of inheritance.

E   15. Which of the following descriptions of Mendel is INCORRECT?
  * a. He was simply lucky to work out the laws of genetics.
    b. He focused on contrasting phenotypic characteristics.
    c. He demonstrated that the blending theory of inheritance was wrong.
    d. He kept exact mathematical data and was the first scientist to utilize numerical analysis of results.
    e. He was a monk, a science teacher, and a gardener.

D   16. Which of the following statements about Mendel is false?
    a. He did not know about chromosomes.
    b. He was not aware of Darwin's theory of evolution.
    c. He was well trained in agriculture and mathematics.
  * d. His work was widely recognized even though it did not produce as much controversy as Darwin's work.
    e. His work established a basic understanding of the laws of heredity.

D   17. Mendel found that pea plants expressing a recessive trait
  * a. were pure-breeding.
    b. appeared only in the first generation of a cross between two pure-breeding plants expressing contrasting forms of a trait.
    c. disappeared after the second generation.
    d. could be produced only if one of the parents expressed the recessive trait.
    e. none of these

M   18. Hybrid organisms produced from a cross between two pure-breeding organisms belong to which generation?
    a. P_1
    b. H_1
    c. A_1
  * d. F_1
    e. F_2

MENDEL'S THEORY OF SEGREGATION

M   19. If *R* is dominant to *r*, the offspring of the cross of *RR* with *rr* will
    a. be homozygous.
  * b. display the same phenotype as the *RR* parent.
    c. display the same phenotype as the *rr* parent.
    d. have the same genotype as the *RR* parent.
    e. have the same genotype as the *rr* parent.

E   20. If short hair (*L*) is dominant to long hair (*l*), animals *LL* and *Ll* have the same
    a. parents.
    b. genotypes.
  * c. phenotypes.
    d. alleles.
    e. genes.

M   21. According to Mendel, what kind of genes "disappear" in F_1 pea plants?
    a. sex-linked
    b. dominant
  * c. recessive
    d. codominant
    e. lethal

M   22. If tall (*D*) is dominant to dwarf (*d*), and two homozygous varieties *DD* and *dd* are crossed, then what kind of progeny will be produced?
    a. all intermediate forms
  * b. all tall
    c. all dwarf
    d. 1/2 tall, 1/2 dwarf
    e. 3/4 tall, 1/4 dwarf

M   23. If all offspring of a cross have the genotype *Aa*, the parents of the crosses would most likely be
  * a. *AA* x *aa*.
    b. *Aa* x *Aa*.
    c. *Aa* x *aa*.
    d. *AA* x *Aa*.
    e. none of these

D   24. Short hair (*L*) is dominant to long hair (*l*). If a short-haired animal of unknown origin is crossed with a long-haired animal and they produce one long-haired and one short-haired offspring, this would indicate that
    a. the short-haired animal was pure-breeding.
  * b. the short-haired animal was not pure-breeding.
    c. the long-haired animal was not pure-breeding.
    d. the long-haired animal was pure-breeding.
    e. none of these can be determined with two offspring.

D   25. For Mendel's explanation of inheritance to be correct,
    a. the genes for the traits he studied had to be located on the same chromosome.
  * b. which gametes combine at fertilization had to be due to chance.
    c. genes could not be transmitted independently of each other.
    d. only diploid organisms would demonstrate inheritance patterns.
    e. none of these

M 26. In a Punnett square, the letters within the little boxes represent
  * a. offspring genotypes.
    b. parental genotypes.
    c. gametes.
    d. offspring phenotypes.
    e. parental phenotypes.

D 27. The theory of segregation applies most specifically to events occurring in preparation of
    a. offspring.
    b. zygotes.
    c. homologous chromosomes.
  * d. gametes.
    e. loci.

E 28. The theory of segregation
    a. deals with the alleles governing two different traits.
    b. applies only to linked genes.
    c. applies only to sex-linked genes.
  * d. explains the behavior of a pair of alleles during meiosis.
    e. none of these

E 29. If short hair (L) is dominant to long hair (l), then what fraction of the offspring produced by a cross of Ll x ll will be homozygous dominant?
    a. 1/2
    b. 1/4
    c. 1/3
  * d. none (no chance of this offspring)
    e. none of these is correct

M 30. If short hair (L) is dominant to long hair (l), then to determine the genotype of a short-haired animal it should be crossed with
    a. LL.
    b. Ll.
  * c. ll.
    d. all of these
    e. none of these

D 31. If Mendel had not examined the _____ generation, he would not have discovered his theory of segregation.
    a. P_1
    b. H_1
    c. A_1
    d. F_1
  * e. F_2

D 32. The F_2 phenotypic ratio of a monohybrid cross is
    a. 1:1.
    b. 2:1.
    c. 9:3:3:1.
    d. 1:2:1.
  * e. 3:1.

M 33. If the results of a testcross reveal that all offspring resemble the parents being tested, then it may be concluded that the parents are
    a. heterozygous.
    b. polygenic.
  * c. homozygous.
    d. recessive.
    e. none of these

D 34. A testcross consists of a cross
    a. of two pure-breeding forms to find out which form of a gene is dominant.
    b. between two unknown forms to determine their genotypes.
    c. between an offspring and its parent.
  * d. of an F_1 hybrid to an individual that is homologous recessive.
    e. of two F_2 individuals to produce an F_3 generation.

D 35. A testcross involves
    a. two F_1 hybrids.
    b. an F_1 hybrid and an F_2 offspring.
    c. two parental organisms.
    d. an F_1 hybrid and the homozygous dominant parent.
  * e. an F_1 hybrid and an organism that is homozygous recessive for that trait.

M 36. For monohybrid experiments, a testcross could result in which of the following ratios?
  * a. 1:1
    b. 2:1
    c. 9:3:3:1
    d. 1:2:1
    e. 3:1

M 37. If all the offspring of a testcross are alike and resemble the organism being tested, then that parent is
  * a. homozygous dominant.
    b. homozygous recessive.
    c. heterozygous.
    d. recessive.
    e. incompletely dominant.

INDEPENDENT ASSORTMENT

D 38. In a cross involving plants with round/wrinkled seeds, yellow/green pods, and tall/dwarf stems, the researcher is actually observing _____ traits.
    a. 4
  * b. 3
    c. 6
    d. 12
    e. none of these

D 39. Solid color allele is dominant to striped, and long hair allele is dominant to short hair in a laboratory animal. If the mating of a long solid animal with a short striped animal produced the maximum number of phenotypes, how many would be produced?
   a. 1
   b. 2
 * c. 4
   d. 8

D 40. Some dogs have erect ears; others have drooping ears. Some dogs bark when following a scent; others are silent. Erect ears and barking are due to dominant alleles located on different chromosomes. A dog homozygous for both dominant traits is mated to a droopy-eared, silent follower. The phenotypic ratio expected in the F_1 generation is
   a. 9:3:3:1.
 * b. 100 percent of one phenotype.
   c. 1:1.
   d. 1:2:1.
   e. none of these

M 41. Some dogs have erect ears; others have drooping ears. Some dogs bark when following a scent; others are silent. Erect ears and barking are due to dominant alleles located on different chromosomes. If two dihybrids are crossed,
   a. the most common phenotype is drooping ears and barking.
 * b. all droopy-eared silent dogs are pure-breeding.
   c. the least common phenotype is drooping ears and barking.
   d. there will be no phenotypes or genotypes that resemble the original parents.
   e. there will be no offspring that resemble the F_1 generation.

M 42. Mendel's theory of independent assortment states that
   a. one allele is always dominant to another.
   b. hereditary units from the male and female parents are blended in the offspring.
   c. the two hereditary units that influence a certain trait segregate during gamete formation.
 * d. each hereditary unit is inherited separately from other hereditary units.
   e. all of these

D 43. Which of the following statements about the F_2 generation produced in the dihybrid cross is NOT true?
 * a. All offspring with the same phenotype will have the same genotype.
   b. All offspring with the same genotype will possess the same phenotype.
   c. It will not be possible to determine the genotype of some individuals by their phenotype.
   d. It will be possible to tell the genotype of some offspring by looking at their phenotypes.
   e. Nine genotypes and four phenotypes will be produced.

M 44. Individuals with the genotype $Gg\ Hh\ Ii\ Jj$ will produce how many different kinds of gametes?
   a. 2
   b. 4
   c. 6
   d. 8
 * e. 16

M 45. An individual with a genotype of $Aa\ Bb\ CC$ is able to produce how many different kinds of gametes?
   a. 2
   b. 3
 * c. 4
   d. 7
   e. 8

D 46. An animal has the genotype $Aa\ Cc\ DD\ gg$. How many different gametes can it produce?
   a. 2
   b. 3
 * c. 4
   d. 8
   e. 12

D 47. Mendel would not have seen four different phenotypes in the F_2 generation of his dihybrid crosses if
 * a. the genes had been on the same chromosomes.
   b. the P_1 generation had been homozygous.
   c. purple had been dominant to white.
   d. more than two traits were traced.
   e. all of these

D 48. In cocker spaniels, black coat color (B) is dominant over red (b), and solid color (S) is dominant over spotted (s). If a red male was crossed with a black female to produce a red spotted puppy, the genotypes of the parents (with male genotype first) would be
   a. $Bb\ Ss$ x $Bb\ Ss$.
 * b. $bb\ Ss$ x $Bb\ Ss$.
   c. $bb\ ss$ x $Bb\ Ss$.
   d. $bb\ Ss$ x $Bb\ ss$.
   e. $Bb\ ss$ x $Bb\ ss$.

D 49. If one pair of alleles exhibits simple dominance while the other pair exhibits incomplete dominance, the F_2 phenotype produced from a cross of $AA\ BB$ with $aa\ bb$ will produce a _____ ratio.
   a. 1:1:1:1
   b. 9:3:3:1
   c. 1:4:6:4:1
   d. 1:2:1
 * e. 3:6:3:1:2:1

D 50. In cocker spaniels, black coat color (B) is dominant over red (b), and solid color (S) is dominant over spotted (s). If a red spotted male was crossed with a black solid female and all the offspring from several crosses expressed only the dominant traits, the genotype of the female would be
 * a. $BB\ SS$.
   b. $Bb\ SS$.
   c. $Bb\ Ss$.
   d. $BB\ Ss$.
   e. none of these

D 51. In cocker spaniels, black coat color (*B*) is dominant over red (*b*), and solid color (*S*) is dominant over spotted (*s*). If two black solid dogs were crossed several times and the total offspring were eighteen black solid and five black spotted puppies, the genotypes of the parents would most likely be
   a. *Bb Ss* x *Bb Ss*.
   b. *Bb Ss* x *Bb SS*.
   c. *BB Ss* x *Bb ss*.
   * d. *BB Ss* x *Bb Ss*.
   e. *Bb ss* x *Bb SS*.

M 52. In cocker spaniels, black coat color (*B*) is dominant over red (*b*), and solid color (*S*) is dominant over spotted (*s*). If two dihybrids (*Bb Ss*) were crossed, the most common phenotype would be
   * a. black and solid.
   b. black and spotted.
   c. red and solid.
   d. red and spotted.
   e. none of these

M 53. In cocker spaniels, black coat color (*B*) is dominant over red (*b*), and solid color (*S*) is dominant over spotted (*s*). If two dihybrids (*Bb Ss*) were crossed, which would be produced?
   a. black and spotted pure-breeding forms
   b. black and solid pure-breeding forms
   c. red and solid pure-breeding forms
   d. red and spotted pure-breeding forms
   * e. all of these

D 54. In cocker spaniels, black coat color (*B*) is dominant over red (*b*), and solid color (*S*) is dominant over spotted (*s*). If two dihybrids (*Bb Ss*) were crossed, what fraction of the black solid offspring would be homozygous?
   a. 4/16
   b. 9/16
   * c. 1/9
   d. 3/16
   e. 3/4

D 55. In cocker spaniels, black coat color (*B*) is dominant over red (*b*), and solid color (*S*) is dominant over spotted (*s*). In the F_2 generation of a cross between *BB ss* with *bb SS*, what fraction of the offspring would be expected to be black and spotted?
   a. 1/16
   b. 9/16
   c. 1/9
   * d. 3/16
   e. 3/4

D 56. In cocker spaniels, black coat color (*B*) is dominant over red (*b*), and solid color (*S*) is dominant over spotted (*s*). A cross of *Bb Ss* with *bb ss* would produce the phenotypic ratio
   a. 9:3:3:1.
   * b. 1:1:1:1.
   c. 1:2:1.
   d. 3:1.
   e. none of these

D 57. In cocker spaniels, black coat color (*B*) is dominant over red (*b*), and solid color (*S*) is dominant over spotted (*s*). If *Bb Ss* were crossed with *Bb ss*, the chance that a black solid individual would be produced is
   a. 3/16.
   b. 1/3.
   c. 9/16.
   * d. 3/8.
   e. 1/16.

D 58. Which of the following would be an exception to the theory of independent assortment?
   a. dominance
   b. recessiveness
   c. incomplete dominance
   d. pleiotropy
   * e. linkage

M 59. Assume that short hair (*L*) is dominant to long hair (*l*) and black hair (*B*) is dominant to brown (*b*). If you found a black short-haired animal, you could determine its genotype by crossing it to an animal with a genotype of
   a. *LL BB*.
   b. *ll BB*.
   c. *ll Bb*.
   * d. *ll bb*.
   e. *LL bb*.

D 60. In the second generation of a cross of *DD RR* with *dd rr,* the most common genotype would be
   a. *DD RR*.
   b. *Dd RR*.
   * c. *Dd Rr*.
   d. *dd RR*.
   e. *dd Rr*.

E 61. The usual F_2 phenotypic ratio of a dihybrid cross is
   a. 1:1.
   b. 2:1.
   * c. 9:3:3:1.
   d. 1:2:1.
   e. 3:1.

M 62. The theory of independent assortment
   * a. cannot be demonstrated in a monohybrid cross.
   b. is illustrated by the behavior of linked genes.
   c. indicates that the expression of one gene is independent of the action of another gene.
   d. states that alleles for the same characteristic separate during meiosis.
   e. is negated by the phenomenon of epistasis.

M 63. If all the offspring of a cross had the genotype *Aa Bb,* the parents of the cross would most likely be
   a. *AA BB* x *aa bb*.
   b. *AA bb* x *aa BB*.
   c. *Aa Bb* x *Aa Bb*.
   d. *Aa bb* x *aa Bb*.
   * e. *AA BB* x *aa bb* or *AA bb* x *aa BB*.

E 64. What fraction of the time will the cross of *Aa Bb Cc* with *Aa Bb Cc* produce an offspring of genotype *aa bb cc*?
* a. 1/64
  b. 1/32
  c. 3/64
  d. 1/16
  e. 9/64

M 65. What fraction of the time will the cross of *Aa Bb Cc* with *Aa Bb Cc* produce an offspring of genotype *Aa bb CC*?
  a. 1/64
* b. 1/32
  c. 3/64
  d. 1/16
  e. 9/64

D 66. What fraction of the time will the cross of *Aa Bb Cc* with *Aa Bb Cc* produce an offspring that expresses the dominant traits *A* and *B* and *cc* (*A__ B__ cc*)?
  a. 1/32
  b. 3/64
  c. 1/16
* d. 9/64
  e. 27/64

D 67. What fraction of the time will the cross of *Aa Bb Cc* with *Aa Bb Cc* produce an offspring that expresses the phenotype represented by the dominant gene *C* (*aa bb C__*)?
  a. 1/32
* b. 3/64
  c. 1/16
  d. 9/64
  e. 27/64

D 68. What fraction of the time will the cross of *Aa Bb Cc* with *Aa Bb Cc* produce an offspring that expresses all three dominant genes?
  a. 3/64
  b. 1/16
  c. 1/8
  d. 9/64
* e. 27/64

D 69. What fraction of the time will the cross of *Aa Bb Cc* with *Aa Bb Cc* produce an offspring that is pure-breeding?
  a. 3/64
  b. 1/16
* c. 1/8
  d. 9/64
  e. 27/64

D 70. The chance of producing an offspring of genotype *Aa BB cc* from a cross of *Aa Bb Cc* with *Aa Bb Cc* is
  a. 1/64.
* b. 1/32.
  c. 3/64.
  d. 1/16.
  e. 3/32.

D 71. The chance of producing an offspring of genotype *Aa Bb cc* from a cross of *Aa BB Cc* with *Aa BB Cc* is
  a. 1/32.
  b. 1/16.
  c. 3/32.
  d. 1/8.
* e. none (no chance of this offspring).

D 72. What fraction of the time will a cross of *Aa Bb Cc* with *Aa BB cc* produce an offspring of genotype *Aa Bb Cc*?
  a. 1/32
  b. 1/16
  c. 3/32
* d. 1/8
  e. none (no chance of this offspring)

D 73. What fraction of the time will a cross of *Aa BB cc* with *Aa Bb CC* produce an offspring of genotype *Aa Bb CC*?
  a. 1/32
  b. 1/16
  c. 3/32
  d. 1/8
* e. none (no chance of this offspring)

M 74. Mendel's dihybrid crosses, but not his monohybrid crosses, showed that
  a. some genes were linked together.
  b. the two alleles controlling a trait were divided equally among the gametes.
* c. alleles for different traits were inherited independently.
  d. one of the pair of alleles is dominant to the other.
  e. the crossing of two different homozygous forms will not produce any offspring in the first generation that will look like either of the parents.

D 75. Mendel's dihybrid crosses provided indirect evidence for all but which one of the following?
  a. independent assortment
  b. dominance
* c. linkage
  d. presence of two factors in parents and offspring
  e. segregation of factors

E 76. An individual with a genetic makeup of *aa BB* is said to be
* a. pure-breeding.
  b. recessive.
  c. hybrid.
  d. dihybrid.
  e. heterozygous.

M 77. A dihybrid cross of two contrasting pure-breeding organisms
  a. produces homozygous offspring.
  b. must produce a phenotype different from either pure-breeding parent.
* c. results in the disappearance of the recessive traits for the first generation.
  d. takes place only in the laboratory under precisely controlled conditions.
  e. will result in the immediate formation of another pure-breeding variety.

DOMINANCE RELATIONS

D 78. Coat color in one breed of mice is controlled by incompletely dominant alleles so that yellow and white are homozygous, while cream is heterozygous. The cross of two cream individuals will produce
   a. all cream offspring.
   b. equal numbers of white and yellow mice, but no cream offspring.
   c. equal numbers of white and cream mice.
   d. equal numbers of yellow and cream mice.
 * e. equal numbers of white and yellow mice, with twice as many creams as the other two colors.

D 79. An incompletely dominant gene controls the color of chickens so that BB produces black, Bb produces a slate-gray color called blue, and bb produces splashed white. A second gene controls comb shape, with the dominant gene R producing a rose comb and r producing a single comb. If a pure-breeding black chicken with a rose comb is mated to a splashed white chicken with a single comb in the F_2 generation, what fraction of the offspring will be black with rose comb?
   a. 9/16
   b. 3/8
 * c. 3/16
   d. 1/8
   e. 1/16

D 80. An incompletely dominant gene controls the color of chickens so that BB produces black, Bb produces a slate-gray color called blue, and bb produces splashed white. A second gene controls comb shape, with the dominant gene R producing a rose comb and r producing a single comb. If a pure-breeding black chicken with rose comb is mated to a splashed white chicken with a single comb in the F_2 generation, what fraction of the offspring will be black with single comb?
   a. 9/16
   b. 3/8
   c. 3/16
   d. 1/8
 * e. 1/16

D 81. An incompletely dominant gene controls the color of chickens so that BB produces black, Bb produces a slate-gray color called blue, and bb produces splashed white. A second gene controls comb shape, with the dominant gene R producing a rose comb and r producing a single comb. If a pure-breeding black chicken with a rose comb is mated to a splashed white chicken with a single comb in the F_2 generation, what fraction of the offspring will be blue with single comb?
   a. 9/16
   b. 3/8
   c. 3/16
 * d. 1/8
   e. 1/16

D 82. An incompletely dominant gene controls the color of chickens so that BB produces black, Bb produces a slate-gray color called blue, and bb produces splashed white. A second gene controls comb shape, with the dominant gene R producing a rose comb and r producing a single comb. If a pure-breeding black chicken with a rose comb is mated to a splashed white chicken with a single comb in the F_2 generation, what fraction of the offspring will be blue with rose comb?
   a. 9/16
 * b. 3/8
   c. 3/16
   d. 1/8
   e. 1/16

M 83. If red (RR) is crossed with white (rr) and produces a pink flower (Rr), and tall (D) is dominant to dwarf (d), the F_2 phenotypic ratio from a cross of $RR\ dd$ with $rr\ DD$ would be
   a. 9:3:3:1.
   b. 1:1:1:1.
   c. 1:2:2:4:1:2:1:2:1.
 * d. 3:6:3:1:2:1.
   e. none of these.

M 84. The F_2 phenotypic ratio of a monohybrid cross involving a gene with incompletely dominant alleles is
   a. 1:1.
   b. 2:1.
   c. 9:3:3:1.
 * d. 1:2:1.
   e. 3:1.

D 85. If shape and color of radishes are due to incompletely dominant genes, crossing two dihybrid heterozygotes will produce how many different phenotypes?
   a. 2
   b. 3
   c. 4
   d. 5
 * e. 9

M 86. In radishes, red and white are the pure-breeding colors and long and round are the pure-breeding shapes, while the hybrids are purple and oval. The cross of a red long radish and a white round radish will produce an F_1 generation of what phenotype?
   a. all long red radishes
   b. all long white radishes
   c. all long purple radishes
   d. all round purple radishes
 * e. none of these

D 87. The type of inheritance that would suggest the concept of blending is
   a. multiple alleles.
   b. autosomal dominance.
   c. codominance.
 * d. incomplete dominance.
   e. codominance and incomplete dominance.

D 88. Roan cattle are the heterozygous hybrids of a cross between a white bull and a red cow. If a roan bull were crossed with a red cow, their offspring would show which of the following ratios?
   a. all roan
   b. 1 red:2 roan:1 white
   c. 1 red:1 white
 * d. 1 red:1 roan
   e. all roan

D 89. In radishes, red and white are the pure-breeding colors and long and round are the pure-breeding shapes, while the hybrids are purple and oval. The cross of a red long radish and a white round radish will produce an F_2 generation in which
   a. the most common phenotype will be oval and purple.
   b. the purple color will occur with all three shapes of radish.
   c. the red color will occur with all three shapes of radish.
   d. all white long forms produced will be pure-breeding.
 * e. all of these

D 90. In radishes, red and white are the pure-breeding colors and long and round are the pure-breeding shapes, while the hybrids are purple and oval. The cross of a red oval with a purple oval will produce all but which of the following phenotypes?
 * a. white and long
   b. purple and oval
   c. red and oval
   d. purple and long
   e. red and long

D 91. In radishes, red and white are the pure-breeding colors and long and round are the pure-breeding shapes, while the hybrids are purple and oval. The cross of a white oval and a purple oval will produce more
   a. red long than white long.
   b. purple round than white long.
 * c. purple oval than purple long.
   d. purple long than purple round.
   e. purple round than white oval.

D 92. In radishes, red and white are the pure-breeding colors and long and round are the pure-breeding shapes, while the hybrids are purple and oval. The cross of a purple oval with a purple oval
   a. is a cross between two pure-breeding forms.
   b. is an example of a testcross.
   c. produces only homozygous pure-breeding forms.
   d. produces only heterozygous offspring.
 * e. none of these

D 93. In radishes, red and white are the pure-breeding colors and long and round are the pure-breeding shapes, while the hybrids are purple and oval. The F_2 generation of a cross between long and white and red and round will produce
   a. offspring that will all express dominant traits.
   b. offspring that will all be phenotypically identical.
   c. offspring that will all be genotypically identical.
 * d. purple round, purple long, white oval, and red oval offspring in equal numbers, as well as other phenotypes.
   e. offspring that will all be phenotypically and genotypically identical.

E 94. In incomplete dominance,
   a. one allele is not dominant to another allele.
   b. the genotype can be determined by the phenotype.
   c. the heterozygote is somewhat intermediate to the two homozygotes.
   d. the intermediate phenotype may be the result of enzyme insufficiency.
 * e. all of these

D 95. If a pure-breeding long-tail cat (*LL*) is crossed with a pure-breeding cat with no tail (rumpy, *ll*), and a cat with a short tail (stumpy) is produced, the simplest explanation is
   a. a mutation.
   b. an X-linked gene.
 * c. an incompletely dominant gene.
   d. a lethal gene.
   e. chromosomal aberration.

D 96. Susan, a mother with type B blood, has a child with type O blood. She claims that Craig, who has type A blood, is the father. He claims that he cannot possibly be the father. Further blood tests ordered by the judge reveal that Craig is *AA*. The judge rules that
   a. Susan is right and Craig must pay child support.
 * b. Craig is right and doesn't have to pay child support.
   c. Susan cannot be the real mother of the child; there must have been an error made at the hospital.
   d. it is impossible to reach a decision based on the limited data available.
   e. none of these

M 97. If a child has an AB blood type, the parents
   a. must both have different blood types.
   b. must be A and B, but not AB.
   c. must both be AB.
   d. can be any blood type.
 * e. can have different blood types, but neither can be blood type O.

E 98. Blood types (A, B, and O) are controlled by
   a. sex-linked genes.
   b. linked genes.
   c. incompletely dominant genes.
 * d. multiple alleles.
   e. none of these

M   99.   The ABO blood types are controlled by
          a. pleiotropy
          b. multiple alleles.
          c. incomplete dominance.
          d. codominance.
     *   e. multiple alleles and codominance.

D 100.   The ABO blood types have _____ different
          genotypes.
          a. 4
     *   b. 6
          c. 8
          d. 12
          e. 16

M 101.   If a child belonged to blood type O, he or she could
          NOT have been produced by which set of parents?
          a. Type A mother and type B father
          b. Type A mother and type O father
     *   c. Type AB mother and type O father
          d. Type O mother and type O father

D 102.   The number of different alleles for ABO blood types in
          the total human population is
          a. 4.
          b. 6.
          c. 9.
          d. undetermined.
     *   e. 3.

D 103.   If a woman of blood type A has a child of blood type
          O, the father may belong to blood type
          a. A, AB, O, but not B.
          b. O only.
     *   c. A, B, O, but not AB.
          d. any blood type other than type A

D 104.   If one parent has type A blood and the other parent has
          type B, then which of the following is possible in the
          children?
          a. only AB
          b. A and AB
          c. B and AB
     *   d. A, B, AB, O
          e. only O

MULTIPLE EFFECTS OF SINGLE GENES

E 105.   A gene that produces multiple effects is called
          a. a multiple allele.
          b. an autosome.
          c. an epistatic gene.
     *   d. a pleiotropic gene.
          e. an incompletely dominant gene.

E 106.   Multiple effects of a single gene is known as
          a. expressivity.
          b. penetrance.
          c. codominance.
     *   d. pleiotropy.
          e. multiple alleles.

E 107.   Pleiotropic genes
          a. act on secondary sexual characteristics.
     *   b. influence more than one aspect of phenotype.
          c. are additive.
          d. produce lethal effects when homozygous.
          e. none of these

M 108.   Which of the following is NOT a known effect in the
          expression of Marfan syndrome?
          a. lanky, loose jointed skeleton
          b. rweakened blood vessels
          c. swollen air sacs in lungs
     *   d. excessive absorption of oxygen causing the blood
              cells to swell
          e. lens displacement in the eyes

INTERACTIONS BETWEEN GENE PAIRS

E 109.   Genes at one locus that affect the expression of genes
          at a different locus are said to be
     *   a. epistatic.
          b. linked.
          c. codominant.
          d. penetrant.
          e. alleles.

M 110.   An F_2 phenotypic ratio of 13:3 is the result of
          a. single recessive epistasis.
          b. double or duplicate recessive epistasis.
          c. single dominant epistasis.
          d. double or duplicate dominant epistasis.
     *   e. one dominant and one recessive gene epistasis.

D 111.   The F_2 phenotypic ratio of 9:3:4 is a result of a cross
          involving
          a. two genes expressing complete dominance.
          b. a gene expressing dominance and another gene
              expressing codominance.
          c. two genes expressing codominance.
     *   d. epistasis in which one gene modifies the
              expression of the other gene.
          e. multiple alleles.

M 112.   An F_2 phenotypic ratio of 9:7 is the result of
          a. single recessive epistasis.
     *   b. double or duplicate recessive epistasis.
          c. single dominant epistasis.
          d. double or duplicate dominant epistasis.
          e. one dominant and one recessive gene epistasis.

D 113.   An F_2 phenotypic ratio of 9:3:4 is the result of
     *   a. single recessive epistasis.
          b. double or duplicate recessive epistasis.
          c. single dominant epistasis.
          d. double or duplicate dominant epistasis.
          e. one dominant and one recessive gene epistasis.

HOW CAN WE EXPLAIN LESS PREDICTABLE VARIATIONS?

E 114. A bell-shaped curve of phenotypic variation is indicative of
    a. incomplete dominance.
*   b. continuous variation.
    c. multiple alleles.
    d. epistasis.
    e. environmental variables on phenotypes.

ENVIRONMENTAL EFFECTS ON PHENOTYPE

E 115. The color of Siamese cats is controlled by
    a. multiple alleles.
    b. quantitative inheritance.
    c. incompletely dominant genes.
    d. nondisjunction.
*   e. variation in temperature, with cold temperature producing dark fur.

E 116. The variation of the color in Siamese cats is due to
    a. incomplete codominance.
    b. inactive X chromosomes.
*   c. environmental effects on phenotypes.
    d. quantitative inheritance.
    e. multiple alleles.

M 117. The reason for the darker fur on the tail, ears, nose, and legs of a Siamese cat is
    a. incomplete dominance.
*   b. the interaction of the environment with gene expression.
    c. quantitative inheritance.
    d. epistasis.
    e. none of these

Problems

M 118. In a certain plant, when individuals with blue flowers are crossed with individuals with blue flowers, only blue flowers are produced. Plants with red flowers crossed with plants with red flowers sometimes produce only red flowers, although other times they produce either red or blue flowers. When plants with red flowers are crossed with plants with blue flowers, sometimes only red flowers are produced; other times either red or blue flowers are produced. Which gene is dominant?

M 119. Which is easier to establish in a pure-breeding population, a dominant or a recessive gene?

M 120. Tall (D) is dominant to dwarf (d). Give the F_2 genotypic and phenotypic ratios of a cross between a pure-breeding tall plant and a pure-breeding dwarf plant.

M 121. If wire hair (W) is dominant to smooth hair (w) and you find a wire-haired puppy, how would you determine its genotype by a genetic breeding experiment? Give both the genotype and phenotype involved with the cross with the unknown.

M 122. In poultry, rose comb is controlled by a dominant allele and its recessive allele controls single comb.
  (a) Give the genotype and phenotype produced from crossing a pure-breeding rose comb chicken with a pure-breeding single comb chicken.
  (b) Give the results of the backcross of the F_1 hybrid with both pure-breeding parents.

M 123. If black fur color is controlled by a dominant allele (B) and brown by its recessive allele (b), give the genotypes of the parents and offspring of a cross of a black male with a brown female that produces 1/2 black offspring and 1/2 brown offspring.

D 124. If 2 spot (S) is dominant to 4 spot (s), give the genotypes for the parents in the following crosses:
  (a) 2 spot x 2 spot yields 2 spot and 4 spot
  (b) 2 spot x 4 spot yields only 2 spot
  (c) 2 spot x 4 spot yields 2 spot and 4 spot
  (d) 2 spot x 2 spot yields only 2 spot
  (e) 4 spot x 4 spot yields only 4 spot

D 125. In humans, normal skin pigmentation is influenced by a dominant gene (C), which allows pigmentation to develop. All individuals who are homozygous for the recessive allele (c) are unable to produce an enzyme needed for melanin formation and are therefore referred to as albino. Two normal parents produce an albino child. What are the chances that the next child will be an albino?

D 126. The allele for albinism (c) is recessive to the allele for normal pigmentation (C). A normally pigmented woman whose father is an albino marries an albino man whose parents are normal. They have three children, two normal and one albino. Give the genotypes for each person listed.

D 127. In garden peas, one pair of alleles controls the height of the plant and a second pair of alleles controls flower color. The allele for tall (D) is dominant to the allele for dwarf (d), and the allele for purple (P) is dominant to the allele for white (p). A tall plant with purple flowers crossed with a dwarf plant with white flowers produces 1/2 tall with purple flowers and 1/2 tall with white flowers. What is the genotype of the parents?

D 128. In garden peas, one pair of alleles controls the height of the plant and a second pair of alleles controls flower color. The allele for tall (D) is dominant to the allele for dwarf (d), and the allele for purple (P) is dominant to the allele for white (p). A tall plant with white flowers crossed with a dwarf plant with purple flowers produces all tall offspring with purple flowers. What is the genotype of the parents?

D 129. In garden peas, one pair of alleles controls the height of the plant and a second pair of alleles controls flower color. The allele for tall (D) is dominant to the allele for dwarf (d), and the allele for purple (P) is dominant to the allele for white (p). A tall plant with purple flowers crossed with a dwarf plant with white flowers produces 1/4 tall purple, 1/4 tall white, 1/4 dwarf purple, and 1/4 dwarf white. What is the genotype of the parents?

D 130. In garden peas, one pair of alleles controls the height of the plant and a second pair of alleles controls flower color. The allele for tall (D) is dominant to the allele for dwarf (d), and the allele for purple (P) is dominant to the allele for white (p). A tall plant with white flowers crossed with a dwarf plant with purple flowers produces 1/4 tall purple, 1/4 tall white, 1/4 dwarf purple, and 1/4 dwarf white. What is the genotype of the parents?

D 131. In garden peas, one pair of alleles controls the height of the plant and a second pair of alleles controls flower color. The allele for tall (D) is dominant to the allele for dwarf (d), and the allele for purple (P) is dominant to the allele for white (p). A tall plant with purple flowers crossed with a tall plant with white flowers produces 3/8 tall purple, 1/8 tall white, 3/8 dwarf purple, and 1/8 dwarf white. What is the genotype of the parents?

D 132. In garden peas, one pair of alleles controls the height of the plant and a second pair of alleles controls flower color. The allele for tall (D) is dominant to the allele for dwarf (d), and the allele for purple (P) is dominant to the allele for white (p). A tall purple crossed with a tall purple produces 3/4 tall purple and 1/4 tall white. What is the genotype of the parents?

D 133. In horses, black coat color is influenced by the dominant allele (B), and chestnut coat color is influenced by the recessive allele (b). Trotting gait is due to a dominant gene (T), pacing gait to the recessive allele (t). If a homozygous black trotter is crossed to a chestnut pacer,
    (a) what will be the appearance of the F_1 and F_2 generations?
    (b) which phenotype will be the most common?
    (c) which genotype will be the most common?
    (d) which of the potential offspring will be certain to breed true?

D 134. In horses, black coat color is influenced by the dominant allele (B), and chestnut coat color by the recessive allele (b). Trotting gait is due to a dominant gene (T), pacing gait to the recessive allele (t). What color horse would you use to find out the genotype of a black trotter? Give the genotype and phenotype.

D 135. Crosses between a yellow rat with a yellow rat always produce yellow. Crosses between a white rat with a white rat always produce white. The alleles affect the same aspect of coat color. The crosses of a white with a yellow produce a cream. What happens if you cross two creams?

D 136. Assume that red plants crossed with white plants give rise to pink plants. Explain how to eliminate red plants if you start with two pinks.

D 137. If long or round are homozygous forms of an incompletely dominant gene and oval is the phenotype of the heterozygote, give the F_2 ratio of the cross between long and round (both genotype and phenotype).

D 138. A breeder of cattle has a herd of white cows and a roan bull. Hair color in this breed is controlled by an incompletely dominant gene. The two homozygous forms are either red or white, and the heterozygous is roan.
    (a) What colors of calves are expected and in what proportions?
    (b) Outline a procedure to develop an all-red herd.

D 139. In radishes, two incompletely dominant genes control color and shape. Red and white radishes are homozygous, whereas the hybrid is purple. Long and round are homozygous and, if crossed, will produce an oval hybrid. Give the F_2 genotypic and phenotypic ratio produced by crossing pure-breed red long radishes with white round varieties.

D 140. In a certain breed of chicken an incompletely dominant gene controls color. The homozygous black, when crossed with the homozygous splashed-white, produces an intermediate gray color pattern referred to as blue. A second gene controls the shape of the comb. The dominant allele (R) produces rose, whereas the recessive allele (r) produces single. Give the F_1 and F_2 genotypic and phenotypic ratios of a cross between a pure-breeding black single and a pure-breeding splashed-white rose.

D 141. There are three alleles controlling the ABO blood types. I^A and I^B are codominant genes so that the combination $I^A I^B$ produces the AB blood type. The third allele, I^O, is recessive to the other two alleles. Indicate which of these parents could produce the given child:

Parents	Child	Yes or No
(a) A x AB	B	
(b) A x O	A	
(c) A x B	O	
(d) A x AB	O	
(e) A x AB	B	
(f) B x B	O	
(g) AB x AB	A	

D 142. In horses there are four alleles at the A locus. Arranged in dominance sequence they are:

A (wild) a^b (bay) a^c (brown) a^d (black)

If you bred several bay mares whose sires were brown to a brown stallion whose sire was black, what type of offspring would be produced, and in what proportion?

D **143.** In rabbits there are four alleles at the c locus. Arranged in dominance sequence they are:

C (agouti), c^{ch}(chinchilla), c^h(Himalayan), and c(albino)

(a) Is it possible to cross two agouti rabbits and produce both chinchilla and Himalayan offspring?

(b) Is it possible to cross two chinchillas and produce 1/2 chinchilla and 1/2 Himalayan?

D **144.** Gray is homozygous while blue is a heterozygous form of a semilethal gene. Give the ratio of the offspring produced in the cross of two blues.

D **145.** A cross of two Kerry horses always produces Kerry. A cross of a Kerry with a Dexter produces 1/2 and 1/2. Crosses of two Dexters produce two Dexters for every Kerry. Explain.

D **146.** In the late 1920s, a mutation occurred in many silver fox farms around the world. The fox farms that sold expensive furs were proud of the quality of their furs, and each advertised that it had the best, purest breed of all the fox farms. The new mutations produced a "platinum" coat pattern that was commercially desirable, so the farms crossed them to get more. The results of their breeding experiments were as follows: (1) silver x silver >>> all silver offspring; (2) silver x platinum >>> equal numbers of silver and platinum; (3) platinum x platinum >>> 2 platinum for each silver offspring. Explain.

D **147.** There is a color pattern inherited in certain mice in which agouti (gray) is homozygous and yellow is heterozygous. A cross of two yellows produces two yellows for each agouti. A second gene, C/c, controls the expression of the color genes: C is the dominant allele that allows color to be expressed, and the recessive gene in the homozygous condition (cc) prevents any color from being expressed.

(a) Give the genotypes of a white parent crossed with a yellow parent that produces 1/2 white, 1/3 yellow, 1/6 agouti offspring.

(b) Give the results of the cross of two forms heterozygous for each gene.

(c) Can you develop a pure-breed population for any of the colors?

D **148.** In poultry, the genes for rose comb (R) and pea comb (P) produce walnut whenever they occur together ($R\_\_ P\_\_$); single-combed individuals have the homozygous condition for both genes ($rr\ pp$).

(a) Give the F_1 and F_2 phenotypic results of a cross of a pure-breeding rose comb ($RR\ pp$) with a pure-breeding pea comb ($rr\ PP$).

(b) Give the phenotypic results of a cross of $Rr\ Pp$ x $rr\ Pp$.

(c) Give the phenotypic results of a cross of $RR\ Pp$ x $rr\ Pp$.

(d) Give the phenotypic results of a cross of $Rr\ pp$ x $rr\ Pp$.

(e) Give the phenotypic results of a cross of $Rr\ Pp$ x $rr\ pp$.

D **149.** Congenital deafness in humans is due to the homozygous condition of either of the recessive genes d or e, or both of these genes. Both dominant D and E are necessary for normal hearing. Gene D/d affects the middle ear, while gene E/e affects the inner ear. It does not matter how good the normal inner ear (as indicated by $E\_\_$) is; if there is something wrong in the middle ear, the individual is unable to hear. The same applies for the other gene. Give the phenotypic results of the following crosses:

(a) $Dd\ EE$ x $Dd\ EE$

(b) $Dd\ Ee$ x $Dd\ Ee$

(c) $dd\ EE$ x $DD\ ee$

(d) $Dd\ EE$ x $Dd\ ee$

(e) $Dd\ EE$ x $DD\ Ee$

D **150.** White fruit color in summer squash is influenced by a dominant allele W, whereas colored fruit must be ww. In the presence of ww, a dominant gene G results in yellow fruit, and if the individual had both recessive genes in the homozygous condition, it would be green. Give the F_2 phenotypic ratios resulting from a cross of a pure-breeding white of genotype $WW\ GG$ with a green.

D **151.** In cultivated stocks, the cross of a variety of white flower plants produced all red flowers in the F_1 generation, but the F_2 generation produced 87 red, 31 cream, and 39 white. Explain these results by giving the genotypes possible for each phenotype.

D **152.** In summer squash, spherical-shaped fruit has been shown to be dominant to elongated fruit. On one occasion two different spherical varieties were crossed and produced all disk-shaped fruits. When these hybrid disk-shaped fruits were crossed they produced 75 disk-shaped fruits, 48 spherical fruits, and 9 elongated fruits. Explain these results.

D 153. In sweet peas, genes *C* and *P* are necessary for colored flowers. In the absence of either (__ *pp* or *cc* __) or both (*cc pp*), the flowers are white. What will be the color of the offspring of the crosses in what proportions for the following?
  (a) *Cc Pp* x *cc pp*
  (b) *Cc Pp* x *Cc Pp*
  (c) *Cc PP* x *Cc pp*
  (d) *Cc pp* x *cc Pp*

D 154. In sweet peas, genes *C* and *P* are necessary for colored flowers. In the absence of either (__ *pp* or *cc* __) or both (*cc pp*), the flowers are white. Give the probable genotype of a plant with colored flowers and a plant with white flowers that produced 38 plants with colored flowers and 42 plants with white flowers.

D 155. In a certain variety of plants a cross between a red-flowered plant and a white-flowered plant produced an all-red flower F_1. In the F_2 there were 140 red, 50 cream, and 65 white.
  (a) Offer an explanation for this F_2 ratio.
  (b) What ratio would be produced in a testcross of the F_1 hybrid?
  (c) What ratio would be produced if all the white F_2 plants were crossed among themselves?

D 156. In a certain breed of chicken two genes control color. A dominant allele (*I*) inhibits the expression of any color gene (*C*). A second recessive gene (*c*) results in albinism when homozygous (*cc*). Give the F_2 phenotypic ratio of a colored chicken *ii CC* with a white *II cc*.

D 157. In mice the allele for colored fur (*C*) is dominant to the allele for albinism (*c*). The allele (*W*) for normal behavior is dominant to that for waltzing movement (*w*). Give the probable genotypes of the parents if they produced the offspring listed after the following crosses:
  (a) Colored normal x white waltzer produced 10 colored normal, 8 colored waltzers, 2 white waltzers, 11 white normal.
  (b) Colored normal x white normal produced 35 colored normal, 13 colored waltzers.
  (c) Colored normal x colored normal produced 37 colored normal, 14 colored waltzers, 9 white normal, and 5 white waltzers.

D 158. Pure-breeding yellow guinea pigs crossed with pure-breeding white ones produce only cream-colored offspring. This pattern indicates incomplete dominance. Rough hair is found to be dominant to smooth hair. Give the F_1 and F_2 genotypic and phenotypic ratios of a cross of a smooth white guinea pig with a homozygous rough yellow guinea pig.

D 159. There are nine coat colors known in foxes. If a red fox were crossed with a double-black fox, all the hybrids would be red above and black below in a pattern known as blended cross. If two blended crosses were mated, the F_2 ratio would be as follows: 1 red, 2 smokey red, 2 cross red, 4 blended cross, 1 standard silver, 2 substandard silver, 1 Alaskan silver, 2 sub-Alaskan silver, and 1 double black.
  (a) Using the letters *A/a* and *B/b* to serve as the genes for these animals, develop a genotype for each variety listed.
  (b) Two crosses will produce all blended-cross offspring. One is used above (red fox x double black); what is the other?
  (c) List the genotype and phenotype of all the pure-breeding foxes.
  (d) Give the genotypic and phenotypic ratio of a cross between two substandard silvers.
  (e) Give the genotype and phenotype of the offspring produced in a cross of a sub-Alaskan silver and a cross red.

D 160. In the garden pea Mendel found that tall (*D*) green pods (*G*) and inflated pods (*C*) were dominant to their alleles, dwarf (*d*) yellow pods (*g*) and constricted pods (*c*). Given the following genotypes, determine the chances of producing the offspring shown.
  (a) *DD Gg Cc* x *Dd Gg cc* ———> *DD gg Cc*
  (b) *DD Gg Cc* x *Dd Gg Cc* ———> tall green pod, constricted pod
  (c) *Dd Gg Cc* x *Dd GG cc* ———> tall green pod, inflated pod
  (d) *Dd Gg Cc* x *Dd Gg Cc* ———> *D__ G__ cc*
  (e) *Dd Gg Cc* x *Dd gg CC* ———> *D__ G__ C__*
  (f) *Dd gg cc* x *DD Gg cc* ———> tall green pod, inflated pod
  (g) *Dd Gg Cc* x *Dd Gg Cc* ———> *Dd Gg Cc*
  (h) *Dd Gg Cc* x *Dd Gg Cc* ———> *dd gg cc*

D 161. In tomatoes, red (*R*) is dominant to yellow (*r*), tall (*D*) is dominant to dwarf (*d*), and smooth (*H*) is dominant to peach or hairy (*h*).
  (a) How many different genotypes are there in relationship to these three characteristics?
  (b) How many different phenotypes are there in relationship to these three characteristics?
  (c) How many different homozygous pure-breeding forms can be produced?

D 162. If you were following the inheritance patterns of two different sets of multiple alleles located on different chromosomes, how many different possible gametes could be produced if locus 1 had five possible alleles and locus 2 had six alleles?

Answers:
118. Red
119. Recessive
120. 1 *DD*, 2 *Dd*, 1 *dd*; 3 tall, 1 dwarf
121. Smooth hair, *ww*

122. (a) *Rr*, rose

(b) *Rr* x *RR* ———> all rose, *Rr* x *rr* Æ
    1/2 rose, 1/2 single

123. Black male (*Bb*) x brown female (*bb*)

offspring: black (*Bb*) brown (*bb*)

124. (a) *Ss* x *Ss* ———> *S__* + *ss*

(b) *Ss* x *ss* ———> *Ss*

(c) *Ss* x *ss* ———> *Ss* + *ss*

(d) *SS* x *S__* ———> *S__*

(e) *ss* x *ss* ———> *ss*

125. 1/4 chance

126. Normal pigmented woman, *Cc;* albino father, *cc;* albino man, *cc;* normal parents, *Cc* + *Cc;*

3 children, 2 normal *Cc*, 1 albino *cc*

127. *DD Pp* x *dd pp*

128. *DD pp* x *dd PP*

129. *Dd Pp* x *dd pp*

130. *Dd pp* x *dd Pp*

131. *Dd Pp* x *Dd pp*

132. Dd Pp x DD Pp

133. (a) F_1: black trotters; F_2: 9 black trotters,
    3 black pacers, 3 chestnut trotters, 1 chestnut pacer

(b) Black pacer

(c) *Bb Tt*

(d) *bb tt*, chestnut pacers

134. *bb tt*, chestnut pacer

135. 1 yellow, 2 cream, 2 white

136. Cross until you get white, and use white in crosses until you cross two whites, then all subsequent plants will be white.

137. 1 *LL*, 2 *Ll*, 1 *ll;* 1 long, 2 oval, 1 round

138. (a) 1/2 white, 1/2 roan

(b) Roan with white —-> roan, roan x roan ----->
    red, roan x red —-> red, red x red ----> red

139. 1 *LL RR* long red, 2 *LL Rr* long purple, 2 *Ll RR* oval red, 4 *Ll RR* oval purple, 1 *ll RR* round red, 1 *ll Rr* round oval, 1 *Ll rr* long white, 2 *Ll rr* oval white, 1 *ll rr* round white

140. F_1: *Bb Rr* blue rose; F_2: 3 *BB R__* black rose,
    6 *Bb R__* blue rose, 3 *bb R__* splashed-white rose,
    1 *BB rr* black single, 2 *Bb rr* blue single,
    1 *bb rr* splashed-white single

141. (a) yes; (b) yes; (c) yes; (d) no;
    (e) yes; (f) yes; (g) yes

142. $a^b a^c$ x $a^c a^d$; 1/2 bay, 1/2 brown

143. (a) no; (b) not likely but possible—would expect a 3:1

144. 1 gray, 2 blues (1 lethal)

145. Kerry is homozygous (*DD*), Dexter is heterozygous (*Dd*), *dd* is lethal.

146. *PP* (silver), *Pp* (platinum), *pp* (lethal)

147. (a) *Yy Cc* x *Yy cc*

(b) *Yy Cc* x *Yy Cc* ———> 3/12 *YY C__* agouti,
    6/12 *Yy C__* yellow, 3/12 *__cc* albino

(c) white and agouti

148. (a) F_1: *Rr Pp* walnut; F_2: 9 *R__P__* walnut, 3 *R__pp* rose,
    3 *rr P__* pea, 1 *rr pp* single

(b) 3/8 walnut, 3/8 pea, 1/8 rose, 1/8 single

(c) 3/4 walnut, 1/4 rose

(d) 1/4 walnut, 1/4 rose, 1/4 pea, 1/4 single

(e) 1/4 walnut, 1/4 rose, 1/4 pea, 1/4 single

149. (a) 3/4 normal, 1/4 deaf

(b) 9/16 normal, 7/16 deaf

(c) all normal

(d) 3/4 normal, 1/4 deaf

(e) all normal

150. 12/16 *W__ __ __* white, 3/16 *ww G __* yellow, 1/16 *ww gg* green

151. *R*-red, *r*-cream, *A*-pigment, *a*-albino

9 *R__ A__* red, 3 *rr A__* cream, 4 *__aa* white

152. 9 *D__ S__* disk, 3 *D__ ss* spherical, 3 *dd S__* spherical, 1 *dd ss* elongated; presence of both dominant genes produces disk, whereas the presence of either one of the genes as homozygous recessive produces spherical, and both recessive produces elongated fruit.

153. (a) 1/4 color, 3/4 white

(b) 9/16 color, 7/16 white

(c) 3/4 color, 1/4 white

(d) 1/4 color, 3/4 white

154. *Cc Pp* x *CC pp*

155. (a) *R*-red, *r*-cream, *A*-color, *a*-albino; 9 *R__A__* red, 3 *rr A__* cream, 4 *__ aa* white

(b) 1/4 red, 1/4 cream, 1/2 white

(c) all offspring would be white because all would be *__aa*

156. 9 *I__ C__* + 3 *I__ cc* + 1 *ii cc* = 13 white + 3 *ii C__* = 3 color

157. (a) *Cc Ww* x *cc ww*

(b) *CC Ww* x *cc Ww*

(c) *Cc Ww* x *Cc Ww*

158. F_1: rough cream *Yy Rr*; F_2: 3 *YY R__* yellow rough, 6 *Yy R__* cream rough, 3 *yy R__* white rough, 1 *YY rr* yellow smooth, 2 *Yy rr* cream smooth, 1 *yy rr* white smooth

159. (a) 1 *AA BB* red
    2 *AA Bb* smokey red
    2 *Aa BB* cross red
    4 *Aa Bb* blended cross
    1 *aa BB* standard silver
    2 *aa Bb* substandard silver
    1 *AA bb* Alaskan silver
    2 *Aa bb* sub-Alaskan silver
    1 *aa bb* double black

(b) *aa BB* standard silver x *AA bb* Alaskan silver

(c)   *AA BB* red, *AA bb* Alaskan silver,
       aa BB standard silver, *aa bb* double black

(d)   1 standard silver *aa BB*
       2 substandard silver *aa Bb*, 1 double black *aa bb*

(e)   1 smokey red *AA Bb*, 2 blended cross *Aa Bb*,
       1 substandard silver *aa Bb*

160. (a)   (1/2) (1/4) (1/2) = 1/16
     (b)   (1) (3/4) (1/4) = 3/16
     (c)   (3/4) (1) (1/2) = 3/8
     (d)   (3/4) (3/4) (1/4) = 9/64
     (e)   (3/4) (1/2) (1) = 3/8
     (f)   (1) (1/2) 0 = 0
     (g)   (2/4) (2/4) (2/4) = 8/64
     (h)   (1/4) (1/4) (1/4) = 1/64

161. (a)   27   (b)   8   (c)   8

162.   30 possibilities

Classification Questions

Answer questions 163–167 using the group of answers below.

     a.   4
     b.   6
     c.   8
     d   12
     e.   24

D   **163.**   In a dihybrid cross between a parent that is a double heterozygote (*Aa Bb*) and a parent that is homozygous dominant for one gene and heterozygous for the other (*AA Bb*), how many unique genotypes potentially will be present in their offspring?

D   **164.**   In a dihybrid cross between a parent that is a double heterozygote (*Aa Bb*) and a parent that is homozygous recessive for one gene and heterozygous for the other (*aa Bb*), how many unique phenotypes potentially will be present in their offspring?

D   **165.**   In a dihybrid cross between a parent that is a double heterozygote (*Aa Bb*) and a parent that is a double homozygous recessive (*aa bb*), how many unique phenotypes potentially will be present in their offspring?

D   **166.**   Plant species X is diploid ($2n = 24$) and has a quantitative trait, the expression of which is controlled by gene loci on each of its chromosomes. What is the maximum number of alleles for this trait that any one individual of species X could have?

D   **167.**   Animal species X is tetraploid ($4n = 12$). Following gene duplication and translocation, a given gene is found on each chromosome. How many alleles for this gene can be present in an individual of this species?

Answers   163. b   164. a   165. a

             166. e   167. d

Selecting the Exception

D   **168.**   Four of the five answers listed below are dominant traits. Select the exception.
     a.   green pod
     b.   purple flower
     c.   yellow seed coat
*   d.   dwarf plant
     e.   axial flower position

E   **169.**   Four of the five answers listed below describe the heterozygous condition. Select the exception.
*   a.   homozygous
     b.   carrier
     c.   heterozygotes
     d.   hybrid
     e.   *Aa*

M   **170.**   Four of the five answers listed below describe the gene makeup. Select the exception.
     a.   pure-breeding
     b.   homozygous
     c.   heterozygous
     d.   carrier
*   e.   phenotype

M   **171.**   Four of the five answers listed below are accepted as valid explanations of genetic behavior. Select the exception.
*   a.   blending
     b.   dominance
     c.   segregation
     d.   independent assortment
     e.   probability

E   **172.**   Four of the five answers listed below are pure-breeding. Select the exception.
     a.   *AA BB*
*   b.   *Aa BB*
     c.   *AA bb*
     d   *aa BB*
     e.   *aa bb*

D   **173.**   Four of the five answers listed below could be produced by epistasis. Select the exception.
     a.   9:7
     b.   12:3:1
     c.   9:6:1
     d   9:3:4
*   e.   3:1

D   **174**   Four of the five answers listed below are dihybrid ratios. Select the exception.
     a.   9:3:3:1
*   b.   1:1
     c.   9:7
     d   1:2:3:4:1:2:1:2:1
     e.   1:1:1:1

CHAPTER 12
HUMAN GENETICS

Multiple-Choice Questions

E   1. The first, and most famous, genetics experiments were done using
    *   a. garden peas.
        b. fruit flies.
        c. bread mold.
        d. humans.
        e. laboratory mice.

E   2. Who was the first to describe chromosomes?
        a. Morgan
        b. Mendel
        c. Sturtevant
        d. Weismann
    *   e. Flemming

E   3. Who discovered the process of meiosis?
        a. Morgan
        b. Mendel
        c. Sturtevant
    *   d. Weismann
        e. Flemming

M   4. Weismann proposed that
        a. the number of chromosomes is reduced by one-half in the sex cells.
        b. the number of chromosomes is doubled by mitosis.
        c. half the chromosomes in a diploid cell come from the father and the other half from the mother.
        d. fertilization restores the number of chromosomes.
    *   e. all except b

M   5. When Mendel's research was discovered in the early 1900s,
    *   a. Weismann had confirmed the basic proposals.
        b. the concept of segregation had to be discarded.
        c. independent assortment was proven untrue.
        d. chromosomes had not yet been described.
        e. the "Father of Genetics" denied involvement with it.

CHROMOSOMES AND INHERITANCE

M   6. Genes are
        a. located on chromosomes.
        b. inherited in the same way as chromosomes.
        c. arranged in linear sequence on chromosomes.
        d. assorted independently during meiosis.
    *   e. all of these

E   7. Chromosomes other than those involved in sex determination are known as
        a. nucleosomes.
        b. heterosomes.
        c. alleles.
    *   d. autosomes.
        e. liposomes.

E   8. Sex chromosomes
        a. determine gender.
        b. vary from one sex to another.
        c. carry some genes that have nothing to do with sex.
        d. were unknown to Mendel.
    *   e. all of these

M   9. DNA coding regions that affect the same trait are called
        a. homologues.
    *   b. alleles.
        c. autosomes.
        d. loci.
        e. gametes.

E   10. The location of a gene on a chromosome is its
        a. centromere.
    *   b. locus.
        c. autosome.
        d. allele.
        e. none of these

M   11. A karyotype
        a. compares one set of chromosomes to another.
    *   b. is a visual display of chromosomes arranged according to size.
        c. is a photograph of cells undergoing mitosis during anaphase.
        d. of a normal human cell shows 48 chromosomes.
        e. cannot be used to identify individual chromosomes beyond the fact that two chromosomes are homologues.

FOCUS ON SCIENCE: KARYOTYPING MADE EASY

E   12. In karyotyping, individual chromosomes may be distinguished from others by
        a. a comparison of chromosome lengths.
        b. bands produced on chromosomes by differential staining.
        c. the position of centromeres.
    *   d. all of these
        e. none of these

M   13. Karyotyping is usually done using what kind of cells?
        a. muscle
    *   b. blood
        c. cartilage
        d. sex
        e. epidermal

M 14. Which chemical is used to keep chromosomes from separating during metaphase?
 a. Giemsa stain
 b. acetone
 * c. colchicine
 d. alcohol
 e. formaldehyde

M 15. Colchicine interferes with the function of
 * a. microtubules.
 b. ribosomes.
 c. centrioles.
 d. centromeres.
 e. chromosomes.

M 16. Karyotype analysis
 a. is a means of detecting and reducing mutagenic agents.
 b. is a surgical technique that separates chromosomes that have failed to segregate properly during meiosis II.
 * c. is used in prenatal diagnosis to detect chromosomal mutations and metabolic disorders in embryos.
 d. substitutes defective alleles with normal ones.
 e. all of these

M 17. Karyotyping involves taking pictures of chromosomes during
 a. prophase.
 b. telophase.
 * c. metaphase.
 d. interphase.
 e. anaphase.

SEX DETERMINATION IN HUMANS

D 18. With respect to chromosomes, the difference between normal human males and females is defined by which of the following?
 a. In females, one X is deleted.
 b. Females possess one X and one Y.
 * c. In males an X is replaced by a Y.
 d. Females have three X's.
 e. Males have two X's and a Y.

D 19. Which of the following statements is false?
 a. The SRY gene is absent in all females.
 b. The SRY gene apparently is the gene that controls the development of male sexuality.
 * c. The development of maleness is by default because males lack 2 X chromosomes.
 d. Maleness develops in the embryo before femaleness.
 e. There is no difference in external genitalia of males or females until four weeks after conception when the genes determining sex begin to be expressed.

D 20. Concerning the sex chromosomes, which of the following is correct?
 a. The Y chromosome carries a greater number of nonsexual traits.
 b. X and Y are different in size but carry nearly equal numbers of genes.
 * c. The X chromosome carries more genes for nonsexual traits.
 d. The X chromosome carries only gender-related genes.
 e. The X chromosome carries the TDF gene.

WHAT MENDEL DIDN'T KNOW: CHROMOSOMES AND RECOMBINATIONS

E 21. Who was the first to use fruit flies in genetics experiments?
 * a. Morgan
 b. Mendel
 c. Sturtevant
 d. Weismann
 e. Flemming

D 22. In his experiments with *Drosophila melanogaster*, Morgan demonstrated that
 a. fertilized eggs have two sets of chromosomes, but eggs and sperm have only one set in each gamete.
 b. aneuploidy exists in karyotypes that have undergone deletions and inversions in specific chromosomes.
 c. colchicine is effective in producing polyploidy in F_2 generations.
 * d. certain genes are located only on an X chromosome and have no corresponding alleles on the Y chromosome.

M 23. An X-linked carrier is a
 a. homozygous dominant female.
 * b. heterozygous female.
 c. homozygous recessive female.
 d. homozygous male.
 e. heterozygous male.

D 24. A human X-linked gene is
 a. found only in males.
 b. more frequently expressed in females.
 c. found on the Y chromosome.
 d. transmitted from father to son.
 * e. found on the X chromosome.

M 25. All of the genes located on a given chromosome constitute a
 a. karyotype.
 b. bridging cross.
 c. wild-type allele.
 * d. linkage group.
 e. none of these

E 26. If two genes are on the same chromosome,
    a. crossing over occurs frequently.
    b. they assort independently.
*   c. they are in the same linkage group.
    d. they are segregated during meiosis.
    e. an inversion will usually occur.

E 27. Who proposed the law of independent assortment?
    a. Morgan
*   b. Mendel
    c. Sturtevant
    d. Weismann
    e. Flemming

D 28. In genetic analyses, researchers know that linkage of genes will introduce exceptions to the principle of
    a. dominance.
    b. segregation.
    c. recessiveness.
*   d. independent assortment.
    e. chromosomal inheritance.

M 29. Genes that are located on the same chromosome
    a. tend to be inherited together.
    b. will appear together in the gamete.
    c. are said to be linked.
    d. may be separated during synapsis and crossing over.
*   e. all of these

D 30. If alleles L, M, and N are on the maternal chromosome and l, m, and n are on the paternal chromosome, the only way that a gamete from a heterozygote will produce a gamete with alleles l, m, and N is through
    a. nondisjunction.
    b. the laws of segregation.
    c. the law of independent assortment.
*   d. crossing over.
    e. chromosome aberration.

D 31. If the paternal chromosome has alleles L, M, and n and the maternal chromosomes have l, m, and N, then the chromosome that cannot be produced by crossing over is
    a. LMN
*   b. LMn
    c. LmN
    d. Lmn
    e. lmn

M 32. Genetic recombination as a result of crossing over occurs more readily in genes
    a. that are on the sex chromosomes.
    b. that are on the autosomes.
    c. that are located close together on the same chromosome.
*   d. that are located far apart on the same chromosome.
    e. that are located on different chromosomes.

D 33. Gene mapping
    a. applies only to genes located on the same chromosomes.
    b. represents actual physical distance between genes.
*   c. is based upon the frequency of crossing over.
    d. can be accomplished only by using the sex chromosomes.

D 34. Which of the following statements is false?
    a. Crossing over tends to reduce the frequency that two linked genes are inherited together.
    b. Independent assortment of homologous chromosomes during meiosis increases variation.
    c. Crossing over leads to variation.
    d. Abnormal number or structure of chromosomes may influence the course of evolution.
*   e. The closer together genes are found on a chromosome the greater is the chance that crossing over will occur between them.

M 35. If two genes are almost always found in the same gamete,
*   a. they are located close together on the same chromosome.
    b. they are located on nonhomologous chromosomes.
    c. they are located far apart on the same chromosome.
    d. they are found on the sex chromosome.
    e. all except "they are located far apart on the same chromosome."

D 36. Which of the following statements is correct?
    a. The ability to map the position of genes on a chromosome depends on the frequency of crossing over.
    b. The map distances between genes on a chromosome map mark only relative distances between them, depending on crossover frequency.
    c. The chance of a crossover only partially depends upon the distance between genes.
    d. The map distance in a chromosome map refers to actual physical distance between genes.
*   e. The ability to map the position of genes on a chromosome depends on the frequency of crossing over; and The map distances between genes on a chromosome map mark only relative distances between them, depending on crossover frequency.

M 37. Linkage mapping is a technique that determines
    a. the relationship between chromatids.
*   b. the positions of genes on chromosomes relative to one another.
    c. the positions of chiasmata.
    d. the sex of offspring.
    e. the probability of a deletion.

HUMAN GENETIC ANALYSIS

E **38.** Which of the following would be the least satisfactory organism for genetic research?
* a. humans
  b. bacteria
  c. corn
  d. fruit flies
  e. peas

E **39.** In a pedigree chart, a male showing the specific trait being studied is indicated by a
* a. darkened square.
  b. clear square.
  c. darkened diamond.
  d. clear triangle.
  e. darkened circle.

E **40.** In a pedigree chart, a female who does not demonstrate the trait being studied is represented by a
  a. darkened square.
  b. clear diamond.
* c. clear circle.
  d. darkened triangle.
  e. darkened oval.

D **41.** If a study of several pedigrees demonstrated that two parents express a characteristic and none of their children express it, then the trait is controlled by
  a. a codominant gene.
* b. a simple dominant gene.
  c. a recessive gene.
  d. a sex-linked gene.
  e. No conclusion can be drawn.

D **42.** If a study of several pedigrees demonstrated that two parents are normal but their children express a trait, then the trait is controlled by a
  a. codominant gene.
  b. simple dominant gene.
* c. recessive gene.
  d. sex-linked gene.
  e. No conclusion can be drawn.

M **43.** Each of the following would be classified as a genetic disorder except _____ , which is an abnormality.
  a. albinism
* b. webbed toes
  c. hemophilia
  d. Down syndrome
  e. XYY

EXAMPLES OF INHERITANCE PATTERNS

D **44.** An autosomal recessive disorder
  a. requires that only one parent be a carrier.
  b. displays its symptoms only in heterozygotes.
  c. is more frequent in males than females.
* d. will appear only in children of parents who both carry the gene.
  e. is dominant in females.

M **45.** The probability of producing a normal child by two parents who are carriers for an autosomal recessive disorder is
  a. 50 percent.
  b. 0 percent.
  c. 100 percent.
  d. 25 percent.
* e. 75 percent.

M **46.** Galactosemia
  a. is an X-linked recessive trait expressed more commonly in males.
  b. occurs more frequently in some ethnic groups than others.
  c. is an autosomal recessive inheritance.
  d. must be homozygous to be expressed.
* e. is an autosomal recessive inheritance and must be homozygous to be expressed.

M **47.** Like many genetic disorders, galactosemia is a disruption of a metabolic pathway due to a malfunctioning
  a. reactant.
  b. cofactor.
* c. enzyme.
  d. energy source.
  e. product.

D **48.** Which of the following diseases could be eliminated in one generation if everyone that develops or will develop the disease could be sterilized or persuaded not to have children?
  a. hemophilia
  b. albinism
  c. sickle-cell anemia
* d. galactosemia
  e. Huntington's disorder

D **49.** A woman is diagnosed to have the genetic disease known as Huntington's disorder. It is a rare defect caused by an autosomal dominant allele. The chance for any one of her children to inherit the disease is
  a. dependent on the sex of the child.
  b. 1/3.
* c. 1/2.
  d. 3/4.

D **50.** In an autosomal dominant disorder such as Huntington's, two carrier parents have the probability of passing the gene on to _____ percent of their children.
  a. 50
  b. 0
  c. 100
  d. 25
* e. 75

M **51.** Queen Victoria
* a. was a carrier of hemophilia.
  b. had a hemophilic parent.
  c. had hemophilia.
  d. married a man with hemophilia.
  e. had a hemophilic parent and married a man with hemophilia.

M   **52.** Hemophilia
     a. is rare in the human population.
     b. is more common among men.
     c. was common in English royalty.
     d. is an X-linked recessive trait.
*   e. all of these

D   **53.** Males tend to be affected in greater numbers by X-linked recessive genetic disorders than are females because
     a. females have two dominant genes for the disorder.
*   b. males have only one recessive gene for the disorder.
     c. males have a double dose of the gene.
     d. Y chromosomes are not as strong as X chromosomes.

M   **54.** Which of the following would be considered a carrier of a sex-linked recessive defect?
     a. a man with the defect
     b. a woman with the defect
     c. a father of a son with the defect
*   d. the normal daughter whose father had the defect
     e. a son of two unaffected parents

M   **55.** A woman heterozygous for color blindness (an X-linked recessive allele) marries a man with normal color vision. What is the probability that their first child will be color blind?
*   a. 25 percent
     b. 50 percent
     c. 75 percent
     d. 100 percent
     e. none of these

D   **56.** A color-blind man and a woman with normal vision whose father was color blind have a son. Color blindness, in this case, is caused by an X-linked recessive gene. If only the male offspring are considered, the probability that their son is color blind is
     a. .25 (or 25 percent).
*   b. .50 (or 50 percent).
     c. .75 (or 75 percent).
     d. 1.00 (or 100 percent).
     e. none of these

M   **57.** Red-green color blindness is an X-linked recessive trait in humans. A color-blind woman and a man with normal vision have a son. What is the probability that the son is color blind?
*   a. 100 percent
     b. 75 percent
     c. 50 percent
     d. 25 percent
     e. 0 percent

M   **58.** Red-green color blindness is an X-linked recessive trait in humans. What is the probability that a color-blind woman and a man with normal vision will have a color-blind daughter?
     a. 100 percent
     b. 75 percent
     c. 50 percent
     d. 25 percent
*   e. 0 percent

M   **59.** What could the children of a color-blind woman and a man with normal vision be?
     a. All will be color blind.
     b. None will be color blind.
     c. Daughters will be color blind and sons will be normal.
*   d. Sons will be color blind and daughters will be normal.

M   **60.** If a daughter expresses an X-linked recessive gene, she inherited the trait from
     a. her mother.
     b. her father.
*   c. both parents.
     d. neither parent.
     e. her grandmother.

M   **61.** A human X-linked recessive gene may be
     a. found on the Y chromosome.
     b. passed to daughters from their fathers.
     c. passed to sons from their mothers.
     d. expressed more commonly among females.
*   e. passed to daughters from their fathers and passed to sons from their mothers.

M   **62.** Color blindness is an X-linked trait in humans. If a color-blind woman marries a man with normal vision, the children will be
     a. all color-blind daughters, but normal sons.
*   b. all color-blind sons, but carrier daughters.
     c. all normal sons, but carrier daughters.
     d. all color-blind children.
     e. all normal children.

FOCUS ON HEALTH: **PROGERIA—TOO YOUNG TO BE OLD**

D   **63.** Hutchinson-Gilford progeria (the aging disease)
     a. is controlled by a simple recessive gene.
     b. is a sex-linked disease more common in males.
*   c. occurs only in those individuals in which a mutation arises and is not found in other members of the family.
     d. is the result of the failure of chromosomes to separate so that an individual receives 3 instead of 2 chromosomes.

CHANGES IN CHROMOSOME STRUCTURE

M 64. A chromosome's gene sequence that was ABCDEFG before modification and ABCDLMNOP afterward is an example of
   a. inversion.
   b. deletion.
   c. duplication.
 * d. translocation.
   e. aneuploidy.

M 65. A chromosome's gene sequence that was ABCDEFG before modification and ABCDCDEFG afterward is an example of
   a. inversion.
   b. deletion.
 * c. duplication.
   d. translocation.
   e. aneuploidy.

E 66. A chromosome that has been broken and rejoined in a reversal sequence has undergone
 * a. inversion.
   b. deletion.
   c. duplication.
   d. translocation.
   e. aneuploidy.

E 67. Chromosomal aberrations can be produced by exposure to
   a. viruses.
   b. radiation.
   c. various chemicals.
   d. viruses and radiation, only.
 * e. viruses, radiation, and various chemicals.

E 68. A chromosome's gene sequence that was ABCDEFG before damage and ABCFG after is an example of
   a. inversion.
 * b. deletion.
   c. duplication.
   d. translocation.
   e. aneuploidy.

E 69. A chromosome's gene sequence that was ABCDEFG before damage and ABFEDCG after is an example of
 * a. inversion.
   b. deletion.
   c. duplication.
   d. translocation.
   e. aneuploidy.

M 70. Certain human cancer cells may demonstrate which of the following?
   a. deletion
   b. inversion
 * c. translocation
   d. duplication
   e. none of these

M 71. Which of the following is a transfer of genes between nonhomologous chromosomes?
   a. crossing over
   b. aneuploidy
   c. trisomy
 * d. translocation
   e. duplication

CHANGES IN CHROMOSOME NUMBER

M 72. Polyploidy is more common in plants than animals because
   a. diploid gametes are more common in plants.
   b. sterile plants can reproduce asexually.
   c. plants generally do not have sex chromosomes.
   d. plants can self-fertilize.
 * e. all of these

M 73. Polyploidy
   a. can occur naturally.
   b. occurs when there are more than two sets of chromosomes.
   c. can be artificially induced by colchicine.
   d. is responsible for some of our major foods.
 * e. all of these

M 74. Triploids
   a. are usually sterile.
   b. are produced by the fusion of a diploid and a haploid.
   c. cannot undergo meiosis.
   d. are polyploids.
 * e. all of these

D 75. Which of the following does NOT belong with the other four?
   a. inversion
 * b. polyploidy
   c. deletion
   d. duplication
   e. translocation

M 76. The condition occurring when an organism has a $2n + 1$ chromosome composition is known as
   a. monosomy.
   b. deletion.
   c. diploid.
 * d. aneuploidy.
   e. both deletion and aneuploidy.

E 77. If a gamete is missing one chromosome,
   a. the chromosome number is expressed as $2n - 1$.
   b. then one chromosome is without its homologue.
   c. the condition is called monosomy.
   d. only the chromosome number is expressed as $2n - 1$, and the condition is called monosomy.
 * e. only the chromosome number is expressed as $2n - 1$, one chromosome is without its homologue, and the condition is called monosomy.

D   **78.** If nondisjunction occurs during meiosis,
- a. the resulting sex cells will be heterogametes.
- * b. one-half of the resulting cells will exhibit trisomy and the other half monosomy.
- c. diploid cells will be produced.
- d. all gametes would lack a chromosome and these gametes would be infertile.

E   **79.** The failure of chromosomes to separate during mitosis or meiosis is called
- a. genetic displacement.
- b. trisomy.
- c. crossing over.
- * d. nondisjunction.
- e. disjunction.

D   **80.** Which of the following is different from the other four?
- * a. nondisjunction
- b. duplication
- c. inversion
- d. deletion
- e. translocation

E   **81.** Down syndrome involves trisomy
- a. 3.
- b. 5.
- c. 15.
- d. 19.
- * e. 21.

M   **82.** In Down syndrome,
- * a. as the age of the mother increases, the chance of the defect occurring in the unborn children increases.
- b. the father seems to have very little influence on the defect.
- c. most embryos abort before complete term.
- d. a person with the defect cannot have a normal child.
- e. none of these

E   **83.** Syndrome means
- a. a chromosome disorder.
- b. a simple genetic disease.
- * c. a set of symptoms that occur together.
- d. an incurable disease.
- e. a rare inborn defect.

CASE STUDIES: CHANGES IN THE NUMBER OF SEX CHROMOSOMES

E   **84.** Which of the following designates a normal human female?
- a. XXY
- b. XY
- * c. XX
- d. XYY
- e. XO

D   **85.** Which of the following conditions is characterized by a karyotype with 45 chromosomes?
- * a. Turner syndrome
- b. Down syndrome
- c. testicular feminization syndrome
- d. Klinefelter syndrome
- e. cri-du-chat

D   **86.** Suppose that a hemophilic male (X-linked recessive allele) and a female carrier for the hemophilic trait have a nonhemophilic daughter with Turner syndrome. Nondisjunction could have occurred in
- a. both parents.
- b. neither parent.
- * c. the father only.
- d. the mother only.
- e. none of these

M   **87.** The sex chromosome composition of a person with Turner syndrome is
- a. XXX.
- * b. XO.
- c. XXY.
- d. XYY.
- e. none of these

D   **88.** Nondisjunction involving the X chromosomes may occur during oogenesis and produce two kinds of eggs. If normal sperm fertilize these two types, which of the following pairs of genotypes are possible?
- a. XX and XY
- * b. XXY and XO
- c. XYY and XO
- d. XYY and YO
- e. none of these

D   **89.** The chromosome composition of a slightly taller female with learning difficulty but generally normal appearance is most probably
- a. XO.
- b. XX.
- * c. XXX.
- d. XXY.
- e. XYY.

E   **90.** Which of the following designates a normal human male?
- a. YY
- b. XX
- * c. XY
- d. XO
- e. XYY

E   **91.** The sex chromosome composition of a person with Klinefelter syndrome is
- a. XXX.
- b. XO.
- * c. XXY.
- d. XYY.
- e. none of these

M 92. A genetic abnormality that may result in sterile males with mental retardation or breast enlargement is
   * a. XXY.
   b. XYY.
   c. Turner syndrome.
   d. Down syndrome.
   e. none of these

M 93. Males that tend to be taller than average and show mild mental retardation may be designated
   a. XXY.
   * b. XYY.
   c. Turner syndrome.
   d. Down syndrome.
   e. none of these

D 94. Aneuploidy would describe all of the following except
   a. Turner syndrome.
   b. Klinefelter syndrome.
   * c. translocation.
   d. XYY.
   e. Down syndrome.

D 95. Which of the following is NOT true?
   a. Down syndrome is an example of aneuploidy.
   b. Human polyploids are lethal.
   * c. Most euploidy embryos miscarry.
   d. The rate of aneuploidy is higher in humans than in other mammals.
   e. On the average, one out of two newly fertilized eggs is an aneuploid.

M 96. Which is NOT a chromosomal abnormality?
   a. deletion
   b. extra chromosomes
   c. translocation (exchange of parts between nonhomologs)
   * d. crossing over
   e. inversion

FOCUS ON SCIENCE: PROSPECTS IN HUMAN GENETICS

M 97. Treatments for genetic disorders currently involve
   a. substituting normal for defective parents.
   b. substituting normal for defective genes.
   c. supplying a missing gene.
   * d. supplying missing enzymes or gene products.
   e. all of these

M 98. Phenotypic treatments for genetic disorders include
   a. preventing the disorders in the carriers.
   b. eliminating the defective gene.
   c. preventing a disorder from being passed on.
   * d. preventing a disorder from being expressed.
   e. all of these

M 99. Phenotypic treatments
   * a. may increase the number of defective genes in a population.
   b. do not affect the number of defective genes in a population.
   c. decrease the number of defective genes in a population.
   d. are the ultimate cures for genetic disorders.
   e. have no biological value for either the individual or the population.

E 100. PKU can be detected by
   a. karyotyping.
   b. urine analysis.
   c. blood tests.
   d. saliva tests.
   * e. both urine analysis and blood tests.

M 101. Gene replacement therapy
   a. has not yet been used successfully with mammals.
   b. is a surgical technique that separates chromosomes that have failed to segregate properly during meiosis II.
   c. has been used successfully to treat victims of Huntington's disorder by removing the dominant damaging autosomal allele and replacing it with a harmless one.
   * d. substitutes defective alleles with normal ones.
   e. all of these

E 102. Symptoms of phenylketonuria (PKU) may be minimized or suppressed by a diet low in
   a. serine.
   b. glycine.
   * c. phenylalanine.
   d. proline.
   e. glutamic acid.

M 103. Sickle-cell anemics should avoid
   a. phenylalanine.
   * b. strenuous activity.
   c. high oxygen conditions.
   d. sunlight.
   e. diet colas.

M 104. Amniocentesis involves sampling
   a. the fetus directly.
   * b. the fetal cells floating in the amniotic fluid.
   c. sperm.
   d. blood cells.
   e. placental cells.

M 105. Amniocentesis is
   a. a surgical means of repairing deformities.
   b. a form of chemotherapy that modifies or inhibits gene expression or the function of gene products.
   * c. used in prenatal diagnosis to detect chromosomal mutations and metabolic disorders in embryos.
   d. a form of gene replacement therapy.
   e. all of these

D 106. In prenatal diagnosis, the newest procedure that can be performed early in pregnancy involves sampling the
   a. amnion.
   b. allantois.
 * c. chorion.
   d. yolk sac.
   e. umbilical cord.

M 107. The most recent technique for analyzing the genetics of the unborn child involves the sampling of
   a. the fetus directly.
   b. cells in the amniotic fluid.
   c. material from the allantois.
 * d. the chorionic villi.
   e. yolk sac material.

Matching Questions

M 108. Matching I. Choose the most appropriate answer for each.
   1. ___ colchicine
   2. ___ deletion
   3. ___ duplication
   4. ___ inversion
   5. ___ monosomy
   6. ___ translocation
   7. ___ triploidy
   8. ___ trisomy

   A. $3n$; generally sterile
   B. a chromosome segment is permanently transferred to a nonhomologous chromosome
   C. $(2n - 1)$; a gamete deprived of a chromosome
   D. a repeat of a particular DNA sequence in the same chromosome or in nonhomologous ones
   E. $(2n + 1)$; three chromosomes of the same kind are present in a set of chromosomes
   F. a piece of the chromosome is inadvertently left out during the repair process
   G. inhibits microtubule assembly and induces polyploidy
   H. a chromosome segment that has been cut out and rejoined at the same place, but backward

   Answers: 1. G   2. F   3. D   4. H
              5. C   6. B   7. A   8. E

E 109. Matching II. Match the cause with the disorder.
   1. ___ Down syndrome
   2. ___ galactosemia
   3. ___ color blindness
   4. ___ hemophilia
   5. ___ Turner syndrome

   A. autosomal recessive inheritance; lactose metabolism is blocked
   B. nondisjunction of the twenty-first chromosomal pair
   C. X-linked recessive inheritance
   D. nondisjunction of the sex chromosomes

   Answers: 1. B   2. A   3. C
              4. C   5. D

M 110. Matching III. Match each of the following phenotypic defects with its most used method of treatment.
   1. ___ diabetes
   2. ___ cleft lip
   3. ___ phenylketonuria, PKU
   4. ___ sickle-cell anemia
   5. ___ albinism

   A. chemotherapy
   B. diet modification
   C. environmental adjustments
   D. surgical correction

   Answers: 1. B   2. D   3. B
              4. C   5. C

Problems

D 111. In cats the allele B produces black, whereas b produces yellow. Neither gene is dominant, and in the heterozygous state the phenotype is a combination of yellow and black spots called tortoise-shell. The alleles B and b are X-linked. If a tortoise-shell cat has three tortoise-shell kittens and two black kittens, give the genotype and phenotype of the tomcat that produced them, and give the sex of the kittens.

D 112. An X-linked recessive gene (c) produces red-green color blindness. A normal woman whose father was color blind marries a color-blind man.
   a. What are the possible genotypes for the mother of the color-blind man?
   b. What are the possible genotypes for the father of the color-blind man?
   c. What are the chances that the first son will be color blind?
   d. What are the chances that the first daughter will be color blind?

D 113. In cats an X-linked pair of alleles, *B* and *b*, control color of fur. The alleles are incompletely dominant: *B* produces black, *b* produces yellow, and *Bb* produces tortoise-shell.
   a. A yellow cat had a litter of two tortoise-shell and one yellow kittens. What is the sex of the yellow kitten?
   b. A tortoise-shell cat brings home a litter of black, yellow, and tortoise-shell kittens. The color of which sex would tell you the color of the tomcat that produced them?
   c. A yellow male is crossed with a tortoise-shell female. If the female has all male kittens in her litter of four, what color(s) would they be?
   d. A tortoise-shell cat brings home her litter of black, yellow, and tortoise-shell kittens. By what method could you possibly decide whether the male parent was the black tomcat next door?

D 114. If a father and a son are both color blind and the mother is normal, is it likely that the son inherited color blindness from his father?

D 115. If a human recessive X-linked characteristic occurred with a 10 percent frequency, what would its frequency be in males and females?

D 116. In humans, an X-linked disorder called coloboma iridia (a fissure in the iris) is a recessive trait. A normal couple has an afflicted daughter. The husband sues the wife for divorce on the grounds of infidelity. Would you find in his favor?

D 117. In *Drosophila* a narrow reduced eye is called a bar-eye. It is due to a dominant X-linked allele (*B*), whereas the full wild-type is due to the recessive gene (*B* +). Give the F_1 and F_2 genotypic and phenotypic expectations of a cross of a homozygous wild-type female with a bar-eyed male.

D 118. If the gene for yellow body color (*y*) is an X-linked recessive and its dominant counterpart (*y+*) produces wild body colors, give the phenotypes expected and their frequencies for the following four crosses:
   a. yellow female x wild male
   b. wild carrier female x wild male
   c. wild carrier female x yellow male
   d. homozygous wild female x yellow male

D 119. Two *Drosophila* are crossed several times, with a total number of offspring of 106 females and 48 males. There is too great a deviation from the expected 1:1 ratio for chance alone to account for the difference. What other factor could account for this difference?

D 120. White eyes in *Drosophila* is a mutation that turned out to be an X-linked recessive. Would you expect that the first time the white eye was discovered it was in a male or female?

D 121. Hemophilia is an X-linked recessive gene. A normal woman whose father had hemophilia marries a normal man. What are the chances of hemophilia in their children?

D 122. Color blindness is an X-linked recessive gene. Two normal-visioned parents produce a color-blind child.
   a. Is this child male or female?
   b. What are the genotypes of the parents?
   c. What are the chances that their next child will be a color-blind daughter?

D 123. If an X-linked recessive gene is expressed in 4 percent of the men, what proportion of women would express the recessive trait?

D 124. Red-green color blindness is an X-linked recessive trait. Two normal-visioned parents have a color-blind son. Indicate the genotype and phenotype of each parent and the son.

D 125. There is an autosomal gene that controls baldness, and its expression is sex-influenced, so that the gene for baldness (*B*) is dominant in males but recessive in females. In females the allele B^1 for nonbaldness is dominant over the gene for baldness. If a heterozygous nonbald woman marries a nonbald man, what will be the appearance of their children? Work out the possibilities for each sex.

D 126. Short index fingers (shorter than ring finger) are dominant in males and recessive in females, whereas long index fingers (as long as or longer than ring fingers) are dominant in females and recessive in males. Give the F_2 genotype and phenotype resulting from the cross of a male with long index fingers with a female with short index fingers.

Answers:

111. *BY* black, tortoise-shell female, black males
112. a. *Cc* or *cc*   b. *CY* or *cY*
     c. 1/2   d. 1/2
113. a. male   b. female
     c. 1/2 yellow 1/2 black   d.   black female kitten
114. No, males inherit all sex-linked traits from the mother.
115. Males 10 percent, females 1 percent
116. Yes, the daughter would have to inherit the recessive trait from both parents.
117. *B+B+* x *BY* — — —> F_1: *B+B* wild female *B+Y* wild male
     F_2: 1/4 *BY* bar male
     1/4 *B* + *Y* wild male 1/4 *B* + *B* + wild female 1/4 *B* + *B* wild female
118. a.   yellow male wild female
     b.   1/4 wild male, 1/4 yellow male, 1/4 wild female, 1/4 wild carrier female
     c.   1/4 wild male, 1/4 yellow male, 1/4 yellow female, 1/4 wild carrier female
     d.   1/2 wild carrier female, 1/2 wild male
119. a sex-linked recessive lethal gene expressed in the males, who received it from their mothers
120. Male
121. All females normal but 1/2 of them would be carriers; 1/2 of the males would have hemophilia, the other 1/2 normal.
122. a.   male   b. *Cc* x *CY*   c.   no chance to produce a color-blind daughter

123. $4/100 \times 4/100 = 16/10,000$, or 4 out of 2,500

124. father CY, mother Cc, son cY

125. $BB^1 \times B^1B^1 \longrightarrow BB^1 + B^1B^1$; all daughters nonbald, 1/2 sons bald, 1/2 sons nonbald

126. F_2: 3/4 males with short fingers, 1/4 males with long fingers F_2: 3/4 females with long fingers, 1/4 females with short fingers

Classification Questions

Answer questions 127–131 in reference to the five items listed below.

    a. 12
    b. 23
    c. 24
    d. 46
    e. 47

D   **127.** How many chromosomes does each somatic cell have in a human male who has two X chromosomes?

D   **128.** Following a gene duplication event involving only five loci, how many chromosomes will a human female have?

D   **129.** How many chromosomes are present in the somatic cells of a child born with Down syndrome (trisomy 21)?

D   **130.** How many chromosomes are present in each cell of the germ cell line for a tetraploid species where its normal complement of chromosomes is 48?

D   **131.** The normal sperm cell of species X carries 11 chromosomes. Following nondisjunction in the formation of secondary spermatocytes and their subsequent fertilization of normal ova, some of the zygotes will have 21 chromosomes, others will have 22, and the remainder will have how many chromosomes?

Answers   127. e   128. d   129. e

             130. c   131. b

Answer questions 132–136 in reference to the five processes listed below. Note that to answer these questions you need to know that the sequence of amino acids directly reflects the sequence of genes that coded for their placement.

    a. an inversion
    b. a deletion
    c. a gene duplication
    d. a translocation
    e. an addition

D   **132.** Homologous sets of genes ABCDEF and aBCdEF are located on nonhomologous chromosomes. Crossing over between them is suppressed because their locations are the result of this.

D   **133.** Homologous sets of genes ABCDEF and AEDCBF are located on homologous chromosomes. Crossing over between them is suppressed because of this.

D   **134.** A small region of a protein from three species is sequenced, and found to be as follows:

species X is alanine, glycine, glycine, threonine, alanine
species Y is alanine, glycine, threonine, alanine
species Z is alanine, valine, glycine, threonine, alanine

The difference in the amino acid sequence of species Y is most likely due to this.

D   **135.** A small region of a protein from three species is sequenced, and found to be as follows:

species X is alanine, valine, threonine, alanine
species Y is alanine, glycine, threonine, alanine
species Z is alanine, valine, glycine, threonine, alanine

The difference in the amino acid sequence of species Z is most likely due to this.

D   **136.** The nucleotide sequences of homologous regions of DNA of two species are AATGCCCCGTTA and AATGCCCCGCTTA. If this is not the result of a nucleotide base-pair addition, then it is most likely the result of this.

Answers   132. d   133. a   134. b

             135. e   136. b

Answer questions 137–141 in reference to the five disorders listed below:

    a. galactosemia
    b. Turner syndrome
    c. AIDS
    d. hemophilia
    e. Down syndrome

D   **137.** For this disorder, both a phenotypic cure and a genotypic cure are *potentially* possible.

D   **138.** This disorder is an autosomal recessive disorder.

M   **139.** This disorder is an X-linked recessive trait.

E   **140.** This disorder is also known as trisomy 21.

D 141. This disorder is due to a sex chromosome abnormality probably caused by nondisjunction of sex chromosomes at meiosis.

Answers   137. a   138. a   139. d

              140. e   141. b

Answer questions 142–146 in reference to the five items listed below:

    a. surgical correction
    b. chemotherapy
    c. genetic screening
    d. genetic counseling
    e. gene therapy

M 142. Identification of persons with sickle-cell anemia can be done by this method.

M 143. This method is most often used to provide a phenotypic cure for a genetic disorder.

M 144. Once the risks have been determined, this method is an effective way of dealing with a genetic disorder prior to its occurrence in a child.

M 145. Radiation treatment of a cancer victim is an example of this.

M 146. The substitution of a normal allele for a defective allele via the methods of genetic engineering would be an example of this.

Answers   142. c   143. a   144. d

              145. b   146. e

Selecting the Exception

D 147. Four of the five answers listed below provide evidence that genes are located on chromosomes. Select the exception.
    a. The chromosome number is cut in half by meiosis.
    b. Original chromosome number is restored by fertilization.
    c. Some genes tend to be inherited together.
*   d. Environmental factors may influence gene expression.
    e. There are two sets of chromosomes, one maternal, one paternal, in diploid forms.

D 148. Four of the five answers listed below are related conditions in which abnormal numbers of chromosomes are present. Select the exception.
    a. monosomy
    b. aneuploidy
    c. nondisjunction
*   d. complete chromosome set
    e. trisomy

M 149. Four of the five answers listed below are terms related to a normal set of chromosomes by quantity. Select the exception.
*   a. aneuploid
    b. haploid
    c. tetraploid
    d. polyploid
    e. diploid

D 150. Four of the five answers listed below describe sets of chromosomes with extra numbers. Select the exception.
    a. polyploid
    b. tetraploid
*   c. diploid
    d. triploid
    e. allopolyploid

E 151. Four of the five answers listed below are organisms widely used in genetic research. Select the exception.
    a. peas
    b. fruit flies
    c. *Neurospora*
*   d. dogfish shark
    e. *E. coli*

D 152. Four of the five answers listed below are conditions caused by chromosomal nondisjunction. Select the exception.
    a. Down syndrome
*   b. Huntington's disorder
    c. Turner syndrome
    d. Klinefelter syndrome
    e. trisomy 21

M 153. Four of the five answers listed below are therapeutic measures applied to affected individuals. Select the exception.
*   a. prenatal diagnosis
    b. chemotherapy
    c. surgical correction
    d. diet modification
    e. environmental adjustment

M 154. Four of the five answers listed below are methods used to reduce the number of defective genes in a population. Select the exception.
    a. genetic counseling
    b. gene replacement
    c. mutagen reduction
*   d. diet modification
    e. genetic screening

D 155. Four of the five answers listed below are caused by recessive genes. Select the exception.
*   a. Huntington's disorder
    b. phenylketonuria
    c. color blindness
    d. hemophilia
    e. albinism

CHAPTER 13
DNA STRUCTURE AND FUNCTION

Multiple-Choice Questions

M 1. Friedrich Miescher is credited with
    a. proposing DNA as the hereditary material.
    b. finding a cure for pneumonia.
    c. telling us that A=T and G=C.
 * d. discovering nucleic acids.

DISCOVERY OF DNA FUNCTION

D 2. When Fred Griffith injected mice with a mixture of dead, pathogenic, encapsulated S cells and living unencapsulated R cells of *Streptococcus pneumoniae,* he discovered that
 * a. the previously harmless strain (S) had inherited the ability to kill mice.
    b. the dead mice teemed with living pathogenic (R) cells.
    c. the killer strain (R) was encased in a protective capsule.
    d. the dead mice teemed with living pathogenic (R) cells and the killer strain (R) was encased in a protective capsule.
    e. all of these

D 3. Fred Griffith's experiments
    a. produced a vaccine against bacterial pneumonia.
    b. demonstrated that rough (R) bacteria cause pneumonia.
 * c. provided evidence that genetic material from one bacterial culture could be transferred to another culture.
    d. showed that rough bacteria injected into mice will be changed by the mice to smooth (S) bacteria.
    e. converted harmless smooth bacteria into lethal rough bacteria.

M 4. The significance of Fred Griffith's experiment in which he used two strains of *Streptococcus pneumoniae* is that
    a. the semiconservative nature of DNA replication was finally demonstrated.
 * b. it demonstrated that harmless cells had become permanently transformed through a change in the bacterial hereditary system.
    c. it established that pure DNA extracted from disease-causing bacteria transformed harmless strains into killer strains.
    d. it demonstrated that radioactively labeled bacteriophages transfer their DNA but not their protein coats to their host bacteria.
    e. all of these

M 5. Which of the following statements is NOT true about Fred Griffith's experiments?
    a. Mice injected with smooth (S) bacteria die.
 * b. Mice injected with heat-killed smooth bacteria die.
    c. Mice injected with heat-killed smooth bacteria and live rough (R) bacteria die.
    d. Mice injected with rough bacteria live.
    e. Smooth bacteria are transformed into harmless rough bacteria.

E 6. Which scientist(s) identified the transforming substance involved in changing rough (R) bacteria to smooth (S)?
 * a. Avery
    b. Griffith
    c. Chargaff
    d. Hershey and Chase
    e. Pauling

E 7. Bacteriophages are
    a. large bacteria.
    b. pathogens (disease-producing bacteria).
 * c. viruses.
    d. cellular components.
    e. protistans.

M 8. The significance of the experiments in which ^{32}P and ^{35}S were used is that
    a. the semiconservative nature of DNA replication was finally demonstrated.
    b. it demonstrated that harmless bacterial cells had become permanently transformed through a change in the bacterial hereditary system.
    c. it established that pure DNA extracted from disease-causing bacteria transformed harmless strains into killer strains.
 * d. it demonstrated that radioactively labeled bacteriophages transfer their DNA but not their protein coats to their host bacteria.
    e. none of these

M 9. In the cycle of viral infection, which of the following is the last process to occur?
    a. invasion of viruses into the body
    b. replication of viral particles by bacteria
 * c. lysis of the bacteria
    d. attachment of virus to bacteria
    e. injection of nucleic acid into the bacteria

D 10. If a mixture of viruses labeled with radioactive sulfur and phosphorus is placed in a bacterial culture,
    a. the bacteria will absorb radioactive sulfur.
    * b. the bacteria will absorb radioactive phosphorus.
    c. the bacteria will absorb both radioactive sulfur and phosphorus.
    d. the bacteria will not absorb either sulfur or phosphorus.
    e. the viruses will not attach to the bacteria.

M 11. Nucleic acid contains
    a. sulfur.
    * b. phosphorus.
    c. potassium.
    d. iron.
    e. manganese.

D 12. Which of the following statements is false?
    a. Protein molecules contain no phosphorus.
    * b. Hershey and Chase discovered that ^{35}S and not ^{32}P had been incorporated into the hereditary system of the bacteria.
    c. Bacteriophages are viruses that inject their nucleic acid genetic code into bacteria and use the bacterial genetic apparatus to make viral proteins.
    d. Each nucleotide is composed of a five-carbon sugar, a phosphate group, and either a purine or pyrimidine.
    e. Viruses are particles of nucleic acid encased in protein.

M 13. The experiments of which of the following researchers clearly distinguished DNA as the hereditary material (as opposed to protein)?
    a. Pauling
    * b. Hershey and Chase
    c. Griffith
    d. Watson and Crick
    e. Avery

M 14. Sulfur is
    * a. found in proteins, but not nucleic acids.
    b. a vital component of .
    c. found in nucleic acids, but not proteins.
    d. needed for bacteriophages to attach to bacteria.
    e. needed for the enzyme that splits the wall of bacteria.

DNA STRUCTURE

E 15. The building blocks of nucleic acids are
    a. amino acids.
    * b. nucleotides.
    c. pentose sugars.
    d. phosphate groups.
    e. nitrogenous bases.

D 16. Which of the following terms is NOT related to the other four?
    * a. amino acids
    b. nucleotides
    c. pentose sugars
    d. phosphate groups
    e. nitrogenous bases

M 17. A nucleotide may contain
    a. a purine.
    b. a pentose.
    c. a phosphate group.
    d. a pyrimidine.
    * e. all of these

M 18. Which scientist(s) discovered the basis for the base-pair rule, which states that the amounts of adenine and thymine match, as do the amounts of cytosine and guanine?
    a. Avery
    b. Griffith
    * c. Chargaff
    d. Hershey and Chase
    e. Pauling

M 19. DNA varies from species to species in its
    a. base-pair bonding.
    b. relative amounts of nucleotide bases.
    c. sequence of base pairs.
    d. base-pair bonding and sequence of base pairs.
    * e. relative amounts of nucleotide bases and sequence of base pairs.

E 20. From x-ray diffraction data, which of the following was determined about DNA?
    a. The molecule had uniform diameter.
    b. The molecule was long and narrow.
    c. Part of the molecule repeated itself often.
    d. The shape of the molecule could be spiral.
    * e. all of these

M 21. Rosalind Franklin's research contribution was essential in
    a. establishing the double-stranded nature of DNA.
    b. establishing the principle of base pairing.
    * c. establishing most of the principal structural features of DNA.
    d. sequencing DNA molecules.
    e. determining the bonding energy of DNA molecules.

M 22. Rosalind Franklin used which technique to determine many of the physical characteristics of DNA?
    a. transformation
    b. transmission electron microscopy
    c. density-gradient centrifugation
    * d. x-ray diffraction
    e. all of these

M 23. James Watson and Francis Crick
    a. established the double-stranded nature of DNA.
    b. confirmed the principle of base pairing.
    c. explained how DNA's structure permitted it to be replicated.
    d. proposed the concept of the double helix.
   * e. all of these

E 24. In the bonding of nitrogenous bases,
    a. adenine is paired with cytosine.
    b. adenine is paired with guanine.
    c. cytosine is paired with thymine.
   * d. guanine is paired with cytosine.

M 25. In the bonding of two nucleotides,
    a. hydrogen bonds are used.
    b. adenine and thymine bind together.
    c. purines bind with pyrimidines.
    d. double-ring nitrogenous bases connect to single-ring bases.
   * e. all of these

E 26. The DNA molecule could be compared to a
    a. hair pin.
   * b. ladder.
    c. key.
    d. globular mass.
    e. flat plate.

M 27. In DNA, complementary base pairing occurs between
    a. cytosine and uracil.
    b. adenine and guanine.
    c. adenine and uracil.
   * d. adenine and thymine.
    e. all of these

E 28. Adenine and guanine are
   * a. double-ringed purines.
    b. single-ringed purines.
    c. double-ringed pyrimidines.
    d. single-ringed pyrimidines.
    e. amino acids.

D 29. If a purine bonded to a purine in DNA, the molecule would _____ in that region.
    a. be constricted
    b. be perfectly normal
    c. lose a sugar-phosphate unit
    d. unwind
   * e. bulge

M 30. In the comparison between a spiral staircase and a DNA molecule, the steps would correspond to
    a. sugars.
    b. hydrogen bonds.
   * c. base pairs.
    d. nucleotides.
    e. phosphates.

E 31. In DNA molecules,
   * a. the nucleotides are arranged in a linear, unbranched pattern.
    b. the nitrogenous bases are found on the outside of the molecule.
    c. the sugar-phosphate pattern runs the same way on each DNA strand.
    d. all of these
    e. none of these

M 32. Which of the following statements is true?
   * a. The hydrogen bonding of cytosine to guanine is an example of complementary base pairing.
    b. Adenine always pairs up with guanine in DNA, and cytosine always teams up with thymine.
    c. Each of the four nucleotides in a DNA molecule has the same nitrogen-containing base.
    d. When adenine base pairs with thymine, they are linked by three hydrogen bonds.
    e. In the DNA of all species, the amount of purines never equals the amount of pyrimidines.

E 33. Each DNA strand has a backbone that consists of alternating
    a. purines and pyrimidines.
    b. nitrogen-containing bases.
    c. hydrogen bonds.
   * d. sugar and phosphate molecules.
    e. amines and purines.

M 34. Who among the following was NOT involved in working out the structure of DNA?
   * a. Avery
    b. Watson
    c. Wilkins
    d. Franklin
    e. Chargaff

DNA REPLICATION AND REPAIR

D 35. The ultimate explanation for resemblances of traits from one generation to another is
    a. gamete formation.
   * b. semiconservative DNA replication.
    c. sexual reproduction.
    d. protein synthesis.
    e. bloodlines.

M 36. The appropriate adjective to describe DNA replication is
    a. nondisruptive.
   * b. semiconservative.
    c. progressive.
    d. natural.
    e. lytic.

E   37. Replication of DNA
          a. produces RNA molecules.
          b. produces only new DNA.
     *   c. produces two molecules, each of which is half-
              new and half-old DNA joined lengthwise to each
              other.
          d. generates excessive DNA, which eventually
              causes the nucleus to divide.
          e. is too complex to characterize.

M   38. DNA strands serve as which of the following during
          DNA synthesis?
          a. replicate
          b. substitute
     *   c. template
          d. source of nucleotides
          e. all of these

D   39. After three replications of a single DNA molecule,
          what percent of the resulting double helices contain
          one strand of the "original" DNA?
          a. 0 percent
     *   b. 25 percent
          c. 50 percent
          d. 75 percent
          e. 100 percent

D   40. The primary function of DNA ligase is to
          a. cut the two strands of the DNA molecule prior to
              replication.
          b. attach free nucleotides to the growing chain.
          c. remove bases that might have been inserted
              incorrectly.
     *   d. seal new short stretches of nucleotides into one
              continuous strand..
          e. fragment old DNA that is no longer of use to the
              cell.

M   41. DNA polymerase
          a. is an enzyme.
          b. adds new nucleotides to a strand.
          c. proofreads DNA strands to see that they are
              correct.
          d. derives energy from ATP for synthesis of DNA
              strands.
     *   e. all of these

Matching Questions

D   42. Matching. Choose the one most appropriate answer
          for each.
          1. ___ Avery and colleagues
          2. ___ Chargaff
          3. ___ Franklin
          4. ___ Griffith
          5. ___ Hershey and Chase
          6. ___ Pauling
          7. ___ Miescher
          8. ___ Watson and Crick

          A. discovered that the hereditary system of one
              strain of bacteria could be transformed by
              materials from another strain of bacteria
          B. first to discover DNA and isolate it from fish
              sperm
          C. in 1944, reported that DNA was the
              "transforming principle"
          D. the first to build a scale model of DNA and
              to describe it explicitly in a publication
          E. the first to demonstrate, through the use of
              radioactive isotopes, that DNA, not protein,
              was the substance transmitted through
              generations of cells
          F. provided two important clues to the structure
              of DNA; one clue was A = T and C = G
          G. discovered the structure of proteins
          H. obtained excellent x-ray diffraction
              photographs that suggested that DNA was a
              long, thin molecule with regularly repeating
              structures; also said that DNA had to be
              helical like a circular stairway

Answers: 1. C   2. F   3. H

              4. A   5. E   6. G

              7. B   8. D

Classification Questions

Answer questions 43–47 in reference to the five nucleotides listed below:

    a. guanine
    b. cytosine
    c. pyrimidine
    d. thymine
    e. uracil

M   **43.** The data of Erwin Chargaff indicated that within a species the amount of adenine was always equal to the amount of this.

E   **44.** This nucleotide is not incorporated into the structure of the DNA helix.

D   **45.** This nucleotide is a double-ringed molecule.

M   **46.** If one chain of a DNA molecule had a purine at a given position, this would be its complement on the other chain.

D   **47.** Two hydrogen bonds connect adenine to _____ in the DNA molecule.

Answers   43. d   44. e   45. a

               46. c   47. d

Selecting the Exception

M   **48.** Four of the five answers listed below are bases used to construct nucleic acids. Select the exception.
    a. cytosine
    b. adenine
    c. thymine
    d. guanine
  * e. phenylalanine

D   **49.** Four of the five answers listed below are people who helped develop the double helix explanation of DNA. Select the exception.
    a. Wilkins
  * b. Griffith
    c. Watson
    d. Franklin
    e. Crick

D   **50.** Four of the five answers listed below are correctly paired. Select the exception.
  * a. A - C
    b. C - G
    c. A - T
    d. T - A
    e. purine - pyrimidine

D   **51.** Four of the five answers listed below are pairs of people who worked in fields related to genetics. Select the exception.
  * a. Wallace and Darwin
    b. Avery and Griffith
    c. Mendel and Morgan
    d. Watson and Crick
    e. Hershey and Chase

CHAPTER 14
FROM DNA TO PROTEINS

Multiple-Choice Questions

M   1.   A byssus is
    a.   a tooth found on the tongue of a snail.
*   b.   an adhesive that anchors a mussel to a rocky shore.
    c.   an internal digestive cavity of an octopus.
    d.   the reproductive organ of flukes.
    e.   a packet of excess genes found in the mantle of snails.

M   2.   DNA from bacteria differs from DNA in humans in which of the following ways?
    a.   base composition
    b.   sugar-phosphate linkage
*   c.   nucleotide sequence
    d.   bonding of the helix
    e.   all of these

M   3.   A linear stretch of DNA that specifies the sequence of amino acids in a polypeptide is called a(n)
    a.   codon.
    b.   intron.
    c.   messenger.
*   d.   gene.
    e.   enzyme.

E   4.   The DNA molecule usually is made up of how many strands?
    a.   1
*   b.   2
    c.   3
    d.   6
    e.   12

M   5.   The "central dogma" of molecular biology
    a.   explains the structural complexity of genes.
*   b.   describes the flow of information.
    c.   is based upon the role of proteins in controlling life.
    d.   does not explain how genes function.
    e.   explains evolution in terms of molecular biology.

HOW IS RNA TRANSCRIBED FROM DNA?

E   6.   _____ molecules carry protein-assembly instructions from the nucleus to the cytoplasm.
    a.   Template DNA
*   b.   Messenger RNA
    c.   Transfer RNA
    d.   Ribosomal RNA
    e.   all of these

E   7.   The RNA molecule is made up of how many strands?
*   a.   1
    b.   2
    c.   3
    d.   6
    e.   12

D   8.   The changing of a business letter from shorthand to typewritten copy is analogous to
    a.   translation of mRNA.
*   b.   transcription of DNA.
    c.   protein synthesis.
    d.   deciphering the genetic code.
    e.   replication of DNA.

E   9.   All the different kinds of RNA are transcribed in the
    a.   mitochondria.
    b.   cytoplasm.
    c.   ribosomes.
*   d.   nucleus.
    e.   endoplasmic reticulum.

E   10.   The form of RNA that carries the code from the DNA to the site where the protein is assembled is called
*   a.   messenger RNA.
    b.   nuclear RNA.
    c.   ribosomal RNA.
    d.   transfer RNA.
    e.   structural RNA.

M   11.   The nitrogenous base found in DNA but not in RNA is
    a.   adenine.
    b.   cytosine.
    c.   guanine.
    d.   uracil.
*   e.   thymine.

D   12.   DNA and RNA are alike in
    a.   the pentose sugar.
    b.   all the nitrogenous bases used to assemble the genetic code.
    c.   the number of strands.
    d.   their function in genetics.
*   e.   none of these

E   13.   Which substance is found in RNA but not in DNA?
    a.   thymine
    b.   deoxyribose
*   c.   uracil
    d.   guanine
    e.   cytosine

E   14.   The nitrogenous base found in RNA but not in DNA is
    a.   adenine.
    b.   cytosine.
    c.   guanine.
*   d.   uracil.
    e.   thymine.

E   15. Uracil will pair with
          a. ribose.
     *   b. adenine.
          c. cytosine.
          d. thymine.
          e. guanine.

M   16. The synthesis of an RNA molecule from a DNA
          template strand is
          a. replication.
          b. translation.
     *   c. transcription.
          d. DNA synthesis.
          e. metabolism.

E   17. The relationship between strands of RNA and DNA is
          a. antagonistic.
          b. opposite.
     *   c. complementary.
          d. an exact duplicate.
          e. unrelated.

M   18. Transcription
          a. occurs on the surface of the ribosome.
          b. is the final process in the assembly of a protein.
     *   c. occurs during the synthesis of any type of RNA
              from a DNA template.
          d. is catalyzed by DNA polymerase.
          e. all of these

M   19. Transcription
          a. involves both strands of DNA as templates.
          b. uses the enzyme DNA polymerase.
          c. results in a double-stranded end product.
     *   d. produces three different types of RNA molecules.
          e. all of these

M   20. Transcription starts at a region of DNA called a(n)
          a. sequencer.
     *   b. promoter.
          c. activator.
          d. terminator.
          e. transcriber.

M   21. Which of the following dominates the process of
          transcription?
     *   a. RNA polymerase
          b. DNA polymerase
          c. phenylketonuria
          d. transfer RNA
          e. all of these

D   22. Before leaving the nucleus, the RNA molecule
          a. acquires a poly-A tail.
          b. breaks loose from the terminator signal on the
              template.
          c. becomes capped.
          d. is stripped of its introns.
     *   e. all of these

M   23. In transcription,
          a. several RNA molecules are made from the same
              DNA molecule.
          b. promoters are needed so that RNA can bind to
              DNA.
          c. DNA produces messenger RNA.
          d. a specific enzyme called RNA polymerase is
              required.
     *   e. all of these

M   24. The portion of the DNA molecule that is translated is
          composed of
          a. introns.
          b. anticodons.
     *   c. exons.
          d. transcriptons.
          e. exons and transcriptons.

M   25. The portion of the DNA molecule that is not translated
          and is a noncoding portion of DNA is composed of
     *   a. introns.
          b. anticodons.
          c. exons.
          d. transcriptons.
          e. exons and transcriptons.

M   26. Before messenger RNA is mature,
          a. all exons are deleted and removed.
     *   b. a cap and a tail are provided.
          c. anticodons are assembled.
          d. the transfer RNA transfers the messenger RNA to
              the ribosome.
          e. the single RNA strand duplicates itself in much
              the same way as DNA.

E   27. If the DNA triplets were ATG-CGT, the mRNA
          codons would be
          a. AUG-CGU.
          b. ATG-CGT.
     *   c. UAC-GCA.
          d. UAG-CGU.
          e. none of these

D   28. If the DNA triplets were ATG-CGT, the tRNA
          anticodons would be
     *   a. AUG-CGU.
          b. ATG-CGT.
          c. UAC-GCA.
          d. UAG-CGU.
          e. none of these

M   29. Which of the following could NOT be an RNA
          transcript?
          a. AUGCGU
     *   b. ATGCGT
          c. UACGCA
          d. UAGCGU
          e. GCGUUU

M   30. In transcription,
    a. several amino acids are assembled by the
        messenger RNA molecules at one time.
  * b. a special sequence called a promoter is necessary
        for transcription to begin.
    c. certain polypeptide sequences are governed by one
        ribosome, whereas other sequences are produced
        by other ribosomes.
    d. the transfer RNA molecules arrange the messenger
        RNA codons into the appropriate sequence.
    e. none of these

DECIPHERING THE mRNA TRANSCRIPTS

D   31. The genetic code
    a. is universal for all organisms.
    b. is based upon 64 codons made of sequences of
        three nucleotides.
    c. also comes equipped with punctuation marks.
    d. is redundant, that is, each amino has more than
        one codon.
  * e. all of these

E   32. The genetic code is made up of units consisting of how
         many nucleotides?
    a. 2
  * b. 3
    c. 5
    d. 6
    e. 12

D   33. If the codon consisted of only two nucleotides, there
         would be how many different kinds of codons?
    a. 4
    b. 8
  * c. 16
    d. 32
    e. 64

D   34. The insertion of how many nucleotides into a genetic
         sequence does less damage to the code than the
         insertion of other numbers of nucleotides?
    a. 1
    b. 2
  * c. 3
    d. 4
    e. 5

E   35. There are how many different kinds of amino acids in
         proteins?
    a. 3
    b. 6
    c. 12
  * d. 20
    e. 28

M   36. There are how many different kinds of RNA codons?
    a. 3
    b. 12
    c. 28
  * d. 64
    e. 120

E   37. There are how many different kinds of RNA
         nucleotides?
    a. 3
  * b. 4
    c. 5
    d. 6
    e. 12

E   38. The concept that a set of three nucleotides specifies a
         particular amino acid provides the basis for
    a. the one gene, one enzyme hypothesis.
    b. the one gene, one polypeptide hypothesis.
  * c. the genetic code.
    d. biochemical reactions among nucleic acids.
    e. all of these

M   39. Of all the different codons that exist, three of them
    a. are involved in mutations.
    b. do not specify a particular amino acid.
    c. cannot be copied.
    d. provide punctuation or instructions such as "stop."
  * e. do not specify a particular amino acid and provide
        punctuation or instructions such as "stop."

D   40. Crick and Brenner discovered that the presence of
         three extra nucleotides inserted in the middle of a gene
         caused far fewer problems than if only one or two
         extra nucleotides were inserted. They interpreted this
         result to mean that
  * a. the genetic code consists of nonoverlapping
        triplets of nucleotide bases.
    b. the longer the sequence of nucleotides that is
        added to a gene, the more chemically stable the
        resulting DNA is.
    c. there had been significant experimental error in
        their electrophoresis studies.
    d. the wobble effect accounts for the unpredictability
        in codon-anticodon pairing at the third base.
    e. all of these

D   41. The wobble effect
    a. explains why and how there can be 31 kinds of
        transfer RNA molecules.
    b. allows the third codon to vary if the first two
        codons in the anticodon follow the base-pair rule.
    c. indicates that transfer RNA combines with either
        the small or large subunit of ribosomes.
  * d. explains why and how there can be 31 kinds of
        transfer RNA molecules, and allows the third
        codon to vary if the first two codons in the
        anticodon follow the base-pair rule.
    e. explains why and how there can be 31 kinds of
        transfer RNA molecules, allows the third codon to
        vary if the first two codons in the anticodon follow
        the base-pair rule, and indicates that transfer RNA
        combines with either the small or large subunit of
        ribosomes.

E 42. Each "word" in the mRNA language consists of how many letters?
* a. 3
b. 4
c. 5
d. more than 5
e. none of these

D 43. If each nucleotide coded for a single amino acid, how many different types of amino acids could be combined to form proteins?
* a. 4
b. 16
c. 20
d. 64
e. none of these

M 44. Which of the following carries amino acids to ribosomes, where amino acids are linked into the primary structure of a polypeptide?
a. mRNA
* b. tRNA
c. hnRNA
d. rRNA
e. all of these

M 45. Transfer RNA differs from other types of RNA because it
a. transfers genetic instructions from cell nucleus to cytoplasm.
b. specifies the amino acid sequence of a particular protein.
* c. carries an amino acid at one end.
d. contains codons.
e. none of these

D 46. The wobble effect pertains to the matching of
* a. codons with anticodons.
b. codons with exons.
c. exons with introns.
d. template DNA with messenger RNA.
e. messenger RNA with ribosomal RNA.

E 47. Eukaryotic ribosomes function as
a. a single unit.
* b. two-part units.
c. three-part units.
d. four-part units.
e. a multidivisional unit.

D 48. All mRNA transcripts begin with
a. methionine.
b. a ribosome.
* c. AUG.
d. the P site.
e. an anticodon.

HOW IS mRNA TRANSLATED?

D 49. Which of the following statements is false?
a. In chain elongation, the amino acids are added to the chain according to the sequence in the messenger RNA.
b. The messenger RNA molecule is stationary and series of ribosomes called polysomes travel along the molecule manufacturing series of polypeptides at the same time.
c. The shape of transfer RNA molecules is uniform and is maintained by hydrogen bonds.
d. Enzymes found in the ribosome catalyze the formation of the bonds in the new polypeptide.
* e. None of these statements is false.

D 50. The maximum number of tRNAs that can be on one ribosome at one time is
* a. 2.
b. 3.
c. 4^3.
d. unlimited.
e. unknown.

M 51. A polysome is
a. one of the units of a ribosome.
b. the nuclear organelle that synthesizes RNA.
c. an organelle that functions similarly to a ribosome during meiosis.
d. the two units of a ribosome considered together.
* e. an mRNA molecule with several ribosomes attached.

DO MUTATIONS AFFECT PROTEIN SYNTHESIS?

M 52 A gene mutation
a. is a change in the nucleotide sequence of DNA.
b. may be caused by environmental agents.
c. may arise spontaneously.
d. can occur in any organism.
* e. all of these

D 53. Which of the following statements is true?
a. Gene mutations occur independently of each other.
b. Gene mutations are relatively rare.
c. The reason that two antibiotics may be given at one time is due to the very remote possibility that two gene mutations could occur in the same cell at the same time.
d. Mutations are random; that is, it is impossible to predict exactly when a specific gene will mutate but an expected frequency can be assigned.
* e. all of these

D 54. Which event may occur in all viruses, prokaryotes, and eukaryotes?
a. duplication
b. aneuploidy
c. translocation
* d. mutation
e. all of these

E **55.** Mutations can be
   a. random.
   b. beneficial.
   c. lethal.
   d. heritable.
   * e. all of these

M **56.** Frameshift mutations may involve
   a. substitution of nucleotides.
   b. substitution of codons.
   c. substitution of amino acids.
   * d. addition or deletion of one to several base pairs.
   e. all of these

M **57.** Sickle-cell anemia has been traced to what type of mutation?
   a. frameshift
   b. transposable element
   c. mutagenic
   * d. base-pair substitution
   e. viral

D **58.** The difference between normal and sickle-cell hemoglobin is based upon
   a. the number of amino acids in the molecule.
   * b. the substitution of one amino acid for another.
   c. the number and orientation of the amino acid chains attached to the heme portion of the molecule.
   d. the number of oxygen molecules that can be carried.
   e. the type of bone marrow that produces it.

M **59.** In a mutation,
   a. the new codon may specify a different amino acid, but may not change the function of the new protein produced.
   b. the new codon may specify the same amino acid as the old codon.
   c. the new codon and resulting amino acid may destroy the function of the protein specified.
   * d. All of these may be true.

Matching Questions

D **60.** Matching. Choose the best matching element.
   1. ___ anticodon
   2. ___ Beadle and Tatum
   3. ___ codon
   4. ___ Pauling and Itano
   5. ___ Garrod
   6. ___ Khorana, Nirenberg, Holley, etc.
   7. ___ messenger RNA
   8. ___ polysome
   9. ___ promoters
   10. ___ transcription
   11. ___ translation

   A. deciphered the mRNA code words
   B. RNA-directed synthesis of polypeptide chains
   C. sites at which RNA polymerases can bind and initiate transcription
   D. binds to small subunit platform of a ribosome
   E. guided and catalyzed by RNA polymerases
   F. polypeptide chain elongation proceeds independently at each body in this cluster
   G. inborn errors of metabolism
   H. a tRNA triplet opposite an amino acid
   I. *Neurospora;* one-gene, one-enzyme hypothesis
   J. the use of electrophoresis to distinguish sickle-cell proteins
   K. a set of three nucleotides

   Answers: 1. H   2. I   3. K   4. J
   5. G   6. A   7. D   8. F
   9. C   10. E   11. B

Classification Questions

Answer questions 61- 65 in reference to the five RNA codons listed below:

    a. AUG
    b. UAA
    c. UUU
    d. UUA
    e. AAA

D   **61.**   This codon terminates a coding region.

D   **62.**   The anticodon AAA would pair with this codon.

M   **63.**   A single mutation involving the second letter of codon AUA would convert it to this codon.

D   **64.**   A DNA codon of ATT would be complementary to this RNA codon.

D   **65.**   This codon codes for an amino acid and indicates the beginning of a coding region.

Answers   61. b   62. c   63. e

           64. b   65. a

Selecting the Exception

E   **66.**   Three of the four answers listed below are different forms of a class of nucleic acids. Select the exception.
     *   a. template
        b. ribosomal
        c. messenger
        d. transfer

M   **67.**   Three of the four answers listed below are involved in gene action. Select the exception.
        a. replication
        b. transcription
        c. translation
     *   d. polymerization

D   **68.**   Four of the five answers listed below are steps in the process of transcription. Select the exception.
        a. cap put on one end
        b. introns snipped out
     *   c. action by DNA polymerase
        d. poly-A tail placed on one end
        e. exons spliced together

D   **69.**   Four of the five answers listed below are related pairings. Select the exception.
        a. double-stranded DNA – messenger RNA
        b. purine – pyrimidine
        c. codon – anticodon
        d. small subunit – large subunit
     *   e. promoter – terminator

D   **70.**   Four of the five answers listed below describe changes at the chromosomal level. Select the exception.
     *   a. base substitution
        b. duplication
        c. translocation
        d. deletion
        e. inversion

D   **71.**   Four of the five answers listed below are chromosomal abnormalities. Select the exception.
        a. translocation
     *   b. elongation
        c. duplication
        d. deletion
        e. inversion

M   **72.**   Four of the five answers listed below are sources of genetic variation. Select the exception.
        a. crossing over
        b. mutation
     *   c. asexual reproduction
        d. chromosome aberration
        e. sexual reproduction

D   **73.**   Four of the five answers listed below are components of a nucleotide. Select the exception.
        a. pentose sugar
     *   b. amino acid
        c. pyrimidine
        d. phosphate group
        e. purine

D   **74**   Four of the five answers listed below are related by a common number. Select the exception.
        a. number of nucleotides in a codon
        b. number of building blocks (parts) in a nucleotide
        c. number of stop codons
     *   d. number of types of DNA
        e. number of types of RNA

D   **75.**   Three of the four answers listed below are steps in translation. Select the exception.
        a. initiation
     *   b. replication
        c. chain elongation
        d. termination

CHAPTER 15
CONTROLS OVER GENES

Multiple-Choice Questions

TYPES OF CONTROL MECHANISMS

M   1.   The nature of development is based upon
          a.   which genes are active in a given cell.
          b.   when the genes function.
          c.   what gene products appear.
          d.   the amount of cellular products generated.
     *   e.   all of these

E   2.   Molecules that interact with DNA to alter gene
          expression are
          a.   operons.
          b.   promoters.
     *   c.   regulatory proteins.
          d.   repressor amines.
          e.   carbohydrates.

E   3.   In negative control systems, which of the following
          would cause transcription to proceed?
          a.   repressor
          b.   operator
          c.   cooperator
     *   d.   inducer
          e.   DNA

BACTERIAL CONTROL OF TRANSCRIPTION

M   4   Repressor proteins
          a.   prevent binding of RNA polymerase to DNA.
          b.   can be inactivated by an inducer such as lactose.
          c.   provide negative control.
          d.   prevent binding of RNA polymerase to DNA and
               can be inactivated by an inducer such as lactose.
     *   e.   prevent binding of RNA polymerase to DNA, can
               be inactivated by an inducer such as lactose, and
               provide negative control

D   5.   The lactose operon includes
          a.   an operator.
          b.   three structural genes that manufacture lactose-
               metabolizing enzymes.
          c.   a promoter.
          d.   a repressor.
     *   e.   all but a repressor.

E   6.   The obvious advantage of the lactose operon system is
          that
          a.   lactose is not needed as energy for bacteria.
     *   b.   lactose-metabolizing enzymes need not be made
               when lactose is not present.
          c.   the bacteria will make lactose only in the presence
               of the proper enzymes.
          d.   milk is not needed for adult humans' diet.
          e.   glucose can substitute for lactose in the diet of
               intolerant persons.

D   7.   The lactose operon
     *   a.   requires the presence of milk in the environment
               of the bacteria.
          b.   is turned on before a baby is born.
          c.   is a control mechanism that enables vertebrates to
               digest milk.
          d.   causes the production of gas in the digestive tract
               of milk-drinking animals.
          e.   is an excellent model for explaining control
               mechanisms for eukaryotic forms.

M   8.   In prokaryotes, most of the control of gene expression
          is at the _____ level.
     *   a.   transcriptional
          b.   transcript processing
          c.   transport
          d.   translational
          e.   post-translational

D   9.   Which of the following is part of a negative control
          mechanism?
          a.   promoter
     *   b.   repressor
          c.   structural genes that produce lactase
          d.   operator
          e.   all of these

D   10. The positive control of the lactose operon in bacteria is
          a.   activated by a repressor protein.
          b.   independent of glucose concentrations.
     *   c.   activated by a protein known as CAP.
          d.   regulated by RNA polymerase.
          e.   all of these

M   11. During the early part of a young mammal's life, the *E.
          coli* in the young offspring's intestinal tract are
          exposed to high levels of which of the following that
          later generations of *E. coli* will never be exposed to?
          a.   glucose
          b.   ribose
          c.   cellulose
     *   d.   lactose
          e.   fructose

E   12. The model of the prokaryote operon explains the
          regulation of which of the following?
          a.   replication
     *   b.   transcription
          c.   induction
          d.   Lyonization
          e.   none of these

M   13.   In the prokaryote operon model, it is usually the
_____ that inactivates the repressor protein.
       a. enzyme
       b. product
*   c. substrate
       d. promoter

M   14.   When a gene transcription occurs, which of the
following is produced?
       a. more DNA
       b. protein or polypeptide sequences
*   c. messenger RNA
       d. enzymes
       e. genetic defects

D   15.   Which of the following is NOT actually a part of an
operon?
       a. promoter
       b. gene for permease
       c. operator
       d. gene for acetylase
*   e. regulator genes

M   16.   A regulator gene produces which of the following?
*   a. repressor protein
       b. regulatory enzyme
       c. promoter
       d. operator
       e. transcriber

E   17.   A repressor protein binds with
       a. messenger RNA.
*   b. the operator.
       c. the regulator.
       d. a product.
       e. a substrate.

M   18.   Which of the following is the region that is the binding
site for RNA polymerase?
       a. heterogeneous nuclear DNA
       b. repressor gene
*   c. promoter sequence
       d. operator sequence
       e. all of these

D   19.   What is the name of the process in which a molecule
combines with a repressor protein and changes the
shape of the protein so that it no longer binds to the
operator sequence?
*   a. induction
       b. corepression
       c. repression
       d. translation
       e. transcription

D   20.   Which of the following statements is false?
       a. The patterns of gene expression vary from one cell
to another in complex multicellular organisms.
*   b. Less is known about gene controls in unicellular
prokaryotes than in multicellular eukaryotes.
       c. Eukaryotes rely on conversion between active
phosphorylated regulators and inactive forms
more than prokaryotes do.
       d. The timing of the induction (turning on) of genes
varies throughout the life span of an organism
depending upon the gene in question.
       e. Hormones are one of the chief signaling molecules
that allow for variable gene expression.

GENE CONTROLS IN EUKARYOTIC CELLS

D   21.   Which of the following statements is false?
       a. All the cells of any one single individual human
have the same genes.
*   b. Only red blood cells have hemoglobin genes.
       c. Different genes are activated depending on the cell
they are in.
       d. Genetically, liver cells and brain cells differ
mostly in function.
       e. Cells don't express all of their genes all of the
time.

M   22.   Genes located in different regions of the body during
embryonic development may
       a. be turned on and off.
       b. never be turned on.
       c. be turned on and left on.
       d. be activated for only a short time in one cell and a
long time in another cell.
*   e. all of these

E   23.   Which of the following terms refers to the processes
by which cells with identical genotypes become
structurally and functionally distinct from one another?
       a. metamorphosis
       b. metastasis
       c. cleavage
*   d. differentiation
       e. induction

D   24.   The control over the rate that mRNA reaching the
cytoplasm is acted upon by ribosomes is known as
       a. transcriptional controls.
       b. transcript processing controls.
       c. transport control.
*   d. translational controls.
       e. post-translational controls.

D   25.   The conversion of proinsulin into insulin by the
removal of a portion of the polypeptide chain is an
example of
       a. transcriptional control.
       b. transcript processing control.
       c. transport control.
       d. translational control.
*   e. post-translational control.

TYPES OF CONTROL MECHANISMS

D 26. Genes may be controlled by
- a. the way that they are packaged on a chromosome.
- b. the X chromosomes in which they are located.
- c. the dispersion of nucleosomes.
- d. the production of more than one type of mRNA.
- * e. all of these

M 27. Homeotic genes are generally in control of
- a. X chromosome inactivation.
- * b. formation of organs and tissues.
- c. hormone synthesis
- d. dosage compensation
- e. all of these

E 28. Homeotic genes
- a. code for homeodomains.
- b. are involved with regulatory proteins.
- c. are related to the homeobox pf amino acids.
- d. control indirectly the process of transcription.
- * e. all of these

M 29. X chromosome inactivation results in
- a. a total shut down of both female X chromosomes.
- * b. only the shut down of the X chromosome derived from the father
- c. only the shut down of the X chromosome derived from the mother
- * d. the shut down of either the X from the father or the X from the mother.

M 30. Eukaryotic nucleosomes exert control at what level?
- * a. transcriptional
- b. transcript processing
- c. transport
- d. translational
- e. post-transcriptional

M 31. A mammalian female
- * a. usually has one Barr body.
- b. is a mosaic for the X-linked traits she inherits.
- c. uses the paternal X chromosome for a Barr body.
- d. uses the maternal X chromosome for a Barr body.
- e. always has one Barr body and is a mosaic for the X-linked traits she inherits.

M 32. Lyonization of a cat refers to
- a. hybridization.
- b. sterilization.
- * c. mosaic phenotype.
- d. inactivation of one of the X chromosomes.
- e. mosaic phenotype and inactivation of one of the X chromosomes.

E 33. The mosaic effect in human females can be observed in
- a. skin color.
- b. hair color.
- c. distribution of fat cells.
- * d. distribution of sweat glands.
- e. all of these

EXAMPLES OF SIGNALING MECHANISMS

M 34. A hormone would most likely act as a(n) _____ in a cell.
- a. repressor
- b. inhibitor
- * c. activator
- d. promoter
- e. operator

M 35. Among vertebrates, the major controlling agent of gene function is (are)
- a. enzymes.
- b. adjacent cells.
- * c. hormones.
- d. accumulation of end products such as toxins.
- e. absence of precursor molecules.

M 36. Chromosome puffs
- * a. indicate that a gene is transcribing.
- b. are sites of chromosome inversions.
- c. occur when two chromosomes stick together.
- d. occur during metaphase.
- e. none of these

M 37. The puffs that appear on giant chromosomes are accumulations of
- a. DNA.
- b. repressor molecules.
- * c. mRNA.
- d. tRNA.

M 38. A polytene chromosome
- a. is found in the salivary glands of some insect larvae.
- b. is a chromosome that has repeatedly divided and stuck together to produce a giant chromosome.
- c. played a key role in the development of the chromosome theory of inheritance.
- d. shows alternating dark and light bands.
- * e. all of these

E 39. Chromosome puffs are most likely to be observed
- a. during gametogenesis.
- b. during hormone secretion by gland cells.
- * c. in the larval stages of some flies.
- d. in the Barr bodies of certain vertebrates.
- e. during hormone secretion by gland cells and in the larval stages of some flies.

M 40. Giant polytene chromosomes are found in
- * a. salivary glands in fly larvae.
- b. calico cats.
- c. arctic foxes.
- d. albino laboratory rats.
- e. all of these

E 41. A good place to look for giant chromosomes would be in
- a. *E. coli* grown in a fructose medium.
- b. cells from the lining of the human reproductive tract.
- c. the apical meristem of onion plants.
- * d. the salivary glands of fruit flies.

D 42. The fact that prolactin stimulates milk glands but thyroxine does not is due to
 a. the inability of the thyroxine to reach the milk glands.
 b. the lack of ducts leading from the source of thyroxine production to the milk glands.
 c. chance.
 * d. the lack of proper receptors on the milk gland cells.
 e. pregnancy.

M 43. The target for prolactin is the
 a. pituitary gland.
 b. pancreas.
 c. parathyroid.
 * d. mammary gland.
 e. salivary gland.

M 44. The signaling molecule that allows plants to make responses to changing light conditions is
 a. chlorophyll.
 b. prolactin.
 c. ultraviolet.
 * d. phytochrome
 e. polytene.

FOCUS ON SCIENCE: LOST CONTROLS AND CANCER

M 45. When cells are not responding to normal controls over growth and division, they form a tissue mass known as a
 a. metastasis.
 b. malignancy.
 * c. tumor.
 d. carcinogen.
 e. puff.

M 46. Unusual growth of cells that do not pose a threat to surrounding tissues are termed
 a. malignant.
 * b. benign.
 c. metastatic.
 d. carcinogenic.
 e. repressed.

M 47. The *myc* gene
 a. can be translocated from chromosome 8 to chromosome 15.
 b. can lead to Burkitt's lymphoma.
 c. does not cause cancer until it is moved.
 d. can be translocated from chromosome 8 to chromosome 15 and can lead to Burkitt's lymphoma.
 * e. can be translocated from chromosome 8 to chromosome 15, can lead to Burkitt's lymphoma, and does not cause cancer until it is moved.

M 48. Which of the following statements concerning cancer cells is most accurate?
 a. Oncogenes are part of the regulatory section of a chromosome.
 * b. Tumor cells have lost their inhibition to stop dividing.
 c. Oncogenes help control runaway cell division.
 d. Benign tumors usually spread to other body parts.
 e. Metastasis is the spread of benign tumors.

M 49. Cancer cells
 a. have altered plasma membranes.
 b. are unable to attach to other cells.
 c. divide to produce high densities of cells.
 d. have a different metabolism, using glycolysis even when oxygen is available.
 * e. all of these

D 50. Which characteristic seems to be most uniquely correlated with metastasis?
 a. loss of nuclear-cytoplasmic controls governing cell growth and division
 * b. changes in recognition factors on membrane surfaces
 c. "puffing" in the polytene chromosomes
 d. the massive production of cyclic adenosine monophosphate and its secretion into the environment
 e. none of these

D 51. Which of the following statements is false?
 * a Cancer cells divide more rapidly than any cells in the body.
 b. The invasion of cancer cells into normal tissue is known as metastasis.
 c. Malignant tumors differ from benign tumors in that their cells migrate.
 d. Cancer cells have lost the ability to stop dividing.
 e. The parent cell that started a cancer may have been the result of a mutation.

E 52. The spread of a cancer from one site to others in the body is known as
 a. benign tumor.
 * b. metastasis.
 c. malignant tumor.
 d. remission.
 e. both a benign tumor and a malignant tumor.

E 53. The specific name given to a cancer-producing chemical is
 a. pathogen.
 * b. carcinogen.
 c. teratogen.
 d. mutagen.
 e. oncogene.

Matching Questions

M **54.** Matching I. Choose the one most appropriate answer for each.

1. ___ Barr body
2. ___ histone
3. ___ nucleosome
4. ___ homeotic genes
5. ___ oncogene
6. ___ Lyonization
7. ___ metastasis
8. ___ repressor protein

    A. a condensed X chromosome
    B. protein that combines with DNA all along its length
    C. attaches or detaches from operator to regulate transcription
    D. nucleoprotein "bead"
    E. gene capable of inducing cancerous transformations
    F. genes controlling the development of the body plan
    G. migration of cancerous cells
    H. mosaic effect arising from random X chromosome inactivation

Answers: 1. A   2. B   3. D   4. F

            5. E   6. H   7. G   8. C

D **55.** Matching II. Choose the one most appropriate answer for each.

1. ___ control over enzyme activity
2. ___ transcript processing
3. ___ post-translational control
4. ___ transcriptional control
5. ___ transport control

    A. influences the amount and kinds of mRNA assembled from structural genes
    B. snipping out of transcript regions; chemical modification of transcript before it arrives at ribosome control
    C. nuclear envelope selectively regulates passage of transcripts
    D. phosphorylation of translated protein
    E. for example, the interior environmental pH determines whether a protein can act as a cell catalyst

Answers: 1. E   2. B   3. D

            4. A   5. C

Classification Questions

Answer questions 56–60 in reference to the five items of gene regulation listed below:

    a. operon
    b. operator
    c. promoter
    d. lactose
    e. regulator gene

M **56.** This item contains regulator, promoter, and operator regions.

D **57.** A repressor protein can shut down transcription by binding to this item.

M **58.** This item codes for the production of repressor.

D **59.** When the repressor is inactivated, RNA polymerase can bind to this item and allow transcription to occur.

D **60.** The inducer that can activate the operon is represented by this item.

Answers   56. a   57. b   58. e

            59. c   60. d

Selecting the Exception

D **61.** Four of the five answers listed below are features of the lactose operon. Select the exception.
    a. regulator
   *   b. terminator
    c. operator
    d. promoter
    e. structural gene

D **62.** Four of the five answers listed below are types of gene control in eukaryotes. Select the exception.
   *   a. replicational control
    b. transcriptional control
    c. translational control
    d. post-translational control
    e. transcript processing control

M **63.** Four of the five answers listed below are features exhibited by DNA and chromosomes. Select the exception.
    a. looped domain
    b. puff
    c. lampbrush
    d. nucleosome
   *   e. nucleolus

E **64.** Four of the five answers listed below are related by a common gender. Select the exception.
    a. Barr body
   *   b. Y chromosome
    c. calico cat
    d. Lyonization
    e. inactive X

D   65.   Four of the five answers listed below are viruses associated with cancer. Select the exception.
       a.   sarcoma virus
       b.   papovavirus
*   c.   retrovirus
       d.   herpes virus
       e.   adenovirus

M   66.   Four of the five answers listed below are carcinogens. Select the exception.
*   a.   egg white
       b.   asbestos
       c.   radiation with x-ray
       d.   components in cigarette smoke
       e.   ultraviolet radiation

CHAPTER 16
RECOMBINANT DNA AND GENETIC ENGINEERING

Multiple-Choice Questions

MOM, DAD, AND CLOGGED ARTERIES

M   **1.** In the first gene therapy, the normal gene was introduced into the patient through
    a. the lungs.
    b. bone marrow transplants.
    c. nasal inhalants.
    d. muscle injections.
  * e. infusion into the bloodstream.

M   **2.** Recombinant DNA
    a. has occurred in sexually reproducing forms.
    b. can be produced with new biological techniques.
    c. occurs with viral infections of various forms of life.
    d. has produced changes that resulted in evolution.
  * e. all of these

M   **3.** Genetic variations in populations are due to
    a. mutations.
    b. sexual recombination.
    c. crossing over.
    d. genetic breeding programs.
  * e. all of these

E   **4.** New genetic combinations result from
    a. crossing over.
    b. sexual reproduction.
    c. mutations.
    d. exchange of genes between different species.
  * e. all of these

M   **5.** Recombination through crossing over
    a. can occur almost anywhere on homologous chromosomes.
    b. may occur more than once in homologous chromosomes.
    c. results in reciprocal exchanges.
    d. requires a fairly long strand for the exchange process and considerable base pairing.
  * e. all of these

E   **6.** Through natural mechanisms, crossing over occurs between
    a. members of the same species.
    b. members of different species.
  * c. homologous chromosomes.
    d. base pairs on any adjacent chromosomes.
    e. all of these

M   **7.** The goal of genetic engineering is to?
    a. eliminate antibiotic resistance in bacteria.
    b. isolate disease-causing plasmids.
    c. transfer of viral genes.
  * d. modify cells to correct a defect or produce a desired product.

A TOOLKIT FOR MAKING RECOMBINANT DNA

M   **8.** Recombinant DNA technology
    a. uses bacteria to make copies of the desired product.
    b. splices DNAs together.
    c. is possible only between closely related species.
  * d. uses bacteria to make copies of the desired product and splices DNAs together.
    e. uses bacteria to make copies of the desired product, splices DNAs together, and is possible only between closely related species.

E   **9.** Small circular molecules of "extra" DNA in bacteria are called
  * a. plasmids.
    b. desmids.
    c. pili.
    d. F particles.
    e. transferins.

D   **10.** Plasmids
    a. are self-reproducing circular molecules of DNA.
    b. are sites for inserting genes for amplification.
    c. may be transferred between different species of bacteria.
    d. may confer the ability to donate genetic material when bacteria conjugate.
  * e. all of these

M   **11.** After being transferred a plasmid must __?__ to form a recombinant DNA molecule.
    a. be destroyed
  * b. be integrated
    c. undergo mutation
    d. replicate
    e. dissolve

M   **12.** In order for DNA molecules to undergo recombination they
    a. they must be from the same species.
    b. their strands must separate as in replication.
  * c. must be cut and spliced at specific nucleotide sequences.
    d. undergo lysis.
    e. must be identical.

E   **13.** Enzymes used to cut genes in recombinant DNA research are
    a. ligases.
  * b. restriction enzymes.
    c. transcriptases.
    d. DNA polymerases.
    e. replicases.

M 14. The "natural" use of restriction enzymes by bacteria is to
    a. integrate viral DNA.
*   b. destroy viral DNA.
    c. repair "sticky ends."
    d. copy the bacterial genes.
    e. clone DNA.

D 15. Which of the following is false?
    a. Gene transfer and recombination is a common occurrence in nature.
    b. The transfer of genetic material from one organism to another is dependent upon enzymes that cut and tie genes.
    c. Rather than causing lysis of bacteria, some bacteriophages may be incorporated into the bacterial genome.
*   d. The insertion of gene fragments can be accomplished only in the laboratory under artificial conditions.
    e. Once a gene has been incorporated into a bacterium, it may undergo amplification.

M 16. The fragments of chromosomes split by restriction enzymes
    a. have fused ends.
    b. have specific sequences of nucleotides.
    c. have sticky ends.
    d. form a circle.
*   e. have specific sequences of nucleotides and sticky ends.

M 17. Restriction enzymes
    a. often produce staggered cuts in DNA that are useful in splicing genes.
    b. are like most enzymes in being very specific in their action.
    c. are natural defense mechanisms evolved in bacteria to guard against or counteract bacteriophages.
    d. are used along with ligase and plasmids to produce a DNA library.
*   e. all of these

M 18. Restriction enzymes
*   a. work at recognition sites.
    b. function only at "sticky ends."
    c. produce uniform lengths of DNA.
    d. function only in genetic laboratories.
    e. none of these

M 19. Which of the following enzymes joins the paired sticky ends of DNA fragments?
    a. reverse transcriptase
    b. restriction enzymes
*   c. DNA ligase
    d. DNA polymerase
    e. transferase

M 20. RNA can manufacture DNA via the action of
    a. DNA polymerase.
    b. RNA polymerase.
*   c. reverse transcriptase.
    d. ligase.
    e. restriction endonuclease.

D 21. Because it has no introns, researchers prefer to use _____ when working with human genes.
*   a. cDNA
    b. cloned DNA
    c. hybridized DNA
    d. RFLPs
    e. viral DNA

PCR—A FASTER WAY TO AMPLFY DNA

E 22. Which of the following methods of DNA amplification does NOT require cloning?
    a. reverse transcription
*   b. polymerase chain reaction
    c. cloned DNA
    d. reverse transcription and polymerase chain reaction.
    e. polymerase chain reaction and cloned DNA.

D 23. For polymerase chain reaction to occur,
    a. isolated DNA molecules must be primed.
    b. all DNA fragments must be identical.
    c. the DNA must be separated into single strands.
    d. a sticky end must be available for the ligase enzyme to function.
*   e. isolated DNA molecules must be primed and the DNA must be separated into single strands.

M 24. The method used to produce single strands of DNA
    a. is known as amplification.
*   b. is heating a solution of DNA.
    c. uses restriction enzymes.
    d. isolates DNA molecules from the nucleus.

D 25. Separation of DNA fragments by gel electrophoresis
    a. requires priming.
    b. is controlled by the size of the fragment.
    c. is based upon the negative charges of phosphate groups.
    d. is easily accomplished.
*   e. all are correct except "requires priming."

FOCUS ON BIOETHICS: DNA FINGERPRINTS

D 26. The use of RFLPs for "genetic fingerprinting" is based upon
    a. the type of gel used in electrophoresis.
    b. identical alleles at loci.
*   c. differences of locations where enzymes make their cuts.
    d. differences between blood and semen DNA.
    e. bonding of DNA to RNA.

D 27. Which of the following statements about restriction fragment length polymorphism is false?
   a. RFLPs can be used as a genetic fingerprint.
   b. RFLPs are based upon variations in alleles at the same locus.
   c. RFLPs reflect the fact that molecular differences in alleles alter the site where restriction enzymes function.
 * d. RFLPs can be used to distinguish between identical twins.
   e. RFLPs have greatly increased the number of sites involved in mapping the human genome.

HOW IS DNA SEQUENCED?

D 28. Probes for cloned genes use
 * a. complementary nucleotide sequences labeled with radioactive isotopes.
   b. certain media with specific antibodies.
   c. specific enzymes.
   d. certain bacteria sensitive to the genes.
   e. all of these

M 29. The DNA fragments produced by automated DNA sequencing are identified using
   a. radioactive probes.
 * b. laser beams.
   c. ultracentrifugation.
   d. electron microscopy.
   e. restriction enzymes.

FROM HAYSTACKS TO NEEDLES—ISOLATING GENES OF INTEREST

M 30. A collection of DNA fragments produced by restriction enzymes and incorporated into plasmids is called
   a. copied DNA.
   b. transcribed DNA.
   c. DNA amplification.
 * d. a DNA library.
   e. plasmid DNA.

D 31. The method used to determine which host cells pick up a desired plasmid is the use of
   a. fluorescent dyes.
   b. restriction enzymes.
 * c. antibiotics.
   d. marker genes.
   e. a known series of nonsense nucleotides (introns).

D 32. Multiple copies of DNA can be produced by
   a. cloning a DNA library.
   b. genetic amplification.
   c. the use of reverse transcriptase.
   d. the action of DNA polymerase.
 * e. all of these

USING THE GENETIC TRANSCRIPTS

M 33. Which of the following can be modified genetically with the least consequences to its future survival?
   a. humans
   b. rats
   c. carrots
 * d. bacteria
   e. plants

E 34. One of the first successful applications of genetic engineering was the commercial production of
   a. clotting factor.
 * b. insulin.
   c. hemoglobin.
   d. strawberries.
   e. carrot seedlings.

DESIGNER PLANTS

D 35. Which of the following statements is false?
   a. A plant has been genetically engineered with a bioluminescent gene from fireflies so that it glows in the dark.
 * b. Plants that have been generated from cultured cells derived from the same cell are identical clones.
   c. Culturing of individual plant cells increases the mutation rates of their genes.
   d. The insertion of genes into cultured plant cells uses the plasmid of a bacterial pathogen of plants.
   e. Gene insertions are safer than pesticides because they are target-specific.

E 36. Which of the following statements is NOT true?
   a. Plant geneticists are searching for wild ancestors of modern corp plants.
   b. Botanists have grown whole plants from cultured cells.
 * c. Modern crop strains are more resistant than ancient ones.
   d. Researchers have introduced DNA fragments directly into cells using bullets.
   e. Plants can be engineered to produce human proteins.

GENE TRANSFERS IN ANIMALS

M 37. When the gene for rat somatotropin was injected into mouse eggs
   a. nothing happened because these two animals are different species.
   b. the mice grew up as dwarfs.
   c. the gene integrated into the mice chromosomes but did not express itself.
 * d. the mice grew up to larger than normal.
   e. federal authorities immediately prohibited any further such research.

M 38. What would be the value of inserting human genes suspected of causing Alzheimer disease into mice?
   a. to make mice feel more human
   b. to make antibodies which can be injected into suffering patients
*   c. to develop mice that can serve as models for study of this condition
   d. to use the mice for production of a vaccine

E 39. The term "biotech barnyards" refers to
*   a. the production of human products by farm animals.
   b. the development of new species of farm animals.
   c. the increase of milk, egg, wool, etc. production.
   d. ultramodern methods of rearing more animals on less feed.
   e. creation of transgenic animals that can produce several products.

D 40. The human genome project seeks to
*   a. identify the nucleotide sequence of all human genes.
   b. develop a complete DNA library for a human gene.
   c. develop genetic markers for all genetic diseases.
   d. catalog all the varieties of human alleles.
   e. identify all humans that possess genetic defects.

SAFETY ISSUES

E 41 Which of the following statements is true?
   a. There is no danger involved in recombinant DNA research in humans.
   b. There is no danger involved in recombinant DNA research in bacteria.
   c. There is no danger in releasing recombinant organisms into the environment.
*   d. Stringent safety rules make the use of recombinant DNA research possible.
   e. It is safe to conduct recombinant DNA research in plants.

BIOTECHNOLOGY IN A BRAVE NEW WORLD

M 42. Gene therapy
   a. has not yet been used successfully with mammals.
   b. is a surgical technique that separates chromosomes that have failed to segregate properly during meiosis II.
   c. has been used successfully to treat victims of Huntington's disorder by removing the dominant damaging autosomal allele and replacing it with a harmless one.
*   d. replaces defective alleles with normal ones.
   e. all of these

Classification Questions

Answer questions 43–47 in reference to the five items listed below:
   a. restriction enzymes
   b. recombinants
   c. plasmids
   d. clones
   e. restriction sites

M 43. Bacterial populations containing thousands or millions of identical copies of one to several genes are these.

D 44. When one uses the techniques of genetic engineering to move a novel or foreign piece of DNA into the DNA of an organism, these new DNA regions are known as _____.

M 45. The pieces of DNA that are moved by a genetic engineer from one organism to another are first incorporated into these.

E 46. The sole function of these is to cut apart foreign DNA molecules.

D 47. These may contain all of the other entities listed.

Answers   43. d   44. b   45. c
          46. a   47. d

Answer questions 48–52 in reference to the four items listed below:
   a. cDNA
   b. a restriction enzyme
   c. reverse transcriptase
   d. a DNA library

M 48. This is from a viral source and catalyzes reactions to construct DNA strands from mRNA.

M 49. Any DNA copied from mRNA transcripts is known as this.

M 50. A nuclease whose only function is to cut apart foreign DNA entering a cell is this.

M 51. Collections of DNA fragments produced by restriction enzymes and incorporated into cloning vectors is this.

M 52. This is a type of bacterial colony probe constructed of radioactively labeled DNA subunits.

Answers   48. c   49. a   50. b
          51. d   52. a

Selecting the Exception

M 53. Four of the five enzymes below are used in genetic engineering. Select the exception.
    a. ligase
    b. reverse transcriptase
    c. restriction
  * d. replicase
    e. DNA polymerase

M 54. Four of the five statements below are true of cloned DNA. Select the exception.
    a. The plasmid used is the cloning vector.
    b. Identical copies are produced.
  * c. Cloned DNA is produced by reverse transcriptase.
    d. Multiple copies are produced.
    e. Cloned DNA is manufactured in bacteria cells.

M 55. Four of the five answers listed below are aspects of the process known as gene splicing. Select the exception.
    a. cloning vector
    b. restriction enzymes
    c. sticky ends
    d. exposed base pairs
  * e. crossing over

CHAPTER 17
MICROEVOLUTION

Multiple-Choice Questions

D   **1.**   Evolution
  a. may be defined as change in frequency of certain genes in a population.
  b. may be used to explain the disappearance of a genetic trait.
  c. occurred in the past, but does not occur today.
  d. is a property of species not other units of life.
  * e. may be defined as change in frequency of certain genes in a population, and may be used to explain the disappearance of a genetic trait.

M   **2.**   Which of the following statements is false?
  a. Humans may ascribe to God some natural events they do not understand.
  b. Natural disasters have killed and then preserved organisms in the past.
  c. One explanation of natural disasters is punishment by God for humans' bad behavior.
  * d. With our current knowledge and understanding of natural disasters, no one today uses supernatural explanations to explain them.
  e. Both the environment surrounding creatures and the creatures themselves have undergone changes through time.

M   **3.**   The chihuahua is able to survive because humans
  a. protect it from predators.
  b. provide it with food.
  c. eliminate its exposure to environmental extremes.
  d. vaccinate it against disease.
  * e. all of these

M   **4.**   Microevolution is the result of
  a. chance variation.
  b. change in gene frequency.
  c. mutation.
  d. natural selection.
  * e. all of these

E   **5.**   Artificial selection occurs when
  a. the environment controls which organisms will survive.
  * b. humans determine which organisms will survive.
  c. the extremes of the population have a lesser chance to survive.
  d. the extremes of the population have a better chance to survive.
  e. the organisms on one extreme of the population have a better chance to survive than those on the other extreme.

E   **6.**   The word *evolution* as used in biology literally means
  a. natural selection.
  b. genetic drift.
  c. divergence.
  * d. change.
  e. mutation.

EARLY BELIEFS, CONFOUNDING DISCOVERIES

E   **7.**   The great Chain of Being developed from ideas written many centuries earlier by
  * a. Aristotle
  b. Moufet
  c. Linnaeus
  d. Hippocrates
  e. none of these

D   **8.**   People embracing the idea of the great Chain of Being did NOT believe in which of the following?
  a. Spiritual beings were a part of the Chain.
  b. Life forms were divinely created.
  * c. Organisms could appear, disappear, or move up and down the Chain.
  d. Each species was "fixed" at creation.
  e. All the "links" would eventually be discovered.

M   **9.**   Scientists began to question the perfection of the Chain of Being because of
  a. the discovery of new organisms in new parts of the world.
  b. the presence of vestigial structures in some organisms.
  c. the existence of fossil forms.
  d. similarities in the structures found in different forms of life.
  * e. all of these

M   **10.**   The distribution of different organisms over the surface of the earth
  * a. offers evidence for evolution.
  b. provides evidence for a single center of evolution.
  c. appears to be simply a matter of chance.
  d. is not affected by biogeographical features.
  e. is primarily the result of human activities.

E   **11.**   The study of the distribution of plants and animals around the world is
  a. diversity.
  * b. biogeography.
  c. ecology.
  d. natural history.
  e. environmentalism.

M 12. The forelimbs of early mammals were similar in all
features except
a. embryonic origin.
b. position on the body.
c. number.
* d. function.
e. composition.

E 13. The pelvic girdle is
a. part of the backbone of vertebrates.
b. a place where the forelimbs are attached.
* c. a place where the hindlimbs are attached.
d. completely absent in snakes, which do not have
legs.
e. found only during embryonic development and is
not present in many mature vertebrates.

M 14. Pythons have
a. no legs.
b. one pair of internal legs.
c. two pairs of internal legs.
* d. one pair of vestigial (small, useless) legs that can
be seen externally.
e. two pairs of vestigial legs that can be seen
externally.

E 15. The oldest fossils
a. demonstrate the widest distribution.
b. represent the most highly evolved plants and
animals.
* c. are found buried deepest in the ground.
d. are found in Africa.
e. are primitive marine vertebrates.

M 16. Fossils
* a. are found in underground layers called strata.
b. are distributed underground, with the oldest forms
near the top.
c. have more complex structure the deeper they are
buried.
d. are the same throughout the world no matter
where they are found.
e. that are most like living organisms are found
deepest in the ground.

M 17. Fossils found in the lowest geological strata are
generally the most
a. advanced.
b. complex.
* c. primitive.
d. widespread.
e. specialized.

A FLURRY OF NEW THEORIES

M 18. The theory of catastrophism
a. was proposed by Buffon.
b. indicates that a series of disasters necessitated
separate acts of creation to replace species that
became extinct.
c. states that one worldwide disaster led to massive
extinction and subsequent replacement by a new
creation.
* d. held that after a series of massive extinctions the
world was repopulated by the survivors of existing
species.
e. has absolutely no basis in fact because extinctions
just happen with no apparent patterns.

M 19. Cuvier, an anatomist and paleontologist, proposed that
a. all present-day organisms have descended, with
adaptations, from one—or possibly a few—
original organisms.
* b. the earth's history has been marked by several
periods when destruction of populations was
widespread and that, after each such period, the
earth was repopulated.
c. evolutionary changes in organisms are caused by
use and disuse.
d. although evolution is responsible for all the
changes that happen to species, God created the
original members of each species.

D 20. There is no convincing fossil evidence for which of the
following?
a. evolution
b. extinction
c. change
* d. catastrophism
e. uniformitarianism

M 21. Which of the following statements is true?
a. The fossil record supports Cuvier's theory of
catastrophism.
* b. According to the theory of catastrophism, more
species were alive at the beginning of the world
than are now present.
c. According to the theory of catastrophism, new
species developed out of the survivors of the
catastrophes.
d. The theory of catastrophism was based upon
observable responses that organisms made to
catastrophes.
e. According to catastrophism, there were several
distinct periods of creation following each
catastrophe.

E 22. According to Lamarck, the characteristics of
organisms changed because of
a. chance.
* b. an innate drive for perfection.
c. extinction of competitors.
d. special acts of creation.
e. genetic mutation.

E 23. Lamarck's contribution to the theory of evolution was the concept of
   a. natural selection.
   b. catastrophism.
 * c. inheritance of acquired characteristics.
   d. mutation.
   e. geographic distribution of organisms.

D 24. Which of the following would be a modern example of Lamarckianism?
   a. A strain of houseflies resistant to insecticides emerges.
   b. Squirrels separated by a river are found to be unable to interbreed.
 * c. A son is born with a portion of his right index finger missing, the same portion cut off from his father's hand in an accident.
   d. A strain of houseflies resistant to insecticides emerges; and Squirrels separated by a river are found to be unable to interbreed.
   e. A strain of houseflies resistant to insecticides emerges; Squirrels separated by a river are found to be unable to interbreed; and A son is born with a portion of his right index finger missing, the same portion cut off from his father's hand in an accident.

M 25. Lamarck believed
   a. that a substance called fluida moved through the nerves to areas of the body in need of change.
   b. in the inheritance of acquired characteristics.
   c. that giraffes' necks elongated in response to stretching.
   d. that environmental pressures bring about changes in organisms.
 * e. all of these

M 26. Which of the following has no part in today's concept of natural selection?
 * a. inheritance of acquired characteristics
   b. struggle for existence
   c. inherited variation
   d. overproduction of offspring
   e. survival of the best adapted

D 27. Which is NOT a part of Lamarck's theory?
   a. The environment controlled and modified traits.
   b. Characteristics acquired by organisms throughout their lifetimes were transmitted to their offspring.
   c. Organs that are used extensively tend to improve and are found in offspring, whereas those not used will diminish and are not passed on to the offspring.
 * d. Those organisms that are best adapted have a better chance to reproduce than those equipped with inferior adaptations.

E 28. Charles Darwin
   a. studied to be a physician.
   b. studied to become a clergyman.
   c. followed his avocation as a naturalist.
 * d. all of these
   e. none of these

E 29. Darwin's mentor, who obtained a position on H.M.S. *Beagle* for Darwin, was
   a. Alfred Wallace.
 * b. John Henslow.
   c. Jean-Baptiste Lamarck.
   d. Georges Cuvier.
   e. Charles Lyell.

D 30. The value to Darwin of Lyell's ideas on the geologic history of the earth was the
   a. evidence from fossils.
   b. record of catastrophic changes that encouraged evolution.
   c. confirmation of Lamarck's theories.
 * d. enormous lengths of time required for geologic events.
   e. proof of several sites of creation.

M 31. Which theory was helpful to Darwin in the formulation of his theory of evolution?
   a. catastrophism
   b. inheritance of acquired characteristics
 * c. uniformitarianism
   d. continental drift
   e. special creationism

DARWIN'S THEORY TAKES FORM

E 32. Glyptodonts were fossil forms that resembled
   a. ostriches.
 * b. armadillos.
   c. kangaroos.
   d. turtles.
   e. sloths.

D 33. After his return to England, Darwin pondered which of the following questions most heavily?
 * a. What could explain the great numbers of species?
   b. Does the fossil evidence support uniformitarianism?
   c. Are the extinct and living armadillos the same species?
   d. Did Galápagos finches have a common mainland ancestor?
   e. Will natural selection work in England?

E 34. Thomas Malthus proposed that
   a. the food supply multiplied faster than the population.
 * b. the population multiplied faster than the food supply.
   c. the food supply and population multiplied at the same rate.
   d. artificial selection was the key to evolution.
   e. natural selection was the key to evolution.

M 35. The place Darwin visited on his trip around the world that had the greatest impact on his thinking was
   a. the Canary Islands.
   b. Africa.
   c. the Hawaiian Islands.
 * d. the Galápagos Islands.
   e. Brazil.

M 36. The most important evidence that Darwin used to develop his theory of natural selection came from
    a. the Argentine pampas.
    b. his boyhood neighborhood in England.
*   c. the Galápagos Islands.
    d. Australia and New Zealand.
    e. South America.

M 37. Galápagos finches are examples of
    a. scavengers.
    b. morphological isolation.
*   c. adaptive radiation.
    d. punctuated equilibrium.

E 38. Darwin's finches were found on the _____ Islands.
*   a. Galápagos
    b. Canary
    c. Philippine
    d. Hawaiian
    e. Aleutian

E 39. The feature of Darwin's finches that underwent variation was
    a. feet.
*   b. beaks.
    c. feathers.
    d. structure of eggs.
    e. all of these

D 40. Darwin's theory of evolution
    a. was the first theory to propose natural selection.
    b. is no longer accepted by biologists.
*   c. failed to account for the sources of variability.
    d. did not account for differential survival and reproduction.
    e. was based upon the chances of mutation occurring in a population.

D 41. Which of the following was NOT one of Darwin's observations?
*   a. Most individuals have an equal chance to survive and reproduce.
    b. Changes in organisms were gradual and took place over long periods of time.
    c. Members of the same species may exhibit considerable variation.
    d. Some characteristics are heritable and passed on to their offspring.
    e. Some characteristics afford their possessor a better chance of survival.

D 42. Natural selection operates to produce changes in
    a. individuals.
*   b. populations.
    c. races.
    d. phyla.
    e. animals only.

M 43. Which of the following is NOT a factor involved in the theory of evolution?
    a. All organisms reproduce beyond the limits of the environment that supports them.
*   b. Food supplies keep pace with the growth of populations feeding upon them.
    c. Populations of organisms tend to remain relatively stable through time.
    d. There is much variation in the characteristics of organisms making up a population.
    e. Some traits are more adaptive than others.

D 44. One part of Darwin's theory is that individuals with certain traits have an increased competitive edge. The source of these traits is
    a. adaptation to the stress.
    b. development over a lifetime.
*   c. inheritance from birth.
    d. mutation after birth.
    e. all of these

M 45. The operation of natural selection depends upon the fact that
    a. the strong always survive, whereas the weak always die.
*   b. some individuals have a better chance to produce more offspring.
    c. mutations are always harmful.
    d. acquired characteristics are inherited.
    e. reproduction of all members of a species is virtually the same.

E 46. The person credited with being the codiscoverer of evolution was
*   a. Alfred Wallace.
    b. Charles Lyell.
    c. Thomas Malthus.
    d. James Hutton.
    e. John Henslow.

INDIVIDUALS DON'T EVOLVE–POPULATIONS DO

E 47. Which of the following is a group of individuals of the same species for which there are no restrictions to random mating among its members?
    a. individual
    b. species
*   c. population
    d. polyploid
    e. all of these

M 48. Members of a population would be least likely to have which of the following in common?
    a. phenotype
    b. morphological traits
*   c. genotype
    d. physiological traits
    e. behavioral traits

D 49. Only identical twins have the same
   *   a. genotype.
        b. phenotype.
        c. traits.
        d. genotype and phenotype.
        e. genotype, phenotype, and traits.

M 50. Which of these statements is true?
        a. Environment can readily alter some genotypes.
   *   b. Genotype is manifested in phenotype.
        c. Genetic variation is easier seen than phenotypic variation.
        d. Variation dies with individuals.
        e. Phenotype is seen physically in the genotype.

M 51. Which of the following is considered a USUAL cause of variation in sexually reproducing organisms?
        a. changes in chromosome number
        b. mutation
        c. independent assortment of chromosomes
        d. crossing over
   *   e. both independent assortment of chromosomes and crossing over

M 52. Genetic variation is the result of all but which one of the following?
        a. alteration in chromosome structure or number
        b. gene mutation
        c. independent assortment
   *   d. the role of environment in controlling genetic expression
        e. crossing over and genetic recombination

E 53. New combinations of genes may be produced by
        a. immigration.
        b. mutation.
        c. crossing over.
        d. sexual reproduction.
   *   e. all of these

M 54. Introduction of previously nonexistent genes into a population may be accomplished by
        a. nonrandom mating.
   *   b. mutation.
        c. sexual recombination.
        d. the founder effect.

M 55. Which statement is NOT true?
        a. Migration leads to genetic variation.
   *   b. Dominant genes always occur more frequently in a population than recessive genes.
        c. Nonrandom mating may result in changes in gene frequency.
        d. The Hardy-Weinberg law applies to large, stable populations.
        e. Crossing over increases variation.

E 56. The Hardy-Weinberg formula is valuable for the calculation of changes in
        a. population size.
        b. speciation.
   *   c. allele frequencies.
        d. mutation.
        e. dimorphism.

E 57. Of the following, which does NOT characterize a population in Hardy-Weinberg equilibrium?
        a. large population size
        b. no mutation
   *   c. differential reproduction
        d. absence of gene flow

D 58. Genetic equilibrium and gene frequencies would be maintained by all but which one of the following?
        a. development of isolating mechanisms
        b. large population interbreeding freely
   *   c. differential mating and survival
        d. random mating
        e. all of these

D 59. Immigration of individuals into a population in Hardy-Weinberg equilibrium will NOT upset the equilibrium if
   *   a. they are beyond the age of reproduction.
        b. females and males are in equal proportions.
        c. they mate randomly in the new population.
        d. they arrive in large numbers.

M 60. The maintenance of Hardy-Weinberg equilibrium is encouraged
        a. when sexual selection occurs.
        b. when mutations occur.
        c. in small populations.
   *   d. when there is no gene flow between different populations.
        e. all of these

M 61. The Hardy-Weinberg rule
   *   a. is useful in determining the extent to which a sexually reproducing population is evolving.
        b. is used to predict when genetic drift will occur in a sexually reproducing population.
        c. is useful in determining the extent to which polyploidy is occurring in specific plant populations.
        d. is used to predict when specific groups of organisms will become extinct.
        e. all of these

E 62. Which of the following is an example of random mating?
        a. The largest and strongest males develop a harem.
        b. A female bird will mate only with males that perform the best courtship displays.
        c. Members of a sorority usually marry fraternity brothers.
   *   d. Some males mate with any females they encounter.

M 63. The genetic equilibrium of a population can be upset by all but which of the following?
        a. mutations
        b. migration
   *   c. random mating
        d. genetic drift

M 64. Which of the following is NOT a major process of microevolution?
    a. mutation
  * b. divergence
    c. genetic drift
    d. gene flow
    e. natural selection

E 65. New alleles arise by
  * a. mutation.
    b. migration.
    c. genetic drift.
    d. random mating.
    e. independent assortment.

E 66. New genes arise from
    a. genetic drift.
  * b. mutation.
    c. gene flow.
    d. recombination.
    e. natural selection.

M 67. New alleles that appear by mutation
    a. are inherently disadvantageous to their bearers.
    b. are seldom advantageous or disadvantageous in themselves.
    c. either have or lack survival value only in the context of their environment.
  * d. both b and c
    e. both a and b

E 68. Which of the following is a source of new alleles within a population?
    a. genetic recombination
    b. meiosis
  * c. mutation
    d. genetic drift

E 69. Whether a mutation is ultimately considered harmful, neutral, or lethal is often determined by
    a. phenotype.
    b. the will of the individual.
    c. the Hardy-Weinberg formula.
  * d. environment.
    e. fate.

D 70. Which of the following statements is false?
  * a. Neutral mutations are not expressed.
    b. The effect of mutation is based upon the environment where it is found.
    c. Mutations are random but their frequency can be predicted.
    d. Mutations are more likely to be harmful because they represent a difference from alleles that have stood the test of years of selection.
    e. Some harmful genes may build up in a population because of their location close to a favorable gene on a chromosome.

FOCUS ON SCIENCE: WHEN IS A POPULATION NOT EVOLVING

D 71. If the frequency of a recessive gene in a population under genetic equilibrium is 40 percent, in the next generation the frequency of that gene would be
    a. 20 percent.
  * b. 40 percent.
    c. 80 percent.
    d. dependent upon other factors, so it cannot be predicted but must instead be reevaluated each generation.

D 72. If the frequency of expression of a recessive trait in a population is 16 percent, the frequency of the recessive allele would be what percent?
    a. 16
    b. 25
  * c. 40
    d. 50
    e. 67

D 73. If the frequency of a recessive allele is 36 percent, the frequency of the dominant allele would be what percent?
    a. 5
    b. 8
    c. 25
    d. 48
  * e. 64

M 74. In the Hardy-Weinberg equation, the term q^2 refers to the frequency of
    a. a recessive allele of a given locus.
  * b. the homozygous recessive genotype at a given locus.
    c. recessive alleles in a population.
    d. heterozygotes in a population.

D 75. If the frequency of the recessive allele is 30 percent, the frequency of the heterozygous carrier would be what percent?
  * a. 42
    b. 9
    c. 27
    d. 60
    e. 80

D 76. In a population that is in Hardy-Weinberg equilibrium, the frequency of the recessive homozygous genotype is 0.49. The percentage of the population that is heterozygous is
    a. 51.
    b. 49.
  * c. 42.
    d. 7.
    e. 3.

D   77. Suppose that you have a population of guinea pigs in which two-thirds of the alleles for coat color specify black and one-third specify white. According to the Hardy-Weinberg rule, what will be the ratio of these alleles in the gene pool in future generations, provided all the guinea pigs reproduce?
         a.   1:1
    *   b.   2:1
         c.   3:1
         d.   6:1
         e.   7.1

D   78. Of 400 people who dwell on a Pacific island, 16 are homozygous recessive for a trait that has only two different types of alleles in the population. The number of heterozygous people is
         a.   256.
         b.   32.
         c.   64.
    *   d.   128.
         e.   384.

NATURAL SELECTION REVISITED

E   79. Which of the following is NOT a component of Darwin's principle of natural selection?
    *   a.   New alleles are constantly produced through mutation.
         b.   Populations exhibit great variation.
         c.   Organisms produce more offspring than can be sustained by the environment.
         d.   Over time, adaptive phenotypes increase in frequency within a population.

D   80. Natural selection
         a.   actively combs through a population searching for the best combination of genes.
         b.   is a haphazard process based upon chance.
         c.   involves differential survival.
         d.   involves differential reproduction.
    *   e.   involves both differential survival and differential reproduction.

DIRECTIONAL CHANGE IN THE RANGE OF VARIATION

M   81. Directional selection occurs when
         a.   the environment controls which organisms will survive.
         b.   humans determine which organisms will survive.
         c.   the extremes of the population have a lesser chance to survive.
         d.   the extremes of the population have a better chance to survive.
    *   e.   the organisms on one extreme of the population have a better chance to survive than those on the other extreme.

E   82. An insect that exhibits resistance to a pesticide
         a.   developed the resistance in response to the pesticide.
         b.   mutated when exposed to the pesticide.
    *   c.   inherited genes that made it resistant to the pesticide.
         d.   none of these

M   83. When DDT was first introduced, insects were very susceptible to it. The development of resistance to DDT by insects was the result of
         a.   special creation.
    *   b.   natural selection of forms that expressed genes for resistance.
         c.   the high biotic potential of insects.
         d.   a naturally occurring example of inheritance of acquired characteristics.
         e.   mutation induced by DDT.

M   84. Directional selection was demonstrated in
         a.   industrial melanism and the color of peppered moths in England.
         b.   development of resistance to insecticides.
         c.   the development of different island races and species of finches in the Galápagos Islands.
    *   d.   industrial melanism and the color of peppered moths in England and development of resistance to insecticides.
         e.   industrial melanism and the color of peppered moths in England, development of resistance to insecticides, and the development of different island races and species of finches in the Galápagos Islands.

M   85. As the trees in England become less sooty due to pollution controls on factories, which of the following should occur?
         a.   Fewer dark moths should survive.
         b.   Numbers of dark and light moths won't change due to stabilizing selection.
         c.   Genetic mutations will be reversed.
         d.   More light-gray moths should survive.
    *   e.   Fewer dark moths should survive; and More light-gray moths should survive.

M   86. Industrial melanism is an example of _____ selection.
         a.   kin
         b.   disruptive
    *   c.   directional
         d.   stabilizing

SELECTION AGAINST OR IN FAVOR OF EXTREME POSITIONS

M **87.** Stabilizing selection occurs when
   a. the environment controls which organisms will survive.
   b. humans determine which organisms will survive.
 * c. the extremes of the population have a lesser chance to survive.
   d. the extremes of the population have a better chance to survive.
   e. the organisms on one extreme of the population have a better chance to survive than those on the other extreme.

M **88.** In an unchanging environment, selection in a well-adapted population is
   a. directional.
   b. disruptive.
 * c. stabilizing.
   d. absent.

E **89.** In a certain bird species, clutch size (the number of eggs laid by a female in one breeding season) ranges from four to eight, and the most frequent clutch size is six. This phenomenon is an example of
   a. sexual selection.
 * b. stabilizing selection.
   c. disruptive selection.
   d. directional selection.

M **90.** The famous "bell-shaped curve" that usually results when test scores are plotted against number of students is an example of what type of selection?
   a. disruptive
 * b. stabilizing
   c. divergent
   d. variable
   e. directional

M **91.** In stabilizing selection,
   a. differential survival and reproduction favor the extremes of the population.
   b. humans are the chief factor controlling which organisms survive and reproduce.
 * c. the most common type of organisms survive and reproduce.
   d. the characteristics of a population move in one direction or another through time.
   e. variability is encouraged in a population and unusual forms are more common.

D **92.** Which of the following is true?
   a. Nautiloids can swim faster than fish.
   b. Fish are more efficient swimmers than nautiloids.
 * c. The persistence of nautiloids for over 400,000,000 years is an example of stabilizing selection.
   d. Nautiloids have never been anything more than a hanger-on and have never been very successful.
   e. Nautiloids require much more energy than fish to move from place to place.

M **93.** Male mallards have had emerald green head feathers and wings with metallic blue patches for hundreds of years, whereas female mallards have been drab brown-feathered ducks. This phenotypic situation suggests that mallards may be an example of
   a. directional selection.
   b. polyploidy.
   c. allopatric speciation.
 * d. disruptive selection.
   e. sexual isolation.

MAINTAINING VARIABLITY IN A POPULATION

M **94.** Balanced polymorphism is a type of
   a. disruptive selection.
   b. sexual selection.
   c. directional selection.
   d. reproductive isolation.
 * e. stabilizing selection.

D **95.** The decline in the frequency of the sickle-cell anemia allele in the American population is the result of
   a. a lower mutation rate in the United States than in Africa.
   b. the advantage of both homozygous forms over the heterozygous form.
   c. the development of appropriate medical treatment in the United States.
 * d. a decline in the occurrence of malaria in the United States.

D **96.** The persistence of the sickle-cell anemia allele in the African population is the result of
   a. a high rate of mutation of the normal allele to the sickle-cell anemia allele.
 * b. the advantage of the heterozygous form over the homozygous forms.
   c. nonrandom mating.
   d. a decline in the occurrence of malaria in Africa.

M **97.** The Hb^S allele (sickle cell) occurs at a higher frequency in Africa than it does in the United States because
   a. it is a dominant allele in Africa and a recessive one in the United States.
   b. genetic recombination occurs at different rates in different human populations.
 * c. natural selection favors heterozygotes in Africa but favors homozygous normal individuals in the United States.
   d. the African population is descended from a small group of individuals who possessed the allele at a high frequency.

E **98.** The difference in the appearance of the male and the female is known as
   a. polymorphism.
 * b. sexual dimorphism.
   c. the dioecious condition.
   d. the monoecious condition.
   e. a primary sexual characteristic.

E 99. Male northern sea lions are nearly twice the size of females because
   a. males live longer than females.
   b. predators of the sea lions favor males.
 * c. males compete to mate with females.
   d. each male must protect the one female with which he mates.

M 100. Sexual dimorphism has arisen as a result of
   a. stabilizing selection.
   b. kin selection.
 * c. sexual selection.
   d. directional selection.

D 101. For most species that exhibit sexual dimorphism, the selection of a mate is the responsibility of the
   a. male.
   b. parents.
 * c. female.
   d. larger individual, no matter the species.
   e. more colorful individual.

GENE FLOW

M 102. Gene flow
   a. makes adjacent populations more similar.
   b. acts to prevent speciation.
   c. is a microevolutionary process.
   d. counteracts the effects of mutation, natural selection, and genetic drift.
 * e. all of these

M 103. Gene flow
 * a. has a homogenizing influence on a population.
   b. speeds up the divergence of two populations.
   c. increases the genetic variation between populations.
   d. is promoted by isolating mechanisms.

M 104. Which of the following does NOT account for the maintenance of a nonbeneficial allele within a population?
   a. The phenotypic expression of the allele may be neutral in some environments.
   b. The allele may be recessive.
 * c. The allele may affect development, but not the phenotype of the adult.
   d. The allele is tightly linked to highly adaptive genes.

M 105. What accounts for the fact that polydactylism is prevalent and Tay-Sachs disease virtually absent in one human population in the United States while Tay-Sachs disease is prevalent and polydactylism virtually absent in another?
   a. Natural selection has promoted these differences because humans live in many different environments.
   b. Mutation rates differ among different loci.
 * c. There is little gene flow between the two populations.
   d. The populations are small, and therefore genetic drift is a major factor in the determination of allele frequencies.

M 106. When compared to the mainland populations from which they are derived, island populations do NOT exhibit which of the following?
 * a. greater variability
   b. greater extinction rates
   c. fewer heterozygous loci
   d. large chance fluctuations in allele frequencies

D 107. A general warming trend in northern climates might decrease the ice bridges that usually form between islands in the upper Great Lakes. Because animals travel across these bridges, this warming could result in
 * a. decreased gene flow.
   b. more genetic heterogeneity.
   c. healthier populations of animals.
   d. more mutations.
   e. all of these

GENETIC DRIFT

M 108. The evolutionary force that operates primarily through chance is
   a. natural selection.
 * b. genetic drift.
   c. isolation.
   d. mating preference.

M 109. Genetic drift
   a. may lead to a loss of variation in a population.
   b. requires small populations.
   c. occurs in populations with the founder effect.
   d. may occur when conditions produce the bottleneck effect.
 * e. all of these

E 110. The influence of genetic drift on allele frequencies increases as
   a. gene flow increases.
 * b. population size decreases.
   c. mutation rate decreases.
   d. the number of heterozygous loci increases.

M 111. The introduction of a small population onto an island that results in a limited gene pool for a population is an example of
   a. the Hardy-Weinberg law.
   b. genetic drift.
   c. the bottleneck effect.
 * d. the founder principle.
   e. the effect of genetic isolation.

M 112. The biological impact of the "founder effect" is based upon
   a. absence of gene flow.
   b. chance.
   c. migration.
   d. nonrandom mating.
 * e. all of these

D 113. Although there are as many starlings in North America as there are in Europe, genetic variability in the North American population is reduced relative to that in Europe because
   a. there are more environments in Europe.
 * b. the North American population is derived from a small founder population.
   c. there is more gene flow in Europe.
   d. there is less mutation in North America.

M 114. The sharp reduction of the gene pool and the numbers of a population through a severe epidemic is an example of
   a. natural selection.
   b. genetic isolation.
 * c. the bottleneck effect.
   d. the founder principle.
   e. all of these

D 115. If you sampled the genetic characteristics of a large population and found that of the 50 loci analyzed there was very little if any variation, the most likely explanation would be that
   a. a uniform environment selected for these alleles.
   b. there has been a lack of migration and the genetic equilibrium stabilized the population.
   c. strong selection pressures eliminated alternative alleles.
 * d. a bottleneck effect may have occurred in the past to reduce the variability in the population.
   e. a combination of low mutation rates and differential sexual selection produced these results.

M 116. When a population goes through a bottleneck,
 * a. genetic drift is likely to occur.
   b. mutation rates increase.
   c. extinction rates decrease.
   d. natural selection decreases in intensity.

Matching Questions

M 117. Matching. Choose the most appropriate answer for each.
   1. ___ Aristotle
   2. ___ Buffon
   3. ___ Cuvier
   4. ___ Darwin
   5. ___ Lamarck
   6. ___ Lyell
   7. ___ Malthus

   A. wrote Principles of Geology
   B. developed the theory of catastrophism
   C. believed that giraffes have long necks because their short-necked ancestors stretched their necks and passed this change on to their offspring
   D. was a naturalist who sailed on the Beagle and studied finches
   E. wrote Essay on the Principle of Population
   F. wrote Scala Naturae, early ideas of great Chain of Being
   G. believed in several centers of creation and the idea that species may have changed through time

Answers: 1. F   2. G   3. B   4. D
           5. C   6. A   7. E

D **118.** Matching. Choose the most appropriate letter for each.

1. ___ $p + q$
2. ___ species
3. ___ directional selection
4. ___ gene pool
5. ___ balanced polymorphism
6. ___ p^2
7. ___ $2pq$
8. ___ genetic equilibrium
9. ___ q^2

   A. a reference point that implies stability of gene frequencies through generations

   B. encompasses all of those actually or potentially interbreeding populations that are reproductively isolated from other such groups

   C. the genes of an entire population

   D. the frequency of homozygous dominants in a population

   E. the frequencies of dominant and recessive alleles in a population

   F. the frequency of heterozygotes in a population

   G. the frequency of homozygous recessives in a population

   H. HbA and HbS in regions where malaria is found

   I. pesticide-resistant pests

Answers: 1. E   2. B   3. I   4. C

5. H   6. D   7. F   8. A

9. G

Classification Questions

Answer questions 119-123 in reference to the four evolutionary processes listed below:

   a. mutation
   b. gene flow
   c. genetic drift
   d. natural selection

M **119.** This is most likely to lead to the loss of genetic variation in a small population.

E **120.** This process produces new genetic variation within a species.

M **121.** This process can rapidly offset the effects of genetic isolation when two populations come into secondary contact.

M **122.** The reduced contribution of one phenotype in comparison to another to the next generation is an example of this.

M **123.** The occurrence of mimicry is best explained as the ultimate result of this process.

Answers   119. c   120. a   121. b

122. d   123. d

Selecting the Exception

M **124.** Four of the five people listed below were biologists. Select the exception.
   a. Buffon
   * b. Lyell
   c. Wallace
   d. Cuvier
   e. Darwin

E **125.** Four of the five answers below support the concept of evolution. Select the exception.
   a. biogeography
   b. fossils
   c. comparative anatomy
   d. natural selection
   * e. catastrophism

M **126.** Four of the five answers below are true of Darwin's voyage. Select the exception.
   a. lasted five years
   * b. wrote final draft of book on species
   c. sailed aboard the H.M.S. *Beagle*
   d. embarked from England when he was 22 years old
   e. visited the mainland of South America

D **127.** Four of the five answers below are consistent with Darwin's theory of natural selection. Select the exception.
   a. All populations tend to overproduce.
   b. Some members are more adapted to the rigors of competition.
   c. Limited resources put limits on population growth.
   * d. Variation in individuals is not inheritable.
   e. Traits appear and disappear.

M **128.** Four of the five answers listed below are sources of variation in a population. Select the exception.
   a. mutation
   b. sexual reproduction
   c. crossing over
   d. independent assortment
   * e. law of dominance

D **129.** Four of the five answers listed below are characteristics of an unchanging, nonevolving population. Select the exception.
   a. random mating
   b. no mutation
   * c. differential survival
   d. no migration or gene flow
   e. infinitely large population

E **130.** Four of the five answers listed below are characteristics of mutations. Select the exception.
*   a. predictable
    b. lethal or beneficial
    c. random
    d. effects depend upon environment
    e. heritable

M **131.** Four of the five answers listed below are portions of the theory of natural selection. Select the exception.
    a. Variation is heritable.
    b. Heritable traits vary in adaptability.
    c. More organisms are produced than can survive.
*   d. The largest and strongest always contribute more genes to the next generation.
    e. Natural selection is the result of differential reproduction.

M **132.** Four of the five answers listed below are types of selection exhibited by nature. Select the exception.
*   a. artificial
    b. disruptive
    c. stabilizing
    d. directional
    e. sexual

M **133.** Four of the five answers listed below are examples of disruptive selection. Select the exception.
*   a. pesticide resistance
    b. sexual dimorphism
    c. sickle-cell anemia
    d. balanced polymorphism
    e. differential mortality

D **134.** Four of the five answers listed below can upset genetic equilibrium. Select the exception.
*   a. interbreeding
    b. genetic drift
    c. mutation
    d. natural selection
    e. gene flow

CHAPTER 18
SPECIATION

Multiple-Choice Questions

M 1. The genes of snails would probably not be dispersed as widely as ducks because
    a. snails are lower on the evolutionary scale.
    b. ducks eat snails.
    c. snails are hermits in their protective shells.
    d. ducks can swim.
  * e. snails cannot move as rapidly as ducks.

M 2. Speciation is most precisely determined
    a. by careful observation of anatomical traits.
    b. at the moment of conception.
    c. by mutation.
  * d. when interbreeding is not longer possible.
    e. at the time of birth or in early postnatal development.

ON THE ROAD TO SPECIATION

E 3. The word *species* could be translated
    a. group.
  * b. kind.
    c. portion.
    d. type.
    e. section.

E 4. The word *phenotype* designates the
    a. portion of the genes that are not expressed.
    b. type of genes an organism possesses.
    c. amount of change seen from one generation to the next.
  * d. observable aspects of any individual organism.
    e. extent of mutation.

E 5. In the biological species concept of Ernst Mayer, what aspect of a population is critical to determining a species?
    a. physical appearance
    b. similar behavior patterns
  * c. interbreeding capabilities
    d. polyploidy
    e. similar genotypes

M 6. Members of the same species would be expected to
    a. look alike.
    b. be reproductively isolated from one another.
  * c. share the same gene pool.
    d. have the same phenotype.
    e. resist evolution.

M 7. A species is composed of
    a. related organisms.
    b. a group of reproductive females.
  * c. populations that have the potential to interbreed and produce fertile offspring.
    d. organisms located in the same habitat.
    e. all males and females in the same geographical range with the same ecological requirements.

D 8. Which of the following is a characteristic feature that would NOT distinguish two different species?
    a. They have different gene pools.
    b. If hybrids are produced as a result of mating, the offspring are sterile.
    c. Their ranges do not overlap.
  * d. Their courtship patterns are different so that they do not attempt to interbreed.

M 9. Two individuals are members of the same species if they
    a. possess the same number of chromosomes.
    b. breed at the same time.
    c. are phenotypically indistinguishable.
  * d. can mate and produce fertile offspring.

E 10. Complete reproductive isolation is evidence that what has occurred?
    a. extinction
  * b. speciation
    c. polyploidy
    d. hybridization
    e. gene flow

D 11. Which of the following will NOT promote speciation?
    a. gamete differences
  * b. gene flow
    c. season of fertility
    d. natural selection
    e. genetic drift

D 12. Speciation occurs
  * a. after populations become reproductively isolated and diverge.
    b. when mutations generate observable differences.
    c. when transitional forms develop between different populations.
    d. when natural selection pressures reach their maximum.
    e. when humans intervene and establish new breeds.

D   13.   Divergence may lead to
           a. genetic drift.
      *   b. speciation.
           c. balanced polymorphism.
           d. gene flow.
           e. genetic equilibrium.

E   14.   The term *reproductive isolation mechanism* refers to
           a. specific areas where males compete or display for females.
           b. the process by which sexual selection evolves within a population.
      *   c. a blockage of gene flow between populations.
           d. the inability of a species to continue reproduction.

M   15.   Which of the following is NOT an example of an isolating mechanism?
           a. species-specific courtship rituals
      *   b. Hardy-Weinberg equilibrium
           c. incompatible reproductive structures
           d. earthquakes and floods
           e. all of these

M   16.   Incompatibilities between the developing embryo and the maternal organism that cause the embryo to abort spontaneously may prevent individuals of different populations from producing fertile offspring. Such differences may be which of the following?
      *   a. isolating mechanisms
           b. allele frequencies
           c. mutations
           d. founder effects
           e. gene flow

M   17.   The primary reason for hybrid sterility is
           a. the inability of the hybrid to attract a mate.
           b. the difficulty in finding a suitable habitat in which to survive.
           c. that the hybrids are usually weak and have difficulty surviving to reproductive maturity.
      *   d. the difficulty in the pairing of homologous chromosomes.
           e. the inability of the hybrid to develop an appropriate courtship pattern.

E   18.   Isolating mechanisms that take effect before or during fertilization are termed
           a. hybridizing.
      *   b. prezygotic.
           c. genetically divergent.
           d. postzygotic.
           e. persistent.

E   19.   The 13-year and 17-year cicadas are isolated by
           a. space.
           b. behavior.
           c. incompatibility of reproductive body parts.
      *   d. time.
           e. gamete incompatibility.

E   20.   "Seasonal", "daily", "monthly" all describe isolation that can be termed
           a. behavioral.
      *   b. temporal.
           c. mechanical.
           d. gametic.
           e. ecological.

M   21.   Members of two different bird species mate and produce viable fertile offspring. The courtship song of the hybrid is not recognized by members of either parent species. This is an example of
           a. speciation.
           b. balanced polymorphism.
      *   c. behavioral isolation.
           d. sexual selection.
           e. ecological isolation.

M   22.   Suppose you witness the mating of a cat and a dog, obviously two different species, but realize that there will be no viable offspring due to isolating mechanisms that are
           a. mechanical.
      *   b. gametic.
           c. behavioral.
           d. temporal.
           e. ecological.

M   23.   During a study of two closely related animals it did not appear as though they were reproductively isolated until the possibility that their different niches could result in __?__ isolation was noted.
      *   a. ecological
           b. gametic
           c. temporal
           d. behavioral
           e. mechanical

E   24.   Hybrid inviability is an example of what kind of isolation?
           a. gametic
           b. prezygotic
           c. divergent
           d. mechanical
      *   e. postzygotic

M   25.   Mules are an exceptional hybrids because
           a. they are weak.
           b. their survival rate is low.
      *   c. they are sturdy and strong.
           d. they are sterile.
           e. their offspring are sterile.

SPECIATION IN GEOGRAPHICALLY ISOLATED POPULATIONS

E   26.   Allopatric speciation requires
           a. gradual evolutionary changes.
      *   b. geographic isolation.
           c. polyploidy.
           d. adaptive radiation.

E 27. In allopatric speciation, daughter species may arise
      a. abruptly.
      b. in proportion to the parental stock.
      c. in the same homeland.
      d. gradually over rather long periods of time.
   * e. either abruptly or gradually over rather long
          periods of time.

M 28. The greatest contributor(s) to allopatric isolation is
       (are)
   * a. geographical barriers.
      b. differences in reproductive timing.
      c. gametic incompatibility.
      d. hybrid inviability.
      e. behavioral peculiarities.

M 29. The effectiveness of geographical barriers in
       promoting speciation is related to the
      a. size of the barrier.
   * b. ability of the organisms to overcome the barrier.
      c. speed at which the barrier forms.
      d. duration of the barrier before it is torn down.
      e. size of the population it separates.

E 30. Changes in the Mississippi River caused by
       earthquakes are thought to have caused speciation by
      a. divergence.
      b. parapatry.
   * c. allopatry.
      d. gene flow.
      e. sympatry.

M 31. Speciation caused by the separation of the continents
       would be by
      a. divergence.
      b. parapatry.
      c. gene flow.
   * d. allopatry.
      e. sympatry.

E 32. The construction of the Panama Canal led to the
       development of _____ isolation in fish.
      a. morphological
      b. behavioral
      c. genetic
   * d. geographical
      e. chronological

MODELS FOR OTHER SPECIATION ROUTES

M 33. Sympatric speciation occurs
      a. gradually.
      b. rapidly.
      c. in the same homeland.
      d. gradually and in the same homeland.
   * e. rapidly and in the same homeland.

E 34. Which is NOT necessary for sympatric speciation?
      a. organisms living together in same location
      b. "same homeland"
   * c. geographical barriers
      d. existing interbreeding population
      e. reproductively mature individuals

M 35. The cichlids of the African crater lakes are an example
       of
      a. divergence.
      b. parapatry.
      c. gene flow.
      d. allopatry.
   * e. sympatry.

E 36. Sympatric speciation through polyploidy has been a
       frequent phenomenon in the evolution of
      a. insects.
      b. mammals.
      c. bacteria.
   * d. plants.

M 37. Which of the following can result in instant speciation?
      a. development of a physical barrier
   * b   polyploidy
      c. increase in physical size
      d. change in environmental conditions
      e. the introduction of a new predator into an area

D 38. Which of the following is accurate concerning
       polyploidy?
      a. It is more common in animals than plants.
      b. It is the result of mitotic irregularities.
      c. It cannot be passed on to offspring.
   * d   It often arises due to nondisjunction.
      e. It is limited to no more than three sets of
          chromosomes.

E 39. Parapatric speciation would be expected to occur most
       often
      a. in the same homeland.
   * b. near a common border between two populations.
      c. within a group of interbreeding populations.
      d. across obvious geographical barriers.
      e. by divergence from a common interbreeding
          population.

E 40. The border across which genes can flow between two
       populations is called the
   * a. hybrid zone.
      b. parapatric zone.
      c. zone of speciation.
      d. demilitarized zone.
      e. zone of polyploidy.

PATTERNS OF SPECIATION

E 41. A speciation pattern which exhibits branching of
       populations is termed
      a. allopatric.
      b. anagenesis.
      c. nondivergent.
      d. hybridizing.
   * e. cladogenesis.

M 42. Evolutionists use the term anagenesis
   a. to describe a divergence of one species into several.
   b. to indicate branching speciation patterns.
 * c. for speciation from a single, unbranched line of descent.
   d. to describe a divergence of one species into several and to indicate branching speciation patterns.

E 43. Scientists have traditionally drawn evolutionary diagrams in the form of
   a. interlocking circles.
   b. pyramids.
   c. a set of parallel lines.
 * d. a tree.
   e. nested squares or boxes.

E 44. The gradual model of evolutionary change proposes that most morphological change occurs
   a. gradually but without development of new species.
   b. rapidly but without speciation.
 * c. gradually during speciation.
   d. rapidly leading to new species.

E 45. The punctuation model of evolutionary change proposes that most morphological change occurs
   a. gradually but without development of new species.
   b. rapidly but without speciation.
   c. gradually during speciation.
 * d. rapidly leading to new species.

M 46. According to the punctuation model of speciation, an evolutionary diagram descent would be characterized by
 * a. vertical lines with horizontal branchings.
   b. vertical lines with branchings at narrow angles.
   c. broad-angled lines with horizontal branches.
   d. broad-angled lines with branching at narrow angles.

D 47. The lack of transitional forms of organisms would be
   a. more expected in the gradual model than in the punctuation model.
 * b. more expected in the punctuation model than in the gradual model.
   c. equally expected in both models.
   d. expected in neither model.

D 48. Which of the following contributes to adaptive radiation within a lineage?
   a. extinction of competitors
   b. new phenotypic characteristics
   c. genetic uniformity
 * d. extinction of competitors and new phenotypic characteristics
   e. extinction of competitors, new phenotypic characteristics, and genetic uniformity

D 49. Which of the following adaptations would be most important for an animal that is to live on land?
   a. three germ layers
   b. a moist skin without scales
 * c. internal fertilization
   d. external gills with major sense organs concentrated in the head region

D 50. An advantage of the evolution of the penis is that it
   a. increased the efficiency of the reproductive act.
   b. reduced the threat of predation of the fertilized eggs.
   c. removed the requirement to return to the water to breed.
 * d. all of these

E 51. The acquisition of a key evolutionary innovation by a species gives evidence for the concept of
   a. uniformitarianism.
   b. gradualism.
   c. convergence.
 * d. adaptive radiation.
   e. special creation.

E 52. Background extinction is a measure of
   a. the rate of species turnover at the end of geologic eras.
   b. the number of species that suffer extinction at the beginning of geologic eras.
 * c. the steady rate of species turnover within a lineage throughout most of their evolutionary history.
   d. the lowest rate of species turnover within a lineage observed within a geologic era.

M 53. Which of the following is NOT an explanation for mass extinction?
   a. collisions between the earth and other bodies in the solar system
   b. continental movements
 * c. adaptive radiation of new predator species in many lineages
   d. alterations in sea level

M 54. Mass extinctions are usually followed by
   a. periods of recovery.
   b. adaptive radiations.
   c. smaller extinctions.
 * d. periods of recovery and adaptive radiations.
   e. periods of recovery, adaptive radiations, and smaller extinctions.

Matching Questions

D **55.** Matching. Choose the most appropriate letter for each.

1. ___ cladogenesis
2. ___ species
3. ___ isolating mechanism
4. ___ sympatric speciation
5. ___ polyploidy
6. ___ punctuation model
7. ___ mass extinction
8. ___ allopatric speciation
9. ___ adaptive radiation

A. geographic separation of two populations accompanied by gradual divergent evolution between them; reproductive isolation

B. encompasses all of those actually or potentially interbreeding populations that are reproductively isolated from other such groups

C. a population occupying the same distribution range undergoes reproductive isolation

D. morphological changes compressed into brief periods followed by speciation

E. branching pattern of speciation

F. catastrophic, global loss of species

G. a burst of microevolutionary activity within a lineage

H. inheritance of three or more of each type of chromosome

I. prevents gene flow between populations

Answers: 1. E 2. B 3. I
4. C 5. H 6. D
7. F 8. A 9. G

Classification Questions

Answer questions 56-60 in reference to the four microevolutionary processes listed below:

a. mutation
b. gene flow
c. genetic drift
d. natural selection

M **56.** erodes species cohesion

E **57.** original source of alleles

M **58.** preserves species cohesion

M **59.** preserves or erodes species cohesion depending on environmental pressures

M **60.** results from differential survival and reproduction

Answers 56. c 57. a 58. b
59. d 60. d

Answer questions 61-65 in reference to the three macroevolutionary processes listed below:

a. genetic persistence
b. genetic divergence
c. genetic disconnect

M **61.** includes the concept of background extinction

E **62.** postulates the continuity of life from molecular origins to present time

M **63.** brought about by adaptive radiations

M **64.** mass extinctions

M **65.** incorporates the idea of branchings

Answers 61. c 62. a 63. b
64. c 65. b

Selecting the Exception

M **66.** Four of the five answers listed below are used in describing a species. Select the exception.
a. interbreeding
b. sexual reproduction
c. natural
d. populations
* e. appearance

D **67.** Three of the four answers listed below promote evolution. Select the exception.
a. genetic drift
b. mutation
* c. gene flow
d. natural selection

E 68. Four of the five answers listed below are types of prezygotic isolating mechanisms. Select the exception.
   a. temporal
 * b. hybrid inviability
   c. mechanical
   d. ecological
   e. gametic

M 69. Four of the five answers listed below are portions of the theory of natural selection. Select the exception.
   a. Variation is heritable.
   b. Heritable traits vary in adaptability.
   c. More organisms are produced than can survive.
 * d. The largest and strongest always contribute more genes to the next generation.
   e. Natural selection is the result of differential reproduction.

M 70. Four of the five answers listed below are types of speciation. Select the exception.
 * a. postzygotic
   b. allopatric
   d. parapatric
   e. punctuation
   c. sympatric

E 71. Four of the five answers listed below can function to isolate populations. Select the exception.
   a. geography
   b. behavior
   c. time
   d. gametes
 * e. external fertilization

CHAPTER 19
THE MACROEVOLUTIONARY PUZZLE

Multiple-Choice Questions

M   **1.** The idea that fossils were the remnants of ancient forms of life was developed because
     a. fossils were found throughout the world.
     b. unique fossils are found in specific layers of stratified rocks.
     c. fossils resembled living organisms.
     d. fossils could be used to study past geologic events.
*   e. all of these

E   **2.** Which of the following evolve?
*   a. populations
     b. genera
     c. kingdoms
     d. both populations and genera
     e. populations, genera, and kingdoms

M   **3.** Macroevolution refers to changes in all but which one of the following?
     a. phyla
     b. classes
*   c. species
     d. genera
     e. divisions

M   **4.** Macroevolution involves all but which one of the following?
     a. the development of higher taxa
     b. periods of massive extinction at the end of geologic periods
     c. the concept of punctuated equilibrium
*   d. gradual differentiation that leads to speciation

M   **5.** Because organisms evolve from existing species by changes,
*   a. there must be some common thread of relation among all living things.
     b. evolution must be a gradual process.
     c. macroevolution is not likely to occur.
     d. the rates of evolution must be uniform.
     e. the environment controls which changes will be made.

FOSSILS—EVIDENCE OF ANCIENT LIFE

E   **6.** The fossil record is incomplete because
     a. very few organisms were preserved as fossils.
     b. organisms tend to decay before becoming a fossil.
     c. animals with hard parts are preserved more easily.
     d. geologic processes may destroy fossils.
*   e. all of these

E   **7.** Fossils would include
     a. skeletons.
     b. shells.
     c. seeds.
     d. tracks.
*   e. all of these

M   **8.** Which of the following organisms would you expect to find preserved as a fossil?
     a. a jellyfish
*   b. a shelled arthropod such as a trilobite
     c. an earthworm
     d. a nematode
     e. a protistan such as an amoeba.

M   **9.** Which of the following statements is true?
     a. Many fossils have not been discovered, whereas others may have been destroyed.
     b. Some types of organisms are more likely to be preserved than others.
     c. Some environments are more conducive to preserving.
     d. Many fossils have not been discovered, whereas others may have been destroyed; and Some types of organisms are more likely to be preserved than others.
*   e. Many fossils have not been discovered, whereas others may have been destroyed; Some types of organisms are more likely to be preserved than others; and Some environments are more conducive to preserving..

M   **10.** Which of the following habitats is most likely to be rich in fossils?
     a. eroding hillsides
     b. deserts
     c. polar ice caps
*   d. bed of former shallow sea
     e. rocky plateau

E   **11.** The geologic time scale is subdivided on the basis of
     a. the appearance of different radioactive isotopes in different strata.
     b. levels of background extinction.
*   c. periods of mass extinction.
     d. the appearance of different radioactive isotopes in different strata, and levels of background extinction.
     e. the appearance of different radioactive isotopes in different strata, levels of background extinction, and periods of mass extinction.

EVIDENCE FROM BIOGEOGRAPHY

E   12. The large, ancient land mass that contained all the continents was called
    a. Laurasia.
  * b. Pangea.
    c. Gondwana.
    d. Atlantis.
    e. all of these

M   13. Plate tectonic theory is based on
    a. a thermal convection model, in which cool material in the earth's mantle rises and spreads laterally beneath the crustal plates.
    b. the idea that the earth's crust is fragmented into rigid crusts that are sinking slowly beneath crustal plates.
    c. the idea that coacervate formation causes continents to drift apart slowly on their crustal plates.
  * d. observations that the sea floor is slowly spreading away from oceanic ridges due to thermal convection in the mantle.

E   14. The idea that geologic processes have formed the Earth's surface by repeating the same actions over and over is known as
    a. theory of catastrophism.
    b. plate tectonics.
    c. continental drift.
  * d. theory of uniformity.
    e. theory of relativity.

M   15. Diversity of living organisms would be increased by
    a. continental drift.
    b. formation of Pangea.
    c. sea-floor spreading.
    d. movement of Gondwana.
  * e. all but "formation of Pangea."

EVIDENCE FROM COMPARATIVE MORPHOLOGY

M   16. Which of the phrases below completes the stem of the following statement incorrectly? The use of comparative morphology as a demonstration of evolution
    a. assumes that the forms being compared had a common ancestor.
    b. is based upon the premise that an organism's body form is a product of evolution.
    c. can compare embryonic as well as adult structures.
  * d. can compare embryonic structures with adult structures to show relationships.
    e. provides that certain developmental constraints during evolution limit the range of forms possible as adults.

M   17. The convergence in external morphology of sharks, penguins, and porpoises is attributed to
    a. reduced genetic variability in these groups.
  * b. selection pressures that are common to these groups.
    c. reproductive isolation of these groups.
    d. identical genes in all three groups.
    e. use and disuse of the limbs.

M   18. Which of the following serve as examples of morphological convergence?
  * a. sharks, penguins and porpoises
    b. panthers and tigers
    c. apes and monkeys
    d. sharks, skates, and rays
    e. mice, rats, and gerbils

M   19. Phylogenetic relationships, when determined solely by the study of comparative morphology, may be incorrect due to
    a. morphological divergence.
  * b. morphological convergence.
    c. adaptive radiation.
    d. extinction.
    e. homology

D   20. The wings of a bird and the wings of a butterfly are _____ and show morphological _____.
    a. homologous; convergence
  * b. analogous; convergence
    c. homologous; divergence
    d. analogous; divergence

D   21. Which of the following would be considered more primitive based upon the structure of their limbs?
    a. bats
  * b. early reptiles
    c. porpoises
    d. penguins
    e. birds

M   22. The bones in the forelimbs of a mammal
  * a. can often be traced to a common ancestor.
    b. offer no evidence to support the theory of evolution.
    c. perform the same function no matter which species they are in.
    d. may exhibit either analogy or homology but not both when compared to the forelimb of another animal.
    e. show convergence with some invertebrate structures.

D   23. Which of the following structures are analogous but not homologous to each other?
  * a. wing of a bird and the wing of a butterfly
    b. wing of a bird and the wing of a bat
    c. the dew claw of a dog and the little toe of a human
    d. the flipper of an aquatic animal and the arm of a human

M   24.   Sharks, penguins, and porpoises together exhibit
           a. morphological divergence.
           b. parallel evolution.
      *   c. morphological convergence.
           d. regression.
           e. coevolution.

EVIDENCE FROM PATTERNS OF DEVELOPMENT

M   25.   The study of comparative embryology has revealed the
           conservative nature of the genes responsible for
           a. food procurement.
           b. reproductive behavior.
      *   c. embryonic development.
           d. size.
           e. intelligence

D   26.   The fact that many vertebrate embryos are more
           similar to one another than their respective adult stages
           are to one another may ultimately be due to
           a. environment.
           b. hormones.
           c. microevolution.
      *   d. genes.
           e. speciation.

M   27.   The variation in the forms of adult vertebrates
           probably arose through mutations in _____
           genes.
           a. dominant
      *   b. regulatory
           c. oncogenic
           d. promoter
           e. operator

EVIDENCE FROM COMPARATIVE BIOCHEMISTRY

E   28.   Which mutations are NOT subject to natural selection?
           a. lethal
           b. physiological
      *   c. neutral
           d. morphological
           e. beneficial

M   29.   Neutral mutations
      *   a. are not subjected to selection.
           b. occur at different rates at different times during
              evolution.
           c. confer a disadvantage.
           d. do not occur; either a gene enhances survival or it
              does not.
           e. account for the difference between hemoglobin in
              normal blood and that found in sickle-cell anemia.

D   30.   Neutral mutations
           a. code for different proteins.
      *   b. allow the time of divergence between different
              forms to be pinpointed.
           c. can be used to accurately establish the relationship
              between widely differing animals.
           d. are responsible for the variation in the various
              hemoglobin molecules found in mammals.
           e. cannot give us any indication of the rates and
              degrees of evolutionary change.

M   31.   The concept of a molecular clock is based on the idea
           that
      *   a. neutral mutations occur at regular rates.
           b. genetic relatedness can be determined by timing
              antibody-antigen reactions.
           c. radioactive isotopes decay at a constant rate.
           d. speciation is a rapid event.
           e. cytochrome c is very similar in primates.

M   32.   Which of the following is NOT a useful indicator of
           phylogenetic relatedness?
           a. base sequences in DNA
           b. amino acid sequences in a protein
      *   c. similar ecological requirements
           d. similar embryonic development
           e. morphological divergence

D   33.   Comparisons of protein similarity between species can
           reveal the degree of genetic kinship because
           a. the number of protein variations is limited.
      *   b. specific amino acids are dictated by known
              nucleotide sequences.
           c. gel electrophoresis converts proteins to
              nucleotides.
           d. protein can be hybridized with DNA.
           e. DNA is made by directions stored in proteins.

D   34.   Which of the following statements about proteins is
           true?
           a. Neutral mutations may produce changes in the
              primary structure of proteins without affecting
              their function.
           b. It is possible to distinguish among proteins by
              subjecting them to electrophoresis.
           c. Humans, chimpanzees, and Rhesus monkeys have
              all been placed in the order Primates based upon
              the similarity in cytochrome c.
           d. The more closely related two forms are, the
              greater similarity there is in cytochrome c.
      *   e. all of these

D   35.   DNA-DNA hybridization studies
           a. depend upon determining the exact sequence of
              nucleotides in a gene.
           b. can be done using a simple tissue homogenizer
              and computer-assisted analysis.
           c. involve generating new nucleotide sequences by
              using ultracentrifugation.
      *   d. measure the amount of heat necessary to separate
              two single strands of DNA that have been allowed
              to fuse together.
           e. give little clue as to how genes mutate.

M 36. The most conclusive evidence used in establishing the relationship of closely related species is
    a. fossil remains.
    b. taxonomy.
*   c. DNA-DNA hybridization.
    d. homologous structures.
    e. analogous structures.

HOW DO WE INTERPRET THE EVIDENCE?

M 37. The units of evolution are called
    a. cladistics.
    b. families.
    c. phyla.
*   d. taxa.
    e. orders

E 38. The higher taxa are groupings of
    a. orders
    b. classes.
    c. families.
    d. phyla.
*   e. all of these

E 39. The organizing units of classification schemes are
    a. binominal systems.
*   b. higher taxa.
    c. taxonomies.
    d. systematics.
    e. links of the Chain of Being.

M 40. According to Linnaeus,
    a. every different kind of organism has its own species name.
    b. species are fixed, unchanging entities.
    c. organisms are locked into a specific rank in the Chain of Being.
    d. rigid categories should be used in the classification of organisms.
*   e. all of these

E 41. When the binomial system of nomenclature was first developed, different organisms were compared to
    a. pieces in a jigsaw puzzle.
    b. parts of bridges connecting different phyla.
    c. rungs in the ladder of life.
*   d. links in the Chain of Being.
    e. none of these

E 42. Linnaeus may have used all but which of the following to assign names and categories to organisms?
    a. anatomy
    b. behavior
*   c. nucelic acid hybridization
    d. physiology
    e. ecology

M 43. Which of the following groups represents the most closely related organisms?
    a. kingdoms
*   b. species
    c. orders
    d. genera
    e. taxa

M 44. Organisms "X" and "Y" are suspected to be the same species. Which of the following will provide the ultimate proof?
*   a. interbreeding
    b. anatomy
    c. physiology
    d. ecology
    e. behavior

E 45. Scientific names of organisms are written in
    a. French.
    b. English.
*   c. Latin.
    d. German.
    e. Swedish.

E 46. Which of the following is written correctly?
    a. *Felis* domestica
    b. Felis Domestica
    c. *felis domestica*
*   d. *Felis domestica*
    e. *felis Domestica*

M 47. Which of the following is NOT correct?
*   a. The specific name can be used alone.
    b. The generic name can be used alone.
    c. The specific name must be preceded by a generic name.
    d. A family includes related genera.
    e. The kingdom is the most inclusive category.

E 48. "House fly" is the _____ applied to a small, pestiferous insect that is often an uninvited guest at dinner.
    a. scientific name
    b. genus and species
    c. universal name
*   d. English common name
    e. Latin name

E 49. Which of the following includes all the others?
    a. family
*   b. phylum
    c. species
    d. class
    e. order

E 50. Which of the following includes all related genera?
*   a. family
    b. phylum
    c. species
    d. class
    e. order

M 51. Which of the following is the least inclusive category?
    a. family
    b. order
*   c. species
    d. kingdom
    e. genus

M 52. The only taxonomic category in which microevolution can occur is the
   a. genus.
 * b. species.
   c. kingdom.
   d. family.
   e. class.

D 53. The fact that cats and humans are both classified as mammals provides us with which minimum of information?
   a. Humans evolved from cats.
   b. Cats have descended from other cats.
 * c. Both have mammary glands.
   d. The ancestor of humans was a catlike creature.
   e. Cats and humans are unrelated.

M 54. Phylogeny refers to what aspects of individuals?
   a. morphological traits
 * b. evolutionary relationships
   c. physiological characteristics
   d. behavioral features
   e. all of these

E 55. The branch of biology called systematics deals with
   a. taxonomy.
   b. classification.
   c. evolution.
   d. phylogeny.
 * e. all of these

M 56. Systematics assesses diversity through
   a. phylogenetic reconstruction.
   b. taxonomy.
   c. classification.
   d. phylogenetic reconstruction and taxonomy.
 * e. phylogenetic reconstruction, taxonomy, and classification.

D 57. Phylogenetic reconstruction
   a. is based upon homologous structures.
   b. requires an outgroup for comparison with the ingroup.
   c. mimics the scale of nature.
   d. identifies relative relationships.
 * e. all but "mimics the scale of nature" are correct

D 58. Variations in phylogeny based on fossil records are probably most often due to
   a. imperfections in the fossils themselves.
 * b. differences of interpretation by scientists.
   c. inconsistencies in rock strata.
   d. inaccuracies in radioisotope dating.

D 59. The cladistics approach to discovering phylogeny
   a. assesses the significance of homologous structures.
   b. is concerned about common ancestry.
   c. portrays relative relationships among organisms.
 * d. assesses the significance of homologous structures and portrays relative relationships among organisms.
   e. assesses the significance of homologous structures, is concerned about common ancestry, and portrays relative relationships among organisms

D 60. In a cladogram,
 * a. the axis can be considered to be a time line.
   b. features found in only one of the ingroups are very useful in establishing relationships.
   c. the higher the position of a group on the cladogram, the more distant is the most recent common ancestor.
   d. the lower in a cladogram a group is, the more derived features they have in common.
   e. all of these

D 61. Technically speaking, a cladogram conveys
 * a. portrayals of relative relationships.
   b. lines of descendants.
   c. a tree of ancestors.
   d. a classification scheme.
   e. all of these

D 62. Fungi were removed from the Kingdom Plantae in Whittaker's system because
   a. they grow underground.
   b. of unicellularity.
   c. they are prokaryotes.
 * d. they are heterotrophs.
   e. they are multicellular.

M 63. In Whittaker's scheme all prokaryotes belonged to the kingdom
 * a. Monera.
   b. Protista.
   c. Fungi.
   d. Monera and Protista
   e. Protista and Fungi

D 64. The only kingdom NOT characterized by heterotrophy is
   a. Monera.
   b. Protista.
   c. Animalia.
   d. Fungi.
 * e. Plantae.

M 65. Which kingdom includes single-celled organisms with a true nucleus?
   a. Monera.
 * b. Protista.
   c. Animalia.
   d. Fungi.
   e. Plantae.

M   66.   Which kingdom is exclusively heterotrophic including
            many predators and parasites?
            a. Monera.
            b. Protista.
        *   c. Animalia.
            d. Fungi.
            e. Plantae.

E   67.   The creation of a new kingdom for the archaebacteria
            resulted from studies of
            a. phylogeny.
        *   b. DNA.
            c. nutritional modes.
            d. habitat.
            e. mutations.

ON INTERPRETING AND MISINTERPRETING THE PAST

E   68.   *Archaeopteryx* was a transitional form between
            a. birds and mammals.
            b. reptiles and mammals.
        *   c. birds and reptiles.
            d. fish and amphibians.
            e. amphibians and reptiles.

M   69.   *Archaeopteryx*
            a. is an example of a "missing link."
            b. had no teeth.
            c. had feathers.
            d. had a long bony tail.
        *   e. is an example of a "missing link, had feathers, and
                had a long bony tail.

M   70.   The concept of natural selection is still considered a
            theory because
            a. it is only one man's idea.
            b. creationism is now co-equal with it.
        *   c. it is still subject to revision.
            d. there is so little proof for it.
            e. all of these

Matching Questions

D   71.   Matching. Choose the most appropriate letter for each
            blank.
            1. ___ analogy
            2. ___ binominal system
            3. ___ cladogram
            4. ___ DNA-DNA hybridization
            5. ___ fossil
            6. ___ Fungi
            7. ___ molecular clock
            8. ___ Monera
            9. ___ morphological divergence
            10. ___ phylogeny
            11. ___ Plantae
            12. ___ systematics

            A. schemes that reflect evolutionary
                relationships among species
            B. branching diagram representing patterns of
                relationships of whole organisms
            C. body structures similar in function but of
                distant lineage
            D. multicelled eukaryotes; nearly all
                photoautotrophs
            E. recognizable evidence of the past
            F. bacteria; prokaryotic
            G. heterotrophs with extracellular digestion
                and absorption
            H. branch of biology dealing with the patterns
                of diversity in an evolutionary context
            I. two-part Latin name
            J. most exact method of determining
                evolutionary relationship
            K. modification of body structures from a
                common ancestor
            L. use of accumulated neutral mutations to
                determine past evolutionary events

Answers: 1. C   2. I   3. B   4. J

               5. E   6. G   7. L   8. F

               9. K   10. A   11. D   12. H

Classification Questions

Answer questions 72-76 in reference to the five taxonomic categories listed below:

a. genus
b. species
c. order
d. family
e. phylum

E **72.** This category is not included in any of the other listed categories.

E **73.** This category is included in each of the other categories.

M **74.** The term Hominidae is an example of this.

M **75.** This category denotes the taxonomic category of *Homo* (humans).

D **76.** This category is a subdivision of the class taxon.

Answers   72. e   73. b   74. d

75. a   76. c

Selecting the Exception

D **77.** Four of the five answers listed below are habitats favoring fossil preservation. Select the exception.
* a. deserts
  b. swamp
  c. tar pits
  d. seafloor
  e. caves

E **78.** Four of the five answers below are taxonomic categories. Select the exception.
  a. species
  b. class
* c. taxon
  d. order
  e. phylum

E **79.** Four of the five answers below are related to investigations into evolutionary evidence from comparative biochemistry. Select the exception.
  a. neutral mutations
* b. homologous structures
  c. molecular clock
  d. protein comparisons
  e. DNA-DNA hybridizations

M **80.** Four of the five answers below are related in a similar way. Select the exception.
  a. Fungi
  b. Protista
  c. Plantae
* d. Bacteriacea
  e. Animalia

D **81.** Three of the four answers below are related. Select the exception.
* a. chemoautotrophic
  b. heterotrophic
  c. parasitic
  d. predatory

D **82.** Four of the five answers below are members of the same group. Select the exception.
  a. tulips
  b. mosses
  c. conifers
  d. ferns
* e. amoebas

E **83.** Four of the five answers below are members of the same group. Select the exception.
  a. arthropods.
* b. protozoans.
  c. sponges.
  d. flatworms.
  e. annelids.

CHAPTER 20
THE ORIGIN AND EVOLUTION OF LIFE

Multiple-Choice Questions

M 1. According to astronomers, the universe is
   a. contracting.
   b. getting warmer.
   c. the same as it was on the day of creation.
   d. getting smaller.
 * e. expanding.

E 2. The "big bang" refers to
 * a. an event marking the beginning of the universe.
   b. the appearance of life on earth.
   c. the impending end of the universe.
   d. an event marking the beginning of the universe and the appearance of life on earth.

CONDITIONS ON THE EARLY EARTH

E 3. Fossil evidence of the earliest living organisms now dates back
   a. 570 million years.
   b. 1.4 billion years.
 * c. about 3.8 billion years.
   d. more than 5 billion years.
   e. to 4004 B.C.

M 4. Life on earth began how many years ago?
   a. 6,000
   b. 350,000
   c. 35,000,000
   d. 350,000,000
 * e. 3,800,000,000

E 5. The solar system is approximately how many years old?
   a. 10–12 billion
 * b. 4.6–5 billion
   c. 750 million
   d. 400 million
   e. 200 million

E 6. The primitive atmosphere did NOT contain
   a. water vapor.
   b. free nitrogen.
   c. free hydrogen.
 * d. free oxygen.
   e. inert gases.

E 7. Many of the organic compounds essential for life, such as amino acids and nucleotides, could NOT assemble spontaneously in the presence of
   a. hydrogen.
 * b. free oxygen.
   c. carbon dioxide.
   d. nitrogen.
   e. argon.

M 8. The earth is able to maintain water in a liquid state on the surface by virtue of
   a. insufficient life to use up the available water.
   b. the distance of the earth from the sun.
   c. the availability of oxygen in the atmosphere.
   d. the size of the earth.
 * e. the distance of the earth from the sun and the size of the earth.

M 9. The early atmosphere of the earth
 * a. originated when gases from beneath the slowly solidifying crust were vented by vulcanism.
   b. did not exist before 1 billion years ago.
   c. probably consisted of hydrogen, methane, nitrogen, ammonia, and hydrogen sulfide, but no water vapor.
   d. all of these

E 10. Organic compounds break down spontaneously in the presence of _____; hence, life probably never would have emerged if the ancient atmosphere had been the same as the present one.
   a. carbon dioxide
   b. hydrogen
 * c. oxygen
   d. nitrogen
   e. silica

E 11. Experiments like those first performed by Stanley Miller in 1953 demonstrated that
   a. DNA forms readily and reproduces itself.
 * b. many of the lipids, carbohydrates, proteins, and nucleotides required for life can form under abiotic conditions.
   c. complete, functioning prokaryotic cells are formed after approximately three months.
   d. a lipid-protein film will eventually be formed by thermal convection.
   e. all of these

E 12. Which of the following was NOT included in Miller's reaction chamber, which contained substances intended to duplicate the atmosphere of ancient earth?
 * a. carbon dioxide
   b. methane
   c. ammonia
   d. water vapor
   e. methane and ammonia

E 13. Who demonstrated the possibility of producing organic compounds from gases and water if the mixture is bombarded with a continuous spark discharge?
 * a. Miller
   b. Starr
   c. Thompsen
   d. Pauling
   e. Platt

E   14. In several experiments in which energy is supplied to a sealed chamber containing a mixture of gases simulating the primitive earth's atmosphere, what will be formed?
        a. amino acids
        b. sugars
        c. nucleotides
        d. lipids
    *   e. all of these

E   15. The Miller experiment designed to study the early synthesis of organic compounds did NOT include which of the following molecules?
        a. methane
        b. ammonia
        c. water
    *   d. oxygen

M   16. The primitive template that was thought to be used for protein synthesis was
        a. stratified mica crystals.
    *   b. clay compounds.
        c. the bottoms of tidal pools.
        d. dried-out mud flats.
        e. pockets in lava beds.

M   17. Clay compounds were thought to be original sites for the formation of
        a. amino acids.
        b. sugars.
        c. polysaccharides.
    *   d. protein chains.
        e. lipid molecules.

M   18. The formation of polypeptide chains under abiotic conditions was important because they served as
        a. a supply of structural units.
        b. enzymes to catalyze reactions.
        c. subunits in the formation of DNA.
        d. subunits in the formation of RNA.
    *   e. a supply of structural units and enzymes to catalyze reactions.

E   19. The first templates for protein synthesis were
        a. complex carbohydrates.
        b. mineral crystals.
    *   c. layers of clay.
        d. sheets of layered minerals such as mica.
        e. multiple oil liposomes or micelles.

EMERGENCE OF THE FIRST LIVING CELLS

M   20. The most likely molecules to serve as a replacement for clay as a template for protein synthesis are
        a. coenzymes.
    *   b. RNA.
        c. DNA.
        d. other proteins.
        e. complex carbohydrates.

D   21. Which of the following statements is false?
        a. The reactions leading to the first self-replicating systems could not have been completely random.
    *   b. DNA must have been a central part of the first self-replicating system.
        c. Amino acids come in two mirror-image forms, right-handed and left-handed.
        d. The amino acids found on meteorites contain disorganized arrays of left-handed and right-handed forms.
        e. Clay crystals attract only left-handed amino acids out of a mixture of both mirror images.

D   22. What step occurred first in the evolution of life?
        a. formation of lipid spheres
        b. formation of protein-RNA systems
        c. formation of membrane-bound protocells
    *   d. spontaneous formation of lipids, proteins, carbohydrates, and nucleotides under abiotic conditions
        e. formation of ATP

D   23. Which step in the evolution of life is the most complex and occurred last?
        a. formation of lipid spheres
        b. formation of protein-RNA systems
    *   c. formation of membrane-bound protocells
        d. spontaneous formation of lipids, proteins, carbohydrates, and nucleotides under abiotic conditions
        e. formation of ATP

M   24. Sidney Fox found that if heated protein chains were allowed to cool in water, they would
        a. form nitrogen, which would escape as a gas.
        b. form proteinoids.
    *   c. form small, stable spheres or microspheres.
        d. clot and form a complex latticework frame for chemical reactions.
        e. break down into the original amino acids from which the protein chain was made.

D   25. Contemporary hypotheses concerned with the origin of life focus on what two characteristics of living systems?
        a. energy conversion and development of a nucleus
        b. self-replication and utilization of oxygen
    *   c. plasma membranes and self-replication
        d. growth and transcription

ORIGIN OF PROKARYOTIC AND EUKARYOTIC CELLS

E   26. The first organisms
        a. had to be autotrophic.
        b. were parasitic.
    *   c. were heterotrophic.
        d. were aerobes.
        e. all of these

M 27. The first organisms
   a. absorbed their food supplies from the organic molecules that surrounded them.
   b. were eukaryotes.
   c. utilized fermentation for energy production.
   d. utilized ATP.
   * e. all of these except "were eukaryotes."

M 28. The earliest organisms were probably unicellular
   a. autotrophs.
   b. aerobes.
   * c. heterotrophs.
   d. eukaryotes.

M 29. The first organisms were most probably
   a. autotrophic.
   b. multicellular.
   c. protozoans.
   * d. prokaryotic.

D 30. During the Archean era, divergence of the prokaryotes led to all but which of the following?
   a. archaebacteria
   b. eukaryotes
   * c. multicelled organisms
   d. eubacteria
   e. additional prokaryotes

M 31. The early atmosphere
   a. was essentially the same as occurs now.
   * b. was changed drastically by the liberation of oxygen following the evolution of photosynthesis.
   c. was characterized by high concentrations of oxygen and ozone.
   d. was characterized by high concentrations of inert gases before the evolution of living organisms.

M 32. The presence of free oxygen in the atmosphere
   a. was a result of the accumulation of the by-products of photosynthesis.
   b. prevented the further spontaneous generation of life.
   c. provided the opportunity to extract more energy through aerobic respiration.
   d. did not occur immediately after the earth was formed.
   * e. all of these

M 33. When free oxygen (O_2) became available in the atmosphere,
   a. some organisms changed their metabolism.
   b. oxygen was used as a dumping place for hydrogen ions and electrons.
   c. some cells and forms of life became extinct.
   d. aerobic respiration emerged.
   * e. all of these

E 34. Currently it is thought that living organisms first appeared on the earth _____ billion years ago and that multicellular forms appeared _____ billion years ago.
   a. 4.6, 3.5
   b. 3.5, 3.5
   * c. 3.8, 0.9
   d. 2.6, 0.7
   e. 3.5, 0.1

WHERE DID ORGANELLES COME FROM?

D 35. Mitochondrial DNA
   a. is replicated independently from nuclear DNA.
   b. transcribes some RNA and protein used by the mitochondrion.
   c. has some codons that have a different meaning from those of nuclear DNA.
   d. may have been the genetic instructions for an organism that lived symbiotically within a predatory form.
   * e. all of these

D 36. Chloroplasts
   * a. resemble photosynthetic bacteria.
   b. utilize the same pigments regardless of what organism they inhabit.
   c. apparently evolved mitochondria.
   d. utilize DNA derived from the nucleus.
   e. all of these

D 37. Which of the following is the strongest evidence for the hypothesis that present-day eukaryotic aerobes are the descendants of the successful symbiotic association of anaerobes and mitochondria?
   a. Mitochondria can produce ATP.
   b. A mitochondrion can survive indefinitely when removed from a eukaryotic cell.
   * c. A mitochondrion has its own set of DNA molecules.
   d. Fossilized mitochondria are older than the oldest fossilized eukaryotes.

D 38. Mitochondrial DNA
   * a. contains a few codons that specify amino acids other than those specified by codons of nuclear DNA.
   b. uses the same assortment of codons as does the DNA in the nucleus.
   c. can never replicate itself because DNA polymerases are not present in mitochondria.
   d. can never be transcribed or translated because RNA polymerases are not in mitochondria.
   e. can never replicate itself because there are no promoter sequences to initiate transcription.

D 39. The mitochondrion
    a. has its own DNA.
    b. transcribes its own DNA.
    c. has DNA that functions independently of nuclear DNA.
    d. has DNA that is somewhat different from nuclear DNA.
  * e. all of these

M 40. Lynn Margulis and other biologists believe that
    a. the mitochondrial DNA code was a parallel but more ancient code than nuclear DNA.
    b. mitochondria were at one time separate, free-living organisms similar to bacteria, rather than organelles.
    c. mitochondria were obligate symbionts, with both the mitochondrion and the cell it inhabited benefiting from the relationship.
  * d. all of these
    e. none of these

LIFE IN THE PALEOZOIC ERA

M 41. What mud-crawling, mud-burrowing crustaceans eventually had 600 genera living during the Cambrian Period?
    a. jawless fishes
    b. cephalopods
    c. brachiopods
  * d. trilobites
    e. isopods

E 42. Which Paleozoic geologic period is the most recent?
    a. Carboniferous
  * b. Permian
    c. Cambrian
    d. Devonian
    e. Ordovician

E 43. Which Paleozoic geologic period is the most ancient?
    a. Carboniferous
    b. Permian
  * c. Cambrian
    d. Devonian
    e. Ordovician

D 44. Which characterizes the earth during the Cambrian period?
  * a. trilobites abundant, extensive shallow seas at tropical latitudes
    b. active predators, land masses at the poles
    c. adaptive radiation of fishes, land masses at the poles
    d. first eukaryotes, Pangea land mass

M 45. What was the most abundant and conspicuous animal during the Cambrian?
    a. primates
  * b. trilobites
    c. fish
    d. cephalopods
    e. sea scorpions

M 46. Insects became abundant during which period?
  * a. Carboniferous
    b. Devonian
    c. Silurian
    d. Ordovician
    e. Cambrian

E 47. Fossil fuels were formed in which period?
  * a. Carboniferous
    b. Devonian
    c. Silurian
    d. Ordovician
    e. Cambrian

D 48. The great burst of diversification in metazoan families, especially those with marine representatives, occurred during which geologic period?
    a. Silurian
    b. Devonian
  * c. Ordovician
    d. Carboniferous

M 49. The first fishes appeared during which period?
    a. Carboniferous
    b. Devonian
    c. Silurian
  * d. Ordovician
    e. Cambrian

M 50. Much of the fossil fuel used by humans today represents the organic remains of organisms that lived during which geologic era?
  * a. Carboniferous
    b. Devonian
    c. Silurian
    d. Permian

M 51. The origin of reptiles occurred during which period?
  * a. Carboniferous
    b. Devonian
    c. Silurian
    d. Ordovician
    e. Cambrian

D 52. Spore-bearing plants became dominant during which period?
  * a. Carboniferous
    b. Devonian
    c. Silurian
    d. Ordovician
    e. Cambrian

M 53. The largest extinction the world has ever known occurred at the end of which period?
    a. Cretaceous
  * b. Permian
    c. Triassic
    d. Jurassic
    e. Tertiary

LIFE IN THE MESOZOIC ERA

D **54.** Which of the following events did not take place during the Mesozoic?
    a. an asteroid impact and the extinction of the dinosaurs
    b. origination of mammals and gymnosperms as the dominant plants
    c. breakup of Pangea and evolution of angiosperms
  * d. first land vertebrates, the amphibians, arise; adaptive radiation of the fishes
    e. the Age of the Dinosaurs

D **55.** Which of the following plants are the most complex and evolved last?
    a. conifers
    b. cycads
  * c. angiosperms
    d. ginkgos
    e. gymnosperms

E **56.** During which geologic era did Pangea break up?
    a. Archean
    b. Paleozoic
    c. Cenozoic
    d. Proterozoic
  * e. Mesozoic

M **57.** Mammals originated during which period?
    a. Cretaceous
    b. Permian
  * c. Triassic
    d. Jurassic
    e. Tertiary

M **58.** The flowering plants appeared during which period?
  * a. Cretaceous
    b. Permian
    c. Triassic
    d. Jurassic
    e. Tertiary

FOCUS ON SCIENCE: HORRENDOUS END TO DOMINANCE

M **59.** The last mass extinction of dinosaurs on Earth occurred between which two geologic periods?
    a. Devonian and Carboniferous
    b. Silurian and Devonian
    c. Triassic and Permian
  * d. Cretaceous and Tertiary

E **60.** The dinosaurs disappeared at the end of which period?
  * a. Cretaceous
    b. Permian
    c. Triassic
    d. Jurassic
    e. Tertiary

M **61.** The disappearance of dinosaurs is correlated with the transition between which two periods?
    a. Devonian, Carboniferous
    b. Silurian, Devonian
    c. Carboniferous, Permian
  * d. Cretaceous, Tertiary

LIFE IN THE CENOZOIC ERA

E **62.** Which epoch is the most recent?
    a. Eocene
  * b. Pleistocene
    c. Paleocene
    d. Miocene
    e. Pliocene

E **63.** Which geologic era is the most recent?
  * a. Cenozoic
    b. Mesozoic
    c. Proterozoic
    d. Archean
    e. Paleozoic

M **64.** When compared to many higher plant lineages, the duration of the average mammalian lineage is
    a. longer.
  * b. shorter.
    c. of equal length.
    d. too varied to draw any generalizations.

E **65.** The extensive adaptive radiation of the mammals occurred during which geologic era?
    a. Paleozoic
    b. Cretaceous
  * c. Cenozoic
    d. Mesozoic

E **66.** The geologic time scale is subdivided on the basis of
    a. the appearance of different radioactive isotopes in different strata.
    b. levels of background extinction.
  * c. periods of mass extinction.
    d. the appearance of different radioactive isotopes in different strata and levels of background extinction.

E **67.** Geologic time is divided into major divisions known as
  * a. eras.
    b. epochs.
    c. periods.
    d. centuries.
    e. years.

E **68.** Which geologic era is the most ancient?
    a. Cenozoic
    b. Mesozoic
    c. Proterozoic
  * d. Archean
    e. Paleozoic

E   69.   Which geologic era is the most recent?
  *   a. Cenozoic
            b. Mesozoic
            c. Proterozoic
            d. Archean
            e. Paleozoic

Matching Questions

D   70.   Matching. Choose the most appropriate letter .
            1. ___ geologic time scale
            2. ___ Archean
            3. ___ Cenozoic
            4. ___ plate tectonic theory
            5. ___ Mesozoic
            6. ___ Paleozoic
            7. ___ Proterozoic

            A. Mammals, birds, and flowering plants evolved mostly during this era.
            B. an era that harbored the oldest definite fossils known
            C. movement of slabs of earth's crust
            D. an era that ended with the great Permian extinction about 240 million years ago
            E. an era during which free oxygen became abundant in Earth's atmosphere, and the first forms of life evolved into more complex, multicellular types 2.5 billion years ago until 570 million years ago
            F. an era that ended with the massive Cretaceous extinction that wiped out the dinosaurs
            G. time spans of the different eras

Answers: 1. G   2. B   3. A   4. C
              5. F   6. D   7. E

D   71.   Matching. Choose the most appropriate letter(s) for each. A letter may be used more than once, and a blank may contain more than one letter.
            1.   ___ Cambrian
            2.   ___ Carboniferous
            3.   ___ Cretaceous
            4.   ___ Devonian
            5.   ___ Gondwana
            6.   ___ Jurassic
            7.   ___ Ordovician
            8.   ___ Pangea
            9.   ___ Permian
            10. ___ Pliocene
            11. ___ Precambrian (Proterozoic)
            12. ___ Silurian

            A. an epoch of the Cenozoic era
            B. a period of the Mesozoic era
            C. a period of the Paleozoic era
            D. only prokaryotes and primitive eukaryotes existed
            E. a supercontinent that fragmented into Africa, South America, Australia, and Antarctica
            F. a supercontinent formed by all crustal plates colliding at the start of the Permian
            G. the golden age of the dinosaurs
            H. all but one invertebrate phylum had been formed by the end of this period; trilobites predominated
            I. great coastal swamp forests that eventually became coal lived during this period
            J. amphibians appeared during this time; Laurasia formed during this period
            K. the great extinctions of marine life due to shallow seas being drained by continental uplift took place
            L. grasslands formed and plant-eating mammals evolved
            M. jawless fishes originated; major radiations of corals, crinoids, brachiopods, mollusks, cephalopods, and swimming arthropods
            N. period closes with extinction of dinosaurs

Answers: 1. C, H   2. C, I   3. B, N   4. C, J
              5. E   6. B, G   7. C, M   8. F
              9. C, K   10. A, L   11. D   12. C

Classification Questions

81. e   82. d   83. a   84. b

85. a   86. b

Answer questions 72-76 in reference to the five geologic periods listed below:

    a. Cambrian
    b. Ordovician
    c. Silurian
    d. Devonian
    e. Carboniferous

M **72.** Vertebrates, represented by the jawless fishes, first arose during this period.

E **73.** Most of the invertebrate phyla are present in the fossil record as early as this period.

D **74.** The cephalopods underwent a major radiation during this period.

D **75.** The ancestors of modern conifers first arose during this period.

D **76.** The most primitive fossil reptiles are associated with this geologic period.

Answers 72. b   73. a   74. b

           75. d   76. e

Answer questions 77-86 in reference to the five geologic periods listed below:

    a. Permian
    b. Triassic
    c. Jurassic
    d. Cretaceous
    e. Tertiary

D **77.** Birds evolved from reptiles during this period.

M **78.** Mammals evolved from reptiles during this period.

M **79.** This period is referred to as the Age of Reptiles.

M **80.** The mass extinction of the dinosaurs occurred at the end of this period.

M **81.** The evolution of hominids occurred during this period.

D **82.** Flowering plants began their radiation during this period.

M **83.** During this period, all land masses began to combine into a single continent called Pangea.

M **84.** This geologic period falls at the beginning of the Mesozoic Era.

D **85.** Major extinctions of marine organisms occurred at the beginning of this period.

D **86.** The first flying vertebrate evolved during this period.

Answers 77. c   78. b   79. d   80. d

Selecting the Exception

D **87.** Four of the five answers listed below are related by a common era. Select the exception.
    a. Permian
    b. Ordovician
    c. Carboniferous
* d. Cretaceous
    e. Cambrian

D **88.** Four of the five answers listed below are related by a similar relationship. Select the exception.
    a. Mesozoic
* b. Tertiary
    c. Cenozoic
    d. Proterozoic
    e. Archean

D **89.** Four of the five answers listed below are related by a common period. Select the exception.
* a. Pleistocene
    b. Miocene
    c. Oligocene
    d. Pliocene
    e. Paleocene

D **90.** Four of the five answers listed below are periods of mass extinctions. Select the exception.
    a. Ordovician
* b. Silurian
    c. Cretaceous
    d. Permian
    e. Triassic

M **91.** Four of the five answers listed below are components of the mixture used in Miller's experiment. Select the exception.
    a. hydrogen
* b. oxygen
    c. methane
    d. ammonia
    e. water

E **92.** Four of the five answers listed below are related by a common feature. Select the exception.
    a. Tethys Sea
    b. Gondwana
* c. Africa
    d. Pangea
    e. Laurasia

CHAPTER 21
PROKARYOTES AND VIRUSES

Multiple-Choice Questions

M   1.   Which of the following are of the smallest size?
  *   a.   viruses
         b.   bacteria
         c.   fungi
         d.   protistans
         e.   plants

M   2.   The reproduction of microorganisms is self-limiting because
         a.   the accumulation of waste products can be toxic.
         b.   the supply of nutrients may run out.
         c.   other organisms may prey on them.
         d.   the accumulation of waste products can be toxic and the supply of nutrients may run out.
  *   e.   the accumulation of waste products can be toxic, the supply of nutrients may run out, and other organisms may prey on them.

E   3.   Which of the following could be called "pathogens"?
         a.   viruses
         b.   bacteria
         c.   protozoans
         d.   viruses and bacteria only, because they are alive
  *   e.   viruses, bacteria, and protozoans.

CHARACTERISTICS OF PROKARYOTIC CELLS

M   4.   Peptidoglycan is
         a.   found in the chromosomes of most bacteria.
  *   b.   composed of long polysaccharides crosslinked with short polypeptides.
         c.   composed of long polypeptides held together by disulfide bridges.
         d.   a unique combination of protein lipid and fat.

E   5.   All but which one of the following are characteristics of at least some of the bacteria?
         a.   photosynthesis
         b.   heterotrophy
         c.   chemosynthesis
  *   d.   multicellularity

E   6.   Which of the following can bacteria use as an energy source?
         a.   hydrogen sulfide
         b.   nitrites
         c.   sunlight
         d.   ammonia
  *   e.   all of these

M   7.   Which of the following statements is true of all autotrophic bacteria?
         a.   They produce molecular oxygen.
         b.   They synthesize sugar.
         c.   They are anaerobic.
  *   d.   They synthesize ATP.

E   8.   In bacteria, DNA is found
         a.   in the nucleus alone.
         b.   in organelles alone.
         c.   in both the nucleus and organelles.
  *   d.   attached to the cell wall as a single circular thread.
         e.   as particles scattered throughout the entire bacterial cell.

E   9.   Bacteria can obtain their nutrition by
         a.   photosynthesis.
         b.   chemosynthesis.
         c.   heterotrophy.
         d.   photosynthesis and chemosynthesis, only.
  *   e.   all of these

M   10. Bacteria
         a.   have cell walls composed of cellulose.
         b.   reproduce primarily by conjugation.
  *   c.   have a single chromosome.
         d.   are eukaryotic.
         e.   that stain Gram-negative have thick peptidoglycan cell walls.

M   11. Which of the following concerning bacteria is true?
         a.   They are diploid organisms.
         b.   They produce gametes.
  *   c.   They possess circular DNA molecules.
         d.   They are eukaryotic.

E   12. Spherical bacteria are called
         a.   bacilli.
         b.   spirilla.
  *   c.   cocci.
         d.   bacteriophages.
         e.   all of these

M   13. A helical or spiral bacterium is called a
  *   a.   spirillum.
         b.   bacillus.
         c.   coccus.
         d.   bacillus or coccus.

M   14. Which of the following statements is NOT characteristic of bacteria?
  *   a.   Some may be completely naked.
         b.   Some may have hairlike structures called pili.
         c.   Some may have rigid cell walls.
         d.   Some may have flagella and move about.
         e.   Some may have a polysaccharide covering.

M   15.   Gram-positive bacteria react to which of the following, whereas Gram-negative bacteria do not?
          a.   presence of oxygen
    *   b.   presence of a chemical stain
          c.   presence of light
          d.   absence of carbohydrates
          e.   presence of magnetic fields

D   16.   Which of the following distinguishes the bacterial flagellum from those of eukaryotes?
          a.   quantity per cell
          b.   general appearance
          c.   function
    *   d.   mechanism of movement
          e.   all of these

E   17.   Which of the following allow the bacteria to join together to transfer genes?
          a.   flagella
          b.   pores
          c.   connecting channels
    *   d.   pili
          e.   stylets

PROKARYOTIC GROWTH AND REPRODUCTION

D   18.   Which of the following statements is false?
          a   Pili enable bacteria to attach to another bacterium or to the surface membranes of their hosts.
          b.   Some plasmids confer resistance to various antibiotics.
          c.   Plasmids can act in a way that allows a bacterium to donate DNA during conjugation.
          d.   In bacterial photosynthesis, oxygen is not a by-product.
    *   e.   Plasmids permit bacteria to carry on autotrophic reactions such as chemosynthesis.

E   19.   All but which one of the following bacterial structures are external or peripherally located?
          a.   flagellum
          b.   pilus
    *   c.   plasmid
          d.   capsule
          e.   peptidoglycan

D   20.   In what way does prokaryotic fission resemble eukaryotic mitosis?
          a.   movement of chromosomes
    *   b.   genetically identical daughter cells
          c.   intracellular mechanisms
          d.   genetically identical daughter cells and intracellular mechanisms
          e.   movement of chromosomes, genetically identical daughter cells, and intracellular mechanisms

E   21.   Small circular molecules of DNA in bacteria are called
    *   a.   plasmids.
          b.   desmids.
          c.   pili.
          d.   F particles.
          e.   transferins.

D   22.   Plasmids
          a.   are self-reproducing circular molecules of DNA.
          b.   are sites for inserting genes for amplification.
          c.   may be transferred between different species of bacteria.
          d.   may confer the ability to donate genetic material when bacteria conjugate.
    *   e.   all of these

M   23.   The process by which one bacterial cell transfers DNA to another is
          a.   fission.
          b.   gametic fusion.
    *   c.   conjugation.
          d.   lysis.
          e.   none of these

M   24.   During conjugation between two *E. coli* cells, which of the following would most likely occur?
          a.   transfer of an antibiotic
          b.   transfer of a plasmid
          c.   transfer of viral genes
          d.   lysogeny
    *   e.   transfer of a plasmid and transfer of viral genes

PROKARYOTIC CLASSIFICATION

E   25.   One of the newest techniques used to identify bacteria is to determine their
          a.   diseases.
          b.   reproductive types.
          c.   metabolic processes.
    *   d.   nucleotide sequences.
          e.   metabolic by-products.

M   26.   Traditionally, bacteria have been grouped on the basis of all but which one of the following?
          a.   mode of nutrition
    *   b.   evolutionary relationships
          c.   response to staining techniques
          d.   energy source
          e.   pathogenicity or nonpathogenicity

ARCHAEBACTERIA

E   27.   Which is a swamp gas?
          a.   carbon monoxide
          b.   carbon dioxide
          c.   ammonia sulfide
    *   d.   methane
          e.   hydrogen sulfide

E   28.   The type of bacterium most likely to be found in a swamp is
          a.   thermophilic.
          b.   halophilic.
          c.   cyanobacteria.
    *   d.   methanogens.
          e.   *E. coli.*

M 29. Which type of bacterium is restricted to the waste piles of coal mines?
* a. thermophiles
b. halophiles
c. cyanobacteria
d. methanogens
e. *E. coli*

D 30. Which of the following makes archaebacteria different from other monerans?
* a. absence of peptidoglycan
b. two chromosomes
c. existence of organelles
d. aerobic

M 31. The methane-producing bacteria belong to
* a. archaebacteria.
b. prokaryotes.
c. eukaryotes.
d. urkaryotes.
e. eubacteria.

M 32. Which terms accurately describe the archaebacteria?
a. extinct, aerobic
b. extinct, anaerobic
c. present, aerobic
* d. present, anaerobic

M 33. The archaebacteria can be described by all but which one of the following?
a. anaerobic
b. chemosynthetic
* c. pathogenic
d. halophilic
e. heterotrophic

EUBACTERIA—THE TRUE BACTERIA

D 34. Which of the following bacteria are the least related to the others?
a. archaebacteria
b. extreme halophiles
* c. chemosynthetic eubacteria
d. extreme thermophiles
e. methanogens

D 35. Endospores are produced by
a. chrysophytes.
* b. monerans.
c. protozoans.
d. viruses.

M 36. When nutrients are scarce, some bacteria
a. engage in conjugation.
b. switch to photosynthesis.
* c. form endospores.
d. become pathogenic.
e. die.

M 37. Endospores
a. are the innermost of two daughter cells.
b. enable some bacteria to survive for a 1,000 years.
c. may contain concentrated poisons.
* d. all of these

E 38. The strongest poison known to humans is produced by
* a. *Clostridium botulinum.*
b. *Clostridium tetani.*
c. fer-de-lance snakes.
d. certain nettles in Java.
e. vines and is called curare.

D 39. Hospitals use autoclaves to kill endospores and resistant bacteria through
a. heat and chemicals.
b. chemicals and pressure.
* c. heat and pressure.
d. heat alone.
e. pressure alone.

M 40. The bacterium *E. coli*
a. is a normal inhabitant of the human intestinal tract.
b. produces conditions that prevent invasion by other bacteria.
c. enhances digestion, especially of fats.
d. produces vitamin K.
* e. all of these

D 41. Which of the following statements concerning the bacterium *E. coli* is NOT true?
a. It synthesizes vitamins that are essential to its mammalian host.
b. It can act as a pathogen.
c. It can prevent colonization of the gut by pathogens.
* d. It is capable of photosynthesis.

M 42. *E. coli*
a. is rarely found in the intestinal tract of people who live in industrially developed countries.
* b. may cause high infant mortality by producing severe diarrhea.
c. is photosynthetic and autotrophic.
d. causes fecal material to move through the colon at a slow rate and frequently causes constipation.
e. all of these

M 43. *E. coli*
a. is a normal inhabitant of human intestinal tracts.
b. has some strains that produce toxins and cause disease.
c. may be the leading cause of infant mortality in developing countries.
d. produces vitamin K and compounds used in fat digestion.
* e. all of these

M 44. Heterocysts are regions in filamentous cyanobacteria
a. that can break and allow for reproduction by fragmentation.
b. where endospores are formed.
c. where the filament is attached to its substrates.
* d. where nitrogen fixation occurs.
e. where photosynthesis occurs.

M 45. *Borrelia burgdorferi* is the cause of
   a. tetanus.
   b. syphilis.
 * c. Lyme disease.
   d. legionnaires disease.
   e. severe diarrhea.

M 46. Bacteria are able to sense
   a. magnetic fields.
   b. light.
   c. gravity.
   d. oxygen concentration.
 * e. all of these

M 47. In many aspects, bacteria are more "advanced" in their _____ than in their _____.
   a. reproduction; structure
   b. metabolism; genetic composition
   c. chemical composition; classification
 * d. behavior; structure

THE VIRUSES

D 48. Which of the following statements is false?
   a. A single bacterium could potentially produce over 1 billion bacteria in less than a day.
   b. Over a million viruses could be found in the space equivalent to the dot of an i.
   c. Microorganisms fit into almost all categories of life-styles such as pathogens, parasites, autotrophs, and decomposers.
 * d. Although viruses are not alive, they can reproduce independently under appropriate conditions.
   e. Viruses have nucleic acids and proteins, but no organelles.

E 49. Which statement is inaccurate?
   a. Viruses are not able to move by themselves.
   b. Viruses are not able to reproduce by themselves.
 * c. Viruses are not structurally organized.
   d. Some biologists consider viruses to be forms of life and other biologists consider them to be nonlife.
   e. Viruses contain instructions to manufacture themselves.

M 50. A virus is characterized by all but which one of the following?
 * a. enzymes of respiration
   b. nucleic acid core
   c. noncellular organization
   d. protein coat

M 51. Most scientists do not consider viruses to be "alive" because
   a. they have no genes.
 * b. their metabolic machinery is borrowed from the host cell.
   c. they are unable to reproduce.
   d. no definite structural features are seen under the microscope.
   e. all of these

M 52. Which of the following is false?
 * a. The outer coats of all viruses are alike.
   b. The virus uses either DNA or RNA at its core, but not both.
   c. Viruses can be replicated only after they enter a living cell.
   d. Most viruses have a protein coat or covering.
   e. A virus may not kill a host cell but may become inactive for a period of latency.

M 53. Which of the following statements about viruses is true?
   a. They were the first forms of life to evolve.
   b. They do not attack plants.
   c. They are able to reproduce without using other organisms.
   d. They are made of protein only.
 * e. They include some forms that are able to attack bacteria.

M 54. A virus described as having "tail fibers attached to a sheath extending from the head" would be identified as a
   a. complex virus.
   b. helical virus.
   c. bacteriophage.
 * d. complex virus and a bacteriophage.
   e. helical virus and a bacteriophage.

D 55. Which disease is NOT caused by a virus?
   a. smallpox
   b. polio
   c. influenza
 * d. syphilis
   e. herpes

D 56. Which virus is an RNA virus?
   a. adenovirus
 * b. retrovirus
   c. parvovirus
   d. herpesvirus
   e. papovavirus

E 57. Plant viruses are transmitted primarily by
   a. wind.
   b. water.
   c. bacteria.
 * d. animals.

M 58. Retroviruses are characterized by
   a. an RNA core.
   b. temperate pathways of replication.
   c. the enzyme reverse transcriptase.
   d. being the causative agent for AIDS.
 * e. all of these

M 59. Flu pandemics are caused by the spread of
   a. pathogenic bacteria.
 * b. RNA viruses.
   c. DNA viruses.
   d. parasitic protozoans.

D   **60.** Herpes viruses that produce latent infections include all but which one of the following?
    a. infectious mononucleosis
    b. genital herpes
    c. chicken pox
*   d. hepatitis
    e. cancer

M   **61.** Which of the following statements is false?
    a. Shingles is an example of latency in animal viruses.
    b. Animal viruses enter a cell through endocytosis.
    c. Plant viruses are introduced into plant cells by insects.
*   d. Viruses are the smallest infective agents known.
    e. For a virus to produce a disease in plants, it must go through the cell wall and enter the cell's cytoplasm.

D   **62.** Which of the following is NOT caused by one of the herpes viruses?
    a herpes simplex and cold sores
*   b. benign and malignant warts
    c. chicken pox and shingles
    d genital herpes
    e. infectious mononucleosis and some cancers

D   **63.** Which of the following pairings of virus and mode of entry is INCORRECTLY matched?
    a. bacteriophage: digestion of host cell wall
*   b. herpes: puncture wound
    c. plant virus: insect feeding
    d chicken pox: endocytosis
    e. T4: hole in bacterial wall

M   **64.** Lengthy periods of latency are most often associated with viruses that infect
*   a. animal cells.
    b. plant cells.
    c. bacteria.
    d other viruses.
    e. viroids.

M   **65.** Contagious diseases are spread by
    a. vectors.
*   b. direct contact.
    c. indirect contact.
    d inhalation.
    e. all of these

D   **66.** Which of the following is correct regarding plant viruses?
    a. They are mostly DNA viruses.
    b. Most of them cause little outward change in plant appearance.
    c. The capsid is spiral-shaped.
    d All plant viruses cause disease.
*   e. RNA viruses cause the most plant diseases.

M   **67.** Which of the following statements is false? Antibiotics
    a. serve as an agent of natural selection in pathogenic bacteria.
*   b. are effective against viruses.
    c. may produce potent side effects.
    d. are normal metabolic by-products of certain microorganisms.
    e. when used by women often have to be accompanied by antifungal drugs to control yeast infections.

VIRAL MULTIPLICATION CYCLES

M   **68.** The lysogenic pathway is characterized by
*   a. passive replication of viral DNA.
    b. extensive transcription of viral DNA.
    c. destruction of the bacterial host.
    d passive replication of viral DNA and extensive transcription of viral DNA.
    e. passive replication of viral DNA, extensive transcription of viral DNA, and destruction of the bacterial host.

E   **69.** When a virus takes over the machinery of a cell, it forces the cell to manufacture
    a. more mitochondria for energy for the virus.
    b. more liposomes to isolate themselves from water.
    c. more food particles.
*   d more viral particles.
    e. more Golgi bodies so that the cell will secrete the excess viruses.

D   **70.** In viral replication, all but which one of the following occur before capsid formation?
    a. attachment to host cell
    b. nucleic acid replication
*   c. release of new viral particles
    d injection of viral nucleic acid into cell

M   **71.** Latency in viruses is associated with all but which one of the following?
    a. replication
*   b lysogenic pathways
    c. gene integration
    d lytic cycle
    e. retroviruses

D   **72.** All but which one of the following are true of retroviruses?
*   a. Viral RNA becomes integrated into host genome.
    b. Temperate pathways are followed.
    c. They infect animal cells.
    d They are responsible for AIDS infection.
    e. Transcriptase enzymes are coded for by viral genes.

E   **73.** Viroids differ from viruses in that the former lack
    a. nucleic acid.
*   b protein.
    c. the ability to reproduce.
    d nucleic acid and protein

D 74. Infective proteins are known as
         a. retroviruses.
         b. vivoids.
         c. viruses.
    *   d. prions.
         e. none of these, because nucleic acids are needed
             for infections

Classification Questions

Answer questions 75-79 using the five groups listed below:
         a. halophiles
         b. cyanobacteria
         c. thermophiles
         d. actinomycetes
         e. methanogens

D 75. These bacteria live in temperatures that are not usually
        conducive to life.

M 76. These produce "swamp gas.".

D 77. These bacteria can live in water of very high salt
        concentration.

M 78. These can form heterocysts, valuable in nitrogen
        fixation.

M 79. These can serve as a source of antibiotics.

Answers   75. c   76. e   77. a

             78. b   79. d

Selecting the Exception

E 80. Three of the four answers listed below are descriptions
        of bacterial shape. Select the exception.
         a. coccus
         b. bacillus
    *   c. pili
         d. spiral

M 81. Four of the five answers listed below are bacterial
        structures. Select the exception.
         a. endospore
         b. pili
         c. capsule
    *   d. eyespot
         e. heterocyst

D 82. Four of the five answers listed below are related by a
        common category. Select the exception.
         a. rhinoviruses
    *   b. poxviruses
         c. togaviruses
         d. retroviruses
         e. enteroviruses

D 83. Four of the five answers listed below are related by a
        similar category. Select the exception.
         a. herpesviruses
         b. papovaviruses
         c. parvoviruses
    *   d. paramyxoviruses
         e. adenoviruses

D 84. Four of the five answers listed below are related by a
        common association. Select the exception.
         a. archaebacteria
         b. methanogens
         c. halophiles
    *   d. cyanobacteria
         e. thermophiles

D 85. Four of the five answers listed below have a common
        relationship. Select the exception.
         a. protistans
         b. plants
         c. animals
         d. fungi
    *   e. methanogens

M 86. Four of the five answers listed below are found in
        viruses. Select the exception.
         a. coat
    *   b. prions
         c. DNA
         d. tail fibers
         e. envelope

CHAPTER 22
PROTISTANS

Multiple-Choice Questions

AN EMERGING EVOLUTIONARY ROAD MAP

E **1.** Which of the following does NOT belong to the protistans?
* a. bacteria
  b. protozoans
  c. chrysophytes
  d. dinoflagellates
  e. euglenoids

D **2.** All but which of the following are members of the same kingdom?
  a. *Amoeba*
* b. *Clostridium*
  c. *Euglena*
  d. *Trypanosoma*

E **3.** Most protistans are
  a. autotrophic.
  b. heterotrophic.
* c. unicellular.
  d. multicellular.

E **4.** The simplest of the eukaryotes are the
* a. protistans.
  b. plants.
  c. fungi.
  d. animals.
  e. both a and c

M **5.** Which of the following is mismatched?
  a. slime mold—multinucleated blob of cytoplasm
  b. sporozoans—nonmotile parasites
* c. Sarcodina—ciliates
  d. Chrysophyta—golden algae and diatoms
  e. Mastigophora—flagellated protozoans

E **6.** Protozoans have traditionally been classified on the basis of their
  a. photosynthetic nature.
  b. life cycle.
  c. unique structures.
* d. type of motility.
  e. feeding habitats.

M **7.** The term "algae" is used primarily for organisms in the kingdom(s)
  a. Monera.
* b. Protista.
  c. Plantae.
  d. Monera and Protista only.
  e. Monera, Protista, and Plantae.

M **8.** Which of the following is NOT true of *Euglena*?
* a. It moves by pseudopodia.
  b. It contains chloroplasts.
  c. It absorbs nutrients such as vitamins from its environment in a heterotrophic manner.
  d. Its cell body is not surrounded by a cell wall.
  e. none of these; all statements are true

E **9** A pellicle is a (an)
  a. defensive organ.
* b. covering.
  c. organelle of motion.
  d. storage organ.
  e. component of the nucleus.

M **10.** Euglenoids
  a. sometimes reproduce faster than their chloroplasts, so that colorless euglenids are produced.
  b. may become a serious parasitic infection in some small children.
  c. reproduce by conjugation.
* d. usually can survive only in light.

M **11.** Certain euglenoids are unique among the protistans in that they
  a. possess flagella.
  b. reproduce by longitudinal fission.
* c. are heterotrophic and autotrophic.
  d. are multicellular.

ANCIENT LINEAGES OF FLAGELLATED PROTOZOANS

D **12.** Which of the following diseases is NOT caused by a flagellated protozoan?
* a. malaria
  b. sleeping sickness
  c. Chagas disease
  d. vaginal trichomonas
  e. intestinal giardiasis

M **13.** Protozoans cause all but which of the following diseases?
  a. dysentery
  b. African sleeping sickness
  c. malaria
* d. elephantiasis
  e. trichomonal infections of the reproductive tract

D **14.** All but which of the following are protozoan parasites of humans?
  a. *Trypanosoma*
  b. *Trichomonas*
* c. *Euglena*
  d. *Entamoeba*

AMOEBOID PROTOZOANS

E 15. Pseudopodia are characteristic of which of the following groups of protozoans?
    a. ciliated
    b. flagellated
*   c. amoeboid
    d. sporozoan

E 16. Which of the following organisms does NOT move by pseudopods?
    a. amoebas
    b. foraminiferans
*   c. diatoms
    d. heliozoans
    e. radiolarians

M 17. The term phytoplankton
    a. is a taxonomic division of the algae.
*   b. is a common term for unicellular, photoautotrophs.
    c. includes both unicellular and multicellular forms.
    d. refers to small, aquatic plants.

CILIATED PROTOZOANS

E 18. Structurally, the most complex unicellular organisms are
    a. viruses.
    b. bacteria.
    c. dinoflagellates.
*   d. ciliates.
    e. amoebas

E 19. *Paramecium* is a representative of the
    a. sporozoans.
    b. amoebas.
    c. flagellates.
    d. euglenoids.
*   e. ciliates.

D 20. Which of the following specialized structures is NOT correctly paired with a function?
    a. gullet—ingestion
    b. cilia—food gathering
*   c. contractile vacuole—digestion
    d. anal pore—waste elimination
    e. ribosome—protein synthesis

E 21. When under attack ciliates can eject sticky threads called
    a. vacuoles.
*   b. trichocysts.
    c. cysts.
    d. pseudopods.
    e. pellicles.

M 22. Which of the following has a simple sort of sexual reproduction called conjugation?
*   a. ciliates
    b. flagellates
    c. sporozoans
    d. amoebas
    e. euglenoids

SPOROZOANS

M 23. The least mobile protistans include
    a. euglenoids.
    b. ciliates.
*   c. sporozoans.
    d. dinoflagellates.
    e. flagellates.

M 24. The sporozoan parasite *Plasmodium* infects cells of which of the following?
    a. blood
    b. liver
    c. brain
*   d. both blood and liver
    e. blood, liver, and brain

THE CELL FROM HELL AND OTHER DINOFLAGELLATES

M 25. "Red tides" and extensive fish kills are caused by population "blooms" of
    a. *Euglena.*
*   b. specific dinoflagellates.
    c. diatoms.
    d. *Plasmodium.*
    e. fish.

M 26. Dinoflagellates
    a. may produce red tides that poison and kill fish.
    b. produce a poison that builds up in the tissues of mussels and may kill humans that eat infected mussels.
    c. may undergo a population explosion that turns the ocean red or various colors.
    d. are mostly photosynthetic marine plankton.
*   e. all of these

M 27. Dinoflagellates are characterized by all but which of the following?
    a. They secrete neurotoxins that can kill fish.
    b. They spin like tops as they swim.
    c. They poison shellfish such as clams, oysters, scallops, and mussels.
*   d. They have two shells that fit together like petri plates.
    e. They are photosynthetic.

M 28. "Red tide" neurotoxins are produced by members of which phylum?
    a. Chrysophyta
*   b. Pyrrophyta
    c. Sarcomastigophora
    d. Ciliophora

OOMYCOTES—ANCIENT STRAMENOPILES

M 29. The failure of the potato crop and the subsequent Irish famine was due mainly to a fungus belonging to which group?
    a. chytrids
    b. imperfect fungi
    c. club fungi
    d. ascomycetes
*   e. water molds

PHOTOSYNTHETIC STRAMENOPILES—CHRYSOPHYTES AND DINOFLAGELLATES

M 30. Diatoms are characterized by all but which of the following?
    a. overlapping shells
    b. classification as chrysophytes
    c. silica composition
*   d. flagella
    e. perforations in the shell

M 31. The gritty substance you may feel on your teeth after using toothpaste is actually
    a. small deposits of sand.
*   b. diatomaceous earth.
    c. cellulose from dinoflagellates.
    d. a synthetic abrasive.

D 32. The pigment that makes chrysophytes golden-brown is
    a. phycobilin.
    b. chlorophyll.
    c. algin.
*   d. fucoxanthin.
    e. carrageenan.

M 33. *Macrocystis*, kelp, and *Sargassum* are examples of
    a. Rhodophyta.
    b. Chlorophyta.
*   c. Phaeophyta.
    d. Bryophyta.
    e. Pterophyta.

M 34. Holdfasts, gas-filled floats, and a thick leathery surface are found in species of
    a. red algae.
*   b. brown algae.
    c. bryophytes.
    d. green algae.
    e. blue-green algae.

M 35. Of the following which is characterized by complex structural morphology, sporophyte-dominant structures, and an abundance of xanthophylls?
    a. Rhodophyta
*   b. Phaeophyta
    c. Chlorophyta
    d. Bryophyta

M 36. Which of the following parts of a brown alga does not have a counterpart in land plants?
    a. blade
    b. stipe
*   c. float
    d. holdfast

M 37. A source for a thickening, emulsifying agent found in ice cream, salad dressing, beer, toothpaste, cough syrup, and floor polish is the
    a. seed plants.
    b. ferns.
*   c. brown algae.
    d. red algae.
    e. green algae.

D 38. All but which of the following terms may be used in descriptions of brown algae?
    a. Phaeophyta
    b. algin
    c. kelp
    d. xanthophyll
*   e. phycobilin

E 39. The largest algae would be included in which of the following groups?
*   a. brown algae
    b. red algae
    c. green algae
    d. blue-green algae

GREEN ALGAE AND THEIR CLOSEST RELATIVES

E 40. Most freshwater algae belong to which phylum?
    a. Rhodophyta
*   b. Chlorophyta
    c. Phaeophyta
    d. Bryophyta
    e. Pterophyta

D 41. Green algae (chlorophytes) are thought to be the ancestors of land plants for all but which of the following reasons?
    a. All have carotenoids and xanthophylls.
    b. All have chlorophyll *a* and *b*.
*   c. They developed a cuticle and rhizoids that are characteristic of primitive land plants.
    d. They store excess carbohydrates as starch.
    e. all of these

M 42. Which pigment is NOT characteristic of Chlorophyta?
    a. chlorophyll *a*
    b. xanthophyll
    c. carotenoids
*   d. phycoerythrins
    e. chlorophyll *b*

M 43. The unicellular alga *Chlamydomonas*
    a. lacks an asexual stage.
    b. lacks a sexual stage.
    c. lacks a haploid and a diploid phase.
*   d. possesses both a haploid and a diploid phase.

D 44. Green algae and land plants are similar in all but which of the following characteristics?
    a. types and proportions of photosynthetic pigments
    b. storage of carbohydrate in the form of starch
    c. cell walls composed of cellulose
  * d. haploid dominant life cycles

RED ALGAE

E 45. The red algae are classified as
  * a. Rhodophyta.
    b. Chlorophyta.
    c. Phaeophyta.
    d. Bryophyta.
    e. Pterophyta.

M 46. Red algae
  * a. are primarily marine organisms.
    b. are thought to have developed from green algae.
    c. contain xanthophylls as their main accessory pigments.
    d. all of these

D 47. Red algae can live in deeper water because of
  * a. phycobilins.
    b. holdfasts.
    c. chlorophyll *a*.
    d. stonelike cell walls.
    e. their preference for freshwater habitats.

M 48. Agar is produced by
    a. brown algae.
  * b. red algae.
    c. phycobilins.
    d. brown and red algae.
    e. red algae and phycobilins.

SLIME MOLDS

M 49. Slime molds are classified as
  * a. protistans.
    b. fungi.
    c. protozoans.
    d. protistans and protozoans
    e. protistans, fungi, and protozoans

M 50. The signal for aggregation and communal activity by cellular slime molds is
    a. a pheromone.
  * b. cyclic AMP.
    c. glycoprotein slime.
    d. RNA.
    e. unidentified as yet.

M 51. Cellular slime molds can be distinguished from plasmodial slime molds on the basis of
    a. reproductive structures.
    b. spore formation.
  * c. nuclei per cell.
    d. slime trails.
    e. food requirements.

Classification Questions

Answer questions 52-56 using the five groups listed below:
    a. sporozoans
    b. amoebas
    c. euglenoids
    d. dinoflagellates
    e. trypanosomes

D 52. This group of protozoans has no locomotor organelles.

M 53. Possesses eyespot for detecting light needed for photosynthesis.

D 54. Move by means of pseudopodia.

M 55. Neurotoxin from this group can kill humans.

M 56. Chagas disease and African sleeping sickness are caused by members of this group.

Answers   52. a   53. c   54. b
             55. d   56. e

Answer questions 57-61 in reference to the four groups of protozoans listed below:
    a. Chrysophyta
    b. Sarcodina
    c. Sporozoa
    d. Ciliophora

E 57. The common amoeba, *Amoeba proteus,* is a member of this group.

M 58. The radiolarians, which produce glass shells, are members of this group.

M 59. The malarial parasite *Plasmodium* is a member of this group.

D 60. This group includes the very unique diatoms.

M 61. An organism commonly used in competition experiments is the *Paramecium,* which belongs to this group.

Answers   57. b   58. b   59. c
             60. a   61. d

Selecting the Exception

M 62. Four of the five answers listed below are members of the same kingdom. Select the exception.
  * a. archaebacteria
    b. protozoans
    c. chrysophytes
    d. dinoflagellates
    e. euglenoids

M   63. Four of the five answers listed below are protistan structures. Select the exception.
        a. cell membrane
    *   b. pili
        c. mitochondrion
        d. eyespot
        e. food vacuole

D   64. Four of the five answers listed below are related by a common category. Select the exception.
        a. amoebas
    *   b. euglenas
        c. foraminiferans
        d. radiolarians
        e. heliozoans

D   65. Four of the five answers listed below are related by a similar category. Select the exception.
        a. golden algae
        b. red algae
        c. green algae
    *   d. blue-green algae
        e. brown algae

D   66. Four of the five answers listed below are protozoans. Select the exception.
        a. amoeboids
    *   b. dinoflagellates
        c. ciliates
        d. sporozoans
        e. flagellates

D   67. Four of the five answers listed below are amoeboid protozoans. Select the exception.
        a. amoebae
        b. foraminiferans
        c. heliozoans
        d. radiolarians
    *   e. diatoms

D   68. Four of the five answers listed below are related by a common association. Select the exception.
        a. Pyrrophyta
        b. Chlorophyta
        c. Chrysophyta
    *   d. Cyanobacteria
        e. Rhodophyta

M   69. Four of the five answers listed below are organelles found in eukaryotes. Select the exception.
        a. mitochondria
    *   b. mesosomes
        c. chloroplasts
        d. nuclei
        e. vacuoles

CHAPTER 23
PLANTS

Multiple-Choice Questions

M 1. The evolution of plants
    a. started in aquatic environments.
    b. was marked by the development of specialized tissues such as vascular tissue.
    c. led to the development of specialized organs.
    d. demonstrated a trend toward radiating into drier environments.
  * e. all of these

TRENDS IN PLANT EVOLUTION

E 2. All of the following are bryophytes except
    a. mosses
  * b. ferns
    c. liverworts
    d. hornworts
    e. nonvascular plants

M 3. Which of the following produces no seeds?
    a. cycads
    b. conifers
  * c. horsetails
    d. ginkgos
    e. tomato

M 4. All but which of the following would be associated with vascular plants?
    a. root systems
  * b. bryophytes
    c. angiosperms
    d. gymnosperms
    e. shoot systems

E 5. Green plants need which of the following?
    a. sunlight energy
    b. water
    c. carbon dioxide
    d. minerals
  * e. all of these

M 6. Which of the following is true of xylem?
    a. conducts water downward in the plant
    b. transports food upward in the plant
  * c. transports water and minerals
    d. transfers materials from stem to leaf

D 7. All but which of the following describe trends in plant evolution?
    a. nonvascular to vascular
  * b. spores of two types to spores of one type
    c. motile gametes
    d. seedless to seeds
    e. haploid to diploid dominance

D 8. Which of the following is NOT a trend evident in plant evolution?
    a. increasing independence from water
    b. development of vascular tissue
  * c. increasing dominance of the gametophyte generation
    d. evolution from homospory (one type of spore) to heterospory (two types of spores)
    e. development of the importance of the diploid phase of the life cycle

M 9. The cuticle of a plant is primarily for
  * a. retention of water.
    b. conduction of fluids.
    c. absorption of carbon dioxide.
    d. protection from strong sunlight.
    e. all of these

M 10. In the life cycle of primitive plants, which of the following predominates?
  * a. haploid stage
    b. diploid stage
    c. large sporophyte body
    d. both diploid stage and large sporophyte body
    e. both haploid stage and large sproophyte body

M 11. Ferns are more advanced than mosses because mosses lack which structure found in ferns?
    a. spores
    b. cuticle
  * c. xylem
    d. sporophytes
    e. pollen

D 12. By _____ years ago, plants had invaded land successfully.
    a. 2.0 billion
    b. 7.0 billion
    c. 750 million
  * d. 450 million
    e. 260 million

M 13. Sporangia are borne by
    a. the sporophyte stage.
    b. diploid organisms.
    c. spores.
  * d. the sporophyte stage in diploid organisms.
    e. the spores of the sporophyte stage in diploid organisms.

M 14. The first haploid cell in the life cycle of a plant is the
    a. zygote.
    b. gamete.
    c. gametophyte plant.
  * d. spore.
    e. spore mother cell.

D 15. In the life cycle of vascular plants, meiosis occurs
    a. immediately before fertilization.
    b. during the production of gametes.
    c. as a way of reducing the number of chromosomes in a zygote.
*   d. in the process of spore formation.
    e. in the gametangia.

M 16. The life cycle of simple plants such as algae is dominated by the
    a. haploid phase.
    b. diploid phase.
    c. gametophyte.
*   d. haploid phase in the gametophyte.
    e. diploid phase in the gametophyte.

M 17. Stomata are responsible for
    a. water escape from the leaves.
    b. carbon dioxide entry.
    c. mineral absorption.
*   d. water escape from the leaves and carbon dioxide entry.
    e. water escape from the leaves, carbon dioxide entry, and mineral absorption.

M 18. All but which of the following are characteristic of the major trends in terrestrial autotroph evolution?
    a. development of vascular tissue
    b. adaptation to environmental stress
    c. heterospory
    d. fertilization by biotic vectors
*   e. reduction of the sporophyte phase

M 19. Gametophytes are
    a. haploid plants that produce spores.
    b. diploid plants that produce spores.
*   c. haploid plants that produce gametes.
    d. diploid plants that produce gametes.
    e. diploid or haploid plants that produce gametes.

M 20. In complex land plants, the diploid stage is resistant to adverse environmental conditions, such as dwindling water supplies and cold weather. The diploid stage progresses through which sequence?
    a. gametophyte———>male and female gametes
    b. spores———>sporophyte
*   c. zygote———>sporophyte
    d. zygote———>gametophyte

M 21. The increased complexity among the different divisions of land plants is paralleled by increased complexity of which of the following?
    a. male gamete
    b. female gamete
    c. gametophyte
*   d. sporophyte
    e. all of these

M 22. A gametophyte is
    a. a gamete-producing plant.
    b. haploid.
    c. the plant produced by the fusion of gametes.
    d. the dominant generation in the higher plants.
*   e. both a gamete-producing plant and haploid.

D 23. Which of the following is true concerning the male gametophyte?
    a. The male gametophyte develops from the pollen grain.
*   b. The pollen grain is the male gametophyte.
    c. The pollen grain develops from the male gametophyte.
    d. The male gametophyte is the pollen tube.

D 24. Which of the following is true concerning seeds?
    a. Ferns produce seeds.
*   b. Seeds form from the female gametophyte.
    c. Pollen grains mature into seeds.
    d. Most seeds are heterosporous.
    e. All of these are true.

D 25. The heterosporous condition led to evolution of
    a. gymnosperms and angiosperms.
    b. pollen grains and seeds.
    c. male and female plant parts.
    d. pollen grains and seeds in male and female plant parts.
*   e. gymnosperms and angiosperms which bear pollen grains and seeds in male and female plant parts.

THE BRYOPHYTES

E 26. The mosses and liverworts are members of which division?
    a. Psilophyta
    b. Lycophyta
    c. Sphenophyta
*   d. Bryophyta
    e. Pterophyta

D 27. Which of the following statements is true?
*   a. Bryophytes have a water-conserving cuticle.
    b. The liverworts and mosses lack true leaves and stems but possess true roots.
    c. The sperm and eggs of Bryophyta are naked and lack any adaptations to keep them from drying out.
    d. Bryophytes do not reproduce sexually except under unusual environmental conditions.
    e. Bryophytes produce male and female gametophytes that are identical in appearance and are identical to sporophytes.

D 28. Bryophytes differ from all other land plants in that they
    a. possess swimming sperm.
*   b. have independent gametophytes and dependent sporophytes.
    c. were the first forms to successfully invade land.
    d. exhibit alternation of generations.
    e. possess gametangia that produce sperm and eggs.

D 29. Which statement about Bryophyta is NOT true?
  * a. The sporophyte is haploid.
    b. The sporangium produces spores.
    c. The sporophyte is parasitic and attached to the gametophyte.
    d. Meiosis precedes spore formation.
    e. Bryophytes require water for sexual reproduction.

M 30. Which of the following do not possess vascular tissue?
    a. angiosperms
  * b. bryophytes
    c. conifers
    d. ferns
    e. ginkgoes

D 31. Which of the following statements is false?
    a. The conifers were the dominant plants during the Mesozoic.
    b. The ferns arose from the mosses by the development of vascular tissue.
    c. Both pollen and seeds first evolved in flowering plants.
  * d. The first terrestrial plants likely possessed vascular tissue.

E 32. Mosses are
    a. algae.
  * b. bryophytes.
    c. vascular plants.
    d. gymnosperms.
    e. extinct.

M 33. Which of the following statements is false?
    a. Mosses do not have xylem and phloem.
    b. Mosses do not have true leaves.
    c. Mosses do not have true stems.
    d. Mosses use rhizoids, not roots, for attachment and absorption.
  * e. Mosses are different from all other plants in that they have an independent sporophyte generation and a dependent gametophyte generation.

M 34. All but which of the following are bryophytes?
    a. hornworts
    b. liverworts
  * c. lycophytes
    d. mosses

M 35. Which of the following statements concerning production of bryophyte reproductive cells is true?
    a. Spores and gametes are produced during meiosis.
    b. Spores and gametes are produced during mitosis.
  * c. Spores are produced during meiosis, whereas gametes are produced during mitosis.
    d. Spores are produced during mitosis, whereas gametes are produced during meiosis.

EXISTING SEEDLESS VASCULAR PLANTS

M 36. In horsetails, lycophytes, and whisk ferns,
  * a. spores give rise to gametophytes.
    b. the main plant body is a gametophyte.
    c. the sporophyte bears sperm- and egg-producing organs.
    d. all of these

D 37. Which of the following is NOT true of seedless vascular plants?
    a. Sporophytes are independent of gametophytes.
  * b. Water is not needed for gamete transport.
    c. Sporophytes have vascular tissue.
    d. Seeds are not produced.
    e. Living members still exist.

M 38. Rhizomes in the whisk ferns serve the same function as _____ in more advanced land plants.
    a. leaves
    b. stems
  * c. roots
    d. seeds
    e. flowers

M 39. Strobili are
    a. gametangia.
  * b. cone-shaped spore sacs.
    c. homospores.
    d. accessory stems.
    e. horizontal stems.

E 40. The feature of horsetails that was useful to pioneers of the American West was
    a. rhizomes.
  * b. silica in the stems.
    c. photosynthetic cells.
    d. cones at the tips.

D 41. Which of the following statements concerning fertilization in ferns is (are) true?
    a. It occurs within the female structure.
    b. It requires water.
    c. The fertilization product is a seed.
  * d. It occurs within the female structure; and It requires water.
    e. It occurs within the female structure; It requires water; and The fertilization product is a seed.

E 42. What is the name given to the "leaves" of a fern?
    a. rhizome
    b. rhizoid
  * c. frond
    d. sorus
    e. bronchus

M 43. Which of the following statements is false?
   a. The ferns differ from the other vascular plants because they lack seeds.
   b. The ferns differ from other vascular plants by having an independent sporophyte generation.
   c. The ferns are restricted to wet environments because of the requirements of the gametophytes.
 * d. Ferns have true roots, stems, and leaves.
   e. Ferns possess both xylem and phloem.

M 44. Which of the following statements is false?
   a. The gametophytes of the ferns are free-living.
   b. Mycorrhizae were essential for the survival and evolution of some land plants.
 * c. All the ferns and related primitive vascular plants are heterosporous, and homospory did not evolve until the gymnosperms.
   d. The ferns and their relatives formed the giant swamp forests that produced the fossil fuels.
   e. Many of the ferns and their relatives have underground stems called rhizomes.

M 45. A sorus is
   a. a collection of rust-colored disease spots on a fern.
   b. the fern gametophyte.
   c. an egg-producing structure.
   d. where the sperm are produced.
 * e. a collection of spore chambers.

THE RISE OF SEED-BEARING PLANTS

E 46. Which of the following are seed plants?
   a. cycads
   b. ginkgoes
   c. conifers
   d. angiosperms
 * e. all of these

M 47. Which of the following will eventually produce a mature pollen grain?
   a. megaspore
   b. microsporangium
 * c. microspore
   d. microgamete
   e. all of these

M 48. Microspores mature into
   a. ovules.
   b. seeds.
 * c. pollen grains.
   d. anthers.

E 49. The seed develops from the
   a. gametophyte.
   b. ovary.
 * c. ovule.
   d. pollen grain.
   e. zygote.

M 50. Which structure will develop into a seed?
   a. archegonium
   b. female gametophyte
 * c. ovule
   d. ovary

GYMNOSPERMS–PLANTS WITH "NAKED" SEEDS

M 51. Which of the following is NOT a fern or closely related to ferns?
   a. Lycophyta
 * b. Cycadophyta
   c. Pterophyta
   d. Sphenophyta
   e. all of these

E 52. Which of the following plants are widely planted in cities because of their resistance to insect predators, air pollution, and disease?
   a. lycopods
 * b. ginkgoes
   c. Dutch elms
   d. conifers
   e. grasses

E 53. Which of the following is NOT a conifer?
   a. pine
   b. fir
   c. cedar
 * d. ginkgo
   e. cypress

D 54. Which of the following plants is NOT a gymnosperm?
   a. cycad
   b. spruce
 * c. palm
   d. ginkgo

M 55. Gymnosperms
 * a. were the first plants not to have swimming sperm and were therefore freed from the need for water to reproduce.
   b. are divided into two groups, the monocots and dicots.
   c. were the first plants to develop vascular tissues.
   d. were the first plants to develop flowers to attract insects.

E 56. What are major sources of pulp, lumber, and numerous industrial products?
   a. cycads
   b. ginkgoes
 * c. conifers
   d. hardwoods
   e. all of these

M 57. Which of these organisms, sometimes called living fossils, is represented by only one species?
   a. *Equisetum,* or horsetails
   b. lycophytes, or club mosses
   c. gnetophyte
 * d. ginkgo
   e. cycad

M 58. The first organisms that did not require water for reproduction were the
   a. ferns.
   b. lycophytes.
   c. cycads.
   d. flowering plants.
 * e. gymnosperms.

A CLOSER LOOK AT THE CONIFERS

M 59. In pine trees, the immature male gametophyte is
   a. a megaspore.
   b. the embryonic pine seed.
   c. a pollen tube.
 * d. a pollen grain.
   e. all of these

D 60. What occurs within the female cone of a pine tree?
   a. meiosis
   b. mitosis
   c. fertilization
   d. both meiosis and mitosis
 * e. meiosis, mitosis, and fertilization.

E 61. A pine tree is
   a. an angiosperm.
   b. a haploid plant body.
 * c. a sporophyte.
   d. a living fossil.
   e. all of these

M 62. A pine seed is composed primarily of
   a. the embryo.
   b. female gametophyte.
   c. seed coats.
   d. the embryo and seed coats.
 * e. the embryo, seed coats, and female gametophyte.

M 63. Which of the following statements about pine cones is correct?
   a. Cones are exclusively female structures.
   b. Cones are the result of pollination.
   c. One type of cone produces microspores.
   d. Seeds are enclosed in cones.
 * e. One type of cone produces microspores; and Seeds are enclosed in cones.

ANGIOSPERMS–THE FLOWERING, SEED-BEARING PLANTS

E 64. The first group with flowers was the
   a. algae.
   b. fern allies.
   c. ferns.
 * d. angiosperms.
   e. gymnosperms.

M 65. The flowering plants and gymnosperms differ from other plants by
   a. the possession of vascular tissue.
   b. the presence of nonmotile gametes.
   c. the presence of two types of spores.
   d. dominance by the diploid generation.
 * e. both the possession of vascular tissue and dominance by the diploid generation.

M 66. Angiosperms are more advanced than gymnosperms because gymnosperms lack which structure found in angiosperms?
   a. independent gametophytes
   b. pollen grains
 * c. fruits
   d. roots

E 67. The group of plants that has the most species is the
   a. mosses.
   b. ferns.
   c. gymnosperms.
 * d. dicots.
   e. monocots.

M 68. The rapid expansion of angiosperms late in the Mesozoic era appears to be related to their coevolution with
   a. dinosaurs.
   b. gymnosperms.
 * c. insects.
   d. mammals.
   e. birds.

M 69. Angiosperms
   a. are the most successful of all plants.
   b. are the most diverse of all plants.
   c. are represented by a number of heterotrophic plants.
   d. have embryos that are provided with food by an endosperm, a unique structure found only within the angiosperms.
 * e. all of these

M 70. All but which of the following are monocots?
   a. iris
   b. wheat
 * c. maple
   d. grass

M 71. Dependence on animal vectors for fertilization and dispersal is characteristic of many species of
   a. ferns.
 * b. angiosperms.
   c. mosses.
   d. conifers.

D 72. The majority of vascular plants possess or are characterized by
    a. leaves.
    b. nonindependent gametophytes.
    c. seeds.
    d. leaves and nonindependent gametophytes.
*   e. leaves, nonindependent gametophytes, and seeds.

M 73. The vast majority of plant species are
    a. algae.
    b. bryophytes.
    c. gymnosperms.
*   d. angiosperms.

M 74. Which is the correct sequence in the evolution of plants?
    a. algae, conifers, flowering plants, ferns
    b. ferns, algae, conifers, flowering plants
*   c. algae, ferns, conifers, flowering plants
    d. ferns, conifers, algae, flowering plants

Matching Questions

D 75. Matching. Choose the most appropriate answer for each.
    1. ___ dicots
    2. ___ conifers
    3. ___ club mosses
    4. ___ cycads
    5. ___ ferns
    6. ___ flowering plants
    7. ___ ginkgos
    8. ___ horsetails
    9. ___ mosses, liverworts
    10. ___ angiosperm

    A. have rhizoids, cuticle, and protected embryo sporophyte
    B. "vessel seed"
    C. non-seed-bearing, heart-shaped gametophytes; spore-bearing leaves with sori
    D. *Lycopodium;* cone-bearing sporophyte; free-living gametophyte
    E. only one species left
    F. cypress and redwood; heterosporous; mostly evergreen
    G. confined to tropics or warm, temperate zones; resemble squat cone-bearing palm trees
    H. two seed leaves
    I. *Equisetum;* homosporous; rhizomes present; aerial stems jointed
    J. have coevolved with pollinating vectors

Answers: 1. H   2. F   3. D   4. G
        5. C   6. J   7. E   8. I
        9. A   10. B

Classification Questions

Answer questions 76-80 in reference to the five divisions of vascular plants listed below:
    a. lycophytes
    b. sphenophytes
    c. pterophytes
    d. conifers
    e. angiosperms

E 76. The tree ferns that are common in today's tropical forests are members of this division.

D 77. The giant ground pines of the Carboniferous Period often reached heights of 50–100 feet. These were members of this division.

M 78. Orchids are members of this division.

D 79. This is heterosporous with well-developed seed and pollen-bearing cones.

M 80. This seed is enclosed in an ovary, which, when ripened, may form a fruit.

Answers   76. c   77. a   78. e   79. d
             80. e

Selecting the Exception

D 81. Four of the five answers listed below are related by the quantity of chromosomes present. Select the exception.
    a. spores
*   b. sporophyte
    c. egg
    d. sperm
    e. gametophyte

D 82. Three of the four answers listed below are related by absence of vascular tissue. Select the exception.
*   a. ferns
    b. liverworts
    c. mosses
    d. hornworts

D 83. Four of the five answers listed below are groups in which the sporophyte is dominant. Select the exception.
*   a. bryophytes
    b. lycophytes
    c. angiosperms
    d. gnetophytes
    e. sphenophytes

D   84. Four of the five answers listed below are
          heterosporous. Select the exception.
          a. angiosperms
          b. cycads
          c. ginkgo
          d. conifers
      *   e. ferns

E   85. Four of the five answers listed below are conifers.
          Select the exception.
          a. hemlock
          b. spruce
          c. fir
      *   d. palm
          e. pine

M   86. Four of the five answers listed below are monocots.
          Select the exception.
          a. grass
          b. onion
      *   c. melon
          d. orchid
          e. pineapple

M   87. Four of the five answers listed below are seed
          producers. Select the exception.
      *   a. ferns
          b. conifers
          c. dicots
          d. ginkgos
          e. monocots

D   88. Four of the five answers listed below are portions of
          the gametophyte generation. Select the exception.
          a. pollen grains
          b. megaspore
      *   c. ovule
          d. pollen tube
          e. male gametophyte

D   89. Four of the five answers below are related by the
          presence of vascular tissue. Select the exception.
          a. whisk ferns
      *   b. mosses
          c. pine trees
          d. flowering plants
          e. horsetails

CHAPTER 24
FUNGI

Multiple-Choice Questions

CHARACTERISTICS OF FUNGI

E **1.** The life cycles are known for how many major groups of fungi?
   a. one
   b. two
 * c. three
   d. four
   e. none

M **2.** The major groups of fungi are assigned names on the basis of
   a. feeding structures.
   b. mode of nutrition.
   c. ecological role.
 * d. reproductive structures.
   e. when they appear in the fossil record.

E **3.** In the ecological community, fungi are
   a. producers if the sun is shining.
   b. consumers of materials digested by their hosts.
 * c. decomposers of organic matter.
   d. consumers of materials digested by their hosts and decomposers of organic matter.
   e. producers if the sun is shining, consumers of materials digested by their hosts, and decomposers of organic matter.

M **4.** In fungi, food materials are digested
   a. within food vacuoles.
 * b. outside the body.
   c. intracellularly.
   d. by the mitochondria.
   e. by the host organism.

D **5.** The value of fungi in the scheme of nature is described by which of the following statements?
   a. Fungi "fix" nitrogen from the air for use by plants.
   b. Fungi trap sunlight energy in carbohydrates.
 * c. Fungi release elements from organic matter.
   d. Fungi suppress population explosions by parasitizing overproductive animals.
   e. Fungi can do any of the above, depending on the species and environment.

E **6.** Saprobes are
   a. cytoplasmic organelles.
   b. metabolic by-products.
 * c. organisms that feed on dead material.
   d. parasites of plants.
   e. an evolutionary dead end.

E **7.** Fungi
   a. are producers.
 * b. are generally saprobes.
   c. usually have life cycles in which the diploid phase dominates.
   d. include *Fucus* and liverworts.
   e. are typically marine forms.

M **8.** Which fungi rely on extracellular digestion and absorption of energy-rich substances from living organisms?
   a. slime molds
   b. saprobic fungi
 * c. parasitic fungi
   d. plasmodial fungi
   e. autotrophic fungi

E **9.** All fungi are
   a. unicellular.
   b. multicellular.
   c. autotrophic.
 * d. heterotrophic.

M **10.** All fungi
   a. are saprobes.
 * b. perform extracellular digestion.
   c. are parasites.
   d. are saprobes and perform extracellular digestion.
   e. are saprobes, perform extracellular digestion, and are parasites.

M **11.** The principal difference between a saprophytic and parasitic mode of nutrition is
   a. the quality of the nutrients.
   b. not noticeable in fungi.
   c. the same as intracellular versus extracellular digestion.
 * d. determined by whether the food source is living or nonliving.
   e. seen only in animals.

M **12.** Which of the following could NOT be used to describe any fungus?
   a. saprophytic
   b. decomposer
   c. parasitic
 * d. autotrophic
   e. heterotrophic

M **13.** A fungus would be expected to exist as
 * a. a colorless multicellular organism that absorbs the food from its environment.
   b. a small motile organism that would be nocturnal.
   c. an eukaryotic organism that could carry on both photosynthesis and respiration.
   d. an organism that functions as a decomposer in the dark and a producer in the light.
   e. a symbiont or parasite only.

E 14. Most true fungi send out cellular filaments called
    a. mycelia.
  * b. hyphae.
    c. mycorrhizae.
    d. asci.
    e. gills.

D 15. All but which of the following statements concerning fungal body plans are true?
  * a. A mesh of hyphae is composed of mycelia.
    b. Branching filaments are called hyphae.
    c. Cytoplasm can flow from one cell to another.
    d. Cell walls contain chitin.
    e. Some filaments become modified into reproductive structures.

D 16. The chief advantage of the growth habit of the mycelium is
  * a. a large surface-to-volume ratio.
    b. the ability to penetrate organic material.
    c. that it allows for more rapid growth than any other approach.
    d. that it enables the organism to spread through the soil.
    e. that it allows growth in many directions at the same time.

M 17. The walls of fungi contain
    a. cellulose.
    b. lignin.
  * c. chitin.
    d. pectin.
    e. protein.

CONSIDER THE CLUB FUNGI

M 18. The club fungi are members of which of the following?
    a. Ascomycota
  * b. Basidiomycota
    c. Imperfect fungi
    d. Oomycota
    e. Zygomycota

M 19. Mushrooms are members of which of the following?
    a. Ascomycota
  * b. Basidiomycota
    c. Imperfect fungi
    d. Oomycota
    e. Zygomycota

M 20. The most reliable way to distinguish edible mushrooms from poisonous ones is to
    a. look for basidiospores.
    b. distinguish their colors.
    c. reject any with a brownish tint.
  * d. rely on mycologists—fungus experts.

D 21. Members of the Basidiomycota include all but which of the following?
    a. shelf fungi
    b. mushrooms
  * c. downy mildew of grapes and late blight of potatoes
    d. puffballs
    e. toadstools and poisonous mushrooms

E 22. The Basidiomycota include the
    a. sac fungi.
  * b. club fungi.
    c. water molds.
    d. imperfect fungi.
    e. none of these

E 23. Spores can be produced by all but which of the following?
    a. sporangia
    b. mitosis
  * c. gametangia
    d. meiosis

M 24. Which of the following is a diploid stage in the life cycle of fungi?
    a. spores
    b. vegetative growth of hyphae
  * c. zygote
    d. gametes
    e. cells produced by budding or fragmentation

M 25. In what way do fungi reproduce?
    a. asexually, through spores
    b. budding of the parent body
    c. sexually, through gametes
    d. asexually, through spores and budding of the parent body
  * e. asexually, through spores; budding of the parent body; and sexually, through gametes

M 26. A fungal cell that contains two separate haploid nuclei is known as a
    a. mycelium.
    b. hypha.
    c. gametangium.
  * d. dikaryon (dikaryotic).

SPORES AND MORE SPORES

D 27. The major difference between a mature zygospore and a spore produced in the zygomycete sporangium is that the mature zygospore
    a. produces gametes.
    b. is metabolically active.
  * c. is diploid.
    d. is produced asexually.

M 28. Zygospores are produced by
    a. plants only.
  * b. fungi only.
    c. algae only.
    d. plants and fungi.
    e. none of these

M 29. Which organism is a zygomycete?
   a. water mold
   b. smut or rust
 * c. bread mold
   d. mushroom

D 30. The life cycle of a zygomycete differs markedly from that of animals because in this fungus,
   a. there is no sexual stage.
 * b. mitosis occurs in the haploid stage.
   c. there is no fusion of nuclei.
   d. meiosis never occurs.
   e. a diploid stage is unknown.

M 31. Rhizoids are
   a. vegetative hyphae.
 * b. rootlike absorbing filaments.
   c. fruiting bodies.
   d. sexually reproductive organs.
   e. fragments of a mycelium.

M 32. The sac fungi are members of the
 * a. Ascomycota.
   b. Basidiomycota.
   c. Imperfect fungi.
   d. Oomycota.
   e. Zygomycota.

M 33. Yeasts are members of which of the following?
 * a. Ascomycota
   b. Basidiomycota
   c. Imperfect fungi
   d. Oomycota
   e. Zygomycota

E 34. Baking bread and making wine are dependent on organisms that can be identified as
   a. yeasts.
   b. sac fungi.
   c. ascomycota.
   d. yeasts and sac fungi.
 * e. yeasts, sac fungi, and ascomycota

M 35. Edible fungi belong mainly to
   a. Ascomycota.
   b. Basidiomycota.
   c. imperfect fungi.
 * d. Ascomycota and Basidiomycota, only.
   e. Basidiomycota and imperfect fungi, only.

D 36. Which of the following are NOT members of the Ascomycota?
   a yeast
 * b. smuts and rusts
   c. truffles and morels
   d. *Neurospora*
   e. ergot of rye, Dutch elm disease, and chestnut blight

D 37. *Aspergillus* and *Penicillium* are related because both
   a. produce antibiotics.
 * b. reproduce using ascospores.
   c. are club fungi.
   d. parasitize human mucous membranes.
   e. lack known sexual stages.

D 38. Imperfect fungi are those that lack (or do not show)
   a. spores.
 * b. sexual reproduction.
   c. cross walls within hyphae.
   d. rhizoids.

M 39. The structure that people typically refer to as a "mushroom" is in reality the
 * a. basidiocarp.
   b. mycelium.
   c. ascocarp.
   d. hyphal mass.
   e. zygospore.

D 40. Which of the following reproductive structures is incorrectly matched with the group in which it is found?
   a. zygospore: zygomycetes
   b. ascus: sac fungi
 * c. conidia: club fungi
   d. basidiospores: mushrooms
   e. spores: imperfect fungi

THE SYMBIONTS REVISITED

M 41. Lichens are a symbiotic relationship between
   a. a club fungus and a green alga.
   b. a club fungus and a cyanobacterium.
   c. sac fungi and green algae.
   d. sac fungi and cyanobacteria.
 * e. all of these

M 42. Which factor is the most important algal contribution to the fungal component of a lichen?
   a. improved water conservation
   b. mechanical protection from being blown away
 * c. photosynthetically derived food
   d. less overlap between individual algal cells
   e. pigment for camouflage

M 43. A lichen is a composite organism made up of
   a. two different fungi.
 * b. a fungus and an alga.
   c. a fungus and a gymnosperm.
   d. a fungus and a bryophyte.

D 44. In lichens, the more "independent" member is the
 * a. alga.
   b. fungus.
   c. mycorrhiza.
   d. imperfect fungus.
   e. water mold.

D 45. Which of the following is NOT one of the species found in lichens?
   a. sac fungi
   b. green algae
   c. club fungi
   d. cyanobacteria
 * e. imperfect fungi

E   46. Lichens are unable to grow
        a. on bare rocks.
        b. on tree trunks.
    *   c. in polluted areas.
        d. in cold temperatures, such as in the tundra.
        e. none of these

M   47. Despite their tolerance for harsh climates, lichens are particularly intolerant of
        a. drought.
        b. cold.
        c. sunlight.
    *   d. airborne toxic materials.
        e. shade.

E   48. Mycorrhizae are
        a. roots.
        b. bacteria.
    *   c. fungus roots.
        d. isolated plants.
        e. small animals found in agricultural soils.

M   49. Mycorrhizae
        a. increase plant growth.
        b. are symbionts.
        c. allow a plant to absorb more water.
        d. increase the surface area for absorption of water and minerals.
    *   e. all of these

M   50. Algae are to lichens as _____ are to mycorrhizae.
        a. club fungi
    *   b. tree roots
        c. water molds
        d. plant leaves
        e. mosses

Classification Questions

Answer questions 51–55 in reference to the five groups of fungi listed below:

        a. Zygomycetes
        b. Sac fungi
        c. Club fungi
        d. Imperfect fungi

M   51. The common mushroom bought in the average supermarket is most likely a member of this group.

D   52. *Penicillium,* the source of antibiotics, was formerly a member of this group

M   53. The yeast used in the fermentation of grape juice to produce the wines of the world is a member of this group.

D   54. The common black bread mold is a member of this group.

M   55. The delicious, edible morel is a member of this group.

Answers   51. c   52. d   53. b

            54. a   55. c

Selecting the Exception

M   56. Four of the five answers listed below are terms used in describing fungi. Select the exception.
        a. hyphae
    *   b. peptidoglycan
        c. dikaryotic stage
        d. spore
        e. mycelium

D   57. Four of the five answers listed below are related to a common fungal group. Select the exception.
    *   a. asci
        b. zygomycetes
        c. *Rhizopus*
        d. zygote
        e. spore former

M   58. Four of the five answers below can be used in describing aspects of fungal reproduction. Select the exception.
        a. spores
    *   b. pollen
        c. dikaryotic
        d. gametangia
        e. asci

E   59. Four of the five answers below can be used to describe fungal life. Select the exception.
        a. heterotrophic
        b. saprobic
        c. parasitic
        d. decomposer
    *   e. autotrophic

E   60. Four of the five answers below can be used to describe fungal reproductive structures. Select the exception.
        a. asci
    *   b. hyphae
        c. basidia
        d. conidia
        e. spores

CHAPTER 25
ANIMALS: THE INVERTEBRATES

Multiple-Choice Questions

M   **1.** The Burgess Shale is located in
     a. Central America.
*   b. British Columbia.
     c. Olduvai Gorge in Central Africa.
     d. Siberia.
     e. Australia.

M   **2.** The Burgess Shale
*   a. attests to the adaptive radiation of early animals.
     b. provides fossil evidence of the invasion of land by vertebrates.
     c. is one of the richest fossil-fuel deposits in the world.
     d. provides a record of the divergence of the fishes.
     e. has a massive collection of Mesozoic dinosaurs.

M   **3.** Which of the following are on the same branch of the evolutionary tree your text uses?
*   a. rotifers and roundworms
     b. cnidarians and flatworms
     c. annelids and roundworms
     d. earthworms and roundworms
     e. jellyfish and sponges

OVERVIEW OF THE ANIMAL KINGDOM

M   **4.** Which of the following statements is NOT true?
     a. Mammals are vertebrates.
     b. Invertebrates have no backbone.
*   c. There are more vertebrate species than invertebrates.
     d. The phylogenetic tree of animals begins with the sponges.
     e. Arthropods have the most species.

M   **5.** Which of the following characteristics is NOT true of all animal phyla?
     a. multicellular
*   b. organ systems
     c. heterotrophic
     d. diploid
     e. sexual reproduction

M   **6.** All animals are
*   a. multicellular, heterotrophic, and diploid.
     b. multicellular, heterotrophic, and haploid.
     c. multicellular, autotrophic, and diploid.
     d. multicellular, autotrophic, and haploid.

M   **7.** Which of the following insulates various internal organs from the stresses of body-wall movement and bathes them in a liquid through which nutrients and waste products can diffuse?
*   a. a coelom
     b. mesoderm
     c. a mantle
     d. a water-vascular system
     e. all of these

M   **8.** A digestive tract is said to be complete if it
     a. possesses specialized regions for different digestive tasks.
     b. produces acids and contains enzymes.
*   c. is a one-way tube with a mouth and an anus.
     d. is surrounded by muscle.

M   **9.** Major trends in the evolution of animals include
     a. cephalization, the development of a definite head region.
     b. the development of types of symmetry.
     c. variation in coelomic cavities.
     d. the development of segments.
*   e. all of these

D   **10.** Creeping behavior and a mouth located toward the head end of the body may have led, in some evolutionary lines, to
     a. development of a circulatory system with blood.
     b. sexual reproduction.
     c. feeding on nutrients suspended in the water (filter feeding).
*   d. concentration of sense organs in the head region.
     e. radial symmetry.

E   **11.** The most successful of the invertebrate phyla with respect to the numbers of species is
     a. Annelida.
*   b. Arthropoda.
     c. Mollusca.
     d. Echinodermata.
     e. Nematoda.

M   **12.** Which of the following organisms exhibits cephalization?
*   a. snail
     b. sea anemone
     c. sea star
     d. sponge

D 13. Which of the following statements is false?
   a. The development of a coelom was necessary before organisms could develop a large size.
   b. Segmentation allows increasing specialization of body parts.
   c. The development of an elongated gut allows specialized regions to carry out different functions.
* d. Organisms with radial symmetry developed into the ultimate predators.
   e. None of these is false.

M 14. The second greatest number of species in an animal phylum is found in
   a. nematodes.
* b. mollusks.
   c. platyhelminths.
   d. echinoderms.
   e. cnidarians.

D 15. An animal with bilateral symmetry
   a. has left and right sides.
   b. usually displays cephalization.
   c. produces mirror images regardless of the number of "cuts" through the central axis.
* d. has left and right sides and usually displays cephalization.
   e. has left and right sides, usually displays cephalization, and produces mirror images regardless of the number of "cuts" through the central axis.

M 16. Which of the following lack a "true" coelom?
   a. flatworms
   b. annelids
   c. roundworms
* d. flatworms and roundworms
   e. flatworms and annelids

M 17. All but which of the following statements are true of animal segmentation?
* a. Truly segmented animals will display uniform segments from anterior to posterior.
   b. Segmentation is a prelude to specialization of appendages.
   c. Sometimes segmentation is more visible internally than externally.
   d. Segments may be fused together.

PUZZLES ABOUT ORIGINS

E 18. *Trichoplax* is a
   a. sponge.
   b. cnidarian.
* c. placozoan.
   d. ctenophoran.
   e. flatworm.

SPONGES–SUCCESS IN SIMPLICITY

E 19. Poriferans are
   a. herbivores.
* b. filter feeders.
   c. scavengers.
   d. predators.
   e. carnivores.

D 20. Unlike most other animals, sponges lack
   a. a digestive tract.
   b. a symmetrical body plan.
   c. nerve cells.
   d. a digestive tract and a symmetrical body plan.
* e. a digestive tract, a symmetrical body plan, and nerve cells.

D 21. Cells of the outer surface of a sponge obtain nutrients by
   a. absorbing food that diffuses from the central cavity.
   b. capturing food in their microvilli.
* c. absorbing food distributed by amoeboid cells.
   d. phagocytosing bacteria and other small food items.

M 22. Sponges have only which one of the following?
   a. symmetry
   b. organs
   c. anus
* d. skeleton
   e. appendages

M 23. Feeding in sponges is dependent on
   a. collar cells.
   b. pores.
   c. water flow.
   d. pores and water flow.
* e. collar cells, pores, and water flow.

D 24. Which of the following groups does NOT have tissues?
   a. nematodes
* b. sponges
   c. echinoderms
   d. flatworms
   e. cnidarians

M 25. Gemmules
   a. are used in respiration.
   b. capture food.
   c. function in excretion.
   d. serve in digestion.
* e. are reproductive agents.

CNIDARIANS–TISSUES EMERGE

E 26. Mesoglea is found in which of the following groups?
   a. Porifera
* b. Cnidaria
   c. Nematoda
   d. Annelida
   e. Mollusca

E   27.   Nematocysts are
          a. reproductive cells.
          b. excretory organs.
          c. sets of muscle cells.
          d. circulatory cells.
     *   e. defensive cells.

M   28.   Nematocysts are found only in
     *   a. cnidarians.
          b. nematodes.
          c. crustaceans.
          d. echinoderms.

E   29.   "Nerve net" describes the nervous system of
          a. flatworms.
     *   b. cnidarians.
          c. annelids.
          d. sponges.
          e. none of these

E   30.   The bulk of a jellyfish consists of
          a. mesoderm.
          b. mesohyl.
          c. mesophyll.
     *   d. mesoglea.
          e. mesogel.

M   31.   Which of the following phyla is characterized by
          radially symmetrical members?
          a. Arthropoda
     *   b. Cnidaria
          c. Platyhelminthes
          d. Chordata
          e. Annelida

M   32.   Cnidarians do NOT have
          a. tentacles equipped with nematocysts.
     *   b. three germ layers.
          c. radial symmetry.
          d. a gastrovascular cavity.
          e. medusa stages.

M   33.   Which of the following is a stage in the life cycle of
          Obelia, a cnidarian?
          a. medusa
          b. planula
          c. polyp
     *   d. all of these

M   34.   A planula is
          a. a sedentary, attached, tree-shaped form found in
              corals.
     *   b. a swimming larval form with an outer ciliated
              epidermis.
          c. a kind of parasitic worm.
          d. a fleshy lobe that extends laterally from the body
              wall of a marine worm.
          e. a rasplike tongue.

M   35.   In the life cycle of a typical cnidarian, which of the
          following would most likely be free-swimming?
          a. medusa
          b. polyp
          c. planula
     *   d. medusa and planula

D   36.   Members of a colony would be described best by
          which of the following words?
          a. dependent
          b. independent
     *   c. interdependent
          d. nondependent

ACOELOMATE ANIMALS–AND THE SIMPLEST ORGAN SYSTEMS

M   37.   Which body plan is characterized by simple gas
          exchange mechanisms, two-way traffic through a
          highly branched, saclike gut, and a thin, flat body with
          all cells fairly close to the gut?
          a. cnidarian
          b. nematode
          c. echinoderm
     *   d. flatworm

M   38.   Bilateral symmetry is characteristic of
          a. cnidarians.
          b. sponges.
          c. jellyfish.
     *   d. flatworms.
          e. *Hydra*

M   39.   Mesodermal tissue is absent in
          a. sponges.
          b. cnidarians.
          c. flatworms.
     *   d. sponges and cnidarians.
          e. sponges, cnidarians, and flatworms.

E   40.   The first phylum on the evolutionary tree with three
          germ layers was
          a. Cnidaria.
     *   b. Platyhelminthes.
          c. Annelida.
          d. Arthropoda.
          e. Nematoda.

M   41.   The organs of excretion in flatworms are
          a. nephridia.
          b. contractile vacuoles.
          c. Malpighian tubules.
     *   d. protonephridia.
          e. book lungs.

M   42.   Animals that are hermaphroditic usually
          a. fertilize their own eggs.
     *   b. cross-fertilize.
          c. donate eggs to other individuals.
          d. none of these
          e. all of these

D   43.   An organism that possesses a scolex and proglottids
          lacks
          a. bilateral symmetry.
     *   b. a coelom.
          c. mesodermal tissue.
          d. bilateral symmetry and a coelom.
          e. bilateral symmetry, a coelom, and mesodermal
              tissue.

M 44. A scolex is
 * a. the anterior attachment organ of a tapeworm.
   b. the feeding organ of a fluke.
   c. an appendage of a sandworm.
   d. the egg of a sea star.
   e. the larva of an aquatic insect.

D 45. The tapeworm might be called the "ultimate" parasite because it
   a. has no need of a host.
   b. can fertilize itself indefinitely.
   c. is immortal.
 * d. has no digestive tract.
   e. is flat.

D 46. All but which of the following have a circulatory system?
 * a. flukes
   b. insects
   c. earthworms
   d. crayfish
   e. both flukes and insects

ROUNDWORMS

M 47. Which of the following have a tough cuticle, longitudinal muscles, a complete digestive system, and are facultative anaerobes?
 * a. nematodes
   b. cnidarians
   c. flatworms
   d. echinoderms
   e. poriferans

M 48. A segmented body plan does NOT occur in which of the following groups?
   a. arthropods
   b. chordates
   c. annelids
 * d. nematodes

M 49. Hookworms and pinworms are
 * a. nematodes.
   b. flatworms.
   c. annelids.
   d. circular worms.
   e. flukes.

D 50. For roundworms living in the intestine of a vertebrate, the cuticle would most probably serve in what capacity?
   a. water retention
   b. nutrient absorption
 * c. protection from digestive enzymes
   d. excretion of metabolic wastes
   e. sensory detection

E 51. Which of the following is mismatched?
   a. sponges—gemmules
   b. cnidarians—polyp
 * c. nematodes—segmentation
   d. flatworms—flame cell
   e. flatworms—scolex

M 52. Which of the following does NOT include parasites?
   a. flatworms
   b. roundworms
   c. nematodes
 * d. cnidarians
   e. none of these

FOCUS ON HEALTH: A ROGUE'S GALLERY OF WORMS

D 53. In the life cycle of the fluke responsible for schistosomiasis, the intermediate host is
   a. a human.
   b. another fluke.
 * c. a snail.
   d. unknown at this time.

M 54. A common intermediate host for most flukes are
   a. mosquitoes.
 * b. snails.
   c. mice.
   d. flies.
   e. clams.

ROTIFERS

M 55. In size, rotifers would be most comparable to which of the following?
   a. flukes
   b. nematodes
 * c. protistans
   d. jellyfishes
   e. sponges

M 56. Rotifers take their name from
   a. their tumbling movements through the water.
 * b. actions of anterior cilia.
   c. their radial symmetry.
   d. rotational action around the central body axis.

E 57. Rotifers possess
   a. cilia.
   b. jaws.
   c. protonephridia.
   d. nerve cells.
 * e. all of these

M 58. Which of the following is mismatched?
   a. insects—exoskeleton
   b. tapeworms—proglottids
   c. flatworms—bilateral symmetry
 * d. roundworms—incomplete digestive system
   e. rotifers—protonephridia

A MAJOR DIVERGENCE

D 59. Which of the following are deuterostomes?
   a. annelids
 * b. chordates
   c. arthropods
   d. mollusks
   e. all of these

D   60.   Which of the following is a deuterostome?
*   a.   bird
     b.   squid
     c.   fly
     d.   earthworm
     e.   centipede

M   61.   Which of the following is NOT a protostome?
     a.   earthworm
     b.   crayfish
*   c.   sea star
     d.   squid
     e.   clam

D   62.   Which of the following is applicable in describing a deuterostome?
     a.   spiral cleavage
     b.   first embryonic indentation becomes mouth
*   c.   coelom develops from gut outpouchings
     d.   mollusca

M   63.   Which of the following is mismatched?
     a.   cnidarians—nematocysts
     b.   poriferans—spicules
     c.   platyhelminths—bilateral symmetry
*   d.   echinoderms—protostomes
     e.   annelids—segmented body

D   64.   Which of the following is true of deuterostomes?
*   a.   Radial cleavage occurs.
     b.   The first opening that develops becomes the anus.
     c.   The coelom arises from tissues at the side of the blastopore (opening of gut).
     d.   Radial cleavage occurs; and The first opening that develops becomes the anus.
     e.   Radial cleavage occurs; The first opening that develops becomes the anus; and The coelom arises from tissues at the side of the blastopore (opening of gut).

A SAMPLING OF MOLLUSKS

E   65.   A mantle is found only among the
     a.   Arthropoda.
     b.   Annelida.
     c.   Echinodermata.
*   d.   Mollusca.
     e.   Chordata.

E   66.   A radula is an organ found in
     a.   mollusks.
     b.   chitons.
     c.   bivalves.
*   d.   mollusks and chitons.
     e.   mollusks, chitons, and bivalves.

M   67.   Oval body, eight dorsal plates, grazer on rocky coasts is descriptive of
     a.   gastropods.
     b.   snails.
     c.   clams.
     d.   slugs.
*   e.   chitons.

M   68.   A radula is which of the following?
     a.   foot
*   b.   feeding organ
     c.   ear
     d.   sensitive hair
     e.   balance organ

EVOLUTIONARY EXPERIMENTS WITH MOLLUSCAN BODY PLANS

M   69.   Torsion of the body is characteristic of
     a.   mollusks in general.
*   b.   gastropods.
     c.   bivalves.
     d.   squids.
     e.   none of these

D   70.   Torsion could cause which of the following problems?
     a.   blockage of the digestive tract
     b.   misdirected signals in the nerve cord
     c.   self-fertilization of eggs
*   d.   intake of digestive wastes with food
     e.   excessive loss of metabolic water

D   71.   Bivalves lack which of the following molluscan features?
     a.   foot
*   b.   head
     c.   mantle
     d.   shells
     e.   visceral mass

D   72.   Which of the following features do bivalves share with sponges?
     a.   lack of symmetry
     b.   flagellated collar cells
*   c.   suspension feeding
     d.   siphons
     e.   none of these

D   73.   Which of the following is in the phylum characterized by a mantle and a radula?
     a.   lobster
     b.   rotifer
*   c.   octopus
     d.   sand dollar

M   74.   The mollusks with the most complex nervous systems are
     a.   chitons.
*   b.   cephalopods.
     c.   gastropods.
     d.   bivalves.

D   75.   Cephalopods are the only mollusks that possess
     a.   a mantle.
     b.   gills.
*   c.   closed circulation.
     d.   shells.
     e.   closed circulation and shells.

M 76. Which of the following is NOT a characteristic of mollusks?
   a. radula
   b. mantle
   c. ctenidia
 * d. radial cleavage
   e. shell

ANNELIDS–SEGMENTS GALORE

D 77. Which of the following is an organism that possesses setae and nephridia, and exhibits coordinated movements of circular and longitudinal muscle?
   a. millipede
   b. tapeworm
 * c. polychaete
   d. hookworm
   e. flatworm

D 78. Earthworms can perform all but which of the following?
 * a. chewing of food
   b. respiration
   c. tillage of the soil
   d. movement using setae
   e. excretion of water

D 79. The feeding mode of leeches can be described as
   a. predaceous.
   b. internal parasitism.
   c. external bloodsucking.
 * d. predaceous and external bloodsucking.
   e. predaceous, external bloodsucking, and internal parasitism.

D 80. Polychaetes are the only annelids that possess
   a. setae.
   b. jaws or teeth.
 * c. parapods.
   d. ganglia.
   e. a complete digestive tract.

M 81. Which annelid structure may resemble the ancestral structure from which the vertebrate kidney evolved?
   a. trachea
 * b. nephridium
   c. mantle
   d. parapodia
   e. none of these

E 82. Nephridia are
   a. circulatory organs.
   b. respiratory organs.
 * c. excretory organs.
   d. endocrine organs.
   e. part of the nervous system.

M 83. Which of the following features do annelids share in common with roundworms?
   a. pseudocoelom
 * b. cuticle
   c. segmented body
   d. setae
   e. nephridia

M 84. The movement of earthworms is dependent on
   a. circular muscles.
   b. longitudinal muscles.
   c. hydrostatic skeleton.
   d. setae.
 * e. all of these

E 85. Which of the following is NOT related to the other three?
   a. free-living flatworms
 * b. earthworms
   c. flukes
   d. tapeworms

M 86. Which of the following has a gut with two openings, a mouth and an anus?
   a. Cnidaria
 * b. Annelida
   c. Platyhelminthes
   d. Porifera

ARTHROPODS–THE MOST SUCCESSFUL ORGANISMS ON EARTH

M 87. The animal phylum that contains the greatest number of named species is
   a. Mollusca.
 * b. Arthropoda.
   c. Nematoda.
   d. Chordata.
   e. Annelida

M 88. Exoskeletons are most characteristic of which of the following?
   a. Mollusca
 * b. Arthropoda
   c. Echinodermata
   d. Chordata
   e. Annelida

E 89. What are the unique devices used by insects in atmospheric respiration ?
   a. gills.
   b. lunglike chambers.
 * c. tracheas.
   d. mantles
   e. pedipalps

M 90. The exoskeleton of a butterfly does NOT provide which of the following?
   a. physical protection
   b. physical support
   c. an antidesiccant surface
 * d. a respiratory surface

E 91. Molting in arthropods involves primarily a change in
   a. body form and maturity.
   b. sex.
 * c. body size.
   d. eating habits.
   e. sensory structures.

M 92. Which of the following is a disadvantage of an exoskeleton?
* a. It must be shed for its owner to grow.
b. It does not provide as efficient a muscle anchorage as an endoskeleton.
c. It allows for excess water loss.
d. It is not flexible enough to allow a full range of movement.
e. It is not able to absorb pigments for sufficient camouflage.

M 93. The appendages of members of several phyla share common functions; however, only certain appendages of arthropods are capable of
a. walking.
* b. flight.
c. feeding.
d. copulation.
e. swimming.

M 94. The arthropod eye is especially adept at
a. detecting motion.
b. seeing long distances.
c. surveying a wide field.
* d. detecting motion and surveying a wide field.
e. detecting motion, surveying a wide field, and seeing long distances.

E 95. The most successful forms of life that have ever evolved are the
a. vertebrates.
* b. insects.
c. humans.
d. protozoans.
e. mollusks

D 96. Which of the following is NOT an organ for excreting excess water from the body?
a. nephridium
b. flame cell
* c. trachea
d. Malpighian tubule
e. siphon

A LOOK AT SPIDERS AND THEIR KIN

D 97. Which of the following is NOT a chelicerate?
a. tick
* b. mosquito
c. spider
d. horseshoe crab
e. scorpion

E 98. Spiders use which of the following mouthparts for subduing prey?
a. mandibles
b. pedipalps
* c. chelicerae
d. maxillae
e. labial palps

M 99. An unidentified arthropod with no antennae and eight pairs of legs.could be closely related to
a. grasshoppers.
* b. ticks.
c. crayfish.
d. millipedes.
e. trilobites.

D 100. Which animal belongs to a subphylum different from that of the other four?
a. horseshoe crab
* b. shrimp
c. mite
d. spider
e. scorpion

A LOOK AT CRUSTACEANS

M 101. Which of the following groups can be distinguished from the other arthropods by its possession of two pairs of antennae?
a. insects
b. millipedes
c. chelicerates
* d. crustaceans
e. trilobites

HOW MANY LEGS?

M 102. Based on the criterion of segmentation, which organism most closely resembles the earliest ancestral arthropod?
a. dragonfly
* b. millipede
c. tick
d. crab
e. scorpion

M 103. A wormlike arthropod with a flattened body and carnivorous eating habits would be identified as a
a. crustacean.
b. millipede.
c. spider.
d. trilobite.
* e. centipede.

A LOOK AT INSECT DIVERSITY

M 104. Which of the following adaptations has contributed to the success of the insects?
a. specialized sensory organs
b. wings
c. high reproductive capacity
d. specialized sensory organs and wings
* e. specialized sensory organs, wings, and high reproductive capacity

M 105. In the course of evolution, the thorax of an insect has become specialized for
  a. digestion.
  b. reproduction.
  * c. locomotion.
  d. excretion.
  e. sensation

THE PUZZLING ECHINODERMS

D 106. Which phylum is strictly marine, with no freshwater or terrestrial forms?
  * a. Echinodermata
  b. Platyhelminthes
  c. Cnidaria
  d. Mollusca
  e. Annelida

M 107. A water-vascular system is characteristic of the phylum
  a. Arthropoda.
  b. Annelida.
  c. Chordata.
  d. Mollusca.
  * e. Echinodermata.

D 108. Parasites of humans are found in all but which of the following phyla?
  a. Platyhelminthes
  b. Nematoda
  c. Annelida
  * d. Echinodermata
  e. Arthropoda

D 109. Which of the following groups contains organisms that produce free-living larvae?
  a. cnidarians
  b. echinoderms
  c. arthropods
  d. cnidarians and echinoderms
  * e. cnidarians, echinoderms, and arthropods

M 110. The water-vascular system is unique to
  a. cnidarians.
  b. bivalves.
  * c. echinoderms.
  d. annelids.
  e. arthropods.

M 111. The water-vascular system is used primarily for
  a. excretion of excess water.
  * b. locomotion.
  c. respiration.
  d. circulation.
  e. sensation.

E 112. A feature found only in echinoderms is the
  a. radula.
  * b. water-vascular system.
  c. nephridium.
  d. nematocyst.
  e. mandible.

E 113. The most unusual feature of the echinoderms is
  a. a motile larval form.
  b. the presence of a radula.
  c. radial symmetry.
  * d. a water-vascular system.
  e. the protonephridial network.

E 114. Which phylum is represented by marine members only?
  a. Mollusca
  * b. Echinodermata
  c. Platyhelminthes
  d. Annelida

Matching Questions

D 115. Matching. Choose the most appropriate answer for each.
  1. ___ millipede
  2. ___ annelids
  3. ___ arthropods
  4. ___ placozoan
  5. ___ cnidarians
  6. ___ echinoderms
  7. ___ flatworms
  8. ___ rotifers
  9. ___ mollusks
  10. ___ roundworms
  11. ___ sponges

  A. two pairs of legs per segment
  B. the simplest animal
  C. planarians, flukes, tapeworms
  D. nematodes
  E. snails, squids, clams
  F. wheel animals
  G. collar cells present
  H. jellyfish and corals
  I. crustaceans, ticks, and insects
  J. polychaetes, earthworms, leeches
  K. sea urchins, sea stars

Answers: 1. A   2. J   3. I   4. B
            5. H   6. K   7. C   8. F
            9. E   10. D   11. G

Classification Questions

Answer questions 116-120 in reference to the five animal phyla listed below:

> a. Porifera
> b. Cnidaria
> c. Platyhelminthes
> d. Nematoda
> e. Annelida

D **116.** Members of this phylum have a pseudocoelomic cavity.

D **117.** Members of this group have a brain with nerve cords, a saclike or branched gut, and lack a circulatory system.

M **118.** Members of this phylum have a brain with a ventral nerve cord, a complete gut, and a circulatory system that is usually closed.

E **119.** This phylum contains the most primitive species of the animal kingdom.

M **120.** Tapeworms are members of this phylum.

Answers   116. d   117. c   118. e

   119. a   120. c

Answer questions 121-125 in reference to the five animal phyla listed below:

> a. Annelida
> b. Arthropoda
> c. Mollusca
> d. Echinodermata
> e. Rotifera

D **121.** Trilobites were members of this phylum.

M **122.** The larval stage in this phylum has bilateral symmetry, whereas the adult stage exhibits radial symmetry.

M **123.** Although most are enclosed by hardened shells, this phylum name literally means "soft body."

E **124.** This phylum has the greatest number of species.

D **125.** Wheel animals are in this phylum.

Answers   121. b   122. d   123. c

   124. b   125. e

Selecting the Exception

M **126.** Four of the five answers listed below are characteristics of the majority of animals. Select the exception.
   a. multicellular
 * b. exhibit alternation of generations
   c. usually motile at least during part of their life cycle
   d. usually diploid, sexually reproducing forms of life
   e. usually heterotrophic

D **127.** Four of the five answers listed below are related. Select the exception.
   a. jellyfish
   b. hydra
 * c. tunicates
   d. corals
   e. sea anemones

D **128.** Four of the five answers listed below are related. Select the exception.
   a. sea star
 * b. sea anemone
   c. sea urchin
   d. sea lily
   e. sea cucumber

D **129.** Four of the five answers listed below possess some type of coelom. Select the exception.
   a. nematodes
   b. annelids
   c. arthropods
   d. mollusks
 * e. platyhelminths

M **130.** Four of the five answers listed below are features found in sponges. Select the exception.
 * a. mesoglea
   b. spicule
   c. gemmule
   d. osculum
   e. collar and amoeboid cells

M **131.** Four of the five answers listed below are characteristics of cnidarians. Select the exception.
   a. planula larvae
   b. polyp form
   c. mesoglea
   d. nematocyst
 * e. pharynx

M **132.** Four of the five answers listed below relate to flatworms. Select the exception.
   a. proglottid
 * b. seta
   c. scolex
   d. flame cell
   e. first form to develop a mesoderm

M **133.** Four of the five answers listed below are parasitic. Select the exception.
 * a. planaria
   b. flukes
   c. nematodes
   d. leeches
   e. tapeworms

D **134.** Three of the four answers listed below are features of deuterostome development. Select the exception.
   a. first opening develops into the anus
   b. radial cleavage
   c. pouches on wall of gut separate to form the coelom
 * d. spiral cleavage

D 135. Four of the five answers listed below have a common relationship. Select the exception.
a. first segmented form
b. possess nephridia
* c. jointed appendages
d. setae
e. complete gut with closed circulatory system and coelom

E 136. Four of the five answers listed below have a common relationship. Select the exception.
a. crabs
b. shrimps
c. lobsters
* d. centipedes
e. barnacles

M 137. Four of the five answers listed below are crayfish appendages. Select the exception.
a. antennae
b. maxillae
* c. pedipalps
d. swimmerets
e. chelipeds

M 138. Four of the five answers listed below are grasshopper mouthparts. Select the exception.
* a. proboscis
b. maxilla
c. palps
d. mandible
e. labrum

M 139. Four of the five answers listed below are molluscan body features. Select the exception.
a. ctenidia
b. head and foot
c. mantle
* d. carapace
e. radula

M 140. Four of the five answers listed below are characteristics of adult sea stars. Select the exception.
a. spiny skin
b. tube foot
c. water-vascular system
* d. bilateral symmetry
e. ampulla

CHAPTER 26
ANIMALS: THE VERTEBRATES

Multiple-Choice Questions

M **1.** The duckbilled platypus has _____ characteristics.
   a. avian
   b. reptilian
   c. amphibian
   d. mammalian
 * e. all but "amphibian"

M **2.** Which of the following characteristics is unique to the duckbilled platypus?
   a. possession of a cloaca
 * b. separate sensory systems for land and water
   c. pelvic girdle
   d. mouth
   e. flattened tail

M **3.** The duckbilled platypus is found in
 * a. Australia.
   b. the Galápagos Islands.
   c. New Zealand.
   d. Borneo.
   e. Greenland.

THE CHORDATE HERITAGE

M **4** Which of the following statements is NOT true?
   a. All chordates have notochords.
   b. All chordates have pharyngeal pouches or perforations.
   c. All chordates have dorsal tubular nerve cords.
 * d. All chordates are vertebrates.
   e. Chordates are found in all major types of environments.

E **5.** The notochord is most closely associated with the
   a. nervous system.
   b. spinal cord.
 * c. skeletal system.
   d. skin system.

E **6.** The only chordate feature still present in the human adult is
   a. pharyngeal gill slits.
 * b. nerve cord.
   c. notochord.
   d. tail.
   e. all of these

E **7.** Which of the following statements is false?
 * a. All vertebrates have a ventral tubular nervous system.
   b. All vertebrates have a tail at some stage in their life cycle.
   c. All vertebrates have a notochord at some stage in their life cycle.
   d. All vertebrates have pharyngeal gill slits at some stage in their life cycle.

M **8.** Which of the following is NOT a feature that is found exclusively among all vertebrates?
   a. notochord
   b. pharyngeal gill slits
 * c. four legs
   d. post-anal tail
   e. dorsal nerve cord

M **9.** In filter-feeding chordates, which structure has cilia that create water currents and mucous sheets that capture nutrients suspended in the water?
   a. notochord
   b. differentially permeable membrane
   c. filiform tongue
 * d. gill slit
   e. jaw

M **10.** The invertebrate chordates are
 * a. filter feeders.
   b. scavengers.
   c. herbivores.
   d. predators.
   e. parasites.

M **11.** A form of metamorphosis is found in
   a. tunicates.
   b. insects.
   c. amphibians.
   d. tunicates and amphibians.
 * e. tunicates, amphibians, and insects.

M **12.** Which of the following is a diagnostic feature of the sea squirts that forms the basis for its classification?
   a. metamorphosis from a motile larva to a sessile adult
   b. a heart that allows circulation of blood
 * c. a notochord located in the tail of the larva
   d. sexual reproduction during the larval stage
   e. the presence of a tunic or coat over the body of the adult

M 13. During the life of a tunicate, the notochord
a. is present throughout life.
* b. appears in the larva only.
c. develops during adulthood.
d. is completely absent.
e. changes into the nerve cord.

E 14. The "tunic" of tunicate refers to
* a. a body covering.
b. the type of food-gathering mechanism.
c. muscle arrangements in the larva.
d. the immature stage of a true fish.

E 15. "Sessile" could properly be used when referring to
* a. sea squirts.
b. ostracoderms.
c. amphibians.
d. true fishes.
e. all of these

M 16. Suspension feeding is used by
a. sea squirts.
b. clams.
c. sponges.
d. lancelets.
* e. all of these

M 17. Lancelets possess which of the following all their lives?
a. notochord
b. gill slits
c. nerve cord
d. notochord and nerve cord
* e. notochord, nerve cord, and gill slits

E 18. Lancelets are
a. predators.
* b. filter feeders.
c. scavengers.
d. parasites.
e. scrapers that feed on the ocean bottom.

TRENDS IN VERTEBRATE EVOLUTION

M 19. Which phylum is most closely related phylogenetically to the first vertebrates?
* a. Echinodermata
b. Arthropoda
c. Mollusca
d. Annelida
e. none of these

E 20. Which of the following is NOT a subphylum of Chordata?
a. Urochordata
* b. Hemichordata
c. Cephalochordata
d. Vertebrata

M 21. Which of the following is NOT one of the trends of vertebrate evolution?
a. conversion of the support for locomotion from the notochord to the vertebral column
b. expansion of the nerve cord to form the brain and spinal cord
c. changes in the respiratory system from gills to lungs with accompanying changes in the circulatory system
* d. increases in size, speed, strength, and physical processes
e. modification of limbs for more efficient movement

D 22. The evolution of vertebrates
a. is believed to have proceeded from cephalochordates.
b. is most closely tied to urochordates.
* c. is probably in a lineage apart from present-day invertebrate chordates.
d. possibly proceeded from cephalochordates to hemichordates.

E 23. Which of the following would be considered to be more primitive and perhaps ancestral to the others?
a. urochordates
b. hemichordates
* c. hypothetical ancestral deuterostome
d. cephalochordates
e. agnathans

D 24. In vertebrate evolution, the appearance of the vertebral column led most directly to development of
a. limbs such as arms and legs.
* b. jaws.
c. sense organs and the nervous system.
d. more efficient breathing systems.
e. greater speed of locomotion.

M 25. In fishes ancestral to land vertebrates, pouches in the gut wall developed into
a. heart chambers.
b. the notochord.
c. lobes of the liver.
* d. lungs.
e. vocal cords.

M 26. The ostracoderms were
a. an ancient group of spiny, thin echinoderms.
b. a group of primitive protochordates.
* c. primitive fishes without jaws.
d. one of the first terrestrial vertebrates.
e. reptiles with a bony skin.

M 27. The chief predators of the ostracoderms were
a. sharks.
b. ichthyosaurs, swimming reptiles.
c. large agnathans.
* d. sea scorpions two meters long.
e. trilobites.

M 28. Ostracoderms lost out in evolutionary competition to animals
   a. with more protective body coverings.
   b. who were filter feeders.
   c. with lungs.
   * d. that had begun to develop jaws.
   e. with an exoskeleton.

M 29. Placoderms were the first fishes to display
   * a. jaws.
   b. gill openings.
   c. cartilaginous skeletons.
   d. jaws and gill openings.
   e. jaws, gill openings, and cartilaginous skeletons.

M 30. Which of the following classes is represented only by fossil forms?
   a. Agnatha
   b. Amphibia
   c. Aves
   * d. Placodermi
   e. Chondrichthyes

M 31. The chief advance of the placoderms was the development of
   a. paired fins for efficient movement.
   * b. paired jaws that enabled them to bite and feed.
   c. bony plates for protection.
   d. an efficient set of lungs.
   e. a strengthened notochord.

EXISTING JAWLESS FISHES

M 32. The most primitive, but still existing, vertebrates are members of the class
   * a. Agnatha.
   b. Amphibia.
   c. Chondrichthyes.
   d. Aves.
   e. Osteichthyes.

M 33. The agnathans were not considered to be very formidable vertebrate challengers to the invertebrates with which they coexisted because they
   a. were poor swimmers due to the lack of paired fins needed for coordinated movement.
   b. lacked paired jaws.
   c. did not have protective plates like the ostracoderms.
   d. were filter feeders that did not compete with predator invertebrates.
   * e. all of these

M 34. The feeding habits of lampreys are best described as
   a. suspension feeding.
   b. predatory.
   * c. parasitic.
   d. scavenging.
   e. all of these

M 35. The first class to evolve was the
   a. Aves.
   b. Reptilia.
   c. Osteichthyes.
   * d. Agnatha.

D 36. The term *agnathan* could be used to describe
   a. ostracoderms.
   b. placoderms.
   c. hagfish.
   * d. ostracoderms and hagfish.
   e. placoderms and hagfish.

M 37. The vertebrate jaw first appeared in
   * a. fishes.
   b. amphibians.
   c. reptiles.
   d. birds.
   e. mammals.

EXISTING JAWED FISHES

E 38. Sharks, rays, and skates belong to the class
   a. Aves.
   b. Amphibia.
   * c. Chondrichthyes.
   d. Osteichthyes.
   e. Reptilia.

E 39. Sharks differ from most other fish in that they lack
   a. lungs.
   b. scales.
   * c. bone.
   d. paired appendages.

M 40. The feeding behavior of true fishes selected for highly developed
   a. parapodia.
   b. notochords.
   * c. sense organs.
   d. gill slits.
   e. motile organs.

M 41. In true fishes, the gills primarily serve which function?
   * a. gas exchange
   b. feeding
   c. water elimination
   d. both feeding and gas exchange
   e. all of these

M 42. Which sequence most accurately describes the complete path of blood through the circulatory system of a fish?
   a. atrium——>ventricle——>gill capillaries ——>atrium——>ventricle——>all other capillaries
   b. atrium——>ventricle——>gill capillaries
   c. gill capillaries——>atrium——>ventricle ——>all other capillaries
   * d. gill capillaries——>all other capillaries ——>atrium——>ventricle

D 43. All but which of the following have cartilaginous skeletons?
    a. sharks
    b. lampreys
  * c. perch
    d. rays

M 44. Which of the following statements is false?
    a. Shark's teeth are modified scales that are continuously shed and replaced.
    b. Many fish use a swim bladder to provide buoyancy control.
  * c. The bony fishes were the ancestors of the cartilaginous fishes.
    d. The ray-finned fishes are the most numerous and diverse of the fish groups.
    e. The lobe-finned fish gave rise to the ray-finned fish.

M 45. Which of the following is associated with lobe-finned fish?
    a. cartilage
    b. replaceable teeth
    c. dermal rays
  * d. lungs
    e. none of these

E 46. The vertebrate lung first appeared in which organisms?
  * a. fishes
    b. amphibians
    c. reptiles
    d. birds
    e. mammals

THE RISE OF AMPHIBIANS

D 47. Amphibians most likely evolved from
  * a. fish with lobed fins.
    b. ray-finned fish.
    c. reptiles.
    d. agnathans.
    e. placoderms.

E 48. The only class that does NOT include animals with scales covering any part of the body is
    a. Aves.
  * b. Amphibia.
    c. Reptilia.
    d. Osteichthyes.

E 49. Amphibians are completely dependent on an aquatic environment for
    a. respiration.
    b. feeding.
  * c. reproduction.
    d. respiration and reproduction.
    e. respiration, reproduction, and feeding.

M 50. Amphibians are distinguished from earlier vertebrates by
    a. the development of eggs capable of hatching on land.
    b. metamorphosis.
  * c. the development of limbs capable of moving on land.
    d. the presence of scales to prevent desiccation.
    e. absence of gills in any stage of development.

M 51. A water environment provides more of which of the following than does air?
    a. support
    b. buoyancy
    c. constancy of temperature
  * d. oxygen
    e. resistance to movement

D 52. When the vertebrates invaded land, they encountered several conditions. Which of the following most favored the invasion?
    a. an increased gravitational force not encountered in water
    b. more efficient lungs due to increased oxygen content of air
    c. more extreme temperature variations
  * d. absence of predators and competitors
    e. absence of prey

M 53. The vertebrate sense that underwent the least developmental change with the invasion of land was
    a. smell.
    b. hearing.
    c. vision.
  * d. touch.
    e. balance.

M 54. Members of the _____ are noted for the ability of larval forms to reproduce sexually.
    a. Aves
    b. Osteichthyes
  * c. Amphibia
    d. Reptilia
    e. Mammalia

M 55. Frogs
    a. have a three-chambered heart.
    b. have an open circulatory system.
    c. use their skin and pharynx as respiratory surfaces.
    d. have a tongue that is anchored at the front of the mouth.
  * e. all but "have an open circulatory system" are true

E 56. The heart in amphibians
    a. pumps blood more rapidly than does the heart of fish.
    b. is efficient enough for amphibians but would not be for birds and mammals.
    c. has three chambers (one ventricle and two atria).
    d. is part of a double circuit of blood flow
  * e. all of these

M 57. Which class has a heart with two atria and one ventricle?
  a. Aves
  * b. Amphibia
  c. Chondrichthyes
  d. Osteichthyes
  e. Mammalia

E 58. Exchange of respiratory gases through the skin is a characteristic of many
  a. fish.
  * b. amphibians.
  c. reptiles.
  d. mammals.
  e. birds

M 59. In which group are retention of larval characteristic and sexual maturity seen in the same body?
  a. toads
  * b. salamanders
  c. frogs
  d. caecilians

D 60. In the evolution of vertebrates, the first evidence of separate pulmonary and systemic circuits for blood flow is seen in
  a. bony fishes.
  b. cartilaginous fishes.
  c. reptiles.
  d. birds.
  * e. amphibians.

THE RISE OF AMNIOTES

M 61. Vertebrate colonization of terrestrial habitats increased dramatically with the evolution of
  a. lungs.
  b. paired appendages.
  * c. shelled eggs.
  d. the four-chambered heart.
  e. scales.

M 62. In the Late Carboniferous, reptiles were able to move into new habitats because of
  a. the increase in numbers of insect prey.
  b. internal fertilization.
  c. the amniotic egg.
  d. internal fertilization and the amniotic egg, only.
  * e. the increase in numbers of insect prey, internal fertilization, and the amniotic egg.

M 63. The early amniotes
  * a. developed a land egg.
  b. had a four-chambered heart.
  c. had lungs equipped with air sacs.
  d. were bipedal and gave rise to the mammals.

M 64. Amniotes differ from earlier vertebrates by
  a. their large size.
  b. their three-chambered heart.
  * c. internal fertilization.
  d. the possession of a slimy skin.
  e. having external scales.

E 65. The first group to exhibit an amniotic egg belonged to the
  a. Aves.
  b. Amphibia.
  * c. Reptilia.
  d. Osteichthyes.
  e. Mammalia.

D 66. Reptiles resemble _____ in not being able to _____.
  a. fish; leave the water
  b. birds; breathe using lungs
  c. ostracoderms; utilize their jaws
  * d. amphibians; maintain a constant body temperature

M 67. The amniotes differ from the amphibians in that they
  a. have a more developed cerebral cortex.
  b. have scales that prevented desiccation.
  c. have internal fertilization.
  d. use a shelled amniotic egg.
  * e. all of these

A SAMPLING OF EXISTING REPTILES

D 68. The most primitive of the current reptiles based upon the time of divergence from the stem reptiles are the
  a. crocodiles.
  b. snakes.
  c. tuataras.
  d. lizards.
  * e. turtles.

D 69. Which of the following statements is false?
  a. Turtle shells may contribute to heat retention during hot weather.
  b. Turtles do not have teeth.
  * c. Turtle shells are enlarged in marine forms.
  d. Turtles must return to land to lay eggs.
  e. In some turtles, the temperatures in the egg's environment control the sex of the developing embryo.

M 70. Which of the following statements is false?
  * a. Lizards are a very small component of the present-day reptiles.
  b. Lizards gave rise to the snakes.
  c. Lizards are primarily insect eaters.
  d. Lizards can break off their tails to serve as a distraction to predators.
  e. Lizards are most numerous in deserts and tropical forests.

BIRDS

M 71. The reptile group believed to be most closely related to the birds is
  a. turtles.
  b. snakes.
  c. lizards.
  d. tuataras.
  * e. crocodilians.

D 72. An organism that possesses feathers must also possess
    a. malpighian tubules.
    b. a three-chambered heart.
*   c. a dorsal nerve cord.
    d. a pseudocoelom.
    e. replaceable teeth

E 73. Birds differ from earlier vertebrates by
    a. their lack of scales.
    b. the land egg.
*   c. the ability to maintain a constant body temperature.
    d. the ability to fertilize eggs internally.
    e. their possession of a dorsal nerve cord.

D 74. Birds and mammals share which of the following characteristics?
    a. ectothermy (body temperature regulated by environment)
    b. body hair
*   c. four-chambered heart
    d. lung design
    e. amniotic egg

M 75. Adaptations for flight in birds include all but which of the following?
*   a. sound production
    b. lightweight bones
    c. feathers
    d. efficient respiration
    e. four-chambered heart

THE RISE OF MAMMALS

M 76. Which adaptation(s) is (are) common to insects and mammals?
*   a. jointed appendages
    b. closed circulatory system
    c. lungs
    d. jointed appendages and closed circulatory system
    e. jointed appendages, closed circulatory system, and lungs.

M 77. Egg-laying mammals
    a. cannot feed their young with milk.
*   b. have no teeth.
    c. are hairless.
    d. are confined to South America.
    e. bear their young into pouches.

PORTFOLIO OF EXISTING MAMMALS

D 78. Which of the following statements concerning the placenta is incorrect?
    a. It nourishes the young in the uterus.
    b. Nutrients pass to the fetus.
*   c. It is entirely a maternal structure.
    d. It promotes faster growth than does the pouch of marsupials.
    e. It cleans the fetal blood of impurities.

TRENDS IN PRIMATE EVOLUTION

E 79. Which is NOT an anthropoid?
    a. orangutan
*   b. lemur
    c. spider monkey
    d. gibbon

M 80. Humans are least closely related to the
    a. chimpanzee.
    b. orangutan.
    c. gorilla.
*   d. tarsier.
    e. gibbon.

M 81. Which group includes all the others?
    a. tarsoids
    b. hominoids
    c. prosimians
    d. anthropoids
*   e. primates

M 82. Humans belong to all but which one of the following?
    a. hominids
    b. hominoids
*   c. prosimians
    d. anthropoids
    e. primates

E 83. Which of the following can be included in the group called "hominids"?
    a. monkeys
*   b. humans
    c. apes
    d. humans and apes, only
    e. monkeys, humans, and apes

E 84. The evolutionary trend of bipedalism refers to the
    a. ability of only humans to ride a bicycle.
*   b. human ability to habitually walk on two feet.
    c. use of two hands to swing through the trees as monkeys do.
    d. development of a prehensile hand.
    e. use of feet as well as hands for grasping.

E 85. Well-developed molars would be most valuable to
    a. cats.
    b. meat-eaters.
*   c. cows.
    d. dogs.
    e. birds.

M 86. The study of teeth tells the researcher what about an animal?
    a. its diet
    b. its life-style
    c. its intelligence
*   d. its diet and life-style
    e. its diet, life-style, and intelligence

M 87. In the course of the evolution of existing primate groups, there has been a general decrease in
* a. number of offspring produced by a female.
   b. body size.
   c. life span.
   d. duration of infant dependency.

E 88. All but which factor were important evolutionary adaptations in primates?
   a. enhanced stereoscopic vision
   b. upright position
   c. an opposable thumb
* d. the development of a restricted or specialized diet
   e. the ability to move the limbs and head freely in any direction

M 89. Behavioral trends in primate evolution include
   a. longer life spans.
   b. longer learning period and dependence on parents.
   c. lower reproductive rate.
   d. longer periods between pregnancies.
* e. all of these

M 90. Which characteristic is NOT considered to have been a key character in early primate evolution?
   a. eyes adapted for discerning color and shape in a three-dimensional field
   b. body and limbs adapted for bipedalism
* c. greater jaw and dental specialization
   d. more complex cultural behavior
   e. opposable thumb and forefinger

E 91. The ability to grasp objects by wrapping the hand around them is termed
   a. opposable.
   b. grabbing.
* c. prehensile.
   d. grappling.
   e. hooking.

E 92. The ability to hold a paintbrush as an artist does is to the thumb and fingers being
   a. prehensile.
   b. in line with each other.
   c. bendable.
   d. muscular.
* e. opposable.

M 93. The most recent level of evolution in primates is considered to be in
   a. brain expansion.
* b. behavior and culture.
   c. dentition.
   d. hand grip.
   e. daytime vision.

M 94. The location of the eyes on the front of the head in later primates was especially important in
   a. seeing color.
   b. detecting light intensity.
   c. predatory behavior.
* d. seeing in three dimensions.
   e. mating.

FROM EARLY PRIMATES TO HOMINIDS

M 95. In the evolution of the arboreal primates, which of the following features would NOT be an important evolutionary advancement?
   a. opposable thumbs
   b. stereoscopic vision
* c. elongated snout with well-developed sense of smell
   d. the ability to see in color
   e. a brain with a well-developed ability to judge distances and with the ability to quickly compensate for misjudgments

E 96. The primates first arose about how many million years ago?
   a. 75
* b. 60
   c. 50
   d. 40
   e. 30

M 97. The most primitive living primate is the
   a. Old World monkey.
   b. lemur.
   c. New World monkey.
* d. tree shrew.
   e. tarsier.

E 98. All of the placental mammals apparently arose from ancestral forms of
* a. Insectivora, which includes omnivorous shrews and moles.
   b. Carnivora, which includes dogs, cats, and seals.
   c. Rodentia, which includes mice and beavers.
   d. Metatheria, which includes the opossum and kangaroo.
   e. Primates, which means first.

M 99. Primitive primates generally live
* a. in tropical and subtropical forest canopies.
   b. in temperate savanna and grassland habitats.
   c. near rivers, lakes, and streams in the East African Rift Valley.
   d. in caves with abundant supplies of insects.
   e. all of these

M 100. The first known primates were characterized as
* a. arboreal and nocturnal.
   b. ground-dwelling and nocturnal.
   c. arboreal and diurnal.
   d. ground-dwelling and diurnal.

M 101. The diet of the direct ancestors of primates did NOT include
* a. grass.
   b. insects.
   c. fruits.
   d. seeds.

M 102. In comparison to the Oligocene, the climate at the start of the Miocene
    a. remained the same.
    b. became wetter and warmer.
*   c. became drier and cooler.
    d. became wetter and cooler.
    e. became drier and warmer.

M 103. Which group is considered most ancient?
    a. *Homo erectus*
    b. *Australopithecus afarensis*
    c. *Australopithecus africanus*
    d. *Homo sapiens*
*   e. *Catopithecus*

M 104. The anthropoids of the Oligocene lived in
    a. hot, dry deserts.
    b. grassy, savannas.
*   c. forests.
    d. the watery swamps.
    e. cool, and pleasant mountains.

M 105. The great adaptive radiation of hominoids in the Miocene is attributable to
    a. the proliferation of complex forests.
*   b. an extended cooling and drying trend.
    c. the advent of bipedalism.
    d. the evolution of a large brain.
    e. changes in tooth structure.

M 106. Hominids evolved when the climate was
    a. wet and hotter.
    b. wet and cooler.
    c. dry and hotter.
*   d. dry and cooler.

M 107. The hominids are characterized by
    a. further expansion and elaboration of the brain.
    b. bipedalism.
    c. omnivorous feeding behavior.
    d. further expansion and elaboration of the brain plus bipedalism.
*   e. further expansion and elaboration of the brain plus bipedalism and omnivorous feeding behavior.

D 108. How long ago did the hominid evolutionary line diverge from that leading to the great apes?
    a. about 3 million years ago
*   b. somewhere between 10 million and 5 million years ago
    c. during the Eocene epoch
    d. less than 2 million years ago
    e. about 1.5 million years ago

E 109. Hominids are characterized as being
    a. insectivores.
    b. herbivores.
    c. carnivores.
*   d. omnivores.
    e. none of these

E 110. The early hominid fossils are found in
*   a. Africa.
    b. Asia.
    c. Australia.
    d. the South Pacific.
    e. Europe.

M 111. The most important feature of the recent evolution of humans has been
    a. increase in size.
    b. habitat changes.
*   c. cultural evolution.
    d. social behavior.
    e. morphological changes.

M 112. Perhaps the greatest asset possessed by early hominids was
    a. their use of many different kinds of foods.
    b. the ability to walk without using the forelimbs.
    c. a heavy, muscular build.
*   d. the ability to reason and learn.
    e. less hair on the body.

M 113. Fossils of the earliest known hominids are approximately how many millions of years old?
    a. more than 20
    b. about 10
*   c. between 4 and 2
    d. less than 0.5

M 114. The primate fossil named Lucy was a(n)
    a. dryopith.
*   b. australopith.
    c. cercopith.
    d. prosimian.
    e. hominid.

M 115. Which of the following is a hominid?
    a. chimpanzee
*   b. *Australopithecus*
    c. baboon
    d. chimpanzee and *Australopithecus*
    e. chimpanzee, *Australopithecus,* and baboon

M 116. The conclusion that early hominids were bipedal is based on examination of
    a. the angles made by the bones that articulate with the pelvis.
    b. fossil footprints.
    c. imprints of motor cortex in fossilized craniums.
*   d. the angles made by the bones that articulate with the pelvis and fossil footprints.
    e. the angles made by the bones that articulate with the pelvis, fossil footprints, and imprints of motor cortex in fossilized craniums.

M   117.   Australopiths
            a. were bipedal.
            b. had their body weight centered under the pelvis.
            c. had a cranial capacity of over 600 cubic
                centimeters.
    *   d. were bipedal and had their body weight centered
                under the pelvis.
            e. were bipedal, had their body weight centered
                under the pelvis, and had a cranial capacity of over
                600 cubic centimeters.

D   118.   Bipedal behavior and a skeleton adapted for
            bipedalism were not weeded out by natural selection
            because they
            a. improved stability during locomotion.
    *   b. enabled the forelimbs to efficiently manipulate the
                environment.
            c. accelerated the development of binocular vision.
            d. improved stability during locomotion and enabled
                the forelimbs to efficiently manipulate the
                environment.
            e. improved stability during locomotion, enabled the
                forelimbs to efficiently manipulate the
                environment, and accelerated the development of
                binocular vision.

EMERGENCE OF EARLY HUMANS

M   119.   It is thought that the earliest tools were used by
            hominids to
            a. assist in locomotion.
            b. provide protection.
    *   c. facilitate the processing of food.
            d. ward off predators.

M   120.   The first toolmakers were
            a. *Australopithecus africanus.*
            b. *Australopithecus robustus.*
            c. *Australopithecus boisei.*
    *   d. *Homo habilis .*
            e. *Homo erectus.*

E   121.   The oldest hominid fossils have been found in
            a. North America.
            b. Eurasia.
    *   c. Africa.
            d. Australia.

M   122.   Fossil evidence suggests that the earliest members of
            the genus *Homo* were
            a. social.
            b. omnivorous.
            c. toolmakers.
            d. social and omnivorous.
    *   e. social, omnivorous, and toolmakers.

M   123.   The first to make use of controlled fires were
            a. *Australopithecus africanus.*
            b. *Australopithecus robustus.*
            c. *Australopithecus boisei.*
            d. *Homo habilis .*
    *   e. *Homo erectus.*

D   124.   Although the phylogenetic lineages for hominids are
            not definitive, which of the following statements is
            NOT a possibility?
    *   a. *Homo* preceded *Australopithecus.*
            b. *Homo sapiens* is the most recent.
            c. *Australopithecus* is probably more ancient than
                Homo.
            d. *Homo erectus* preceded *Homo sapiens.*
            e. *Homo* and *Australopithecus* may have evolved at
                the same time.

M   125.   The geographical distribution of hominids changed
            dramatically during the Pleistocene due to the
            migrations of
            a. *Australopithecus robustus.*
            b. *Australopithecus boisei.*
    *   c. *Homo erectus.*
            d. *Homo sapiens.*

THE EMERGENCE OF MODERN HUMANS

M   126.   Which of the following statements about Neandertals
            is false?
            a. The oldest Neandertal fossils are 500,000 years
                old.
            b. Neandertal settlements show little evidence of
                tools.
            c. Neandertal brains were larger than those of
                modern humans.
    *   d. The oldest Neandertal fossils are 500,000 years
                old; and Neandertal settlements show little
                evidence of tools.
            e. The oldest Neandertal fossils are 500,000 years
                old; and Neandertal settlements show little
                evidence of tools; and Neandertal brains were
                larger than those of modern humans.

M   127.   Neandertals were members of
            a. *Australopithecus robustus.*
            b. *Australopithecus boisei.*
            c. *Homo habilis* (early *Homo*).
            d. *Homo erectus.*
    *   e. *Homo sapiens.*

M   128.   About 40,000 years ago, what kind of evolution
            replaced biological evolution in the shaping of modern
            humans?
    *   a. cultural
            b. behavioral
            c. chemical
            d. psychological
            e. morphological

M   129.   A hominid of Europe and Asia that became extinct
            nearly 30,000 years ago was
            a. a dryopith.
            b. *Australopithecus.*
            c. *Homo erectus.*
    *   d. Neandertals.

D 130. "Long, chinless face, thick-walled skull, and heavy-browed" would be a partial description of
    a. *Australopithecus robustus*.
    b. *Australopithecus boisei*.
    c. *Homo habilis* (early *Homo*).
*   d. *Homo erectus*.
    e. *Homo sapiens*.

D 131. "Smaller teeth and jaws, presence of a chin, thin facial bones, larger brain, and rounder, higher skull" would be a partial description
    a. *Australopithecus robustus*.
    b. *Australopithecus boisei*.
    c. *Homo habilis* (early *Homo*).
    d. *Homo erectus*.
*   e. *Homo sapiens*.

Matching Questions

D 132. Matching I. Choose the one most appropriate letter for each blank.
    1. ___ birds
    2. ___ bony fishes
    3. ___ caecilians
    4. ___ humans
    5. ___ lampreys
    6. ___ lancelets
    7. ___ opossum
    8. ___ ostracoderms
    9. ___ placoderms
    10. ___ platypus
    11. ___ salamanders
    12. ___ sharks
    13. ___ snakes
    14. ___ tunicates

    A. cartilaginous skeleton; jaws
    B. jawless fishes; now extinct
    C. placental mammal
    D. legless amphibian
    E. invertebrate chordate; no metamorphosis
    F. endotherm with feathers
    G. limbless reptile
    H. most primitive fishes with jaws
    I. modern-day parasitic agnathan
    J. marsupial
    K. adult is called "sea squirt"
    L. egg-laying mammal
    M. swim bladder for buoyancy
    N. may be sexually mature but not adult

Answers: 1. F   2. M   3. D   4. C
            5. I   6. E   7. J   8. B

    9. H   10. L   11. N   12. A
    13. G   14. K

D 133. Matching II. Choose the one most appropriate answer for each.
    1. ___ anthropoids
    2. ___ australopith
    3. ___ ceboids
    4. ___ Cenozoic
    5. ___ cercopithecoids
    6. ___ dryopiths
    7. ___ hominoids
    8. ___ Miocene
    9. ___ Neandertals
    10. ___ Primates
    11. ___ Pliocene
    12. ___ prosimians

    A. a group that includes apes and humans
    B. a population of *Homo sapiens* that lived from at least 100,000 to as recently as 35,000 years ago; tool users and artisans
    C. the order that includes animals with freely swiveling limbs, mobile grasping digits, upright body posture, good depth perception, and exquisite neural control
    D. organisms in a suborder that includes New World and Old World monkeys, apes, and humans
    E. an era that began 65 to 63 million years ago; characterized by the evolution of birds, mammals, and flowering plants
    F. a group that includes New World monkeys only
    G. a term denoting multicellular animals
    H. an epoch of the Cenozoic lasting from 25 million to 7 million years ago; characterized by the appearance of primitive apes, whales, and grazing animals
    I. organisms in a suborder that includes tree shrews, tarsiers, lemurs, and others
    J. an epoch of the Cenozoic lasting from 7 million to 2 million years ago; characterized by the appearance of distinctly modern plants and animals
    K. a group that includes Old World monkeys only
    L. bipedal organisms from about 3.8 to 1 million years ago, with essentially human bodies and ape-shaped heads; brains no larger than those of chimpanzees
    M. transitional apelike forms that could climb about in trees and walk on the ground

Answers: 1. D   2. L   3. F   4. E

5. K   6. M   7. A   8. H

9. B   10. C   11. J   12. I

D   **134.**   Matching III. Choose the one most appropriate answer for each.

1. ___ *Australopithecus*
2. ___ *Homo erectus*
3. ___ *Homo sapiens*
4. ___ Neandertals

    A.   lived from approximately 100,000 to 30,000 years ago; skilled toolmakers and artisans

    B.   lived about 1.5 million years ago until 300,000 years ago; cranial capacity approximately 1,000 cubic centimeters; bipedal

    C.   lived about 30 million years ago near Fayum

    D.   humans since 300,000 years ago

    E.   Lucy; between 3.8 to 1 million years ago

Answers: 1. E   2. B   3. D   4. A

Classification Questions

Answer questions 135-139 in reference to the five classes listed below:

    a. Agnatha
    b. Chondrichthyes
    c. Osteichthyes
    d. Amphibia
    e. Reptilia

E   **135.**   Members of this class are fully terrestrial except for reproduction.

M   **136.**   Ostracoderms could qualify for membership in this class.

M   **137.**   Members of this class have cartilaginous skeletons but also possess jaws.

M   **138.**   Some species of this class live in water but are not dependent upon an aquatic environment.

D   **139.**   Members of one unusual class may have been ancestors of amphibians.

Answers   135. d   136. a   137. b

138. e   139. c

Answer questions 140-144 in reference to the four primates listed below:

    a. *Sahelanthropus*
    b. *Australopithecus afarensis*
    c. *Australopithecus boisei*
    d. *Australopithecus robustus*

M   **140.**   This primate is the oldest in the fossil record.

M   **141.**   This primate is the most recent in the fossil record.

M   **142.**   This primate may have given rise to the genus *Homo*.

D   **143.**   The fossil Lucy is a representative of this species.

D   **144.**   This primate is most likely to have been the common ancestor of the great apes and humans.

Answers   140. a   141. c   142. b

143. b   144. a

Answer questions 145-148 in reference to the four hominids listed below:

    a. *Homo habilis*
    b. *Homo erectus*
    c. *Homo sapiens*
    d. *Australopithecus afarensis*

M   **145.**   The Neandertals belong to this species.

M   **146.**   Our own species evolved from this species.

M   **147.**   This species was the first known to use fire.

D   **148.**   This species was the first definitely known to use tools.

Answers   145. c   146. b   147. b   148. a

Selecting the Exception

M   **149.**   Four of the five answers below are members of the same group. Select the exception.
   *   a. lampreys
    b. sharks
    c. rays
    d. skates
    e. chimaeras

D   **150.**   Four of the five answers below are correct pairings of group name and common name. Select the exception.
    a. Chondrichthyes: sharks
   *   b. Urochordata: lancelets
    c. Amphibia: toads
    d. Reptilia: lizards
    e. Agnatha: hagfish

M   **151.**   Four of the five answers below are classes of living chordates. Select the exception.
    a. Agnatha
    b. Osteichthyes
    c. Reptilia
   *   d. Placodermi
    e. Chondrichthyes

M 152. Four of the five answers below are related by a common group. Select the exception.
   a. frogs
   b. toads
 * c. tuataras
   d. salamanders
   e. caecilians

M 153. Four of the five answers below are principal characteristics of all chordates. Select the exception.
   a. tail
 * b. bony vertebra
   c. notochord
   d. nerve cord
   e. pharyngeal gill slits

M 154. Four of the five answers below are breathing mechanisms in chordates. Select the exception.
   a. skin
   b. gills
 * c. tracheas
   d. lungs
   e. lining of pharynx and mouth

M 155. Four of the five answers below characterize a group of chordates. Select the exception.
   a. feathers
 * b. ectothermic
   c. four-chambered heart
   d. hollow skeleton
   e. no teeth

D 156. Four of the five answers listed below are related. Select the exception.
   a. lancelet
   b. jawed fish
   c. jawless fish
   d. tunicate
 * e. squid

M 157. Three of the four answers listed below are prosimians. Select the exception.
   a. tree shrews
 * b. monkey
   c. lemurs
   d. lorises

E 158. Four of the five answers listed below are anthropoids. Select the exception.
 * a. tarsier
   b. Old World monkey
   c. human
   d. ape
   e. gorilla

M 159. Three of the four answers listed below are trends in hominid evolution. Select the exception.
   a. strong social bonding
   b. enhanced vision
 * c. upright vertebral column
   d. omnivorous feeding behavior

D 160. Four of the five answers listed below are related by a similar evolutionary characteristic in *Homo*. Select the exception.
   a. small thin face
   b. high skull
   c. large cranial capacity
   d. larger body size
 * e. specialized teeth

CHAPTER 27
BIODIVERSITY IN PERSPECTIVE

Multiple-Choice Questions

E 1. When James Cook explored Easter Island, he saw the people and the land were experiencing the long-term the results of
    a. drought
    * b. overpopulation
    c. a typhoon
    d. global warming
    e. war

E 2. The effects that Captain James Cook saw on Easter Island were more dramatic because
    a. it was located in an exotic place.
    b. he was not familiar with Pacific cultures.
    c. the destruction had occurred just a month before.
    * d. of the island's small size.
    e. the statues on the beach.

ON MASS EXTINCTIONS AND SLOW RECOVERIES

E 3. Which of the following statements is not true?
    a. Global biodiversity is greater than ever.
    * b. The diversity of biological species is lower than ever.
    c. Extinction is a continuing process.
    d. Some scientists believe an extinction crisis is currently underway.

M 4. Genetic divergences accelerated during the Cambrian period due to
    a. asteroid bombardment.
    b. mutations.
    c. conservation.
    * d. the presence of oxygen.
    e. global warming.

M 5. Recovery from a mass extinction requires about how long?
    a. 100,000 years
    b. none of these because recovery is never possible
    c. about as long as the extinction required
    d. less than 1 million years
    * e. 20 to 100 million years

M 6. Which of the following is least likely to be a cause of extinction?
    a. asteroid impact
    b. human activity
    * c. adaptive radiation
    d. tectonic activity
    e. climate change

M 7. Which of the following is most likely the cause of the current extinction crisis?
    a. asteroid impact
    * b. human activity
    c. adaptive radiation
    d. tectonic activity
    e. climate change

THE NEWLY ENDANGERED SPECIES

E 8. A species that is extremely vulnerable to extinction is designated as
    a. riparian.
    b. endemic.
    * c. endangered.
    d. fragmented.
    e. an indicator.

E 9. Endemic means a species
    * a. originated in one geographic region and lives nowhere else.
    b. could cause an epidemic at any time.
    c. is on its way to extinction.
    d. can live in only one habitat.
    e. is extinct.

E 10. Which of the following would NOT be a contributing factor in species extinction?
    a. habitat loss
    b. overharvesting
    c. habitat fragmentation
    * d. conservation biology
    e. illegal wildlife trading

M 11. Habitat fragmentation can reduce biodiversity by
    * a. creating patches too small to maintain breeding.
    b. increasing the effects of chemical pollution.
    c. eliminating vast tracts of forests.
    d. introducing exotic species into a habitat.

M 12. Inhabitable regions surrounded by unsuitable habitat describes
    a. indicator species.
    b. ecoregions.
    c. hot spots.
    * d. habitat islands.
    e. biogeography.

M 13. Destruction of 50 percent of a habitat island will drive _____ of its species to extinction.
    a. 75 percent
    b. nearly all
    c. 25 percent
    d. one-half
    * e. one-tenth

E   14.   Because migratory birds live in all major regions and climate zones, they are good
      a.   habitat island indicators.
      b.   exotic species.
   * c.   indicator species.
      d.   habitat fragmenters.
      e.   pollution carriers.

M   15.   Exotic species that are introduced into a non-native habitat usually
      a.   interbreed with native species.
   * b.   drive endemic species to extinction.
      c.   die out due to competition from native species.
      d.   blend in with endemic species.
      e.   create habitat islands for themselves.

FOCUS ON THE ENVIRONMENT: CASE STUDY: THE ONCE AND FUTURE REEFS

E   16.   One of the most sensitive indicators of biodiversity disruption in the oceans is the life forms found on
      a.   islands.
      b.   the sea floor.
   * c.   coral reefs.
      d.   the open waters.
      e.   the sandy beaches.

FOCUS ON SCIENCE: RACHEL'S WARNING

E   17.   The modern environmental movement can be traced to Rachel Carson's book
      a.   *Origin of Species.*
      b.   *Pesticides in Perspective.*
      c.   *Endangered Species.*
      d.   *Conservation Biology.*
   * e.   *Silent Spring.*

CONSERVATION BIOLOGY

D   18.   The wild maize (*Zea diploperennis*) found by a Mexican college student was significant because it
      a.   lives more than one growing season.
      b.   is more resistant to disease.
   * c.   lives more than one growing season and is more resistant to disease.
      d.   produces much greater yields per acre than domestic corn.
      e.   lives more than one growing season, is more resistant to disease, and produces much greater yields per acre than domestic corn.

E   19.   By the year 2050, the world human population is expected to reach
      a.   20 billion.
      b.   6 billion.
      c.   265 million.
   * d.   9 billion.
      e.   none of these due to mass extinction

M   20.   Perhaps the most significant impact of human population increase is the
      a.   increased possibility for wars.
      b.   disregard for human rights.
   * c.   exponential need for life's resources.
      d.   lack of living space.
      e.   increase in crime.

M   21.   Conservation biology includes a(an)
      a.   survey of biological diversity.
      b.   look at the evolutionary origins of diversity.
      c.   ecological considerations of diversity.
      d.   effort to maintain biodiversity.
   * e.   all of these

E   22.   Habitats with the most species in greatest danger of extinction are called
      a.   ecoregions.
      b.   indicator species.
      c.   riparian zones.
   * d.   hot spots.
      e.   conservation islands.

M   23.   Which of the following pairs of words are most closely related?
   * a.   hot spots: indicator species
      b.   habitat island: strip logging
      c.   conservation: habitat loss
      d.   coral reef: Rachel Carson
      e.   endemic: exotic

M   24.   In making a systematic survey of biodiversity, the first level of inquiry is
      a.   at the ecoregion level.
      b.   among the riparian zones.
   * c.   in hot spots.
      d.   at the regional research station.
      e.   on a global scale.

E   25.   A broad land or ocean region defined by climate, geography, and producers is called
   * a.   an ecoregion.
      b.   a hot spot.
      c.   a realm.
      d.   a habitat island.

M   26.   Future value of ecoregions can be determined by
      a.   destroying portions of the regions.
      b.   indicator species.
   * c.   bioeconomic analysis.
      d.   selling it on the global market.

M   27.   Bioeconomic analysis looks at
      a.   long-term economic benefits.
      b.   short-term gains.
      c.   cost/benefit ratios.
      d.   sustainability of biodiversity.
   * e.   all of these.

RECONCILING BIODIVERSITY WITH HUMAN DEMANDS

E   **28.** Given a choice, most humans will choose to
   a. protect endangered species.
   b. do what is best for mankind.
   c. conserve.
   d. maintain biodiversity for all humankind.
*   e. preserve their own lives.

M   **29.** Gary Hartshorn has proposed a profitable, sustainable method of harvesting called
   a. riparian ranching.
   b. habitat fragmentation.
*   c. strip logging.
   d. sustainable forestation.
   e. clear cutting.

M   **30.** A relatively narrow corridor of vegetation along a stream or river is called a
   a. ecoregion.
*   b. riparian zone.
   c. habitat island.
   d. hot zone.
   e. refuge.

Matching Questions

D   **31.** Matching   Choose the one most appropriate answer for each.

   1. ___   conservation biology
   2. ___   coral reef
   3. ___   ecoregion
   4. ___   endangered species
   5. ___   habitat fragmentation
   6. ___   habitat island
   7. ___   habitat loss
   8. ___   hot spot
   9. ___   indicator species
   10. ___   strip logging
   11. ___   riparian zone

   A. a reduction in suitable places to live
   B. organisms that give "early warning" signal of changes in biodiversity
   C. new method of harvesting trees to preserve diversity
   D. a field of research whose goal is conservation of biodiversity
   E. endemic species vulnerable to extinction
   F. broad land or ocean region defined by climate, geography, and producers
   G. ocean structure of amazing biological complexity
   H. locations where species are in greatest danger of extinction
   I. a national park is an example
   J. narrow corridor of vegetation long stream or river
   K. isolated patches of habitat

Answers: 1. D   2. G   3. F   4. E

   5. K   6. I   7. A   8. H

   9. B   10. C   11. J

Classification Questions

Answer questions 32-36 in reference to the four "habitat" items listed below:

    a. habitat fragmentation
    b. habitat island
    c. habitat loss
    d. habitat

M   **32.** This describes where a species lives.

M   **33.** This could reduce a habitat's boundaries making species more vulnerable to predators.

M   **34.** This could be the result of chemical pollution.

D   **35.** This is inhabited area surrounded by unsuitable habitat.

D   **36.** This action may result in a lack of sufficient resources to sustain the population.

Answers   32. d   33. a   34. c
                 35. b   36. a

Selecting the Exception

E   **37.** Three of the four answers listed below are possible causes of extinction. Select the exception.
    a. asteroid impact
*   b. conservation
    c. tectonic change
    d. human activity

M   **38.** Three of the four answers listed below are possible effects of habitat fragmentation on biodiversity. Select the exception.
*   a. chemical pollution may cause mass evacuation of the habitat
    b. species become more vulnerable to predators
    c. population numbers may be too small to maintain breeding
    d. food and other resources may be too scarce

M   **39.** Three of the four answers listed below are approaches to biodiversity conservation. Select the exception.
    a. riparian ranching
    b. strip logging
*   c. introduction of exotic species
    d. research on species hot spots

M   **40.** Four of the five answers listed below can become threats to species survival. Select the exception.
    a. habitat losses
    b. introduction of exotic species
    c. overharvesting
    d. illegal wildlife trading
*   e. strip logging

CHAPTER 28
HOW PLANTS AND ANIMALS WORK

Multiple-Choice Questions

E   **1.** The barheaded goose can survive high altitude flight because
     a. it has extremely strong wings.
     b. it stops to rest often.
     c. updrafts lift its tiny body.
  * d. its hemoglobin binds more oxygen.
     e. it has a very large heart.

E   **2.** Which of the following is the study of an organism's form?
     a. philosophy
  * b. anatomy
     c. phylogeny
     d. taxonomy
     e. physiology

E   **3.** Which of the following terms applies to the functioning of the human body?
     a. cytology
     b. anatomy
     c. psychology
  * d. physiology
     e. endocrinology

LEVELS OF STRUCTURAL ORGANIZATION

E   **4.** Chemical and structural bridges link groups or layers of like cells, uniting them in structure and function as a cohesive
     a. organ.
     b. organ system.
  * c. tissue.
     d. cuticle.

E   **5.** Which of the following represents the correct hierarchy of organization in the human body?
     a. cells——>tissues——>organ systems ——>organs
  * b. cells——>tissues——>organs——>organ systems
     c. tissues——>cells——>organs——>organ systems
     d. tissues——>organs——>cells——>organ systems

M   **6.** The minimum level of organization required for a "division of labor" is the _____ level.
     a. cellular
     b. organ
  * c. tissue
     d. organ system
     e. body

E   **7.** Growth __?__ but development __?__.
     a. is qualitative; is quantitative
  * b. is measured by increased cell numbers; is measured by increased cell specialization
     c. occurs only in infants; occurs only in adolescents
     d. continues throughout life; stops at puberty

M   **8.** Extracellular fluid would NOT include
     a. plasma.
     b. blood.
     c. interstitial fluid.
  * d. cytoplasm.
     e. any of the above

D   **9.** When nutrients are supplied to a cell, the last fluid through which they must pass before encountering the plasma membrane is the
     a. plasma.
  * b. interstitial fluid.
     c. blood.
     d. intracellular fluid.
     e. cerebrospinal fluid.

THE NATURE OF ADAPTATION

M   **10.** Long-term adaptation
     a. is inheritable.
     b. includes aspects of form and function.
     c. is the outcome of natural selection.
     d. improves the odds of survival and reproducing.
  * e. includes all of these.

MECHANISMS OF HOMEOSTASIS IN ANIMALS

M   **11.** Which of the following are examples of integrators?
  * a. brain, spinal cord
     b. muscles, glands
     c. sensory cells in eye, tongue, and ear
     d. bones
     e. none of these

E   **12.** Which of the following is most directly associated with a stimulus?
     a. integrators
  * b. receptors
     c. effectors
     d. central nervous system
     e. all of these

D   **13.** Which of the following is the correct sequence involved in the regulation of organ systems?
     a. stimulus, receptor, integrator, response, effector
     b. stimulus, response, integrator, receptor, effector
  * c. stimulus, receptor, integrator, effector, response
     d. stimulus, integrator, receptor, effector, response
     e. stimulus, effector, integrator, receptor, response

M   14.   An effector can be
          a.   muscle.
          b.   nerve.
          c.   gland.
          d.   receptor.
     *   e.   both muscle and gland.

E   15   Control of body temperature is an example of which of
         the following?
          a.   homeostatic mechanism
          b.   positive feedback system
          c.   endocrine function
          d.   negative feedback system
     *   e.   both homeostatic mechanism and negative
               feedback system

E   16.   In feedback systems,
          a.   two sets of organs may act in opposition to each
               other.
          b.   a set point may be established.
          c.   receptors are required to monitor changing
               conditions.
          d.   changes in environmental conditions (either internal
               or external) result in a response by the organism.
     *   e.   all of these

M   17.   Which of the following involves a positive feedback
          stimulation?
          a.   temperature control
     *   b.   sexual stimulation
          c.   glucose concentration
          d.   absorption of toxins
          e.   muscle contraction

DOES THE CONCEPT OF HOMEOSTASIS APPLY TO PLANTS?

M   18.   Which of the following is NOT an example of
          compartmentalization?
          a.   thickened walls around plant wounds
          b.   secretion of phenols
          c.   resins
          d.   response to fungal attack
     *   e.   circadian rhythms

M   19.   Rhythmic leaf folding is an example of
          a.   adaptation.
          b.   division of labor.
     *   c.   circadian rhythms.
          d.   homeostasis.
          e.   negative feedback.

COMMUNICATION AMONG CELLS, TISSUES, AND ORGANS

M   20.   Target cells
          a.   are found only in specific endocrine glands.
          b.   are equipped with specific receptor molecules.
          c.   are muscle cells.
          d.   may occur in any part of the body.
     *   e.   are equipped with specific receptor molecules and
               may occur in any part of the body.

M   21.   Which of the following statements is true?
     *   a.   Although hormones are carried to all parts of the
               body, they produce effects only in cells with
               proper receptors.
          b.   Hormones are limited to steroid compounds.
          c.   Hormones are secreted by specialized exocrine
               glands.
          d.   Most hormones are controlled by positive
               feedback mechanisms involving the pituitary
               gland.

M   22.   The important feature of all cells that react to a specific
          hormone is the
          a.   type of blood supply they receive.
          b.   proximity of the endocrine gland.
     *   c.   presence of an appropriate receptor molecule.
          d.   characteristics of their plasma membranes.
          e.   presence of specific genes responsive to the
               hormone.

M   23.   The basic unit of the nervous system is
          a.   neuroglia.
     *   b.   the neuron.
          c.   the brain.
          d.   a nerve.
          e.   a nerve impulse

RECURRING CHALLENGES TO SURVIVAL

D   24.   The net direction that an ion or molecule moves is
          a.   dependent upon the size of the molecule.
          b.   unpredictable because movement is random.
          c.   controlled by the temperature of the medium.
          d.   controlled by the membranes in the vicinity.
     *   e.   the result of concentration differences.

E   25   Movement of a molecule against a concentration
         gradient is
          a.   simple diffusion.
          b.   facilitated diffusion.
          c.   osmosis.
     *   d.   active transport.
          e.   bulk flow.

D   26.   If the volume of a cell increases, its surface area will
          a.   decrease.
          b.   remain the same.
          c.   increase proportionately.
          d.   increase to a greater degree.
     *   e.   increase to a lesser degree.

D   27.   Volume increases by the _____ of the diameter,
          and surface area increases by the _____.
          a.   square; doubling
          b.   square; cube
     *   c.   cube; square
          d.   cube; cube

E   28.   The vascular tissues of plants are composed of
          a.   epidermis and ground meristem.
          b.   ground tissue.
     *   c.   xylem and phloem.
          d.   arteries and veins.
          e.   sap and water.

Matching Questions

D **29.** Matching Choose the one most appropriate answer for each.

 1. ___ ABC model
 2. ___ effector
 3. ___ habitat
 4. ___ interstitial fluid
 5. ___ myelin
 6. ___ plasma
 7. ___ stimulus
 8. ___ tissue

 A. form of energy that a receptor can detect
 B. where an organism lives
 C. muscles and glands are examples
 D. three groups of genes for floral development
 E. fluid that bathes all cells
 F. fluid in the blood
 G. sheath surrounding axons
 H. groups of cells with a common function

Answers: 1. D 2. C 3. B 4. E
 5. G 6. F 7. A 8. H

Classification Questions

Answer questions 30-35 in reference to the six organization terms listed below:

 a. cell
 b. organ system
 c. growth
 d. organ
 e. development
 f. tissue

M **30.** This term describes the successive stages in the formation of specialized tissues; qualitative.

M **31.** This is a collection of tissues specialized for common function

M **32.** The vertebrate circulatory system is a good example of this term.

D **33.** Here cells are working together for a specialized function.

D **34.** This is quantitative term describing an increase in cell numbers.

E **35.** This is the smallest unit of life.

Answers   30. e   31. d   32. b
 33. f   34 c   35. a

Selecting the Exception

E **36.** Three of the four answers listed below are used to describe participants in the body's division of labor Select the exception.
 a. tissue
 * b. growth
 c. organ
 d organ system

M **37.** Three of the four answers listed below could help a plant wall off threats. Select the exception.
 * a. hormones
 b. phenols
 c. resins
 d compartmentalization

M **38.** Four of the five answers listed below describe adaptations. Select the exception.
 a. salt-tolerant tomatoes.
 b. barheaded geese in the Himalayas
 c. yellow bush pine on Pacific coasts
 d circadian rhythms
 * e myelin sheaths that speed nerve impulses

CHAPTER 29
PLANT TISSUES

Multiple-Choice Questions

OVERVIEW OF THE PLANT BODY

E   1.   Approximately how many species of plants are known?
     a. 100,000
     b. 180,000
 *   c. 295,000
     d. 360,000
     e. 480,000

M   2.   Which of the following are vascular plants?
     a. bryophytes
 *   b. ferns
     c. red algae
     d. green algae
     e. brown algae

E   3.   The conifers, such as pines and junipers, are examples of the
 *   a. gymnosperms.
     b. angiosperms.
     c. bryophytes.
     d. filicinae.
     e. none of these

E   4.   Which of the following is NOT part of the plant shoot system?
     a. stems
 *   b. roots
     c. flowers
     d. leaves
     e. all of these are parts of the shoot system

E   5.   Most of the plant body is composed of
     a. dermal tissue.
     b. root tissue.
 *   c. ground tissue.
     d. vascular tissue.
     e. cork tissue.

M   6.   The tissues of the root and shoot system are classified as
     a. ground tissue.
     b. dermal tissue.
     c. vascular tissue.
     d. ground and dermal tissues
 *   e. ground, dermal, and vascular tissues

D   7.   Which of the following is false?
 *   a. Periderm is a primary tissue.
     b. There is no tissue in animals that corresponds to meristem tissue of plants.
     c. Growth from cell division at the tips of stems and roots produces primary growth.
     d. Divisions of the lateral meristem increase the diameter of the roots and stems.
     e. Lateral meristem produces secondary growth.

M   8.   Perpetually young tissues where cells retain the ability to divide are
     a. vascular.
 *   b. meristematic.
     c. protective.
     d. photosynthetic.
     e. all of these

M   9.   The division of the lateral meristem
     a. results in the production of primary tissue.
     b. causes an increase in the length of roots.
     c. produces floral tissue.
     d. gives rise to the epidermis.
 *   e. increases the diameter of roots and stems.

M   10.   Growth designated as "primary"
     a. occurs along the sides of stems.
 *   b. is dependent upon apical meristem.
     c. increases the diameter of older plants.
     d. is responsible for additions to woody parts.

TYPES OF PLANT TISSUES

D   11.   Which of the following is mismatched?
     a. dermal cells—cutin
     b. sclerenchyma—lignin
 *   c. parenchyma—pectin
     d. xylem—water

M   12.   Plant tissue noted for storage, healing wounds, and regeneration is
     a. vascular cambium.
 *   b. parenchyma.
     c. collenchyma.
     d. sclerenchyma.
     e. none of these

M   13.   Parenchyma cells are specialized for and involved in all but which of the following activities?
     a. photosynthesis
     b. wound healing
 *   c. conduction of food
     d. secretion
     e. food storage

M 14. The chewy, stringy cells in celery are which cells?
   a. xylem
 * b. collenchyma
   c. phloem
   d. sclerenchyma
   e. parenchyma

M 15. Sclereids are found in
   a. root tips.
 * b. seed coats.
   c. mesophyll cells that produce food.
   d. cortex cells that store food.
   e. epidermal cells.

M 16. The gritty stone cells of pears, the hard cells of seed coats, and plant fibers are examples of
   a. xylem.
   b. collenchyma.
   c. phloem.
 * d. sclerenchyma.
   e. parenchyma.

M 17. Which of the following would NOT be considered strengthening or supportive tissue?
   a. collenchyma
   b. xylem
   c. sclerenchyma
 * d. parenchyma
   e. cork

M 18. Polysaccharides are used by plants for
   a. food storage.
   b. cementing cells together.
   c. structural support.
   d. food storage and structural support.
 * e. food storage, structural support, and cementing cells together.

M 19. If a mutation prevented the formation of lignin, which tissue would be most affected?
   a. vascular cambium
   b. parenchyma
   c. collenchyma
 * d. sclerenchyma
   e. all of these

M 20. All but which of the following are associated with sclerenchyma?
   a. lignin
 * b. photosynthesis
   c. transport
   d. sclereids
   e. fibers

M 21. Lignin is to cellulose strands as _____ is to epidermal cells.
   a. cuticulin
   b. epidermerin
   c. pectin
 * d. cutin
   e. chitin

D 22. If cell walls did not vary in thickness or were not perforated,
 * a. xylem and phloem would not be able to function as vascular tissue.
   b. gas exchange could not occur across the stomata.
   c. water could not enter the epidermal cells of the root.
   d. the terminal bud could not cause the stem to elongate.
   e. all of these

E 23. Cells that are the main water-conducting cells of a plant are
   a. sclereids.
 * b. tracheids.
   c. sieve tubes.
   d. parenchyma.
   e. all of these

M 24. The cells that function with the sieve tubes are the
   a. vessels.
 * b. companion cells.
   c. adjunct cells.
   d. sclereids.
   e. periderm.

D 25. Which of the following statements concerning xylem is incorrect?
 * a. Each xylem vessel is one continuous cell.
   b. The direction of flow is mainly from root upward.
   c. Water and minerals are transported.
   d. Tracheids and vessel members participate.
   e. There are pits in the walls.

D 26. Which of the following cells are alive at maturity?
 * a. sieve tube members
   b. vessel members
   c. tracheids
   d. vessel members and tracheids
   e. sieve tube members and vessel members

M 27. Which of the following cells are alive?
   a. tracheids
   b. cork
   c. sclereids
 * d. parenchyma
   e. vessel members

D 28. A cuticle
   a. resists water loss.
   b. covers epidermal cells.
   c. may contain waxes and cutin.
   d. resists attack by microorganisms.
 * e. all of these

E 29. The cell walls of epidermal cells are filled with which of the following to reduce water loss?
 * a. cutin
   b. pectin
   c. lignin
   d. suberin
   e. chitin

E   30. Air and water vapor cross the epidermis via
      a. pits.
      b. perforations.
      c. osmosis.
   * d. stomata.
      e. tracheids.

M   31. The periderm
      a. replaces the epidermis when some plants age.
      b. is a protective tissue.
      c. is a dermal tissue.
      d. is found on woody plants.
   * e. all of these

E   32. A cotyledon is which of the following?
      a. embryonic root
      b. seed cover
      c. flower part
   * d. seed leaf
      e. fruit

D   33. Which of the following is true of monocots?
      a. has two cotyledons
      b. leaf veins usually netlike
      c. pollen grains with three pores
   * d. vascular bundles throughout ground tissue
      e. floral parts in multiples of fours and fives

M   34. Which statement is NOT generally true of monocot stems?
      a. They do not undergo secondary growth.
      b. They are not tapered along their length.
      c. Their vascular bundles are scattered throughout the ground tissue.
   * d. Monocot stems have a single central vascular cylinder.
      e. all of these

E   35. Which of the following is a dicot?
      a. palm
      b. grass
   * c. oak
      d. orchid
      e. lily

PRIMARY STRUCTURE OF SHOOTS

D   36. The vascular bundles of dicots separate the ground tissue into two zones. Which of the following correctly describes the arrangement of these zones?
      a. outermost xylem——>phloem——>pith——>cortex
      b. outermost phloem——>xylem——>pith——>cortex
   * c. outermost cortex——>phloem——>xylem——>pith
      d. outermost pith——>phloem——>xylem——>cortex
      e. outermost cortex——>xylem——>phloem——>pith

D   37. Which of the following statements is true?
      a. An annual ring is composed of alternating rings of phloem and xylem.
   * b. When a tree is girdled, it dies because its roots are deprived of food.
      c. There is no acceptable explanation for apical dominance because the growth patterns of plants vary.
      d. All plants have vascular tissue.

M   38. Dicots have stems
      a. with scattered vascular bundles.
   * b. with a pith and cortex.
      c. with no vascular cambium.
      d. that develop only primary tissues.
      e. none of these

E   39. Buds are produced
      a. in the axils of leaves.
      b. at the very ends of stems.
      c. at the nodes.
      d. by the apical meristem.
   * e. all of these

M   40. All but which of the following are true of buds?
   * a. attached to the stem at internodes
      b. may occur at the tip of the twig
      c. some are called lateral
      d. may give rise to leaves
      e. mostly meristematic tissue

M   41. Which of the following statements is false?
   * a. Axillary buds are found at the tip of the stems.
      b. Internodes are the spaces between leaves.
      c. Cotyledons are leaves within a seed.
      d. Ground tissue is the most common type of tissue in a plant.
      e. Dermal tissue covers the body of the plant.

M   42. Leaves arise
      a. as part of the periderm.
      b. as part of secondary growth.
   * c. at the nodes.
      d. as a result of differentiation of cambium cells.
      e. from the lateral, not the apical, meristem.

A CLOSER LOOK AT LEAVES

M   43. The stalk that supports the individual dicot leaf is the
      a. vascular bundle.
   * b. petiole.
      c. node.
      d. bundle sheath.
      e. stomata.

E 44. Stomata
   a. are found in the root cells.
   b. may be found scattered anywhere throughout the plant.
 * c. allow the movement of gases into and out of plants.
   d. prevent the loss of water from plants.

E 45. Deciduous plants
   a. are nonvascular.
   b. are evergreen.
   c. must shed all their leaves once a year.
 * d. may retain their dead brown leaves over the winter and shed them only when new leaves emerge.

M 46. Which of the following is mismatched?
   a. cotyledon—seed leaf
   b. petiole—leaf stalk
 * c. deciduous—evergreen
   d. veins—vascular bundles
   e. blade—leaf

E 47. The main photosynthetic area of a leaf is composed of
 * a. mesophyll.
   b. cortex.
   c. xylem.
   d. epidermis.
   e. none of these

M 48. Which of the following statements is false?
   a. The greatest amount of photosynthesis takes place in the palisade mesophyll.
 * b. There are more stomata on the upper epidermis than on the lower epidermis.
   c. The palisade mesophyll is more densely packed than the spongy mesophyll.
   d. The surface area of the root system is greater than that of the shoot system.
   e. Root hairs are extensions of single epidermal cells.

M 49. Photosynthesis takes place in the
   a. stomata.
   b. vascular bundles.
   c. cuticle.
   d. lower and upper epidermis.
 * e. mesophyll tissue.

M 50. The veins of leaves are used for
   a. support.
   b. identification.
 * c. transport of water and nutrients.
   d. detachment in the autumn.

M 51. Approximately 30 to 50 percent of a leaf consists of
   a. palisade mesophyll.
   b. water.
   c. spongy mesophyll.
 * d. air spaces.
   e. synthesized carbohydrates.

PRIMARY STRUCTURE OF ROOTS

E 52. Roots are involved in all but which of the following activities?
   a. support
   b. food storage
 * c. food production
   d. anchorage
   e. absorption and conduction

E 53. Mitosis takes place in which region of the root?
   a. zone of maturation
   b. root cap
   c. zone of elongation
 * d. meristem region
   e. region of differentiation

M 54. If you were to penetrate through the epidermal layer of a root, you would next encounter the
   a. xylem.
   b. endodermis.
 * c. cortex.
   d. phloem.
   e. pericycle.

M 55. The tissue found in the center of a root is
 * a. xylem.
   b. endodermis.
   c. cortex.
   d. phloem.
   e. pericycle.

M 56. The layer of cells responsible for branch roots and the development of cork as a root thickens is the
   a. xylem.
   b. endodermis.
   c. cortex.
   d. phloem.
 * e. pericycle.

M 57. Most monocots have numerous _____ roots arising from the stem.
 * a. adventitious
   b. primary
   c. fibrous
   d. secondary
   e. tap

M 58. Which of the following gives rise to lateral roots?
   a. endodermis
   b. cortex
   c. epidermis
 * d. pericycle
   e. pith

D 59. Which of the following is in contact with the soil into which it is growing?
   a. vascular cylinder
   b. apical meristem
 * c. root cap
   d. pericycle
   e. outer cortex

M 60. Root hairs are the extensions of the
　　a. apical meristem.
　*　b. epidermis.
　　c. pericycle.
　　d. vascular bundles.
　　e. root cap.

D 61. Lateral roots are the product of the
　*　a. pericycle.
　　b. vascular cylinder.
　　c. epidermis.
　　d. apical meristem.
　　e. endodermis.

M 62. The carrot
　　a. has a taproot system.
　　b. uses food stored in the root to produce flowers, fruits, and seeds.
　　c. takes two years to complete its life cycle.
　　d. does not develop adventitious roots and has very limited lateral roots.
　*　e. all of these

D 63. Adventitious roots are associated with
　　a. fibrous root systems.
　　b. stems.
　　c. taproot systems.
　*　d. fibrous root systems and stems, only.
　　e. fibrous root systems and taproot systems.

ACCUMULATED SECONDARY GROWTH–THE WOODY PLANTS

E 64. The typical landscaping "shrubs" around homes are mostly
　　a. annuals.
　　b. biennials.
　　c. perennials.
　　d. herbaceous.
　*　e. perennials and herbaceous

E 65. If all of the phloem were stripped from around a tree in a process known as girdling,
　　a. the plant would stop growing.
　　b. the vascular cambium would be destroyed so that the plant could no longer grow.
　　c. the shoot system would get no moisture or minerals.
　*　d. the roots would starve and eventually the plant would die.
　　e. there would be no problems unless the tree became infected by insects and fungi.

M 66. Lateral meristems
　　a. are groups of dividing cells.
　　b. are responsible for increases in the width of a stem or root.
　　c. are called cambium.
　　d. produce secondary growth only.
　*　e. all of these

M 67. Which tissue will NOT be crushed or sloughed off by the growing of the stem?
　*　a. vascular cambium
　　b. epidermis
　　c. cortex
　　d. pith
　　e. endodermis

A CLOSER LOOK AT WOOD AND BARK

D 68. The cell type that is found only in secondary tissue is
　　a. epidermis.
　　b. sclereids.
　*　c. periderm cork cells.
　　d. collenchyma.
　　e. cuticle.

M 69. Which of the following is part of the lateral meristem?
　*　a. cork cambium
　　b. procambium
　　c. protoderm
　　d. ground meristem
　　e. all of these

M 70. Annual growth rings are formed in woody stems principally through the activities of the
　　a. pericycle.
　　b. pith.
　*　c. vascular cambium.
　　d. mesophyll.
　　e. endodermis.

M 71. If a sieve tube in a plant becomes blocked, the plant will experience difficulty in
　　a. carrying on transpiration.
　　b. the transport of minerals.
　*　c. the translocation of food throughout the plant.
　　d. completing cell division and experiencing normal growth.

M 72. Secondary xylem is formed in association with the
　　a. pith.
　*　b. inner face of vascular cambium.
　　c. outer face of vascular cambium.
　　d. inner face of cork cambium.
　　e. outer face of cork cambium.

M 73. In an annual tree ring, the light wood is
　*　a. produced each spring.
　　b. the remnant of the bark produced the year before.
　　c. formed from crushed phloem cells.
　　d. produced in the winter.

M 74. Which of the following environments would be most likely to produce trees without annual rings?
　*　a. tropical rain forest
　　b. northern evergreen forest
　　c. areas with alternating wet and dry seasons
　　d. temperate-deciduous forests
　　e. none of these, because annual rings are characteristic of all trees

D **75.** Which of the following statements is false?
  a. Some perennial plants may consist of primary growth only.
  b. Cork cambium and vascular cambium are cells that form lateral meristems.
  c. Nonwoody plants are herbaceous.
  * d. Phloem is formed on the inside of vascular cambium, whereas xylem is formed on the outside.
  e. Sapwood surrounds heartwood.

Matching Questions

D **76.** Matching I. Choose the one most appropriate answer for each.
  1. ___ companion cells
  2. ___ cork cambium
  3. ___ meristems
  4. ___ palisade mesophyll
  5. ___ pericycle
  6. ___ sclereids
  7. ___ sieve elements
  8. ___ spongy mesophyll
  9. ___ tracheids
  10. ___ vascular bundles
  11. ___ vessel members

  A. gives rise to periderm
  B. nucleate phloem cells that help load and unload the phloem pipe lines
  C. dead cells with perforation plates; more efficient at water conduction than other xylem cells
  D. living nonnucleated cells that conduct food from photosynthetic source area to storage sink area
  E. a cylinder of parenchyma cells outside the vascular tissue but inside the endodermis
  F. clusters of strands containing xylem, phloem, and vascular cambium
  G. dead cells without perforation plates; the principal xylem cells of nonflowering vascular plants
  H. cells with thick secondary walls impregnated with lignin that are especially abundant in fruits and seeds
  I. the principal photosynthetic region of a leaf
  J. regions that can undergo mitosis
  K. gas exchange and storage plus photosynthesis

Answers: 1. B   2. A   3. J   4. I
       5. E   6. H   7. D   8. K
       9. G   10. F   11. C

D **77.** Matching II. Match all applicable letters with the appropriate term(s). Letters may be used more than once, and a blank may contain more than one letter.
  1. ___ collenchyma
  2. ___ cortex
  3. ___ endodermis
  4. ___ epidermis
  5. ___ parenchyma
  6. ___ periderm
  7. ___ phloem
  8. ___ pith
  9. ___ procambium
  10. ___ sclerenchyma
  11. ___ stomata
  12. ___ vascular cambium
  13. ___ xylem

  A. tissue that is part of the ground system
  B. tissue that is part of the vascular system
  C. tissue that is part of the dermal system
  D. develops into the vascular cambium
  E. leaf's photosynthetic tissues (palisade and spongy) are in this category
  F. transports photosynthetic products away from leaves and stem
  G. meristematic tissue
  H. develops into secondary xylem and phloem
  I. transports water and dissolved nutrients up to the stem and leaves
  J. replaces the epidermis in plants that undergo secondary growth
  K. a single layer of cells that helps control the movement of water and dissolved salts into the xylem pipeline
  L. influence the movement of carbon dioxide into the leaf and movement of water out of the leaf
  M. generally, dead cells that provide support and strength to all three tissue systems
  N. ground tissue centrally located within a ring of vascular bundles

Answers: 1. A   2. A   3. A, K
       4. C   5. A, E   6. C, J
       7. B, F   8. A, N   9. D, G
       10. A, M   11. L   12. B, G, H
       13. B, I, M

Classification Questions

Answer questions 78–82 in reference to the five plant tissues listed below:

    a. parenchyma
    b. collenchyma
    c. sclerenchyma
    d. xylem
    e. phloem

D   78. Ground tissue of plants, sometimes containing lignin, that strengthens the adult plant.

E   79. Vascular tissue that conducts and distributes food to plant cells.

E   80. Vascular tissue that conducts water and dissolved salts throughout a plant.

D   81. Vascular tissue of a plant composed of tracheids and vessel members.

D   82. Plant tissue involved in regeneration following a wound.

Answers   78. c   79. e   80. d

               81. d   82. a

Answer questions 83–87 in reference to the five plant tissues listed below:

    a. protoderm
    b. ground meristem
    c. procambium
    d. vascular cambium
    e. cork cambium

D   83. This tissue gives rise to periderm.

D   84. This tissue gives rise to primary tissue forming xylem and phloem.

M   85. This tissue gives rise to primary vascular tissue.

D   86. This tissue gives rise to the protective covering that forms the bark of a tree.

D   87. This tissue gives rise to the xylem and phloem of an older tree.

Answers   83. e   84. c   85. c

               86. e   87. d

Answer questions 88–92 in reference to the four source tissues of plant roots listed below:

    a. primary meristems
    b. primary tissues
    c. pericycle
    d. vascular cambium

M   88. This tissue gives rise to epidermis and cortex.

D   89. This tissue gives rise to protoderm and procambium.

D   90. This tissue gives rise to ground meristem.

M   91. This tissue gives rise to cork cambium.

D   92. This tissue gives rise to secondary phloem and xylem.

Answers   88. b   89. a   90. a

               91. c   92. d

Selecting the Exception

M   93. Four of the five answers listed below are related by a common region of the plant body. Select the exception.
      a. leaf
 *   b. root cap
      c. node
      d. axillary bud
      e. stem

D   94. Four of the five answers listed below are characteristic of monocots. Select the exception.
      a. flower parts in three or multiples of three
      b. pollen grains have one pore
      c. one cotyledon in seed
 *   d. vascular tissue arranged in a ring
      e. veins in leaf are parallel

D   95. Four of the five answers listed below are characteristic of dicots. Select the exception.
      a. secondary growth
      b. net venation
      c. flower parts in fours or fives
      d. two seed leaves
 *   e. pollen grains with one pore or furrow

M   96. Four of the five answers listed below are types of ground tissue. Select the exception.
      a. ground tissue
 *   b. xylem
      c. sclerenchyma
      d. parenchyma
      e. collenchyma

D   97. Four of the five answers listed below are functions of parenchyma tissue. Select the exception.
 *   a. support
      b. heal wounds
      c. store food
      d. conduct photosynthesis
      e. regenerate lost parts

D 98. Four of the five answers listed below are characteristic of sclerenchyma cells. Select the exception.
   a. sclereid
   b. found in seed coats
 * c. retain the ability to divide after differentiation
   d. gritty texture of pear cells
   e. used in manufacture of paper, textiles, and rope

D 99. Four of the five answers listed below are characteristics of xylem. Select the exception.
   a. is dead at maturity
   b. cell walls are impregnated with lignin
 * c. conducts dissolved food
   d. includes tracheids and vessels
   e. has pits in the walls of the cells

D 100. Four of the five answers listed below are characteristics of phloem. Select the exception.
 * a. consists only of cell walls
   b. characterized by channels across plant cell walls
   c. sieve plates found between some cells
   d. includes accessory companion cells
   e. transports sugar

D 101. Four of the five answers listed below are characteristics of epidermal cells. Select the exception.
   a. have a continuous covering
   b. outer walls impregnated with cutin
   c. oil-secreting cells
   d. secrete nectar
 * e. impregnated with suberin

D 102. Four of the five answers listed below are characteristics of periderm. Select the exception.
   a. periderm
   b. suberin
   c. cork
   d. waterproof protection
 * e. primary tissue

D 103. Four of the five answers listed below are tissues capable of cell division. Select the exception.
   a. cork cambium
   b. apical meristem
   c. procambium
 * d. periderm
   e. vascular cambium

M 104. Four of the five answers listed below are limited to the node region. Select the exception.
   a. leaf axil
   b. node
 * c. vascular bundle
   d. lateral bud
   e. leaf meristem

M 105. Four of the five answers listed below are parts of tissue found in a cross section of root. Select the exception.
   a. cortex
 * b. pith
   c. pericycle
   d. endodermis
   e. epidermis

M 106. Four of the five answers listed below are related to vascular tissue. Select the exception.
   a. conduction of water and minerals
   b. vascular bundle
   c. translocation
   d. vein
 * e. pith

M 107. Four of the five answers listed below are functions of roots. Select the exception.
   a. support
 * b. synthesis of food
   c. absorption of water and minerals
   d. conduction of water and solutes
   e. anchorage

M 108. Four of the five answers listed below are related by a similar nature. Select the exception.
   a. adventitious
   b. tap
   c. fibrous
   d. lateral
 * e. insectivorous

D 109. Four of the five answers listed below are features of the pericycle. Select the exception.
   a. outermost tissue in the vascular column
   b. origins of branch roots
   c. found in the root but not in stem
 * d. site for food storage
   e. located inside the endodermis

D 110. Four of the five answers listed below are parts of the vascular cylinder. Select the exception.
 * a. endodermis
   b. procambium
   c. primary xylem
   d. primary phloem
   e. pericycle

M 111. Four of the five answers listed below are types of cells in plants. Select the exception.
   a. cork
   b. parenchyma
 * c. cuticle
   d. sieve tube
   e. tracheid

D 112. Four of the five answers listed below are parts of a leaf. Select the exception.
   a. stoma
   b. cuticle
   c. mesophyll
 * d. node
   e. petiole

CHAPTER 30
PLANT NUTRITION AND TRANSPORT

Multiple-Choice Questions

E   1.   Which of the following statements is false?
   a.   Some plants are carnivorous.
 * b.   It is unsafe to sleep in a dark room filled with
        plants because they will use up all the oxygen.
   c.   Plants lose water only during the day.
   d.   Water is pulled up to the top of a plant by the pull
        of transpiration.
   e.   Plants absorb the majority of needed elements
        from water and soil.

PLANT NUTRIENTS AND THEIR AVAILABILITY
IN SOILS

M   2.   By definition, humus includes all of the following
           except
   a.   feces.
   b.   dead organisms.
   c.   leaf litter.
 * d.   weathered rock.
   e.   decomposing organic matter.

E   3.   The soil particles that hold nutrients best are composed
           of
   a.   sand.
 * b.   clay.
   c.   humus.
   d.   silt.
   e.   quartzite.

E   4.   Topsoil is designated as horizon
 * a.   A.
   b.   B.
   c.   C.
   d.   O.
   e.   Z.

M   5.   The oxygen needed by plants is ultimately derived
           from
   a.   aerobic respiration.
 * b.   photosynthesis.
   c.   anaerobic respiration.
   d.   electrolysis.
   e.   lightning discharges.

E   6.   Which of the following elements is obtained by plants
           directly from the atmosphere?
   a.   nitrogen
   b.   hydrogen
 * c.   carbon
   d.   iron
   e.   sulfur

E   7.   In terms of percent content of dry weight of a plant, the
           two most common elements are
   a.   carbon and hydrogen.
   b.   hydrogen and oxygen.
   c.   carbon and nitrogen.
 * d.   oxygen and carbon.
   e.   hydrogen and nitrogen.

E   8.   Plants in general require how many essential elements
           for their growth and survival?
   a.   6
   b.   12
 * c.   16
   d.   22
   e.   28

E   9.   Which of the following elements required by plants
           does NOT come directly from the soil?
 * a.   carbon
   b.   nitrogen
   c.   magnesium
   d.   potassium
   e.   iron

D   10.   Which element is found as a component of amino
           acids, proteins, chlorophyll, nucleic acids, and
           coenzymes?
 * a.   nitrogen
   b.   potassium
   c.   sulfur
   d.   phosphorus
   e.   magnesium

D   11.   Which element is a component of nucleic acids, ATP,
           and participates in guard cell movements?
   a.   nitrogen
 * b.   potassium
   c.   sulfur
   d.   phosphorus
   e.   magnesium

M   12.   Which of the following is a micronutrient?
   a.   sulfur
 * b.   iron
   c.   magnesium
   d.   potassium
   e.   phosphorus

M   13.   Which of the following elements has a role in electron
           transport and chlorophyll synthesis?
 * a.   iron
   b.   manganese
   c.   phosphorus
   d.   zinc
   e.   boron

M 14. Which of the following elements is a component of both proteins and nucleic acids?
   a. iron
   b. phosphorus
 * c. nitrogen
   d. potassium
   e. sulfur

D 15. Which element is a component of some amino acids, two vitamins, and most proteins?
   a. nitrogen
   b. potassium
 * c. sulfur
   d. phosphorus
   e. magnesium

D 16. Which element is a component of chlorophyll and activates enzymes used in photosynthesis, respiration, and protein synthesis?
   a. nitrogen
   b. potassium
   c. sulfur
   d. phosphorus
 * e. magnesium

D 17. Chlorotic interveinal yellowing of older leaves and leaf droop are caused by a deficiency of
   a. nitrogen.
   b. potassium.
   c. sulfur.
   d. phosphorus.
 * e. magnesium.

E 18. Which of the following is a micronutrient?
   a. sulfur
   b. calcium
   c. phosphorus
 * d. manganese
   e. magnesium

E 19. Chlorotic leaves turn
 * a. yellow.
   b. black.
   c. orange.
   d. red.
   e. transparent.

D 20. A plant will become chlorotic due to a lack of any but which one of the following?
   a. nitrogen
 * b. phosphorus
   c. magnesium
   d. manganese
   e. iron

M 21. Which of the following is NOT an essential element for most land plants?
 * a. sodium, Na
   b. potassium, K
   c. copper, Cu
   d. molybdenum, Mo
   e. all of these are essential

E 22. Most of the macronutrients and micronutrients function as
   a. food for plants.
   b. structural components for cells.
   c. elements needed for the development of mycorrhizae.
 * d. enzyme activators.
   e. all of these

E 23. Leaching is caused by
   a. wind and water movements.
   b. wind only.
 * c. water only.
   d. wind, running water, and ice.
   e. none of these

HOW DO ROOTS ABSORB WATER AND MINERAL IONS?

M 24. The Casparian strip is associated with the
   a. epidermis.
   b. vascular tissue.
   c. cortex.
   d. root hairs.
 * e. endodermis.

M 25. Which of the following statements is false?
   a. Root hairs are composed of single epidermal cells.
   b. Nodules containing bacteria enable plants to increase their absorption of nitrogen.
 * c. Water moves through the Casparian strip.
   d. Water travels along the cells of the cortex but must move through the cytoplasm of endodermal cells.
   e. In plant cells, ATP is produced by both photosynthesis and respiration.

M 26. Which of the following could NOT be used in a description of the Casparian strip?
   a. waxy
   b. endodermis
 * c. permeable
   d. exodermis
   e. waterproof

D 27. The endodermis in the plant root
 * a. regulates the movement of water and minerals into the vascular cylinder.
   b. prevents water from moving through the Casparian strip.
   c. is the outer absorptive surface for water uptake.
   d. forces water to move through the Casparian strip.

M 28. Water absorption depends primarily on
   a. abscisic acid.
   b. cohesion-tension.
 * c. the concentration gradient.
   d. active transport.
   e. the potassium pump.

M 29. Water absorption is greater when the roots are in
 * a. wet soil because more ions are in solution.
   b. dry soil because there is more oxygen available for ATP production.
   c. dry soil because transpiration pull is more effective.
   d. dry soil because the stomata are closed and less sugar is being transported down to the root.

M 30. Which of the following statements is false?
   a. Annual grasses have fibrous root systems.
   b. Most dicots have a large taproot system.
   c. Mycorrhizae are mutually beneficial to the plants they infect.
 * d. Roots explore the soil and actively search for water.
   e. In mycorrhizal infection, the fungus absorbs sugar and nitrogen compounds from the host plant.

M 31. The water and minerals absorbed by the roots usually first enter the
   a. pericycle.
   b. vascular tissue.
   c. cortex.
 * d. root hairs.
   e. endodermis.

M 32. Nodules found on the roots of leguminous plants are involved in supplying which element for the plant?
   a. aluminum
   b. boron
   c. magnesium
 * d. nitrogen
   e. chlorine

E 33. Plants obtain nitrogen
 * a. as the product of nitrogen-fixing bacteria.
   b. by absorption of nutrients released from the minerals that form the underlying rocks.
   c. directly from the atmosphere through their stomata.
   d. only through the application of commercial fertilizers.

M 34. The nodules found on the roots of plants called legumes
   a. are abnormal growths.
   b. house bacteria.
   c. are beneficial to the plant.
   d. are abnormal growths and house bacteria.
 * e. house bacteria and are beneficial to the plant.

E 35. Mycorrhizae are
   a. roots.
   b. bacteria.
 * c. fungus roots.
   d. isolated plants.
   e. small animals found in agricultural soils.

M 36. Mycorrhizae
   a. increase plant growth.
   b. are symbionts.
   c. allow a plant to absorb more water.
   d. increase the surface area for absorption of water and minerals.
 * e. all of these

M 37. What would be the effect of the accidental seepage of a fungicide into the soil surrounding a plant in a mycorrhizal relationship?
   a. The plant would die from lack of nutrients.
 * b. Water and mineral supply to the plant would slow.
   c. The fungicide would cause the leaves to become chlorotic.
   d. The plant would live just as it did before because the fungi are not necessary.

HOW IS WATER TRANSPORTED THROUGH PLANTS?

M 38. Water inside all of the xylem cells is being pulled upward primarily by
   a. turgor pressure.
 * b. negative pressures (tensions).
   c. osmotic gradients.
   d. pressure flow forces.
   e. active transport.

M 39. Which of the following causes transpiration?
   a. hydrogen bonding
 * b. the drying power of air
   c. cohesion-tension
   d. evaporation
   e. all of these

M 40. Which theory of water transport states that hydrogen bonding allows water molecules to maintain a continuous fluid column as water is pulled from roots to leaves?
   a. pressure flow
   b. evaporation
 * c. cohesion-tension
   d. abscission
   e. fusion

M 41. Water moves through a plant because of
   a. transpirational pull.
   b. the cohesion of water molecules.
   c. the strength of hydrogen bonds holding water molecules together.
   d. the replacement of lost water molecules.
 * e. all of these

M 42. Water tension in a transpiring plant
   a. is exerted on a continuous column of water throughout the plant.
   b. is the result of the polar nature of water molecules.
   c. results in the loss of over 90 percent of the water the plant absorbs.
   d. will exert a pull on water molecules lower down in the plant's vascular system.
 * e. all of these

M 43. If houseplants must be left unattended for any length of time, some people recommend placing plastic bags over them. What is the reasoning behind this procedure?
   a. Water will condense on the inside of the bag and water the soil.
   b. Heat will build up in the bag and keep the plant from freezing.
   c. Photosynthesis will be increased due to the concentration of carbon dioxide in the bag.
   * d. Transpiration will be slowed, and more water will remain in the soil.

M 44. A detergent added to the water applied to your houseplants could have what effect?
   a. increase the uptake of minerals by loosening them from surrounding soil particles
   * b. disrupt the cohesion of water in the xylem tubes
   c. poison the companion cells of the xylem tubes
   d. dissolve the cuticle of the root cells

HOW DO STEMS AND LEAVES CONSERVE WATER?

M 45. Most of the water moving into a leaf is lost through
   a. osmotic gradients.
   * b. transpiration.
   c. pressure flow forces.
   d. translocation.
   e. all of these

M 46. Most of the water that enters the plant
   a. leaves the plant through the root system.
   * b. is lost through transpiration.
   c. remains in the plant to form the high concentration of water in plant tissue.
   d. remains in the plant to function in translocation.
   e. is used up in cellular metabolism.

E 47. If a cuticle is removed from a leaf, it will
   a. be unable to carry on photosynthesis.
   b. be unable to carry on transpiration.
   * c. lose water and wilt.
   d. stop growing and turn yellow.

M 48. Of all the water moving into a leaf, about what percent is stored or used in metabolism?
   a. 0
   * b. 2
   c. 10
   d. 70
   e. 90

M 49. Most of the water lost from a leaf comes most directly from
   a. upper epidermal cells.
   b. lower epidermal cells.
   * c. mesophyll cells.
   d. xylem tissue.
   e. phloem cells.

E 50. The waxy covering of the leaf is the
   * a. cuticle.
   b. epidermis.
   c. Casparian strip.
   d. stomata.
   e. none of these

E 51. The openings in leaves that function to exchange gases are called
   a. cuticles.
   * b. stomata.
   c. guard cells.
   d. pits.
   e. pores.

E 52. The cells that surround stomata are
   a. endodermal cells.
   * b. guard cells.
   c. mesophyll cells.
   d. vascular bundle cells.
   e. vessel cells.

D 53. Gas exchange in plants
   a. is not necessary because plants produce their own oxygen.
   * b. cannot occur if there is excess transpiration.
   c. is a one-way process, with carbon dioxide entering the plant and oxygen leaving.
   d. is not required by the roots.

E 54. Which of the following statements is false?
   a. Transpiration creates a tension on water columns in a plant.
   b. Transpiration is the loss of water from a plant in a gaseous form.
   c. Water enters a root because of an osmotic gradient.
   * d. Most of the transpiration in a plant occurs through the cuticle.
   e. Molecules of water exhibit cohesion resulting from hydrogen bonding of water molecules.

E 55. Carbon dioxide enters the plant
   a. at night.
   b. when transpiration occurs.
   c. when the guard cells are turgid.
   d. when potassium ions leave the guard cells.
   * e. when transpiration occurs because guard cells are turgid.

M 56. The stomata
   a. open at night.
   * b. are open when the guard cells are turgid.
   c. close when the turgor pressure of the guard cells increases.
   d. are covered by the cuticle to reduce water loss.
   e. all of these

D 57. Which statement is false?
* a. The stomata open to allow carbon dioxide to enter the leaf, not as a result of environmental conditions.
b. As carbon dioxide levels drop in guard cells, there is an influx of potassium.
c. When potassium ions enter guard cells, water will move in by osmosis.
d. At night, carbon dioxide builds up in guard cells, resulting in the movement of potassium and water out of the guard cells.
e. When the guard cells collapse, the stomata are closed.

E 58. The cuticle
a. conserves water.
b. reduces absorption of carbon dioxide by the plant.
c. reduces transpiration.
d. helps prevent wilting.
* e. all of these

E 59. The stomata are open
a. during the day.
b. when the guard cells are turgid.
c. when the plant is wilted.
d. during the time that plants are actively photosynthesizing.
* e. all but "when the plant is wilted."

M 60. Guard cells
a. surround the stoma.
b. control the opening to the interior of the leaf.
c. become turgid when it becomes light if environmental conditions are not too hot or dry.
d. absorb water from surrounding epidermal cells.
* e. all of these

M 61. Usually, during the daytime,
a. carbon dioxide accumulates in leaf cells.
b. turgor pressure in the guard cell decreases.
* c. water and potassium move into the guard cell.
d. the guard cells close.
e. water is conserved.

D 62. If the transport of potassium into guard cells is inhibited, the expected result would be that
a. stomata would remain open.
b. water would flow into the cells more freely.
* c. stomata would remain closed.
d. greater amounts of carbon dioxide could enter.
e. stomata would remain open and greater amounts of carbon dioxide could enter.

D 63 In CAM plants, such as cacti
a. the stomata are open both day and night.
b. the stomata are open during the day even though the plants cannot afford to lose the water.
c. there are no stomata because the water loss would be too great.
* d. stomata are open at night.
e. guard cells are present but operate the reverse of usual plants.

HOW ARE ORGANIC COMPOUNDS DISTRIBUTED THROUGH PLANTS?

M 64. Products of photosynthesis are
a. used by plant tissues for energy.
b. stored for use by herbivores.
c. transported in soluble form to sinks.
d. interconverted to other forms.
* e. all of these

M 65. The most common form of sugar transported to the roots is
a. glucose.
b. fructose.
* c. sucrose.
d. ribose.
e. starch.

E 66. Carbohydrates are stored in plants in the form of
a. cellulose.
b. sucrose.
* c. starch.
d. fats.
e. glucose.

E 67. Movement of soluble organic material through plants is known as
* a. translocation.
b. active transport.
c. passive transport.
d. transpiration.
e. none of these

E 68. Sugars are carried throughout the plant in which tissue?
a. cortex
b. parenchyma
c. xylem
* d. phloem
e. cambium

M 69. The major food transport substance in plants is
a. oil.
b. glucose.
c. starch.
d. fructose.
* e. sucrose.

E 70. Insects used to study the process of translocation in plants are the
* a. aphids.
b. fruit flies.
c. cockroaches.
d. termites.
e. grasshoppers.

M 71. The role of companion cells in translocation is to
    a. assist vessel members with movement of organic substances.
    b. supply the potassium ions needed for water absorption.
*   c. provide energy to the sieve tube members.
    d. supply the potassium ions needed for water absorption and provide energy to the sieve tube members.
    e. assist vessel members with movement of organic substances, supply the potassium ions needed for water absorption, and provide energy to the sieve tube members.

M 72. The fluid in the phloem
    a. is under negative pressure.
    b. moves by active transport.
*   c. is under pressure equivalent to the air in a tire, or greater.
    d. is responsible for the transpiration pull of material from roots.
    e. is chiefly water with dissolved minerals.

D 73. Sieve tubes are different from vessel cells because they
    a. carry water, not food.
    b. are not connected to each other.
*   c. are alive, not dead like xylem cells.
    d. conduct minerals.
    e. carry water, not food and conduct minerals.

M 74. A parked car that gets spattered by sticky droplets from a tree has been covered by
    a. water and minerals that have been exuded from the tips of leaves.
*   b. droplets of honeydew that have been forced out of aphids.
    c. feces from herbivorous insects.
    d. material released from mistletoe in the upper limbs.
    e. drops of water produced by transpiration.

M 75. Feeding aphids may be anesthetized by exposure to
    a. alcohol.
*   b. carbon dioxide.
    c. methane.
    d. gasoline.
    e. cigarette smoke.

E 76. The movement of materials already in the phloem is described as
    a. source-to-sink.
    b. pressure flow.
    c. cohesion-tension.
    d. active transport.
*   e. source-to-sink and pressure flow.

M 77. The source region in the pressure flow explanation of phloem transport is most often the
    a. root.
    b. flower.
    c. stem.
*   d. leaf.
    e. soil.

M 78. The sink region in the pressure flow explanation of phloem transport could be
    a. growing leaves.
    b. seeds.
    c. fruits.
    d. roots.
*   e. all of these

M 79. Large pressure gradients arise in sieve tube systems by means of
    a. vernalization.
    b. abscission.
*   c. osmosis.
    d. transpiration.
    e. all of these

D 80. Which of the following processes does NOT serve to maintain low pressure at the receiving end of sieve tube pipelines?
    a. Sucrose is converted into cell-wall polysaccharides in the receiving regions.
    b. Sucrose is converted into starch in the receiving regions.
    c. Sucrose is converted to glucose, which is used in cellular respiration at the receiving end.
*   d. High concentrations of dissolved solutes are pumped into the cells of these receiving regions by active transport.
    e. none of these

M 81. The most commonly accepted theory used to explain movement of food in the phloem is
    a. cohesion-tension theory.
*   b. the pressure flow hypothesis.
    c. active transport.
    d. dialysis.
    e. turgor pressure.

M 82. Which of the following statements is true?
    a. There is always a gradient of sucrose concentration from source to sink.
    b. Sucrose is being generated at the source and converted or used at the sink.
    c. Companion cells supply the energy required for translocation.
    d. Sieve tubes are only passive conduits for translocation.
*   e. all of these

Matching Questions

D 83. Matching. Choose the one most appropriate letter for each.

1. ___ Casparian strip
2. ___ companion cells
3. ___ legumes
4. ___ mycorrhiza
5. ___ nodules
6. ___ sieve tube members
7. ___ stylet
8. ___ tracheids and vessels
9. ___ translocation
10. ___ transpiration
11. ___ guard cells

A. responsible for opening and closing of stomata
B. mouthpart of an aphid
C. pipelines of the xylem
D. a mutually beneficial association between a fungus and a young root
E. structures on roots that house nitrogen-fixing bacteria
F. pipelines of the phloem
G. evaporation from stems and leaves
H. actively transport sucrose into sieve tube members
I. dicot plants that tend to establish symbiotic relationships with nitrogen-fixing bacteria
J. transport of organic molecules from source region to sink
K. a waxy band that forces water to diffuse through cells

Answers:

1. K	2. H	3. I
4. D	5. E	6. F
7. B	8. C	9. J
10. G	11. A	

Classification Questions

Answer questions 84–88 in reference to the five plant macronutrients listed below:

a. nitrogen
b. potassium
c. calcium
d. magnesium
e. phosphorus

M 84. This nutrient helps to maintain turgor pressure.

M 85. This nutrient is an extremely important part of ATP.

M 86. This nutrient is an important part of the backbone structure of DNA.

D 87. This nutrient helps to cement cell walls together.

M 88. This nutrient is essential to formation of chlorophyll and acts as a cofactor for many enzymes.

Answers

84. b	85. e	86. e
87. c	88. d	

Answer questions 89–93 in reference to the five plant micronutrients listed below:

a. iron
b. boron
c. manganese
d. zinc
e. copper

D 89. This nutrient is used in synthesis of auxins.

M 90. This nutrient plays an important role in flowering and germination.

M 91. This nutrient is a cofactor in enzymes involved in carbohydrate metabolism.

E 92. This nutrient is an essential component of proteins involved in electron transport.

D 93. This nutrient plays an important role in the movement of plant hormones.

Answers

89. d	90. b	91. e
92. a	93. b	

Selecting the Exception

M 94. Four of the five answers listed below are macronutrients. Select the exception.
* a. manganese
b. potassium
c. calcium
d. magnesium
e. phosphorus

M 95. Four of the five answers listed below are micronutrients. Select the exception.
   a. molybdenum
   b. copper
   * c. nitrogen
   d. iron
   e. chlorine

D 96. Four of the five answers listed below are related by a common chemical nature. Select the exception.
   a. protein
   * b. calcium carbonate
   c. carbohydrate
   d. lipid
   e. nucleic acid

D 97. Four of the five answers listed below are elements whose deficiency symptoms include chlorosis. Select the exception.
   * a. phosphorus
   b. iron
   c. chlorine
   d. copper
   e. magnesium

D 98. Four of the five answers listed below are related by their participation in water movement through plants. Select the exception.
   a. hydrogen bonds
   b. transpiration
   c. cohesion-tension
   d. tension in xylem
   * e. photosynthesis

D 99. Four of the five answers listed below promote transpiration. Select the exception.
   a. potassium ions pumped into guard cells
   b. turgor pressure builds up in guard cells
   c. photosynthesis occurs in guard cells
   d. carbon dioxide enters leaf
   * e. presence of cuticle

D 100. Four of the five answers listed below are actions that cause stomata to open. Select the exception.
   * a. Abscisic acid accumulates in leaves.
   b. Potassium ions build up in guard cells.
   c. Water moves from epidermal cells to guard cells.
   d. Turgor pressure increases in guard cells.
   e. Guard cells carry on photosynthesis.

D 101. Four of the five answers listed below are events that occur when the stomata are open. Select the exception.
   a. ATP is used.
   b. Potassium pump operates.
   c. Active transport is going on.
   * d. Water is conserved.
   e. Guard cells swell with water.

D 102. Four of the five answers listed below are events that occur when water is abundant. Select the exception.
   a. Leaves absorb more carbon dioxide.
   b. Ions are absorbed by the roots.
   c. Less oxygen is absorbed by roots.
   * d. Stomata are closed.
   e. Photosynthesis is not limited by lack of water or carbon dioxide.

D 103. Four of the five answers listed below are sinks for solute deposition. Select the exception.
   a. fruits
   b. roots
   * c. leaves
   d. seeds
   e. rapidly growing tissue

CHAPTER 31
PLANT REPRODUCTION

Multiple-Choice Questions

E   1.   The first seed-bearing plants were produced in the Devonian, about how many million years ago?
     a. 50
     b. 150
     c. 250
   * d. 390
     e. 450

M   2.   Ovules and pollen sacs first arose on the surfaces of scales that were
     a. stems.
     b. leaves.
     c. flowers.
     d. found in cones.
   * e. leaves and found in cones.

M   3.   The evolution of flowers and insects is an example of
     a. parallel evolution.
     b. regressive evolution.
   * c. coevolution.
     d. convergent evolution.
     e. divergent evolution.

E   4.   Insects are attracted to flowers by
     a. nectaries.
     b. specific colors.
     c. specific color patterns.
     d. floral odors.
   * e. all of these

M   5.   Birds and a few insects are able to detect which of the following colors?
     a. yellow
     b. green
     c. blue
   * d. red
     e. violet

E   6.   Which color are most insects unable to see?
     a. yellow
     b. blue
   * c. red
     d. green
     e. orange

D   7.   Foul-smelling flowers may be pollinated by
     a. birds.
   * b. beetles and flies.
     c. bees and bumblebees.
     d. wasps.
     e. bugs and butterflies.

M   8.   Bees will NOT visit flowers of what color?
   * a. red
     b. blue
     c. yellow
     d. purple
     e. white

E   9.   Night-flying moths would be expected to pollinate flowers of what color?
     a. red
     b. blue
     c. yellow
   * d. white
     e. purple

E   10. The function of flowers is to
     a. provide beauty to the environment.
     b. attract insects.
     c. produce sex cells.
     d. enable scientists to classify plants into the proper taxonomic group.
   * e. attract insects and produce sex cells.

REPRODUCTIVE STRUCTURES OF FLOWERING PLANTS

E   11. Which of the following statements is false?
     a. Flowers are reproductive shoots.
   * b. Trees are gametophytes.
     c. Sporophyte plants can reproduce asexually.
     d. Cells produced by mitosis are clones.
     e. Gametophytes are haploid.

M   12. The sporophyte generation
   * a. is essential for a flowering plant to complete its life cycle.
     b. is the dominant generation in the mosses.
     c. is microscopic in the flowering plants.
     d. produces the sexually reproducing cells—sperm and egg.

E   13. Alternation of generations refers to the
     a. expression of recessive traits.
   * b. presence of a diploid and a haploid generation in the life cycle of plants.
     c. presence of the different sexes in two different plants.
     d. occurrence of a sexually reproducing diploid stage followed by an asexually reproducing haploid stage during the life cycle of higher plants.

M   14. All but which of the following are true of angiosperm
          gametophytes?
          a. produce haploid sex cells
          b. arise from cells within the flowers
     *   c. develop independently from the sporophyte
          d. produce eggs or sperm

M   15. The least specialized part of the flower is a
          a. carpel.
          b. stamen.
          c. petal.
     *   d. sepal.
          e. ovule.

E   16. A stamen is
          a. composed of a stigma, a style, and an ovary.
          b. the mature male gametophyte.
     *   c. the site where microspores are produced.
          d. part of the vegetative phase of an angiosperm.
          e. none of these

E   17. The male part of a flower is the
          a. carpel.
     *   b. stamen.
          c. petal.
          d. sepal.
          e. receptacle.

E   18. The male part of a flower includes the
          a. carpel.
          b. stigma.
          c. pollen sacs.
          d. anther.
     *   e. pollen sacs and anther.

E   19. The various flower parts are attached to the
          a. style.
     *   b. receptacle.
          c. stigma.
          d. filament.
          e. calyx.

E   20. The calyx is composed of
          a. petals.
     *   b. sepals.
          c. stigmas.
          d. ovules.
          e. anthers.

E   21. Stamens contain
          a. petals.
          b. sepals.
          c. stigmas.
          d. ovules.
     *   e. anthers.

E   22. The corolla is made up of
          a. sepals.
     *   b. petals.
          c. carpels.
          d. pollen grains.
          e. anthers.

M   23. Which forms the outermost whorl of flower parts?
     *   a. sepals
          b. petals
          c. anthers
          d. carpels
          e. stamens

E   24. The calyx is composed of
          a. petals.
     *   b. sepals.
          c. anthers.
          d. carpels.
          e. receptacle tissue.

M   25. Theoretically, a plant should still be able to reproduce
          sexually even though its _____ have been
          removed.
          a. stamens
     *   b. sepals
          c. anthers
          d. ovaries
          e. carpels

M   26. The term *angiosperm* refers to the _____ of the
          flower.
     *   a. carpel
          b. ovary
          c. ovule
          d. stamens
          e. petals

M   27. Plants with perfect flowers have structures
     *   a. of both sexes.
          b. that are not damaged.
          c. for only one sex.
          d. of both sexes and are not damaged.
          e. for only one sex and are not damaged.

A NEW GENERATION BEGINS

D   28. Which of the following choices represents the correct
          sequence?
          a. microspores——> meiosis——> gametophyte—
              —> sperm
     *   b. meiosis——> microspores——> gametophyte—
              —> sperm
          c. gametophyte——> meiosis——> megaspores—
              —> eggs
          d. meiosis——> gametophyte——> megaspores—
              —> eggs

M   29. Megaspores produce
     *   a. female gametophytes.
          b. spores.
          c. sporophytes.
          d. embryos.
          e. diploid tissue.

M 30. What do gametes, spores, and the gametophyte
generation have in common?
a. They are all diploid.
* b. They are all haploid.
c. They are limited to vascular plants.
d. They have nothing in common.

M 31. Which of the following is part of the gametophyte
generation?
a. carpel
b. anther
* c. tube nucleus
d. seed
e. megaspore

M 32. Which of the following is false?
a. Flowers often exhibit coevolution with their
pollinators.
b. Seeds often exhibit coevolution with their
disseminators.
c. The pollen grain is a haploid microspore.
d. Megaspores are part of the female gametophyte
generation.
* e. Megaspores and microspores arise through
mitosis.

M 33. The process during which the diploid set of
chromosomes becomes haploid is
a. metastasis.
b. fertilization.
c. cleavage.
* d. meiosis.
e. none of these

E 34. Anthers produce
a. ovules.
b. stamens.
* c. microspores.
d. female gametophytes.
e. none of these

M 35. Microspores are produced by
a. carpels.
b. mitosis.
* c. meiosis.
d. parthenogenesis.
e. carpels and meiosis.

M 36. Which of the following is true concerning the pollen
grain?
a. diploid
b. formed from sperm cells
* c. two-celled
d. produced by the pollen tube

E 37. Pollen grains fossilize well because
* a. of their strong, resistant walls.
b. of their small size.
c. they are haploid.
d. they are dry.
e. of the muddy environments into which they fall.

M 38. Megaspores
a. are haploid.
b. are found in the embryo sac.
c. will develop into the gametophyte.
d. are female rather than male.
* e. all of these

M 39. The megaspore usually divides into how many nuclei
before fertilization?
a. 2
b. 4
* c. 8
d. 16
e. 32

E 40. The female gametophyte is the
a. nucellus.
b. ovule.
* c. embryo sac.
d. endosperm.
e. ovary.

E 41. The egg is
a. diploid.
b. tetraploid.
c. polyploid.
d. triploid.
* e. haploid.

E 42. Pollination occurs on the
a. micropyle.
* b. stigma.
c. style.
d. anther.
e. embryo sac.

E 43. The place where pollination occurs is the
* a. stigma.
b. micropyle.
c. anther.
d. receptacle.
e. style.

E 44. The pollen tube grows to or through the
a. stigma.
b. style.
c. ovary.
d. micropyle.
* e. all of these

E 45. The endosperm is
a. diploid.
b. tetraploid.
c. polyploid.
* d. triploid.
e. haploid.

M 46. "Double fertilization" in plants is the union of
a. two eggs and one sperm.
b. two sperm and one egg.
c. two sperm and two eggs.
* d. one sperm to one egg and one sperm to the
endosperm.
e. one sperm to the egg and one sperm to the egg
nucleus.

D 47. In flowering plants, one sperm nucleus fuses with that of an egg, and a zygote forms that develops into an embryo. Another sperm nucleus
   a. fuses with a primary endosperm cell to produce three cells, each with one nucleus.
   b. fuses with a primary endosperm cell to produce one cell with one triploid nucleus.
 * c. fuses with the diploid endosperm mother cell, forming a primary endosperm cell with a single triploid nucleus.
   d. fuses with one of the smaller megaspores to produce what will eventually become the seed coat.
   e. none of these

E 48. The endosperm of a plant
 * a. forms the food supply for the new sporophyte plant.
   b. is composed of haploid tissue.
   c. protects the young embryo within a seed.
   d. provides a connection between the ovary of a flower and a developing seed.

FROM ZYGOTE TO SEEDS AND FRUITS

M 49. Counting the number of seeds in a fruit will give an indication of the number of
   a. carpels.
   b. stamens.
   c. pollen tubes.
 * d. ovules.
   e. flowers.

E 50. Which of the following is NOT a fruit?
   a. peanut
   b. pumpkin
 * c. potato
   d. plum

E 51. The protective layers covering the ovule are the
   a. nucellus.
   b. endosperm.
 * c. integuments.
   d. micropyle.
   e. embryo sac.

E 52. The zygote is
 * a. diploid.
   b. tetraploid.
   c. polyploid.
   d. triploid.
   e. haploid.

E 53. The primary function of the endosperm is
   a. protection.
   b. reproduction.
   c. growth.
 * d. food storage.
   e. water absorption.

E 54. Which of the following develops into seed?
   a. flower
   b. ovary
   c. carpel
 * d. ovule
   e. stamen

E 55. The seed is produced by the development of the
   a. embryo.
 * b. ovule.
   c. ovary.
   d. zygote.
   e. pollen.

M 56. The seed coat forms from the
   a. zygote.
   b. cotyledon.
   c. nucellus.
 * d. integuments.
   e. micropyle.

E 57. A seed leaf is which of the following?
   a. embryo
   b. coleoptile
   c. endosperm
 * d. cotyledon
   e. suspensor

E 58. A seed does NOT include
   a. endosperm.
   b. seed coats.
   c. cotyledons.
 * d. carpels.

D 59. What kind of fruit is formed from carpels of several associated flowers?
   a. aggregate
   b. simple
 * c. multiple
   d. fleshy
   e. dry

M 60. Fruit is produced from the development of the
   a. zygote.
   b. ovule.
   c. flowers.
   d. cotyledon.
 * e. ovary.

D 61. All but which of the following is a simple fruit?
   a. pea
   b. maple
 * c. strawberry
   d. wheat
   e. sunflower

DISPERSAL OF FRUITS AND SEEDS

M 62. The seeds of fleshy fruits are most likely to be spread by
 * a. animals.
   b. water.
   c. wind.
   d. explosion.
   e. insects.

M   63.   Which of the following adaptations of seeds would be expected to be the most common in the temperate parts of the world?

     a.   the requirement that the seed be exposed to hot, dry conditions before germination can occur

     b.   the requirement that the fruit or seeds be exposed to high temperatures such as would be produced by fires

*   c.   the requirement that the seed be exposed to a critical low temperature before it would germinate

     d.   the need to be dispersed from where they originated and to be planted by humans

M   64.   Fleshy fruits, such as cherries, are more likely to be dispersed by _____ than by other means.

     a.   wind

     b.   adhering to animal fur

*   c.   passing through animal guts

     d.   falling to the ground and rotting

     e.   water currents

ASEXUAL REPRODUCTION OF FLOWERING PLANTS

M   65.   All but which of the following terms can be used in describing asexual reproduction?

     a.   clone

     b.   mitosis

     c.   identical

*   d.   meiosis

     e.   parent

M   66.   Which is NOT primarily related to asexual reproduction?

     a.   parthenogenesis

*   b.   pollination

     c.   runner formation

     d.   cloning and tissue culture

     e.   all of these

M   67.   If a plant is said to propagate vegetatively, this means that

*   a.   part of a leaf, a stem, or a root, when torn away from the parent plant and planted under proper conditions, can develop into a new plant.

     b.   it cannot reproduce by forming flowers, fruits, and seeds.

     c.   the leafy part of the gametophyte can grow into a new plant if planted and grown similar to the way most vegetables are grown.

     d.   flowers and fruits from one plant can be grafted onto another closely related plant to produce hybrids.

     e.   all of these

M   68.   Parthenogenesis

*   a.   is a form of asexual reproduction.

     b.   is a type of pollination.

     c.   is a specialized flower.

     d.   is typical of the reproductive cycle of most flowering plants.

     e.   results in germination of most seeds.

E   69.   Strawberries reproduce by

*   a.   runners.

     b.   corms.

     c.   bulbs.

     d.   tubers.

     e.   rhizomes.

E   70.   Potatoes reproduce by

     a.   runners.

     b.   corms.

     c.   bulbs.

*   d.   tubers.

     e.   rhizomes.

E   71.   Grasses reproduce by

     a.   runners.

     b.   corms.

     c.   bulbs.

     d.   tubers.

*   e.   rhizomes.

E   72.   Lilies and onions reproduce by

     a.   runners.

     b.   corms.

*   c.   bulbs.

     d.   tubers.

     e.   rhizomes.

M   73.   Frederick Steward and his coworkers propagated a complete plant from a single cell. What kind of plant was it?

     a.   onion

*   b.   carrot

     c.   radish

     d.   bamboo

     e.   bean

Matching Questions

D **74.** Matching. Choose the one most appropriate answer for each.

1. ___ aggregate fruit
2. ___ anther
3. ___ carpel
4. ___ embryo sac
5. ___ endosperm mother cell
6. ___ megaspores
7. ___ micropyle
8. ___ microspores
9. ___ multiple fruit
10. ___ ovary
11. ___ ovule
12. ___ petal
13. ___ pollen grain
14. ___ sepal
15. ___ stigma

    A. meiospores of anthers

    B. site where pollen tube usually penetrates the ovule

    C. after fertilization, ripens into fruit tissue

    D. a $2n$ cell that will help form nutrients for the developing plant embryo

    E. cluster of matured ovaries attached to a common receptacle

    F. modified leaf with pigments and fragrance-producing cells

    G. immature male gametophyte

    H. female reproductive organ

    I. landing platform for pollen

    J. pollen-bearing structure

    K. meiospores of ovule

    L. outermost whorl of leaf parts on a receptacle; generally green, but sometimes pigmented

    M. female gametophyte

    N. matured ovaries of several flowers fused together into a single mass (for example, pineapple, fig)

    O. after fertilization, will form a seed

Answers:

1. E	2. J	3. H	4. M
5. D	6. K	7. B	8. A
9. N	10. C	11. O	12. F
13. G	14. L	15. I	

Classification Questions

Answer questions 75–79 in reference to the five flower parts listed below:

    a. anther
    b. stigma
    c. ovule
    d. ovary
    e. stamen

E **75.** During fertilization of a flowering plant, the male gamete first adheres to this structure.

M **76.** A pollen tube ultimately grows into this structure.

M **77.** Fertilization of a flowering plant occurs inside of this structure.

M **78.** This structure produces pollen.

M **79.** Male gametogenesis occurs in this structure.

Answers   75. b   76. c   77. c

         78. a   79. a

Answer questions 80–84 in reference to the five flower parts listed below:

    a. megaspore
    b. microspore
    c. ovule
    d. ovary
    e. seed

D **80.** This structure gives rise to the female gametophyte.

D **81.** This structure is female and haploid.

M **82.** This gives rise to haploid pollen grains.

D **83.** The egg is ultimately derived from this structure.

D **84.** During early development, the plant embryo is most intimately associated with this structure.

Answers   80. a   81. a   82. b

         83. a   84. c

Selecting the Exception

E **85.** Four of the five answers listed below are related by gender. Select the exception.
    a. carpel
    b. ovary
  * c. stamen
    d. style
    e. stigma

M 86. Four of the five answers listed below are types of flower whorls. Select the exception.
* a. receptacle
  b. stamen
  c. carpel
  d. petal
  e. sepal

M 87. Four of the five answers listed below are haploid. Select the exception.
  a. gametophyte
* b. zygote
  c. sperm
  d. meiospore
  e. gamete

E 88. Four of the five answers listed below are nonreproductive parts of a flower. Select the exception.
  a. calyx
* b. anther
  c. corolla
  d. petal
  e. sepal

M 89. Four of the five answers listed below are related by a common gender. Select the exception.
  a. micropyle
  b. integument
  c. embryo sac
* d. microspore
  e. egg

E 90. Four of the five answers listed below are the results of fertilization. Select the exception.
  a. fruit
  b. seed
  c. embryo
* d. pollen
  e. endosperm

E 91. Four of the five answers listed below are useful to flowers as means of attracting vectors. Select the exception.
  a. nectar
  b. flower color
  c. color patterns
  d. pollen
* e. wind

M 92. Four of the five answers listed below are parts of a seed. Select the exception.
* a. ovary
  b. cotyledon
  c. embryo
  d. coat
  e. endosperm

M 93. Four of the five answers listed below are defined as simple fruits. Select the exception.
* a. pineapple
  b. maple
  c. pea
  d. lemon
  e. banana

M 94. Four of the five answers listed below are adaptations to aid in dispersal of fruit. Select the exception.
  a. hooks
  b. spines
* c. smooth surface
  d. hairs
  e. sticky substances

E 95. Four of the five answers listed below are types of asexual reproduction. Select the exception.
* a. seed
  b. runner
  c. bulb
  d. parthenogenesis
  e. corm

CHAPTER 32
PLANT GROWTH AND DEVELOPMENT

Multiple-Choice Questions

M   **1.**   Gibberellins
     a.   were first isolated by Japanese working with "foolish" rice plants.
     b.   were first isolated from a fungus.
     c.   are represented by more than 70 different types.
     d.   promote stem elongation.
*   e.   all of these

PATTERNS OF EARLY GROWTH AND DEVELOPMENT–AN OVERVIEW

M   **2.**   Imbibition is
     a.   a synonym for germination.
     b.   the rapid growth that occurs after fertilization.
*   c.   the absorption of water.
     d.   the loss of salt from a plant.
     e.   the digestion of the seed coat.

M   **3.**   All but which of the following could have an effect on seed germination?
     a.   moisture
     b.   temperature
*   c.   minerals
     d.   number of daylight hours
     e.   oxygen

M   **4.**   Cells that retain the ability to divide are called _____ cells.
     a.   parenchyma
*   b.   meristematic
     c.   ground
     d.   epidermal
     e.   mesophyll

M   **5.**   The cells formed by mitosis in a germinating seed are different from one another in all but which one of the ways listed below?
     a.   amount of cytoplasm
*   b.   genetic composition
     c.   hormone content
     d.   enzymes present
     e.   metabolic rate

E   **6.**   In the early growth stages of a seedling, what is responsible for cell enlargement?
     a.   mitosis
     b.   cytoplasmic divisions
     c.   hormonal interactions
*   d.   water uptake
     e.   mitosis and cytoplasmic divisions

D   **7.**   Which of the following statements is false?
     a.   The movement of water into a seed is known as imbibition.
     b.   Water is attracted to hydrophilic proteins in the seed.
*   c.   The shoot system is the first part of a cotyledon to grow.
     d.   When a seed begins germinating, it starts aerobic respiration.
     e.   Germination is completed once the root extends outside the seed.

WHAT THE MAJOR PLANT HORMOES DO

M   **8.**   When a cell begins to enlarge after cell division, the primary cell wall
     a.   is rather elastic and can be stretched.
     b.   becomes thinner because it is stretched.
*   c.   becomes thicker due to the addition of polysaccharides.
     d.   is rather elastic and can be stretched making it thinner.
     e.   is rather elastic, can be stretched, and becomes thicker due to the addition of polysaccharides.

E   **9.**   Chemicals produced by one group of cells that affect distant target cells are called
     a.   secretions.
*   b.   hormones.
     c.   steroids.
     d.   polymers.
     e.   enzymes.

E   **10.**   The target cells for hormones
*   a.   have special receptor sites.
     b.   are located in roots.
     c.   are no different from any other cells.
     d.   are located in the interior of the plant.
     e.   all of these

M   **11.**   Which of the following is NOT accurate in describing a hormone?
*   a.   Hormones produced by a particular species affect only that species.
     b.   Only those cells that have specific receptors can respond to any one hormone.
     c.   Hormones in general are produced by one cell and cause their effects in another cell.
     d.   Hormones are a type of signaling molecule.

M   12.   Synthetic auxins are used as
          a. pesticides.
        * b. herbicides.
          c. fungicides.
          d. insecticides.
          e. all of these

M   13.   2,4-D, a potent dicot weed killer, is a synthetic
        * a. auxin.
          b. gibberellin.
          c. cytokinin.
          d. phytochrome.
          e. none of these

M   14.   The most common synthetic "hormone" is
          a. 3,7-C.
        * b. 2,4-D.
          c. 1,5-K
          d. 3,6-T.
          e. 1,4-X.

E   15.   The plant hormone thought to be involved with
          response to gravity and light is
          a. abscisic acid.
        * b. auxin.
          c. gibberellin.
          d. ethylene.
          e. none of these

M   16.   The function of a coleoptile is
          a. food production.
          b. food storage.
        * c. protection.
          d. translocation.
          e. absorption of water and minerals.

M   17.   A coleoptile
          a. is found in dicot seeds.
        * b. is a protective sheath surrounding the first leaf of
             monocots.
          c. produces the primary root of grasses.
          d. is a tissue specialized for food storage in a seed.
          e. is an impermeable membrane found immediately
             under the seed coat.

M   18.   Studies on the growth of coleoptiles involve
          a. florigen.
          b. ethylene.
        * c. auxin (IAA).
          d. abscisic acid.
          e. gibberellin.

M   19.   Monocots, but NOT dicots, have
          a. nodes.
          b. cotyledons.
        * c. coleoptiles.
          d. hypocotyl hooks.
          e. flowers.

D   20.   Which of the following is mismatched?
          a. cytokinin—retards aging
          b. auxin—promotes cell elongation
        * c. gibberellin—involved in phototropism and
             gravitropism
          d. abscisic acid—promotes stomatal closure
          e. ethylene—promotes leaf abscission

D   21.   Which of the following is mismatched?
          a. cytokinin—promotes cell division
          b. abscisic acid—triggers bud and seed dormancy
        * c. ethylene—breaks dormancy of seeds and buds
          d. auxin—involved in phototropism and gravitropism

M   22.   Gibberellins have their most dramatic effects
          a. on leaves.
          b. in cell elongation.
          c. in fruit ripening.
        * d. in stem lengthening.
          e. on flowers.

M   23.   The plant hormone that promotes cell division is
          a. auxin.
          b. gibberellin.
        * c. cytokinin.
          d. florigen.
          e. ethylene.

M   24.   Root formation in stem cuttings can be improved by
          the application of
        * a. indoleacetic acid.
          b. abscisic acid.
          c. phosphoglyceric acid.
          d. citric acid.

M   25.   What hormone can be used commercially to prolong
          the shelf life of fresh vegetables?
          a. abscisic acid
        * b. cytokinins
          c. auxins
          d. IAA
          e. florigen

M   26.   The plant hormone that promotes dormancy in plants
          and seeds is
        * a. abscisic acid.
          b. auxin.
          c. gibberellin.
          d. ethylene.
          e. none of these

M   27.   In contrast to most other plant hormones, which
          hormone has mostly inhibitory effects?
          a. auxin
          b. gibberellin
          c. cytokinin
        * d. abscisic acid
          e. ethylene

M   28.   The plant hormone that is gaseous is
          a. auxin.
          b. gibberellin.
          c. cytokinin.
          d. florigen.
        * e. ethylene.

M   29. The plant hormone that promotes fruit ripening is
          a. auxin.
          b. gibberellin.
          c. cytokinin.
          d. florigen.
     *   e. ethylene.

ADJUSTING THE DIRECTION AND RATES OF GROWTH

D   30. Perhaps a plant's greatest liability is its inability to
          a. produce growth hormones.
          b. use aerobic respiration.
     *   c. move when conditions around it deteriorate.
          d. produce its own lipids and proteins.
          e. respond to dwindling supplies of nutrients and water.

M   31. Charles Darwin did research on
          a. dwarf pea plants.
     *   b. coleoptiles and phototropism.
          c. flowering.
          d. germination.
          e. fruit ripening.

E   32. What is the principal substance that causes phototropism in stems or leaves?
     *   a. auxin
          b. gibberellin
          c. abscisic acid
          d. ethylene
          e. all of these

M   33. A house plant that has been placed in the window will grow toward the source of light because auxin
          a. becomes more concentrated on the illuminated side of the plant.
     *   b. becomes less concentrated on the illuminated side of the plant.
          c. becomes more concentrated in the roots of the plant.
          d. inhibits the growth of cells on the shady side, so the cells on the sunny side grow faster.

M   34. Which color of light is most effective in producing phototropism?
          a. red
     *   b. blue
          c. yellow
          d. white
          e. green

M   35. The primary root of a seedling grows down
          a. to avoid light.
          b. in response to gravity.
          c. because the cells on the top of the root grow faster than those on the bottom of the root.
          d. in response to different concentrations of auxin.
     *   e. all except "to avoid light."

M   36. Which is the principal substance that regulates thigmotropism?
     *   a. auxin and ethylene
          b. gibberellin
          c. abscisic acid
          d. florigen
          e. none of these

D   37. A decline in health of a plant struck repeatedly by the garden gate is most likely explained as
          a. positive geotropism.
     *   b. negative thigmotropism.
          c. negative phototropism.
          d. positive thigmotropism.
          e. positive photoperiodism.

D   38. Mechanical stress is most closely related to
          a. phototropism.
          b. geotropism.
          c. hydrotropism.
     *   d. thigmotropism.
          e. aerotropism.

M   39. The leaves of some sensitive plants droop when touched because
          a. their cell walls lose their rigidity when touched.
     *   b. some cells lose turgor pressure when touched.
          c. the plant tries to escape from the source of irritation.
          d. nerve impulses trigger effectors to close the leaves.

HOW DO PLANTS KNOW WHEN TO FLOWER?

M   40. Which of the following is NOT promoted by the active form of phytochrome?
          a. seed germination
     *   b. root growth
          c. leaf expansion
          d. stem branching
          e. none of these

D   41. Compared with young trees growing out in the open, young trees growing in a darker forest understory tend to have longer, thinner trunks with less branching; this developmental pattern is principally caused by
          a. phototropism.
          b. thigmotropism.
     *   c. activated phytochrome being converted to inactive phytochrome.
          d. inactive phytochrome being converted to active phytochrome.
          e. none of these

E   42. Which of the following responses is NOT controlled by plant hormones?
          a. the growth form of the plant (apical dominance)
          b. the beginning and ending of dormancy
          c. the bending of an oat coleoptile toward light
     *   d. the production of glucose by the chloroplast

M 43. The pigment responsible for photoperiodism is
   a. chlorophyll.
   b. xanthophyll.
   c. anthocyanin.
 * d. phytochrome.
   e. photoerythrin.

E 44. The absence of which of the following pigments would prevent a plant from responding to the duration of light and darkness?
   a. chlorophyll
   b. xanthophyll
   c. carotene
 * d. phytochrome

E 45. Rhythms that are repeated every 24 hours are collectively and specifically known as
   a. sleep movements.
   b. tropisms.
   c. biorhythms.
 * d. circadian rhythms.
   e. the biological clock.

M 46. The active form of phytochrome is known as
   a. Pp.
   b. Pr.
 * c. Pfr.
   d. Pl.
   e. Pst.

M 47. Active phytochrome controls
   a. flowering and seed set.
   b. seed germination.
   c. stem branching and elongation.
   d. expansion of leaves.
 * e. all of these

M 48. The value of a plant's sleep movements is possibly that they
   a. block moonlight from the lower leaves.
   b. reduce the amount of heat lost from the plant at night.
   c. allow heat transfer between leaves.
   d. speed the process of translocation between plant parts.
 * e. block moonlight from the lower leaves and reduce the amount of heat lost from the plant at night.

M 49. Phytochrome is converted from the inactive to the active form by being exposed to light of what color?
   a. far red
 * b. red
   c. yellow
   d. white
   e. blue

E 50. In the dark, plants cannot
   a. grow.
   b. respire.
   c. move.
 * d. utilize chlorophyll.
   e. form carotenoid pigment.

M 51. All but which of the following are hormones?
   a. IAA
   b. abscisic acid
 * c. phytochrome
   d. cytokinin
   e. All are hormones.

E 52. Photoperiodism is the
   a. duration of flowering in a plant.
   b. amount of light needed by a plant to exhibit normal growth.
 * c. response of a plant to the duration of light and darkness.
   d. light phase of photosynthesis during which photolysis of water occurs.

D 53. Which of the following terms refers to the change in relative daylength?
   a. photoerythrin
   b. phototropism
   c. photorhythmic
   d. photochrome
 * e. photoperiodism

D 54. Even though the autumn may be unusually warm, the leaves from deciduous trees begin to drop during September. Which of the following is the best explanation?
 * a. The trees are responding to shorter days.
   b. The autumn months are usually drier because the summer rains have tapered off.
   c. The effects of phototropism are operating "right on schedule."
   d. There is not enough sunlight to carry on photosynthesis any longer.

M 55. Day-neutral plants are
   a. short-day plants.
 * b. able to bloom when they are old enough.
   c. night-blooming plants.
   d. triggered to bloom by cold weather.
   e. none of these

M 56. Which of the following statements is false?
   a. Long-day plants bloom in the spring.
 * b. Short-day plants bloom around noon.
   c. Short-day plants bloom in late summer and early fall.
   d. Chrysanthemums, cockleburs, and poinsettias are long-day plants.
   e. Day-neutral plants flower when mature enough to do so.

M 57. Short-day plants
   a. flower in late summer.
   b. will not bloom until they have been exposed to a dark period longer than a critical length.
   c. flower in the fall.
   d. will not bloom if their dark period is interrupted by two to five minutes of light.
 * e. all of these

M   58.   In long-day plants,
   a.   extended daylight produces more Pfr.
   b.   the plants bloom more profusely.
   c.   the interruption of the dark period does not upset the flowering sequence.
   d.   flowering is limited to summertime under normal conditions.
   *   e.   all of these

M   59.   An unidentified hormone that interacts with phytochrome to influence flowering is produced in
   a.   roots.
   *   b.   leaves.
   c.   stem.
   d.   flowers.
   e.   petioles.

LIFE CYCLES END, AND TURN AGAIN

E   60.   All the processes that lead to the death of a plant or any of its organs are called
   a.   dormancy.
   b.   vernalization.
   c.   abscission.
   *   d.   senescence.
   e.   none of these

E   61.   The aging of a plant is known as
   *   a.   senescence.
   b.   vernalization.
   c.   abscission.
   d.   dormancy.
   e.   chlorosis.

M   62.   Abscission affects
   a.   leaves.
   b.   fruits.
   c.   flowers.
   *   d.   all of these
   e.   none of these

M   63.   The so-called death signal to a plant is embodied in the concept of
   *   a.   senescence.
   b.   abscission.
   c.   vernalization.
   d.   dormancy.
   e.   photoperiodism.

M   64.   Senescence may be counteracted by
   a.   auxins.
   b.   abscisic acid.
   *   c.   cytokinin.
   d.   gibberellin.
   e.   florigen.

D   65.   Which factor has NOT been implicated in breaking dormancy?
   *   a.   abscisic acid movement from leaves to buds in late summer
   b.   the breakdown of abscisic acid in late autumn and winter
   c.   gibberellin accumulation in buds in late autumn and winter
   d.   an exposure to low temperatures for hundreds of hours
   e.   none of these

M   66.   Dormancy can be triggered by
   a.   low Pfr levels.
   b.   the production of abscisic acid.
   c.   nitrogen deficiency and low soil moisture.
   d.   cold nights.
   *   e.   all of these

E   67.   The requirement of cold weather before a particular plant process occurs (i.e., germination) is known as
   a.   the biological clock.
   *   b.   vernalization.
   c.   photoperiodism.
   d.   biennial life cycle.
   e.   biorhythm.

D   68.   If peach trees growing in specific mild climates of the southern United States do not receive about 850 hours of temperatures below 40 degrees, they will not produce flowers in the spring. This is explained by which of the following terms?
   a.   photoperiodism
   b.   phototropism
   c.   senescence
   *   d.   vernalization
   e.   dormancy

M   69.   Dormancy in a seed may be broken by
   a.   fire.
   b.   passage through the digestive tract of a bird or mammal.
   c.   the seed coat being ruptured by the seed driven across sand by wind or rain.
   d.   digestion of the seed coat by fungi and bacteria.
   *   e.   all of these

M   70.   For some seeds to germinate,
   a.   they must first be exposed to a critical low temperature for a certain length of time.
   b.   they must be exposed to proper environmental conditions of temperature and moisture.
   c.   something must remove the restrictive seed coat.
   d.   something must remove the hormones that promote dormancy.
   *   e.   all of these

D   **71.** If a woody plant in dormancy was placed in a
         greenhouse so that only one limb was exposed to the
         cold winter temperatures, eventually
         a. the whole plant would break dormancy and start
            growing.
         b. the parts of the plant that were inside the
            greenhouse would start blooming.
         c. the limb exposed to the low temperature would
            die.
    *   d. the limb exposed to the low temperature would
            break dormancy.
         e. the limb exposed to the low temperature would
            flower.

Matching Questions

D   **72.** Matching. Choose the one most appropriate answer
         for each. Some letters may not be used.

         1. ___ abscisic acid
         2. ___ annual
         3. ___ biennial
         4. ___ coleoptile
         5. ___ ethylene
         6. ___ florigen
         7. ___ gibberellin
         8. ___ auxin
         9. ___ phytochrome
         10. ___ circadian
         11. ___ short-day plant
         12. ___ target cell
         13. ___ long-day plant
         14. ___ Pfr
         15. ___ vernalization

A. flower each successive year or after several
    years of vegetative growth
B. promotes cell elongation in stems
C. has receptor sites for a particular hormonal
    message
D. a hollow, cylindrical organ that protects
    young leaves growing within it
E. blue-green pigment that absorbs light energy
F. low-temperature stimulation of flowering
G. stimulates stomata closure and might be
    involved in root geotropism
H. stimulates fruit ripening
I. reproduces in spring
J. produces only roots, stems, and leaves the
    first growing season and produces flowers
    the second year
K. occurring on a 24-hour cycle
L. flowers in autumn
M. possible name for elusive hormone that
    controls flowering
N. lives for only one growing season
O. promotes stem elongation in dwarf plants
P. pigment involved in flowering process

Answers: 1. G   2. N   3. J   4. D
              5. H   6. M   7. O   8. B
              9. E   10. K   11. L   12. C
             13. I   14. P   15. F

Classification Questions

Answer questions 73–77 in reference to the five plant hormones
listed below:

         a. auxins
         b. gibberellins
         c. cytokinins
         d. abscisic acid
         e. ethylene

M   **73.** Hormones most closely associated with cell division.

M   **74.** Hormones involved in stem elongation and closely
         related chemically to certain weed killers like 2,4–D.

D   **75.** This hormone controls rate of transpiration.

E   **76.** This hormone is a gas that promotes ripening.

M   **77.** This hormone promotes bud and seed dormancy.

Answers   73. c   74. a   75. d
              76. e   77. d

Selecting the Exception

M 78. Four of the five answers listed below are effects caused by auxin. Select the exception.
    a. used as herbicide
  * b. promotes cell division
    c. promotes cell elongation
    d. functions in tropism
    e. indoleacetic acid

D 79. Four of the five answers listed below are true for gibberellin. Select the exception.
    a. breaks dormancy in seeds in buds
    b. first isolated from a fungus
    c. causes stem elongation
  * d. triggers flower production
    e. overcomes genetic dwarfing

D 80. Four of the five answers listed below are functions of abscisic acid. Select the exception.
    a. may be involved in the dropping of leaves and fruits
    b. promotes stomata closure
    c. promotes seed dormancy
    d. confers resistance to water stress
  * e. stimulates cell elongation

D 81. Four of the five answers listed below are characteristics of ethylene. Select the exception.
    a. the simplest plant hormone
    b. promotes fruit ripening
  * c. triggers cells division
    d. is a gas
    e. effects were observed by ancient Chinese

M 82. Four of the five answers listed below are stimulators that evoke plant tropisms. Select the exception.
    a. gravity
    b. touch
    c. mechanical stress
    d. light
  * e. electrical current

M 83. Four of the five answers listed below are flower responses that follow 24-hour cycles. Select the exception.
    a. sleep movements
    b. flowers open in the morning
    c. circadian rhythm
  * d. photoperiodism
    e. flowers close at night

D 84. Four of the five answers listed below are plant activities affected by phytochrome. Select the exception.
  * a. tropism
    b. stem elongation
    c. seed germination
    d. leaf expansion
    e. formation of flowers, fruits, and seeds

CHAPTER 33
ANIMAL TISSUES AND ORGAN SYSTEMS

Multiple-Choice Questions

M 1. Which of the following is an example of a negative feedback response?
   a. As the uterus contracts, more oxytocin is released to intensify the level of uterine contractions.
   b. The smell of food or the sight of pictures of a sumptuous meal makes a person hungrier.
 * c. Meerkats bask in the sunlight at the beginning of the day but avoid it during the heat of the day.
   d. Sexual stimulation leads to arousal and climax.
   e. Accumulation of undigested food in the bowels leads to the defecation reflex.

E 2. Which of the following terms applies to the functioning of the human body?
   a. cytology
   b. anatomy
   c. psychology
 * d. physiology
   e. endocrinology

E 3. Which of the following terms applies to the structural aspects of the human body?
   a. cytology
 * b. anatomy
   c. psychology
   d. physiology
   e. endocrinology

E 4. Chemical and structural bridges link groups or layers of like cells, uniting them in structure and function as a cohesive
   a. organ.
   b. organ system.
 * c. tissue.
   d. cuticle.

E 5. Which of the following represents the correct hierarchy of organization in the human body?
   a. cells——>tissues——>organ systems——>organs
 * b. cells——>tissues——>organs——>organ systems
   c. tissues——>cells——>organs——>organ systems
   d. tissues——>organs——>cells——>organ systems

M 6. The minimum level of organization required for a "division of labor" is the _____ level.
   a. cellular
   b. organ
 * c. tissue
   d. organ system
   e. body

M 7. Which of the following statements is NOT true?
 * a. Tissues are composed of cells with similar structures but different functions.
   b. There are four major types of tissues found in animals.
   c. Tissues exhibit division of labor.
   d. Tissues are organized to form organs.
   e. All of these are true.

D 8. A cell in the pancreas is unaffected by which of the following features of muscle or bone tissue?
   a. Contraction of muscle cells aids in circulation of blood and lymph.
   b. Bone tissue serves as a reservoir for certain minerals such as calcium and potassium.
   c. Muscle contraction during a reflex action helps to avoid a falling piano.
   d. Bone tissue through hemopoesis results in blood cell production.
 * e. None of these, because all directly or indirectly affect any given cell in the pancreas.

EPITHELIAL TISSUE

E 9. The tissue that lines all internal surfaces is
 * a. epithelium.
   b. loose connective.
   c. supportive connective.
   d. fibrous.
   e. adipose.

D 10. Adhering and gap junctions are found at the
   a. endoplasmic reticulum.
   b. nuclear membrane.
 * c. plasma membrane.
   d. Golgi apparatus.
   e. ribosomes.

D 11. Cells with gap junctions are typical of tissues
   a. that suffer wear, abrasion, and mechanical insults.
   b. such as bone and cartilage that must withstand external forces.
 * c. that require rapid exchange of chemical messages, as is the case for cardiac muscle.
   d. that secrete enzymes or hormones.
   e. all of these

M 12. Which of the following junctions influences the passage of ions and small molecules between cells?
 * a. gap
   b. adhering
   c. loose
   d. tight
   e. plasma

D **13.** Epithelial cells are specialized for all but which of the following functions?
   a. secretion
   b. protection
   c. filtration
   * d. contraction
   e. absorption

E **14.** The secretion of tears, milk, sweat, and oil is a function of what tissue?
   * a. epithelial
   b. loose connective
   c. lymphoid
   d. nervous
   e. adipose

D **15.** Which type of epithelial cell is modified for filtration and diffusion?
   a. cuboidal
   * b. simple squamous
   c. simple columnar
   d. stratified squamous
   e. stratified columnar

M **16.** The type of epithelial cell found in the lining of the stomach, intestinal tract, and part of the respiratory tract is
   a. simple cuboidal.
   b. simple squamous.
   * c. simple columnar.
   d. stratified.
   e. stratified columnar.

E **17.** Exocrine glands secrete
   a. enzymes.
   b. sweat.
   c. milk.
   d. mucus.
   * e. all of these

M **18.** Which of the following is true of the basement membrane?
   a. It overlies the epithelium at its free surface.
   b. It is composed partially of epithelial cells and partially of connective tissue.
   c. It is mostly lipid and embedded celluloid fibers.
   * d. It lies between the epithelium and connective tissue.
   e. It cements the layers of stratified epithelium together.

M **19.** If you microscopically examined a slide and observed a single layer of closely packed cells with microvilli on the free or open side and a basement membrane underlying the sheet of cells, you would expect this to be a slide of
   a. adipose tissue.
   b. dense regular connective tissue.
   * c. epithelial tissue.
   d. muscle tissue.
   e. cartilage.

CONNECTIVE TISSUE

M **20.** Which of the following is NOT defined as connective tissue?
   a. bone
   * b. skeletal muscle
   c. cartilage
   d. collagen
   e. blood

E **21.** What type of tissue is blood?
   a. epithelial
   b. muscular
   * c. connective
   d. adipose
   e. noncellular fluid

M **22.** An extracellular matrix is characteristic of
   a. muscle tissue.
   b. epithelial tissue.
   * c. connective tissue.
   d. nervous tissue.
   e. embryonic tissue.

M **23.** Which of the these is NOT connective tissue?
   a. cartilage
   b. blood
   c. bone
   d. fat
   * e. outer layer of skin

E **24.** Dense fibrous tissues that connect muscle to bone are called
   a. muscles.
   b. cartilage.
   c. ligaments.
   * d. tendons.
   e. all of these

M **25.** Bones are linked together at skeletal joints by
   a. tendons.
   b. intercellular junctions.
   * c. ligaments.
   d. cartilage.
   e. collagen.

M **26.** Collagen fibers are characteristic of which tissue?
   a. muscle
   b. epithelial
   * c. connective
   d. nervous
   e. embryonic

M **27.** Tendons connect
   a. bones to bones.
   b. bones to ligaments.
   * c. muscles to bones.
   d. bones to cartilage.
   e. all of these

E 28. Collagen fibers supply
   a. strength.
   b. elasticity.
   c. energy.
   d. rigidity.
* e. all except "energy."

E 29. Cartilage is found
   a. in the nose.
   b. in the embryonic skeleton.
   c. in the external ear.
   d. between vertebrae.
* e. all of these

E 30. Which element is found in greatest abundance in bone?
   a. potassium
   b. fluorine
* c. calcium
   d. iron
   e. phosphorus

E 31. Adipose tissue cells are filled with
   a. minerals.
* b. fat.
   c. cartilage.
   d. fibers.
   e. muscles.

D 32. Outside the circulatory and lymphatic systems, macrophages
   a. are found in loose, connective tissue.
   b. perform a defensive action.
   c. can become transformed into fibroblasts.
* d. are found in loose, connective tissue and perform a defensive action.
   e. are found in loose, connective tissue, perform a defensive action, and can become transformed into fibroblasts.

D 33. Which of the following correctly matches connective tissue with its deposits?
   a. blood: fats
   b. adipose: polysaccharide
* c. bone: mineral ions
   d. cartilage: calcium

E 34. Which of the following tissues would be associated with the following terms: collagen, matrix, hemoglobin, minerals?
   a. epithelial
   b. nervous
* c. connective
   d. muscle
   e. reproductive

MUSCLE TISSUE

M 35. If its cells are striated and fused at the ends by intercalated disks so that the cells contract as a unit, the tissue is
   a. smooth muscle.
   b. dense fibrous connective.
   c. supportive connective.
* d. cardiac muscle.

E 36. Muscle that is NOT striped and is involuntary is
   a. cardiac.
   b. skeletal.
   c. striated.
* d. smooth.
   e. cardiac and smooth

E 37. Cardiac muscle cells are
   a. involuntary.
   b. voluntary.
   c. striated.
   d. slow contracting.
* e. involuntary and striated.

E 38. Smooth muscles are
   a. striated and voluntary.
   b. isolated, spindle-shaped cells.
   c. found in the walls of hollow structures such as blood vessels and the stomach.
   d. involuntary and nonstriated.
* e. all except "striated and voluntary."

NERVOUS TISSUE

E 39. Rapid communication throughout the body is accomplished by
* a. neurons.
   b. blood.
   c. hormones.
   d. muscles.
   e. connective tissue.

ORGAN SYSTEMS

D 40. A fish embryo was accidentally stabbed by a graduate student in a developmental biology laboratory. Later, the embryo developed into a creature that could not move and had no supportive or circulatory systems. Which embryonic tissue had suffered the damage?
   a. ectoderm
   b. endoderm
* c. mesoderm
   d. protoderm
   e. both ectoderm and protoderm

D 41. A student attempting to learn more about the process of embryological development manipulated an embryo early in the developmental process. The creature that developed was normal in almost every aspect, except for some of the organs lining the digestive tract. The tissue that was disturbed was
   a. ectoderm.
* b. endoderm.
   c. gastroderm.
   d. mesoderm.
   e. both ectoderm and gastroderm

E 42. Muscle cells are produced by
    a. the ectoderm.
    b. the endoderm.
  * c. the mesoderm.
    d. the ectoderm and endoderm.
    e. all of the germ layers.

E 43. The lining of the intestinal tract is produced by
    a. the ectoderm.
  * b. the endoderm.
    c. the mesoderm.
    d. the endoderm and mesoderm.
    e. all of the germ layers.

E 44. The nervous system is produced by
  * a. the ectoderm.
    b. the endoderm.
    c. the mesoderm.
    d. the endoderm and ectoderm.
    e. all of the germ layers.

E 45. The external covering of the body is produced by
  * a. the ectoderm.
    b. the endoderm.
    c. the mesoderm.
    d. the ectoderm and mesoderm.
    e. all of the germ layers.

E 46. The skeletal and circulatory systems are produced by
    a. the ectoderm.
    b. the endoderm.
  * c. the mesoderm.
    d. two of the germ layers.
    e. all of the germ layers.

E 47. The lining of the gut and the stomach, liver, and pancreas are produced by
    a. the ectoderm.
  * b. the endoderm.
    c. the mesoderm.
    d. two of the germ layers.
    e. all of the germ layers.

M 48. Somatic cells can form all but which of the following?
  * a. gametes
    b. epithelia
    c. muscles
    d. digestive organs
    e. Somatic cells form all of these.

M 49. The endocrine system functions in
    a. conduction.
    b. contraction.
  * c. hormonal control of body functioning.
    d. protection against disease.
    e. cell production.

M 50. The maintenance of the volume and composition of body fluids is the direct responsibility of which system?
    a. integumentary
    b. immune
    c. digestive
  * d. urinary
    e. circulatory

E 51. Which system is involved with heat production?
    a. endocrine system
    b. nervous system
  * c. muscular system
    d. respiratory system
    e. skeletal system

E 52. Integration of body functions is controlled by the
    a. respiratory system.
    b. nervous system.
    c. endocrine system.
    d. defense system.
  * e. both nervous system and endocrine system.

M 53. Organs of which of the following systems are the most diffuse and the least likely to be physically connected?
    a. integumentary system
  * b. endocrine system
    c. skeletal system
    d. muscular system
    e. digestive system

E 54. Which system produces blood cells?
    a. endocrine
  * b. skeletal
    c. muscular
    d. defense
    e. integumentary

E 55. Which of the following terms means the structure is located away from the central part of the body?
    a. dorsal
    b. inferior
    c. superior
    d. proximal
  * e. distal

M 56. Of the following organs, which is NOT in the abdominal cavity?
    a. stomach
    b. liver
  * c. heart
    d. intestine
    e. pancreas

E 57. What we usually call the "back" of the human body is really the
    a. anterior.
  * b. posterior.
    c. inferior.
    d. superior.

Matching Questions

D   **58.**   Matching I. Choose the one most appropriate answer for each.

1. ___ adipose tissue
2. ___ blood
3. ___ dense connective tissue
4. ___ glandular epithelium
5. ___ loose connective tissue
6. ___ interstitial fluid
7. ___ neuron
8. ___ epidermis

   A.   ligaments and tendons are made of this

   B.   contains collagen and elastin; acts as a packing material that supports internal organs

   C.   receives, conducts, and initiates signals in response to environmental changes

   D.   stores fatty reserves

   E.   offers resistance to mechanical injury and loss of internal fluids; also a barrier against microorganisms

   F.   secretes extracellular products such as sweat, mucus, tears, and saliva

   G.   fluid ground substance plus free cells; involved in transport , pH, and temperature stability

   H.   extracellular fluid that bathes cells and tissues

Answers: 1. D   2. G   3. A   4. F
             5. B   6. H   7. C   8. E

D   **59.**   Matching II. Choose the one most appropriate answer for each.

1. ___ muscle cells
2. ___ lining of the intestine
3. ___ nervous system
4. ___ external body covering
5. ___ skeletal system
6. ___ circulatory system
7. ___ stomach, liver, and pancreas (excluding the muscles and nerves)

   A.   develop(s) from ectoderm in embryo

   B.   develop(s) from endoderm in embryo

   C.   develop(s) from mesoderm in embryo

Answers: 1. C   2. B   3. A   4. A
             5. C   6. C   7. B

Classification Questions

Answer questions 60- 64 in reference to the five types of connective tissue listed below:

   a.   loose tissue
   b.   dense tissue
   c.   adipose tissue
   d.   cartilage
   e.   blood

E   **60.**   Tendons are composed of this.

E   **61.**   The elasticity of skin is due to the presence of this kind of tissue.

M   **62.**   This tissue plays an important role in stabilizing body temperature.

E   **63.**   This tissue provides nourishment to each of the other connective tissues.

M   **64.**   This tissue plays a particularly important role in the thermoregulation of marine mammals.

Answers   60. b   61. a   62. e
                 63 e   64. c

Answer questions 65- 69 in reference to the five organ systems listed below:

    a. circulatory
    b. lymphatic
    c. digestive
    d. endocrine
    e. respiratory

E   **65.** The first line of defense against infectious bacteria found in food lies in this system.

E   **66.** The immune response is part of this system.

M   **67.** Airborne allergens are first encountered by this system.

E   **68.** Antibodies are distributed throughout the body by this system.

E   **69.** The recovery of excess interstitial fluid is the responsibility of this system.

Answers   65. c   66. b   67. e

                68. a   69. b

Selecting the Exception

M   **70.** Three of the four answers listed below are germ layers. Select the exception.
    a. ectoderm
    b. mesoderm
*   c. blastoderm
    d. endoderm

D   **71.** Four of the five answers listed below are derived from the same germ layer. Select the exception.
    a. kidney
*   b. brain
    c. muscle
    d. respiratory system
    e. skeleton

D   **72.** Four of the five answers listed below are derived from the same germ layer. Select the exception.
    a. lining of intestinal tract
*   b. circulatory system
    c. liver
    d. pancreas
    e. stomach

E   **73** Four of the five answers listed below are parts of the digestive system. Select the exception.
    a. mouth
    b. gall bladder
    c. pancreas
*   d. lungs
    e. large intestine

M   **74.** Four of the five answers listed below are secreted by an exocrine gland. Select the exception.
    a. wax
    b. saliva
*   c. hormone
    d. milk
    e. mucus

D   **75.** Four of the five answers listed below are related by a common tissue type. Select the exception.
    a. adipose
    b. bone
    c. cartilage
    d. blood
*   e. epithelium

D   **76.** Four of the five answers listed below are sites where cartilage is found. Select the exception.
    a. embryonic skeleton
    b. vertebral discs
    c. external ear
    d. end of long bones in skeleton
*   e. the connection of one bone with another

M   **77.** Four of the five answers listed below are functions of the skeleton. Select the exception.
*   a. control of body temperature
    b. production of blood cells
    c. protection
    d. calcium and phosphorus storage
    e. muscle attachment

CHAPTER 34

INTEGRATION AND CONTROL: NERVOUS SYSTEMS

Multiple-Choice Questions

E 1. The basic unit of the nervous system is
  * a. the neuron.
  b. neuroglia.
  c. the brain.
  d. a nerve.
  e. a nerve impulse.

M 2. Which of the following is NOT true concerning sensory neurons?
  a. They have receptor regions for detection of stimuli.
  * b. They lie in the pathway between the interneurons and motor neurons.
  c. They relay information to the spinal cord.
  d. They are part of a reflex arc.
  e. They are one of three types of neurons.

E 3. Which of the following sequences is correct?
  a. receptors——>sensory neurons——>motor neurons——>interneurons
  b. sensory neurons ——>receptors——>motor neurons
  c. motor neurons——>integrators——>sensory neurons
  d. receptors——>motor neurons ——>interneurons——>sensory neurons
  * e. sensory neurons——>interneurons ——>motor neurons

M 4. Neuroglial cells
  a. metabolically support other neurons.
  b. form sheaths around neurons and control the rate of impulse transmission.
  c. form more than half of the volume of the brain.
  d. provide physical support.
  * e. all of these

NEURONS–THE COMMUNICATION SPECIALISTS

E 5. The single long process that extends from a typical motor nerve cell is the
  * a. axon.
  b. neuron.
  c. synapse.
  d. dendrite.
  e. cell body

E 6. The input zone of a neuron is the
  a. axon.
  b. axonal terminals.
  c. cell body.
  d. dendrite.
  * e. both cell body and dendrite.

D 7. Within a single neuron, the direction an impulse follows is
  a. dendrite——>axon——>cell body.
  b. axon——>dendrite——>cell body.
  * c. dendrite——>cell body——>axon.
  d. cell body——>dendrite——>axon.
  e. cell body——>axon——>dendrite.

D 8. When an impulse passes from one neuron to the next, it
  a. is passed directly from dendrite to axon.
  b. passes from axon to cell body to dendrite.
  c. can bypass the cell bodies of both.
  * d. passes from axon to dendrite.
  e. undergoes repolarization.

M 9. Neurons and other cells that produce action potentials are said to show
  a. polarity.
  b. saltatory conduction.
  * c. excitability.
  d. capacitance.
  e. voltage.

M 10. Functionally speaking, a nerve impulse is
  a. a flow of electrons along the outside of the plasma membrane of a neuron.
  b. the movement of cytoplasmic elements through the core of the neuron.
  * c. a series of changes in membrane potentials.
  d. a lengthening and shortening of the membrane extensions of a neuron.

D 11. When a neuron is at rest,
  a. there is a voltage difference across the membrane of about 70 millivolts.
  b. the interior is negatively charged.
  c. it is not responding to a stimulus.
  d. the fluid outside the membrane has more sodium and less potassium than the cytoplasm.
  * e. all of these

M 12. At rest, a nerve cell has a high concentration of _____ inside and a high concentration of _____ outside.
  a. acetylcholine; chlorine
  b. sodium; potassium
  * c. potassium; sodium
  d. calcium; phosphorous
  e. phosphorus; calcium

230

M   13.   The membrane-bound enzyme system that maintains the resting membrane potential is which of the following pumps?
      a.   sodium-phosphorus
*   b.   sodium-potassium
      c.   sodium-chlorine
      d.   phosphorus-calcium
      e.   phosphorus-chlorine

D   14.   The movement of potassium into the neuron when it is at rest is a result of
      a.   diffusion leakage.
      b.   the presence of some open potassium channels.
      c.   the attraction of the positively charged potassium ions by the negatively charged interior of the neuron.
      d.   both diffusion leakage and the presence of some open potassium channels.
*   e.   both the presence of some open potassium channels and the attraction of the positively charged potassium ions by the negatively charged interior of the neuron.

D   15.   Active transport
      a.   helps establish the resting potential of a neuron.
      b.   counters the process of diffusion.
      c.   allows transport of atoms across the plasma membrane of the neuron against the concentration gradient.
      d.   helps establish the resting potential of a neuron and counters the process of diffusion.
*   e.   helps establish the resting potential of a neuron, counters the process of diffusion, and allows transport of atoms across the plasma membrane of the neuron against the concentration gradient.

D   16.   For sodium to accumulate rapidly in a neuron,
*   a.   a stimulus above the threshold must open sodium gates in an accelerating manner.
      b.   the wave of repolarization must occur to reestablish a resting potential.
      c.   there must be a dramatic increase in the negative charge of the cytoplasm.
      d.   a voltage surge must cause the sodium gates to close.
      e.   the potassium gates must open first.

D   17.   Which of the following concerning transport proteins in the neuron membrane is true?
      a.   Only sodium is transported.
      b.   Only potassium is transported.
      c.   Movement is in response to concentration gradients.
*   d.   Energy moves ions against the concentration gradient.

E   18.   The resting potential of a neuron is approximately
      a.   70 microvolts.
*   b.   70 millivolts.
      c.   70 volts.
      d.   70 electrovolts.
      e.   70 megavolts.

HOW ARE ACTION POTENTIALS TRIGGERED AND PROPAGATED?

M   19.   Disturbances in sensory neurons will result in an action potential if the
      a.   stimulus is graded.
      b.   stimulus remains local.
*   c.   graded stimulus reaches a trigger zone.
      d.   localized stimuli do not spread too far.
      e.   stimuli become downgraded to localized ones.

M   20.   The intensity of a nerve impulse is dependent upon the
      a.   diameter of the nerve that transmits the impulse.
*   b.   number of impulses produced per unit time.
      c.   amount of voltage generated by the action potential.
      d.   sense organ that generates the impulse.
      e.   all of these

M   21.   Action potentials are
      a.   faster in neurons than in muscle cells.
      b.   faster in muscles than in neurons.
*   c.   essentially the same in neurons and muscle cells.
      d.   completely different in neurons and muscle cells.

E   22.   Studies of neuronal actions utilize the giant axons of
      a.   horses.
*   b.   squids.
      c.   giraffes.
      d.   whales.
      e.   tapirs.

D   23.   Which of the following occurs first during an action potential?
      a.   Many sodium ions flow into the neuron.
      b.   Voltage-gated sodium channels open.
*   c.   A local disturbance triggers the resting voltage to exceed the threshold level.
      d.   The interior of the neuron becomes positive.
      e.   The interior of the neuron becomes negative.

D   24.   The term that best describes what happens to a neuron as an impulse passes along it is
      a.   polarization
*   b.   depolarization
      c.   ionization
      d.   hypolarization
      e.   transpolarization

D   25.   Which of the following terms most accurately describes the cellular activity associated with the actual passage of a nerve impulse?
      a.   electrical discharge
      b.   action of sodium-potassium pump
*   c.   wave of depolarization
      d.   repolarization
      e.   active transport of ions

D   26.   Which of the following statements is false?
- a. The information that travels along the neural membrane is little more than a transient change in the membrane potential.
- b. A neuron is never really at rest, but must expend energy to keep the membrane potential constant even when no impulse is being processed.
- c. During the short time an action potential occurs, the cytoplasmic side of the membrane becomes positive with respect to the outside.
- *   d. Only nerve cells can exhibit depolarization events.
- e. Action potentials are not transferred from neuron to neuron.

D   27.   What happens first following a neuron stimulation?
- *   a. Sodium ions enter the cell.
- b. Sodium ions leave the cell.
- c. Potassium ions enter the cell.
- d. Potassium ions leave the cell.

D   28.   An action potential is brought about by
- a. a sudden membrane impermeability.
- b. the movement of negatively charged proteins through the neuronal membrane.
- c. the movement of lipoproteins to the outer membrane.
- *   d. a local change in membrane permeability caused by a greater-than-threshold stimulus.
- e. all of these

D   29.   During the passage of a nerve impulse,
- a. sodium ions pass through gated channels.
- b. positive feedback causes more sodium ions to enter the cell.
- c. the interior of the cell becomes positive.
- d. changing voltage increases the number of open gates.
- *   e. all of these

D   30.   The phrase "all or nothing," used in conjunction with discussion about an action potential, means that
- a. a resting membrane potential has been received by the cell.
- *   b. nothing can stop the action potential if the threshold is reached.
- c. the membrane either achieves total equilibrium or remains as far from equilibrium as possible.
- d. propagation along the neuron is saltatory.
- e. none of these

D   31.   Once a threshold is reached,
- a. the number of sodium gates that open depends upon the strength of a stimulus.
- b. a graded local potential will be unable to spread to a trigger zone of the nerve membrane.
- c. the resting potential of a neuron is restored.
- d. the potassium channels in the input zone open.
- *   e. the opening of sodium gates and the accompanying flow of sodium ions is an example of positive feedback.

D   32.   The reason that an action potential is so brief is that
- *   a. a wave of repolarization immediately follows an action potential.
- b. the opening of potassium gates allows the voltage difference across the neural membrane to be restored.
- c. the protein channels for sodium movement remain open.
- d. the sodium-potassium pump restores the electrical gradients.
- e. the membrane limits electrical activity.

D   33.   Which of the following statements is false?
- *   a. An action potential can be generated in an input zone only.
- b. A trigger zone has enough sodium gates to initiate an action potential.
- c. Each portion of a membrane has its own refractory time.
- d. During the refractory period, the sodium gates are shut and the potassium gates open.
- e. During the refractory period, the resting membrane potential has not been restored.

D   34.   The occurrence of an action potential can best be compared to a
- *   a. switch to turn a lamp on and off.
- b. volume control on a stereo.
- c. door to the classroom.
- d. room light dimmer switch.

D   35.   When an expert trumpet player is executing thirty-second notes,
- a. there is a rest (refractory) period between each individual movement of the tongue.
- b. sodium gates must continually close and reopen.
- c. repolarization can be bypassed temporarily.
- *   d. there is a rest (refractory) period between each individual movement of the tongue and sodium gates must continually close and reopen.
- e. there is a rest (refractory) period between each individual movement of the tongue, sodium gates must continually close and reopen, but repolarization can be bypassed temporarily.

E   36.   Before another action potential "spike" can occur
- *   a. there must be a very brief restoration of the resting conditions in the membrane.
- b. the membrane voltage must drop to zero.
- c. the sodium-potassium pump must cease temporarily.
- d. all of the membrane gates must be closed at the same time.

D   37.   During the short recovery period before another action potential
- a. the threshold value is increased.
- b. the threshold value is reduced.
- *   c. the sodium gates are shut and the potassium gates are opened.
- d. both sodium and potassium gates are shut.
- e. the nerve is said to be at the resting potential.

CHEMICAL SYNAPSES

M 38. Transmitter substances
    a. are expelled from the presynaptic cells by exocytosis.
    b. tend to destroy acetylcholine.
    c. enter the postsynaptic cell to continue the passage of the impulse.
    d. interact with membrane receptors of the postsynaptic cells.
    * e. are both expelled from the presynaptic cells by exocytosis and interact with membrane receptors of the postsynaptic cells.

M 39. Which of the following is a junction between two neurons?
    a. Schwann cell
    * b. chemical synapse
    c. node of Ranvier
    d. sodium gate
    e. all of these

M 40. The operation of a synapse
    a. results from the passage of an electrical charge across the gap.
    * b. involves a transmitter substance from vesicles in the presynaptic neuron that acts upon a receptor site in the postsynaptic neuron.
    c. occurs only between two nerves.
    d. is limited only by the action of acetylcholinesterase.

M 41. Which of the following bridges the gap between a neuron sending a message and the neuron receiving it?
    a. threshold value
    b. action potential
    * c. transmitter substance
    d. neurohormone
    e. all of these

D 42. The presynaptic neuron and postsynaptic neuron do not directly contact each other because
    a. one would inhibit the actions of the other.
    b. they never grow to sufficient length.
    c. the synaptic vesicles keep them apart.
    * d. this would cause continuous impulse transmission.
    e. acetylcholine prevents this action.

M 43. Transmitter substances
    a. include acetylcholine.
    b. change the permeability of postsynaptic cells.
    c. may be inhibitory or stimulatory.
    d. elicit graded potentials near the synapse.
    * e. all of these

D 44. Which of the following statements is false?
    a. A nerve will not fire unless a stimulus exceeds the threshold.
    b. An action potential is an all-or-nothing event.
    * c. An action potential continues indefinitely until a quenching signal is released.
    d. An action potential is self-propagating.
    e. An action potential transmission depends on activities at the membrane.

D 45. Which of the following neurotransmitters is mismatched?
    a. acetylcholine—muscle contraction
    b. endorphin—pain perception
    c. norepinephrine—emotions, dreaming, awakening
    * d. serotonin—sexual function
    e. dopamine and GABA—act on the brain

D 46. Organophosphate insecticides kill by inhibiting acetylcholinesterase, an enzyme that degrades acetylcholine. What effect does this have?
    a. It allows continuous volleys of impulses.
    b. Control of vital organs is disrupted.
    c. "Start/stop" signals for breathing and heartbeat are not possible.
    d. Control of vital organs is disrupted; and "Start/stop" signals for breathing and heartbeat are not possible.
    * e. Control of vital organs is disrupted; "Start/stop" signals for breathing and heartbeat are not possible; and It allows continuous volleys of impulses.

M 47. Endorphins are
    a. neuromodulators.
    b. stimulators of brain and nervous activity.
    c. inhibitors of pain perception.
    d. neuromodulators and stimulators of brain and nervous activity.
    * e. neuromodulators and inhibitors of pain perception.

D 48. At an inhibitory synapse,
    a. no transmitter substances are released by the sending cell.
    * b. a transmitter substance produces changes in the receiving cell that drive the membrane potential away from threshold.
    c. no transmitter substance can bind to the receiving cell.
    d. a transmitter substance produces changes in the receiving cell that drive the membrane potential closer to threshold.

D 49. An excitatory postsynaptic potential
    a. is only one of several types of graded potential.
    b. has a hyperpolarizing effect.
    c. will drive the membrane away from its potential.
    * d. is summed with an inhibitory postsynaptic potential at the input zone of a neuron in a process known as synaptic integration.
    e. none of these

M 50. Synaptic integration means that
    a. all positive or excitatory stimuli are added together.
    b. the positive and negative ions neutralize each other.
    * c. excitatory and inhibitory signals are combined in a neuron.
    d. the adjacent neurons interact so that excitatory and inhibitory stimuli cancel each other out.
    e. all of these

D   51.   Which of the following statements is false?
          a.   Synaptic potentials may vary in magnitude.
          b.   Transmitter molecules bind to receptor molecules
               on the postsynaptic cells.
     *   c.   An excitatory postsynaptic potential is
               hyperpolarizing, whereas an inhibitory
               postsynaptic potential is depolarizing.
          d.   Synaptic integration means that signals arriving at
               a neuron can be reinforced or dampened.
          e.   Synaptic integration means that signals arriving at
               a neuron can be sent on or suppressed.

PATHS OF INFORMATION FLOW

M   52.   By definition, a "nerve" is
     *   a.   a bundle of axons.
          b.   a single extension of a neuron.
          c.   the same as a neuron within the central nervous
               system.
          d.   a dendrite.
          e.   a fiber more than 10 inches in length.

M   53.   The myelin sheath
          a.   is formed by the Schwann cell.
          b.   speeds up the transmission of impulses.
          c.   does not surround all nerves.
          d.   is interrupted along the axon by nodes.
     *   e.   all of these

M   54.   The spaces that separate adjacent Schwann cells are
          called
          a.   neuroglia.
          b.   myelin sheaths.
     *   c.   nodes
          d.   dendrites.
          e.   synapses.

M   55.   Conduction from node to node
          a.   occurs only in the central nervous system.
          b.   is a quicker type of nerve conduction.
          c.   occurs between nerves and muscles.
          d.   involves the "jumping" of impulses.
     *   e.   is a quicker type of nerve conduction and involves
               the "jumping" of impulses.

D   56.   A deterioration in the myelin sheaths of motor axons to
          the lower leg would be expected to
          a.   remove the restraints to ion movement and speed
               up impulse transmission.
          b.   cause immobility of the leg due to cessation of
               impulses to leg muscles.
     *   c.   slow the rate of transmission and cause lack of
               motor control.
          d.   have little effect because the sheaths are for
               insulation only.

M   57.   What is the name of the condition in which there is a
          deterioration of the myelin sheaths of the neurons in
          the spinal cord?
          a.   muscular dystrophy
          b.   cancer
          c.   diabetes
     *   d.   multiple sclerosis
          e.   Alzheimer disease

E   58.   The simplest nerve pathway
          a.   is located in the midbrain.
     *   b.   is the reflex arc.
          c.   is found in the lower part of the brain.
          d.   is found in the autonomic nervous system.
          e.   is in the flow of information from a sense receptor
               to the brain.

M   59.   One example of a simple reflex arc involves the
     *   a.   contraction of a muscle when it is stretched.
          b.   conscious message to move part of the body.
          c.   receptor, the brain, and the effector.
          d.   muscle action in a salute when a
               noncommissioned combatant sees an officer.
          e.   contraction of an antagonistic muscle when its
               opposite muscle relaxes.

M   60.   The stretch reflex is
          a.   an adaptation that enables humans to stand
               upright.
          b.   activated by stretch-sensitive receptors inside the
               muscle spindles.
          c.   a simple, stereotyped, and repeatable motor action.
          d.   elicited by a sensory stimulus.
     *   e.   all of these

M   61.   In the knee-jerk reflex arc, the synapse between a
          sensory neuron and a motor neuron occurs where?
          a.   in the brain
          b.   between the receptor and the spinal cord
          c.   within the muscle of the leg
     *   d.   within the spinal cord
          e.   in the nerve leading to the spinal cord

INVERTEBRATE NERVOUS SYSTEMS

M   62.   Which of the following statements is false?
          a.   Reflexes are the simplest of all nervous reactions.
          b.   The nervous system required sense organs before
               organisms could perceive their environment.
     *   c.   Motor neurons lead toward the brain or central
               nervous system.
          d.   Reflex actions are stereotyped and repeatable.
          e.   All of these statements are true.

M   63.   A reflex pathway is the simplest reaction unit because
          it
          a.   involves only one synapse.
          b.   is evaluated and integrated by the medulla, not the
               cerebrum.
     *   c.   involves only two or three neurons.
          d.   does not involve the central nervous system in any
               way.

D 64. In terms of evolution, which of the following is considered to be the oldest?
  a. cephalization
  b. information storage
  c. eyes
  * d. reflexes
  e. reasoning

M 65. *Hydra*, a cnidarian relative of sea anemones, has
  a. radial symmetry.
  b. a "nerve net."
  c. tentacles.
  d. a single opening to the digestive tract.
  * e. all of these

D 66. Which of the following is incorrect concerning a nerve net?
  a. found in animals with radial symmetry
  b. used in reflex actions
  * c. shows evolution of cephalization
  d. operates cells with contractile properties
  e. utilizes sensory cells

M 67. A planula is
  a. a polyp with tentacles.
  b. a portion of the nerve net of a cnidarian.
  c. radially symmetrical.
  * d. a free-swimming larva.
  e. a sessile polyp stage in the life cycle of a cnidarian.

M 68. Cephalization refers to a
  a. type of symmetry.
  b. type of segmentation characteristic of lower forms of life.
  c. group of protective cells found in the tentacles of a polyp.
  d. transitional state in the life cycle of a jellyfish.
  * e. none of these

M 69. Which of the following is the more advanced nervous system?
  a. a diffuse system with scattered nerves
  b. a bilaterally symmetrical system
  c. a radially symmetrical system
  * d. paired nerves, paired sensory structures, and paired brain centers
  e. a nerve net

E 70. Clusters of cell bodies of neurons outside the central nervous system are known as
  a. nerve cords.
  * b. ganglia.
  c. a plexus.
  d. notochords.
  e. nerves.

M 71. Cephalization may have originated in a
  a. flatworm.
  * b. cnidarian planula.
  c. jellyfish.
  d. vertebrate.
  e. grasshopper.

VERTEBRATE NERVOUS SYSTEMS—AN OVERVIEW

E 72. The notochord is
  a. found in the embryos of higher vertebrates.
  b. characteristic of all vertebrates.
  c. replaced by the vertebral column.
  d. characteristic of all chordates.
  * e. all of these

E 73. All vertebrates have
  a. two nerve cords.
  b. a nerve cord in the front of the body.
  c. a nerve cord on the side of the body.
  * d. a hollow dorsal nerve cord.
  e. a hollow ventral nerve cord.

D 74. Which of the following terms is NOT directly connected with the nervous system?
  * a. spinal column
  b. spinal cord
  c. neural tube
  d. nerve cord
  e. All of these are associated with the nervous system.

M 75. The two major divisions of the vertebrate nervous system are the
  a. autonomic and peripheral systems.
  b. sympathetic and parasympathetic systems.
  c. cranial and spinal nerves.
  * d. central and peripheral nervous systems.
  e. brain and spinal cord.

M 76. Which of the following would NOT be defined as a part of the central nervous system?
  a. brain
  b. cerebellum
  c. medulla
  * d. spinal nerves
  e. neuroglia cells

WHAT ARE THE MAJOR EXPRESSWAYS?

M 77. Which of the following statements concerning the peripheral nervous system is false?
  a. Spinal nerves lead to and from the spinal cord.
  b. There are 31 pairs of spinal nerves.
  * c. Cranial nerves lead from the brain directly to the spinal cord.
  d. Some nerves carry only sensory information.
  e. Some nerves are both sensory and motor.

M 78. The major divisions of the peripheral nervous system are
  * a. somatic and autonomic systems.
  b. sympathetic and parasympathetic systems.
  c. peripheral and central systems.
  d. afferent and autonomic systems.
  e. cranial and skeletal nerves.

E 79. All nerves that conduct impulses away from the central nervous system are
 * a. motor only,
 b. sensory only.
 c. motor or sensory depending body location.
 d. spinal nerves.
 e. cranial nerves.

M 80. The sequence of a simple reaction to a stimulus is
 * a. sense organ, sensory neuron, interneuron, motor neuron, effector.
 b. sense organ, sensory neuron, motor neuron, interneuron, effector.
 c. sense organ, motor neuron, sensory neuron, interneuron, effector.
 d. sense organ, motor neuron, interneuron, sensory neuron, effector.

M 81. The autonomic subdivision of the vertebrate nervous system would innervate all but which of the following?
 a. intestinal muscles
 * b. skeletal muscles
 c. heart
 d. pancreas
 e. liver

M 82. Which nerves generally dominate internal events when environmental conditions permit normal body functioning?
 a. ganglia
 b. pacemaker
 c. sympathetic
 * d. parasympathetic
 e. all of these

D 83. Which of the following statements is true?
 a. Both the parasympathetic and sympathetic nervous systems send nerves to all organs.
 b. The sympathetic nervous system that supplies an organ will also provide parasympathetic nerves to it.
 c. Both the sympathetic and parasympathetic have either excitatory or inhibitory effects.
 * d. The sympathetic branch of the sympathetic system usually speeds up the activities of the body.
 e. The parasympathetic system usually speeds up the activities of the body.

E 84. Signals from the parasympathetic nervous system cause which of the following?
 a. rise in blood pressure
 b. increase in pulse rate
 * c. increase in digestive activities
 d. rise in blood sugar level
 e. rise in metabolic rate

M 85. The parasympathetic nervous system includes the
 a. cranial and thoracic nerves.
 b. thoracic and lumbar nerves.
 c. lumbar and sacral nerves.
 d. cervical and lumbar nerves.
 * e. cranial and sacral nerves.

M 86. The sympathetic nervous system includes the
 a. cranial and thoracic nerves.
 * b. thoracic and lumbar nerves.
 c. lumbar and sacral nerves.
 d. cervical and lumbar nerves.
 e. cranial and sacral nerves.

M 87. Activation of the sympathetic nervous system
 * a. causes the pupils of the eye to dilate.
 b. increases the flow of watery saliva.
 c. stimulates peristaltic contractions of the intestinal system.
 d. slows heartbeat and lowers blood pressure.
 e. allows the body to relax rather than prepare for fight or flight.

D 88. The word that best describes the interaction of sympathetic and parasympathetic systems is
 * a. antagonistic.
 b. cooperation.
 c. overriding.
 d. subversive.
 e. ineffective.

M 89. The part of the central nervous system that is composed of parts that are antagonistic to each other is the
 * a. autonomic nervous system composed of the sympathetic and parasympathetic subsystems.
 b. central nervous system composed of the brain and spinal cord.
 c. peripheral nervous system composed of the cranial and spinal nervous system.
 d. none of these; the muscular system is the only system with antagonistic subsets.

D 90. During the "fight-flight" response, which of the following would be in use?
 a. sympathetic nervous system
 b. parasympathetic nervous system
 c. epinephrine
 * d. sympathetic nervous system and epinephrine
 e. parasympathetic nervous system and epinephrine

E 91. Nerve impulses coming into the spinal cord enter via
 a. intervertebral disks.
 b. neuroglia.
 * c. the dorsal roots.
 d. Broca's area.
 e. ventral root.

E 92. Interneurons are found in the
 a. dorsal root.
 * b. spinal cord.
 c. sensory neurons.
 d. motor neurons.
 e. autonomic nervous system.

M 93. The ascending and descending tracts (bundles of sheathed axons) are
 a. found in the gray matter of the spinal cord.
 b. found in the white matter of the spinal cord.
 c. covered with myelin sheaths.
 d. both sensory and motor.
 * e. All except "found in the gray matter of the spinal cord" are correct.

236   Test Bank

D 94. All but which of the following are true of the spinal cord?
    a. houses connections between sensory and motor neurons
    b. serves as a reflex center
*   c. its gray matter serves as passageway for nerve tracts to brain
    d. is covered with meninges
    e. is enclosed by vertebrae

E 95. Areas of the spinal cord appear glistening white because of
    a. naked dendrites.
    b. cell bodies.
    c. neuroglia cells.
    d. lack of meninges.
*   e. myelin sheaths.

THE VERTEBRATE BRAIN

E 96. The hindbrain includes the
    a. thalamus.
    b. pineal gland.
    c. cerebellum.
    d. medulla oblongata.
*   e. cerebellum and medulla oblongata

E 97. The part of the brain that connects one brain center with another is the
    a. cerebrum.
*   b. pons.
    c. cerebellum.
    d. fissure of Rolando.
    e. hypothalamus.

E 98. The center for balance and coordination is the
    a. cerebrum.
    b. pons.
*   c. cerebellum.
    d. thalamus.
    e. hypothalamus.

M 99. The part of the brain that controls the basic responses necessary to maintain life processes (breathing, heartbeat) is the
*   a. medulla oblongata.
    b. corpus callosum.
    c. fissure of Rolando.
    d. cerebellum.
    e. cerebral cortex.

E 100. The midbrain includes the
    a. thalamus.
    b. pineal gland.
*   c. tectum.
    d. medulla oblongata.
    e. olfactory lobes.

E 101. Which structure forms the roof of the midbrain where visual and auditory signals are integrated?
    a. ventricles
    b. meninges
*   c. tectum
    d. olfactory and optic bulbs
    e. pineal gland

E 102. The pituitary gland is controlled by the
    a. pineal gland.
    b. medulla oblongata.
*   c. hypothalamus.
    d. thalamus.
    e. cerebrum.

E 103. The center of consciousness and intelligence is the
    a. medulla oblongata.
    b. thalamus.
    c. pons.
    d. cerebellum.
*   e. cerebrum.

D 104. Destruction of the motor areas in the left cerebral cortex results in the loss of
    a. sensation on the right side of the body.
    b. sensation on the left side of the body.
    c. voluntary movement on the left side of the body.
*   d. voluntary movement on the right side of the body.

E 105. Which part of the mammalian brain is disproportionately larger than the corresponding part of a fish brain?
    a. medulla oblongata
    b. thalamus
    c. pons
    d. cerebellum
*   e. cerebrum

E 106. The part of the brain that shows the greatest proportional increase in size from the lower vertebrates to humans is the increase in the
    a. cerebellum.
*   b. cerebrum.
    c. medulla oblongata.
    d. hypothalamus.

E 107. The part of the brain that deals with the basic drives such as hunger, sex, and thirst is the
    a. cerebrum.
    b. pons.
    c. cerebellum.
    d. thalamus.
*   e. hypothalamus.

E 108. The major relay center of the brain is the
    a. cerebrum.
    b. olfactory area.
    c. cerebellum.
*   d. thalamus.
    e. hypothalamus.

E 109. The mechanism that regulates the movement of substances into and out of the cells of the brain is the
   a. cerebrospinal fluid.
   b. reticular formation.
   c. tectum.
 * d. blood-brain barrier.
   e. brain stem.

D 110. What is the name given to the network of interneurons that extends from the medulla to the cerebrum and is responsible for message integration?
   a. tectum
 * b. reticular formation
   c. hypothalamus
   d. cerebral cortex.
   e. meninges.

E 111. The protective covering of the brain is the
   a. ventricles.
 * b. meninges.
   c. tectum.
   d. olfactory and optic bulbs.
   e. pineal gland.

THE HUMAN CEREBRUM

E 112. The gray matter of the brain is associated with the
 * a. cerebral cortex.
   b. pons.
   c. optic chiasma.
   d. corpus callosum.
   e. thalamus.

E 113. The occipital lobe of the brain is responsible for
   a. coordination of hands and fingers.
   b. speech.
   c. memory.
   d. sense of taste and smell.
 * e. vision.

E 114. The cerebral hemispheres communicate with each other by means of the
   a. cerebral cortex.
   b. corpora cardiaca.
   c. corporothalamus.
 * d. corpus callosum.
   e. corpus allata.

M 115. The left hemisphere of the brain is responsible for
   a. music.
   b. artistic ability.
   c. spatial relationships.
 * d. language skills.
   e. abstract abilities.

M 116. The right hemisphere of the cerebrum is specialized for
   a. verbal ability.
   b. mathematics.
 * c. music interpretation.
   d. control over the right side of the body.

D 117. The primary hearing interpretation portion of the brain is located
 * a. at the rear of the brain.
   b. midway from front to back.
 * c. in the "temple" area.
   d. behind the forehead.
   e. in the cerebellum.

M 118. Emotional states are the responsibility of the
   a. medulla.
   b. corpus callosum.
 * c. limbic system.
   d. cerebral cortex.
   e. cerebellum.

FOCUS ON SCIENCE: SPERRY'S SPLIT-BRAIN EXPERIMENTS

D 119. If the motor cortex on the right side of the brain is destroyed by a stroke, what would be impaired?
   a. movement on both sides of the body
   b. reception of sensory information from the left side of the body
   c. movement by the right side of the body
 * d. movement by the left side of the body
   e. all of these

M 120. To produce a split-brain individual, an operation would need to cut the
 * a. corpus callosum.
   b. reticular formation.
   c. hypothalamus.
   d. fissure of Rolando.
   e. pons.

HOW ARE MEMORIES TUCKED AWAY?

D 121. Studies of memory indicate that
   a. short-term memory is the product of chemical changes in neurons.
   b. long-term memory is limited to a few years' duration.
   c. long-term memories are lost more frequently in amnesia.
 * d. long-term memory depends on structural or chemical changes in the brain.
   e. short-term memory is limited to several hundred bits of information.

FOCUS ON HEALTH: DRUGGING THE BRAIN

E 122. Active chemicals found in chocolate, tea, coffee, and soft drinks are examples of which of the following?
   a. depressant
 * b. stimulant
   c. narcotic analgesic
   d. hallucinogen or psychedelic
   e. antipsychotic

E   123. Pain relievers such as endorphins and enkephalins are
        a. depressants.
        b. stimulants.
    *   c. analgesics.
        d. hallucinogens or psychedelics.
        e. antipsychotics.

E   124. Substances that lower the activity of the brain and inhibit transmission at a synapse are
    *   a. depressants.
        b. stimulants.
        c. narcotic analgesics.
        d. hallucinogens or psychedelics.
        e. antipsychotics.

M   125. Which of the following statements is false?
    *   a. Synapses are direct contacts between nerves.
        b. Both sensory and motor neurons use action potentials to transmit information.
        c. Only the central nervous system is able to interpret the meaning of a stimulus.
        d. Sensory neurons carry impulses toward the central nervous system.
        e. Motor neurons carry impulses away from the central nervous system.

E   126. Substances that could be called hypnotics and that induce sleep are
    *   a. depressants.
        b. stimulants.
        c. narcotic analgesics.
        d. hallucinogens or psychedelics.
        e. antipsychotics.

M   127. Once a person's body becomes adapted to drugs, it takes even greater exposure to that drug to achieve the same level of reaction. This condition is known as
        a. synergism.
        b. habituation.
        c. psychological dependence.
    *   d. tolerance.

M   128. A chemical substance that behaves as a natural analgesic is
        a. an amphetamine.
        b. LSD.
        c. epinephrine.
    *   d. endorphin.
        e. none of these

M   129. A group of chemicals that at low doses reduce fatigue and heighten awareness but at high doses elicit anxiety and irritability while mimicking the effect of norepinephrine are
        a. depressants.
    *   b. stimulants.
        c. narcotic analgesics.
        d. hallucinogens or psychedelics.
        e. antipsychotics.

E   130. Substances that alter sensory perception, cause disorientation, and inhibit the ability to perform complex tasks are
        a. depressants.
        b. stimulants.
        c. narcotic analgesics.
    *   d. hallucinogens or psychedelics.
        e. antipsychotics.

E   131. Barbiturates are
    *   a. depressants.
        b. stimulants.
        c. narcotic analgesics.
        d. hallucinogens or psychedelics.
        e. antipsychotics.

E   132. Substances that sedate the body and relieve pain are
        a. depressants.
        b. stimulants.
    *   c. narcotic analgesics.
        d. hallucinogens or psychedelics.
        e. antipsychotics.

Matching Questions

D **133.** Matching I: Even though there may be more than one correct letter response to some numbered items, discriminate and "juggle" so that you have the one BEST response for each blank.

1. ___ effector
2. ___ EPSP
3. ___ ganglion
4. ___ integrator
5. ___ IPSP
6. ___ interneuron
7. ___ muscle spindle
8. ___ myelin sheath
9. ___ neuroglia
10. ___ receptor
11. ___ rest period
12. ___ response
13. ___ sodium-potassium pump
14. ___ stimulus
15. ___ transmitter substance

A. cells that nurture and support neurons
B. a hyperpolarizing event
C. a neuron cannot propagate an action potential at this time
D. ACh or GABA
E. interneuron in brain or spinal cord
F. establishes basis of resting membrane potential
G. sheathed muscle cells that contain receptors
H. input
I. integrator cell between sensory and motor
J. modified dendrite of a sensory neuron
K. a depolarizing event
L. output
M. motor neuron
N. produced by a specific kind of Schwann cell
O. cluster of cell bodies from different neurons

Answers: 1. M   2. K   3. O   4. E
           5. B   6. I   7. G   8. N
           9. A   10. J   11. C   12. L
           13. F   14. H   15. D

D **134.** Matching II: Choose the most appropriate answer.

1. ___ autonomic nervous system
2. ___ frontal lobe
3. ___ cerebellum
4. ___ corpus callosum
5. ___ ganglion
6. ___ hypothalamus
7. ___ limbic system
8. ___ medulla oblongata
9. ___ midbrain
10. ___ nerve net
11. ___ peripheral nervous system
12. ___ reticular formation
13. ___ meninges
14. ___ transmitter substances
15. ___ white matter

A. integrates body position, motions, balance
B. in cnidarians; based on reflex pathways devoted to swimming and feeding
C. messages from here arouse the brain and maintain wakefulness
D. the cortical region that coordinates muscles required for speech
E. all parts of nerve cells outside the brain and spinal cord
F. acetylcholine is an example
G. reflex control center for breathing, heart rate, and blood pressure
H. axons of the central nervous system that are sheathed with fatty myelin
I. at top of the brainstem bordering the cerebral hemispheres; influences learning and emotional behavior
J. motor neurons that are divided into sympathetic and parasympathetic divisions
K. membrane coverings over brain spinal cord
L. contains the optic lobes; receives and integrates sensory information that is largely sent on to the forebrain for further neural processing
M. connects right and left cerebral hemispheres
N. group of nerve cell bodies encased in connective tissue; forms integrative centers
O. contains centers concerned with body temperature regulation and with salt and water balance

Answers: 1. J   2. D   3. A   4. M
           5. N   6. O   7. I   8. G
           9. L   10. B   11. E   12. C
           13. K   14. F   15. H

Classification Questions

Answer questions 135-139 in reference to the four cell types listed below:

    a. sensory neurons
    b. interneurons
    c. motor neurons
    d. Schwann cells

M **135.** Nerve cells that carry signals to muscle cells are these.

M **136.** These are a type of neuroglia cell.

E **137.** Myelin is formed by these.

E **138.** An animal brain is composed mostly of this cell type.

E **139.** This cell type picks up environmental signals.

Answers   135. c   136. d   137. d

            138. b   139. a

Answer questions 140-144 in reference to the autonomic nervous system associated with the five regions of the human vertebral column listed below:

    a. cervical
    b. thoracic
    c. lumbar
    d. sacral
    e. coccygeal

D **140.** Sympathetic nerves from this region innervate the bladder, uterus, and genitals.

D **141.** Sympathetic nerves from this region innervate the kidney.

D **142.** Parasympathetic nerves from this region innervate the rectum.

D **143.** Sympathetic nerves from this region innervate the heart.

D **144.** Sympathetic nerves from this region pass through the celiac ganglion.

Answers   140. c   141. b   142. d

           143. b   144. b

Answer questions 145-149 in reference to the five regions of the vertebrate brain listed below:

    a. cerebrum
    b. hypothalamus
    c. pons
    d. cerebellum
    e. medulla oblongata

D **145.** This region of the brain contains the reflex centers involved in respiration.

D **146.** This region of the brain controls neural-endocrine activities such as temperature control.

D **147.** This region of the brain controls carbohydrate metabolism.

M **148.** This part of the brain controls the complex coordination of motor activity and limb movement.

D **149.** This region of the brain contains parasympathetic nerves that innervate the heart and lungs.

Answers   145. e   146. b   147. b

          148. d   149. e

Selecting the Exception

M **150.** Four of the five answers listed below are actively involved in nerve impulse transmission. Select the exception.
   * a. neuroglia
       b. neuron
       c. ganglia
       d. nerves
       e. tracts

D **151.** Four of the five answers listed below are true of a neuron at resting potential. Select the exception.
   * a. Interior of neuron is positive.
       b. Exterior of neuron has negative charge.
       c. More sodium ions are outside neuron.
       d. More potassium ions are inside neuron.
       e. Membrane of neuron is polarized.

D **152.** Four of the five answers listed below are used in descriptions of neuron membranes. Select the exception.
       a. gate
       b. pump
       c. wave of depolarization
       d. channel
   * e. synaptic cleft

D **153.** Four of the five answers listed below are used in descriptions of the nerve sheath. Select the exception.
       a. Schwann cell
   * b. threshold
       c. myelin sheath
       d. saltatory conduction
       e. node of Ranvier

M **154.** Four of the five answers listed below are participants in a common function. Select the exception.
       a. sensory neuron
   * b. medulla
       c. interneuron
       d. effector
       e. receptor

D **155.** Four of the five answers listed below are characteristic of bilaterally symmetrical forms. Select the exception.
   * a. sessile, nonmoving
       b. segmentation
       c. cephalization
       d. paired nerves, muscles, sensory structures
       e. right and left halves of the body

M 156. Four of the five answers listed below are parts of the central nervous system. Select the exception.
a. spinal cord
b. medulla
* c. ganglia
d. cerebellum
e. cerebrum

D 157. Four of the five answers listed below are parts of the same nerve grouping. Select the exception.
* a. cranial nerve
b. thoracic nerve
c. lumbar nerve
d. cervical nerve
e. sacral nerve

M 158. Four of the five answers listed below are innervated by the autonomic nervous system. Select the exception.
* a. skeletal muscles
b. smooth muscles
c. heart
d. endocrine glands
e. exocrine glands

D 159. Four of the five answers listed below are actions mediated by the sympathetic nervous system. Select the exception.
a. pulse increases
* b. blood glucose levels drop
c. metabolism increases
d. digestion slows down
e. pupils of the eyes dilate

D 160. Four of the five answers listed below are located within the spinal cord. Select the exception.
* a. dorsal root ganglion
b. interneurons between sensory input and motor outputs
c. major ascending and descending nerve tracts
d. interneurons connecting with other neurons
e. direct reflex connections between sensory and motor neurons

M 161. Four of the five answers listed below are parts of the forebrain. Select the exception.
a. limbic system
b. thalamus
c. olfactory lobes
* d. cerebellum
e. cerebrum

E 162. Four of the five answers listed below are lobes of the brain. Select the exception.
a. parietal
* b. squamosal
c. frontal
d. occipital
e. temporal

M 163. Four of the five answers listed below are classified as white matter. Select the exception.
a. myelin sheath
b. descending tracts
c. corpus callosum
* d. cerebrum
e. ascending tract

M 164. Four of the five answers listed below are stimulants. Select the exception.
* a. heroin
b. caffeine
c. nicotine
d. cocaine
e. amphetamine

M 165. Four of the five answers listed below are depressants. Select the exception.
a. alcohol
b. barbiturates
c. Valium
* d. marijuana
e. Quaalude

D 166. Four of the five answers listed below are analgesics. Select the exception.
a. endorphin
b. opium
c. heroin
d. enkephalin
* e. lithium

CHAPTER 35
SENSORY RECEPTION

Multiple-Choice Questions

M   **1.** In order for bats to capture prey at night, they are equipped with
   *   a. extra-sensitive hearing.
     b. extraordinary sight.
     c. pits that are sensitive to infrared radiation.
     d. a strong sense of smell located in the tongue.
     e. special organs that detect heat.

D   **2.** During echolocation, bats
     a. are unable to hear the faint echoes while they are producing the sounds that produce the echoes.
     b. use ultrasound that is beyond the range of human hearing.
     c. can increase the rate of ultrasonic clicks when they detect prey.
     d. are able to hear returning sounds because they are able to change the frequency (pitch) of the noises they are generating.
   *   e. all but "are able to hear returning sounds because they are able to change the frequency (pitch) of the noises they are generating" are correct

E   **3.** Which sense utilizes mechanical energy?
     a. sense of touch
     b. muscle sense
     c. sense of hearing
     d. sense of balance
   *   e. all of these

E   **4.** Infrared receptors are classified as
     a. chemoreceptors.
     b. mechanoreceptors.
     c. photoreceptors.
   *   d. thermoreceptors.
     e. none of these

E   **5.** Olfactory centers are responsive to
     a. touch.
   *   b. smell.
     c. taste.
     d. sound.
     e. sight.

E   **6.** The carotid body is a
   *   a. chemoreceptor.
     b. photoreceptor.
     c. thermoreceptor.
     d. mechanoreceptor.
     e. movement receiver.

OVERVIEW OF SENSORY PATHWAYS

M   **7** A sensory system includes
     a. a sensory receptor.
     b. nerve pathways from the receptor to the brain.
     c. brain regions where the sensory information is processed.
     d. a sensory receptor and nerve pathways from the receptor to the brain plus nerve pathways from the receptor to the brain.
   *   e. a sensory receptor and nerve pathways from the receptor to the brain plus nerve pathways from the receptor to the brain whose regions will process the sensory information.

D   **8.** Which of the following animals does NOT have a sensory system?
     a. free-living flatworms
     b. tapeworms
     c. cnidarians
   *   d. sponges
     e. nematodes

D   **9** The difference in "sensation" and "perception" when referring to a stimulus lies in
     a. the type of receptor stimulated.
   *   b. understanding the significance of the stimulus.
     c. the number of receptors that depolarize.
     d. feeling exactly what is happening at the site.
     e. responding to the stimulus.

M   **10.** The major function of a receptor is to
     a. control the autonomic functions of the body.
     b. stabilize the internal environment to achieve homeostasis.
     c. produce responses to the various stimuli the body receives.
   *   d. give organisms awareness and sensitivity to their environment.

M   **11.** Which of the following statements is false?
   *   a. All animals placed in the same environment will have the same awareness of it.
     b. Humans and insects see flowers differently.
     c. The carotid bodies monitor the concentration of carbon dioxide in the blood.
     d. Olfactory receptors detect odors.
     e. Pacinian corpuscles are examples of mechanoreceptors.

D 12. Which of the following statements is false?
a. Sensory receptors are able to detect specific stimuli only.
b. Sensation is an awareness of a change in external or internal conditions.
* c. A stimulus will generate impulses that are different depending on where the signals are sent in the brain.
d. Information about a stimulus is coded in the quantity and frequency of action potentials sent to the brain.
e. Specific regions of the brain translate the information about the signal and convert it into a sensation.

M 13. Which of the following is NOT characteristic of sensation?
a. Some sense cells can be activated only by chemicals.
b. Nerve impulses for each of the five senses are essentially the same regardless of the sense considered.
c. Sensory nerve impulses follow the all-or-none law.
* d. All organisms perceive their environments by the same sense organs.

M 14. Differences in intensity of a stimulus
a. do not affect the impulse transmitted.
b. are indicated by the number of nerves activated.
c. control the part of the brain that receives the stimulus.
d. are encoded in the frequency of action potentials on a single axon.
* e. are indicated by the number of nerves activated and are encoded in the frequency of action potentials on a single axon.

D 15. Which of the following statements is false?
a. It is assumed that lower animals are incapable of perception.
* b. Humans, as the most complex organisms, have all of the sensory organs found in lower forms.
c. Mechanoreceptors are responsible for the senses of equilibrium and hearing.
d. Infrared radiation is detected by thermoreceptors.
e. A lobster can react to the boiling water in which it is placed to cook.

M 16. Which of the following statements is true?
a. All action potentials for the same nerve are alike.
b. Receptors respond by graded potential.
c. Different nerves convey different information by going to different areas of the brain.
d. Differences in intensities may be due to the number of receptors and nerves involved in response.
* e. all of these

M 17. A loud sound can be distinguished from a soft whisper because
a. more neurons depolarize.
b. each receptor depolarizes more fully.
c. the frequency of depolarizing neurons increases.
* d. more neurons depolarize and the frequency of depolarizing neurons increases.
e. more neurons depolarize, the frequency of depolarizing neurons increases, and each receptor depolarizes more fully.

M 18. Which of the following statements is false?
a. Neurons in the brain can interpret incoming action potentials only in certain ways.
b. Optic nerve impulses can only be interpreted as light.
* c. Sensory neurons do not follow the all-or-none law.
d. The stronger the stimulus, the more action potentials are generated.
e. A strong stimulus activates many adjacent receptors, thereby increasing the number of action potentials and the level of awareness for the stimulus.

D 19. Which of the following is NOT an example of nerve adaptation?
a. a loss of the sense of pressure of clothes against the skin
b. adjustment to repeated jumping into a body of cold water
* c. response to lack of oxygen at high altitudes
d. eventual loss of awareness of a constant noise
e. the loss of the ability to smell a person's perfume or cologne after being in that person's presence for some time

SOMATIC SENSATIONS

D 20. The extent to which a sense can detect a particular sensation is mainly due to the
a. sensitivity of its receptors.
b. speed of nerve transmission.
* c. brain area devoted to interpretation.
d. transmitter substances in the synapses.
e. amount of stimulus.

M 21. The somatic senses include all but which one of the following sensations?
* a. balance
b. pain near the body surface
c. temperature
d. touch
e. pressure

M 22. Somatic sensations include all but which one of the following?
a. heat and cold
b. pressure and touch
c. pain
d. limb movements and the position of the body in space
* e. sound

M 23. According to the classification given by your authors, somatic senses
 * a. are distributed in several locations over the body.
    b. reside in certain receptor organs located at a few specific locations.
    c. are exemplified by ears and eyes.
    d. include sight and sound.
    e. all of these but "are distributed in several locations over the body."

M 24. Mechanoreceptors are located in
    a. internal organs.
    b. skin.
    c. joints.
    d. tendons.
 * e. all of these

D 25. The feeling of pressure on the skin is the result of
    a. bending of mechanoreceptors.
    b. stimulation only when the stimulus is first applied.
    c. constant stimulation.
 * d. bending of mechanoreceptors and constant stimulation.
    e. bending of mechanoreceptors and stimulation only when the stimulus is first applied.

E 26. The Pacinian corpuscle is used in detecting
    a. sound.
 * b. pressure.
    c. chemicals.
    d. sight.
    e. chemical differences.

M 27. Pain is
    a. detected by nociceptors.
    b. the perception of injury.
    c. dependent on interpretation by the brain.
    d. the perception of injury and dependent on interpretation by the brain.
 * e. detected by nociceptors, the perception of injury, and dependent on interpretation by the brain.

E 28. The pain produced in an internal organ may be perceived as occurring somewhere else. This is called
    a. mixed nerve messages.
 * b. referred pain.
    c. phantom pain.
    d. psychosomatic pain.
    e. hypochondria.

E 29. A stretch receptor is classified as a
    a. chemoreceptor.
 * b. mechanoreceptor.
    c. photoreceptor.
    d. thermoreceptor.
    e. all of these

D 30. The knee-jerk reflex used by physicians to check nerve response is based on
    a. muscle spindles.
    b. stretch receptors.
    c. spinal cord synapses.
    d. muscle spindles and stretch receptors, only.
 * e. muscle spindles, stretch receptors, and spinal cord synapses.

CHEMICAL SENSES

E 31. Receptors in the human nose are
 * a. chemoreceptors.
    b. mechanoreceptors.
    c. photoreceptors.
    d. nocireceptors.
    e. none of these

E 32. Sense receptors for "taste" are located on
    a. insect legs.
    b. octopus tentacles.
    c. antennae.
    d. fish fins.
 * e. all of these

M 33. Pheromones
    a. are social signals.
    b. identify individuals who belong to a group in case they get separated.
    c. may serve as sex attractants.
    d. may be used for an alarm signal.
 * e. all of these

E 34. Female silk moths secrete bombykol as a(n)
    a. way to gather young when they scatter.
    b. message to stay close to the cocoon.
    c. alarm signal.
 * d. sexual attractant.
    e. territory marker.

M 35. Functionally, the two most closely associated senses are
    a. sight and sound.
    b. touch and sight.
 * c. taste and smell.
    d. temperature and pain.
    e. touch and balance.

SENSE OF BALANCE

E 36. One's equilibrium is sensed by a
    a. chemoreceptor.
 * b. mechanoreceptor.
    c. photoreceptor.
    d. thermoreceptor.
    e. none of these

M   37.   Hair cells are important in the sense of
        a. equilibrium.
        b. hearing.
        c. taste.
        d. smell.
   *   e. both equilibrium and hearing.

E   38.   The sense of equilibrium or balance can detect
        a. motion.
        b. acceleration.
        c. gravity.
        d. position.
   *   e. all of these

M   39.   The semicircular canals are
        a. empty.
        b. filled with gas.
   *   c. filled with a liquid.
        d. filled with bones or stones.
        e. filled with sand grains.

E   40.   An otolith is one of the functional parts of the
        a. eye.
        b. Pacinian corpuscle.
   *   c. vestibular apparatus.
        d. taste bud.
        e. pits, or heat-sensing devices, of snakes.

E   41.   How many semicircular canals are in each organ of balance?
        a. 2
   *   b. 3
        c. 4
        d. 5
        e. more than 6

D   42.   Motion sickness is the result of
        a. overstimulation of the hair cells in the vestibular apparatus.
        b. visual input, especially when it is monotonous.
        c. fear and anxiety.
        d. overstimulation of the hair cells in the vestibular apparatus and visual input, especially when it is monotonous, only.
   *   e. overstimulation of the hair cells in the vestibular apparatus, visual input, especially when it is monotonous, and fear and anxiety.

SENSE OF HEARING

E   43.   The acoustical sense deals with the sense of
        a. taste.
        b. smell.
        c. touch.
        d. sight.
   *   e. hearing.

E   44.   The organ of Corti is a
        a. chemoreceptor.
   *   b. mechanoreceptor.
        c. photoreceptor.
        d. nocireceptor.
        e. all of these

M   45.   The principal place in the human ear where sound waves are amplified by means of the vibrations of tiny bones is the
        a. pinna.
        b. ear canal.
   *   c. middle ear.
        d. organ of Corti.
        e. all of these

M   46.   The place where vibrations are translated into patterns of nerve impulses is the
        a. pinna.
        b. ear canal.
        c. middle ear.
   *   d. organ of Corti.
        e. none of these

E   47.   The organ of Corti is located in the
        a. thoracic cavity.
   *   b. inner ear.
        c. abdominal cavity.
        d. brain stem.
        e. semicircular canals.

D   48.   In hearing, the last place that pressure or sound waves pass through is the
        a. bones of the middle ear.
        b. tympanic membrane.
        c. oval window.
        d. round window.
   *   e. tectorial membrane.

E   49.   How many coiled and fluid-filled ducts are found in each cochlea?
        a. 1
        b. 2
   *   c. 3
        d. 4
        e. 5 or more

D   50.   The sense of hearing in both invertebrates and vertebrates is dependent on
        a. fluid displacement.
        b. hair bending.
        c. echolocation.
   *   d. vibration of a membrane.
        e. all of these

D   51.   The sense in which amplitude and frequency can be detected with some accuracy is
        a. sight.
   *   b. hearing.
        c. balance.
        d. taste.
        e. smell.

D   52.   The use of echolocation by bats and dolphins is most like which of the following navigation devices?
   *   a. radar
        b. compass
        c. map
        d. sextant (using star position)

E 53. Movable bones are features of the sense organs associated with
   a. sight.
 * b. hearing.
   c. taste.
   d. smell.
   e. touch.

M 54. Movable bones are found in the
   a. cochlea.
   b. external ear.
 * c. middle ear.
   d. inner ear.
   e. organ of Corti.

M 55. The organ of Corti
   a. functions in the awareness of motion and the sense of equilibrium.
   b. controls the sense of depth perception.
 * c. converts sound vibrations into impulses that enable hearing.
   d. secretes cerebrospinal fluid.
   e. detects light energy.

SENSE OF VISION

M 56. Which of the following has receptors for ultraviolet light?
   a. bears
 * b. bees
   c. birds
   d. reptiles
   e. amphibians

E 57. Eyes are
   a. chemoreceptors.
   b. mechanoreceptors.
 * c. photoreceptors.
   d. nocireceptors.
   e. none of these

D 58. According to the mosaic theory,
   a. the basement membrane's pigment molecules prevent the scattering of light.
   b. light falling on the inner area of an "on center" field activates firing of the cells.
   c. hair cells in the semicircular canals cooperate to detect rotational acceleration.
 * d. each ommatidium detects information about only one small region of the visual field; many ommatidia contribute "bits" to the total image.
   e. all of these

E 59. The repeating units of a compound eye are called
   a. ocelli.
   b. lenses.
   c. rhabdomeres.
 * d. ommatidia.
   e. pupils.

D 60. In contrast to eyes, the eyespots of most invertebrates cannot
   a. detect light.
   b. distinguish darkness from daylight.
 * c. form distinct images.
   d. discern shadows.
   e. possess photoreceptors.

STRUCTURE AND FUNCTION OF VERTEBRATE EYES

E 61. The layer of the eye where photoreceptors are located is the
   a. lens.
   b. cornea.
   c. pupil.
   d. iris.
 * e. retina.

E 62. The adjustable ring of contractile and connective tissues that controls the amount of light entering the eye is the
   a. lens.
   b. cornea.
   c. pupil.
 * d. iris.
   e. retina.

E 63. The white protective fibrous tissue of the eye, often called the white of the eye, is the
   a. lens.
 * b. sclera.
   c. pupil.
   d. iris.
   e. retina.

E 64. The dark middle layer of the eye that prevents the scattering of light is the
   a. fovea.
   b. retina.
   c. sclera.
 * d. choroid.
   e. cornea.

M 65. Accommodation involves the ability to
   a. change the sensitivity of the rods and cones by means of neurotransmitters.
   b. change the curvature of the cornea.
 * c. change the width of the lens by contracting or relaxing certain muscles.
   d. adapt to large changes in light intensity.
   e. all of these

M 66. The ciliary muscle
   a. controls the eardrum.
 * b. controls the shape of the lens to allow focusing.
   c. holds the bones of the middle ear in place.
   d. enables the eyeball to move so that a person may see an object without moving the head.
   e. is responsible for the size of the pupil in different light intensities.

M 67. If the ciliary muscle of the eye is damaged, then
a. color vision will be lost.
b. the amount of light entering the eye cannot be regulated.
* c. proper focusing will be impossible.
d. only peripheral vision is available.
e. "night blindness" will become more evident.

E 68. The outer transparent protective cover of the eyeball is the
a. fovea.
b. retina.
c. sclera.
d. choroid.
* e. cornea.

E 69. The part of the eye that may be colored (e.g., brown, blue, green, or gray) is the
a. retina.
b. sclera.
c. choroid.
d. cornea.
* e. iris.

CASE STUDY—FROM SIGNALING TO VISUAL PERCEPTION

E 70. Rods and cones are located in the
a. lens.
b. cornea.
c. pupil.
d. iris.
* e. retina.

E 71. The highest concentration of cones is in the
* a. fovea.
b. blind spot.
c. sclera.
d. ommatidium.
e. choroid.

D 72. The fovea
a. is the blind spot produced by the optic nerve entering the eye.
* b. is the region of the retina filled with cones that allows the most acute vision.
c. is the region of the retina that has the greatest concentration of rods that enable sight under extremely dim conditions.
d. focuses light on the retina.
e. is the anterior fluid-filled chamber of the eye.

M 73. In the human eye, what provides the greatest visual acuity (the precise discrimination between adjacent points in space)?
a. photoreceptors in the sclera
* b. photoreceptors in the fovea
c. protein filaments in the lens
d. photoreceptors in the optic nerve
e. none of these

E 74. Cones are
a. sensitive to red light.
b. sensitive to green light.
c. sensitive to blue light.
d. relatively insensitive to dim light.
* e. all of these

M 75. Where are bipolar, amacrine, and ganglion cells located?
a. sclera
b. thalamus
c. organ of Corti
* d. retina
e. all of these

E 76. Rhodopsin is a
* a. protein.
b. carbohydrate.
c. vitamin.
d. steroid.
e. alkaloid.

FOCUS ON SCIENCE: DISORDERS OF THE HUMAN EYE

E 77. Nearsightedness is caused by
* a. eye structure that focuses an image in front of the retina.
b. uneven curvature of the cornea.
c. uneven curvature of the lens.
d. eye structure that focuses an image posterior to the retina.
e. all of these

D 78. Which of the following is mismatched?
a. histoplasmosis—retinal destruction
b. trachoma—damage to conjunctiva leading to blindness
c. glaucoma—excess pressure of the aqueous humor
* d. astigmatism—vertical axis is longer than the horizontal axis of the eyeball
e. cataract—gradual clouding of the lens

Matching Questions

D **79.** Matching. Choose the one appropriate answer for each.

1. ___ amplitude
2. ___ cochlea
3. ___ eardrum
4. ___ iris
5. ___ oval window
6. ___ pheromone
7. ___ hammer
8. ___ pitch
9. ___ retina
10. ___ round window
11. ___ semicircular canals

    A. dissipates excess vibrational energy to the middle ear

    B. contains the organ of Corti

    C. separates the outer and middle ears

    D. membrane-covered gateway to inner ear

    E. consists of tissue containing rods and cones

    F. bone in middle ear

    G. peak height and valley depth of sound waves are its basis

    H. maintain balance and position; detect acceleration

    I. depends on how many wave changes per second occur

    J. a substance that elicits a response in members of the same species

    K. regulates size of pupil and amount of incoming light

Answers: 1. G   2. B   3. C   4. K

             5. D   6. J   7. F   8. I

             9. E   10. A   11. H

Classification Questions

Answer questions 80–84 in reference to the four kinds of energy listed below:

    a. chemical
    b. mechanical
    c. thermal
    d. light

E **80.** Receptors on the tongue detect variation in this kind of energy.

M **81.** Olfactory receptors detect this kind of energy.

D **82.** Ears monitor this kind of energy.

E **83.** Ultraviolet radiation detected by insects is in this category.

M **84.** The pain you feel from fire is a result of detecting this kind of energy.

Answers: 80. a   81. a   82. b

             83. d   84. c

Answer questions 85–89 in reference to the five eye structures listed below:

    a. cornea
    b. lens
    c. retina
    d. ommatidium
    e. vitreous body

D **85.** This structure is found in the compound eyes of insects but not in the eyes of vertebrates.

M **86.** This structure forms the transparent front of the eye.

E **87.** This structure primarily acts to focus light waves.

M **88.** This structure is composed of rod- and cone-shaped cells in mammals and birds.

M **89.** This structure acts to maintain the shape of the eye and to transmit light to other structures.

Answers   85. d   86. a   87. b

            88. c   89. e

Selecting the Exception

D **90.** Four of the five answers listed below are related by a similar sense receptor. Select the exception.
    a. touch or pressure
  * b. olfaction
    c. balance (equilibrium)
    d. hearing
    e. muscle sense

M **91.** Four of the five answers listed below are somatic senses. Select the exception.
  * a. light
    b. pressure
    c. touch
    d. temperature
    e. pain

D **92.** Four of the five answers listed below are related by a similar receptor. Select the exception.
    a. otolith
    b. vestibular apparatus
    c. semicircular canal
  * d. cochlea
    e. saccule

M   93.   Four of the five answers listed below are parts of the inner ear. Select the exception.
      *   a.   eardrum
           b.   oval window
           c.   scala tympani
           d.   basilar membrane
           e.   cochlea

M   94.   Three of the four answers listed below are related by a common navigational feature. Select the exception.
           a.   bat
           b.   dolphin
      *   c.   sharks
           d.   whales

D   95.   Three of the four answers listed below are functionally connected to each other. Select the exception.
           a.   hammer
      *   b.   pinna
           c.   stirrup
           d.   anvil

M   96.   Four of the five answers listed below are parts of the same sense organ. Select the exception.
           a.   choroid
           b.   retina
           c.   vitreous humor
      *   d.   ampulla
           e.   sclera

M   97.   Four of the five answers listed below are parts of the same sense organ. Select the exception.
      *   a.   cochlea
           b.   cornea
           c.   sclera
           d.   choroid
           e.   fovea

D   98.   Four of the five answers listed below are parts of the same sense organ. Select the exception.
           a.   ommatidium
      *   b.   retina
           c.   crystalline cone
           d.   photoreceptor
           e.   cornea

D   99.   Three of the four answers listed below are colors for which the cone cells have pigments. Select the exception.
           a.   red
      *   b.   yellow
           c.   blue
           d.   green

M   100.   Four of the five answers listed below are receptors. Select the exception.
      *   a.   muscle
           b.   Pacinian corpuscle
           c.   ommatidium
           d.   statocyst
           e.   ocellus

CHAPTER 36

INTEGRATION: ENDOCRINE CONTROL

Multiple-Choice Questions

D   **1.** From a species standpoint, sex in chimpanzees is
     a. a major force in the social life of the troop.
     b. responsible for developing social alliances.
     c. a way for females to benefit from male attention.
     d. a major force in the social life of the troop and responsible for developing social alliances.
     * e. a major force in the social life of the troop, responsible for developing social alliances, and a way for females to benefit from male attention.

D   **2.** Social position in chimpanzee society ultimately is dependent upon
     a. size and physical strength.
     b. success in play activities and aggressive behavior.
     * c. the number of social alliances claimed by the individual.
     d. the levels of testosterone in the bloodstream.
     e. the genotype of the individual.

THE ENDOCRINE SYSTEM

M   **3.** Target cells
     a. are found only in specific endocrine glands.
     b. are equipped with specific receptor molecules.
     c. are muscle cells.
     d. may occur in any part of the body.
     * e. are equipped with specific receptor molecules and may occur in any part of the body.

M   **4.** Which of the following statements is true?
     * a. Although hormones are carried to all parts of the body, they produce effects only in cells with proper receptors.
     b. Hormones are limited to steroid compounds.
     c. Hormones are secreted by specialized exocrine glands.
     d. Most hormones are controlled by positive feedback mechanisms involving the pituitary gland.

M   **5.** The important feature of all cells that react to a specific hormone is the
     a. type of blood supply they receive.
     b. proximity of the endocrine gland.
     * c. presence of an appropriate receptor molecule.
     d. characteristics of their plasma membranes.
     e. presence of specific genes responsive to the hormone.

E   **6.** Which glands secrete pheromones?
     * a. exocrine
     b. ductless
     c. sebaceous
     d. endocrine
     e. digestive

D   **7.** Pheromones are used primarily for
     a. signaling target cells in the vicinity of the secreting cells.
     b. use as transmitter substances in certain synapses.
     * c. arousing interest in a potential mate.
     d. causing a response in a part of the body some distance from the site of secretion.
     e. all of these, depending on the species

M   **8.** When Bayliss and Starling conducted experiments to determine what caused secretion of pancreatic juice, they
     a. cut the blood supply to the upper digestive tract.
     b. added acid to the small intestine and got secretions of pancreatic juices.
     c. cut the nerve supply to the upper digestive tract.
     d. got a response from the pancreas using extracts of cells lining the intestinal tract.
     * e. All except "cut the blood supply to the upper digestive tract" are true.

E   **9.** The first hormone to be discovered was
     a. insulin.
     b. gastrin.
     * c. secretin.
     d. thyroxine.
     e. estrogen.

E   **10.** The word *hormone* comes from the Greek word meaning
     a. target.
     b. response.
     c. secretion.
     * d. set in motion.
     e. internal gland.

E   **11.** Hormones are distributed throughout the body by the
     a. exocrine system.
     b. lymphatic system.
     c. nervous system.
     * d. blood system.
     e. integumentary system.

M   **12.** The primary purpose of the endocrine system is to
     a. provide a mechanism for rapid response to changes in the body.
     * b. maintain a relatively constant internal environment.
     c. ensure proper growth and development.
     d. allow for a mechanism to control gene action.
     e. all of these

D 13. Based on evolutionary evidence in higher animals, the search for hormones in insects should focus on
   a. the digestive system.
   b. exocrine glands.
   * c. the nervous system.
   d. muscles.
   e. the exoskeleton.

SIGNALING MECHANISMS

M 14. In the testicular feminization syndrome,
   a. no testosterone is produced.
   b. chemicals circulating in the blood deactivate the male hormone.
   * c. the cellular receptor for testosterone in the target cells is defective.
   d. the male with this defect is normal in all respects except that he is sterile.
   e. all of these

D 15. The reason that some individual hormones have so many different effects is that
   a. they influence gene transcription.
   b. they trigger a second messenger system that produces a cascade of effects.
   * c. there are a great many different cells in different tissues that have specific receptors for the hormone.
   d. the hormone is carried throughout the body and only a small amount is needed to produce its effect.
   e. all of these

M 16. Steroid hormones do not require a membrane receptor because they
   a. are small enough to pass directly through the membrane.
   * b. are lipid-soluble in the bilayer.
   c. pass through special channels.
   d. are water-soluble.
   e. dissolve in the cholesterol of the membranes.

M 17. The release of cyclic AMP as a second messenger is a response to
   a. peptide hormones.
   b. steroid hormones.
   c. glycoprotein hormones.
   * d. peptide and glycoprotein hormones.
   e. peptide, steroid, and glycoprotein hormones.

M 18. Which is the predominant second messenger involved in regulating glucose metabolism?
   a. insulin
   b. glucagon
   c. adenyl cyclase
   * d. cAMP
   e. all of these

M 19. Second messengers are molecules of
   a. steroid compounds.
   * b. cyclic AMP.
   c. ADP.
   d. prostaglandin.
   e. intermedin.

M 20. Water-soluble hormones
   a. must be transported by specific carriers in the blood.
   b. have no trouble entering the target cells.
   c. find and react with the surface receptor molecules.
   d. sometimes elicit the production of a second messenger.
   * e. all except "have no trouble entering the target cells" are true

THE HYPOTHALAMUS AND PITUITARY GLAND

E 21. Which gland is often called the master gland?
   a. pineal
   * b. pituitary
   c. thyroid
   d. adrenal
   e. pancreas

E 22. The pituitary gland is controlled by the
   a. pons.
   b. corpus callosum.
   c. medulla oblongata.
   d. thalamus.
   * e. hypothalamus.

D 23. The hypothalamus and pituitary link the activities of the endocrine system and nervous system by
   * a. neurohormones being secreted in response to the summation of neural messages that enter the hypothalamus.
   b. shifts in hormonal concentrations being detected by the anterior pituitary.
   c. pheromones being secreted as a response to photoperiodic stimuli.
   d. the nervous tissue of the anterior lobe of the pituitary sending stimuli to the glandular tissue of the posterior pituitary to produce hormones that will be secreted by the hypothalamus.
   e. all of these

M 24. Which of the following statements is true?
   a. The anterior pituitary gland is essentially nervous tissue.
   b. The anterior pituitary gland secretes only two hormones.
   c. The posterior pituitary gland is the master gland.
   * d. The posterior pituitary gland only stores hormones produced by the hypothalamus.
   e. all of these

M 25. The melanocyte-stimulating hormone
  a. affects kidney functions.
  b. causes melanoma if there is excess secretion.
  c. is found only in humans.
  * d. controls pigmentation in the external protective tissue.
  e. maintains normal reproductive or estrus cycle.

D 26. Which of the following is an example of an organ that is nervous in origin, structure, and function but secretes substances into the bloodstream?
  a. anterior pituitary
  * b. posterior pituitary
  c. pancreas
  d. adrenal cortex
  e. testis

E 27. If you were cast up on a desert island with no fresh water to drink, the level of which of the following would rise in your bloodstream in an effort to conserve water?
  a. erythropoietin
  b. oxytocin
  c. insulin
  * d. antidiuretic hormone
  e. glucose

E 28. The antidiuretic hormone
  a. controls water balance.
  b. controls the concentration of urea in the urine.
  c. influences blood pressure.
  d. changes the permeability of the urine-conducting tubules so that the interstitial fluid increases.
  * e. all of these

E 29. Oxytocin affects the
  * a. uterine wall.
  b. voluntary muscles throughout the body.
  c. nervous tissue.
  d. target cells in the brain.
  e. target cells in the digestive tract.

M 30. The control over milk production, water balance, and labor in childbirth is mediated by the _____ gland.
  a. pineal
  b. anterior pituitary
  * c. posterior pituitary
  d. parathyroid
  e. thyroid

E 31. The immediate stimulus for the release of milk from the female breast is the
  a. culmination of the maternal instinct.
  b. excessive accumulation of milk.
  * c. mechanical stimulation of the breast by sucking.
  d. time of day.
  e. interaction of hormones.

D 32. Antidiuretic hormone and oxytocin are products of
  a. endocrine glands.
  * b. neurosecretory cells.
  c. blood capillaries.
  d. the anterior pituitary.
  e. kidney and uterine wall cells, respectively.

M 33. A drop in blood volume would trigger the body to secrete
  a. parathyroid hormones.
  b. somatotropin.
  * c. antidiuretic hormone.
  d. insulin.
  e. glucocorticoids.

D 34. Positive feedback systems are characteristic of the
  a. male reproductive system and the pituitary gland.
  b. relative amounts of insulin and glucagon circulating in the bloodstream.
  * c. secretion of oxytocin and the onset and continuation of labor.
  d. release of antidiuretic hormone and the excretion of sodium by the kidney.

M 35. Which of the following substances is NOT secreted by neurosecretory cells?
  a. oxytocin
  b. antidiuretic hormones
  c. epinephrine
  * d. histamine
  e. dopamine

E 36. The anterior pituitary secretions produce their effects in the
  a. gonads.
  b. thyroid glands.
  c. adrenal glands.
  d. mammary glands.
  * e. all of these

E 37. ACTH (corticotropin)
  a. is secreted by the posterior pituitary.
  b. has target cells in the autonomic nervous system.
  * c. has target cells in the adrenal cortex.
  d. has target cells in the adrenal medulla.
  e. initiates the autoimmune response.

M 38. The luteinizing hormone
  * a. stimulates ovulation.
  b. has no function in males.
  c. is produced by the corpus luteum.
  d. stimulates milk production.
  e. promotes sperm formation.

M 39. The pituitary hormone associated with metabolic rate and with growth and development is
  a. ACTH.
  * b. TSH.
  c. FSH.
  d. LH.
  e. STH or GH.

M 40. The most general of the pituitary hormones, in that it may affect almost any cell in the body, is
    a. the adrenocorticotropic hormone.
    b. the thyroid-stimulating hormone.
    c. gonadotropin.
*   d. somatotropin.
    e. prolactin.

M 41. Prolactin
*   a. stimulates the mammary glands to produce milk.
    b. affects only mammals because they alone have mammary glands.
    c. causes the development of breasts and other secondary sexual characteristics in the male.
    d. acts in concert with FSH to produce milk.
    e. has secondary effects on reducing the size of the uterus after birth.

E 42. The growth hormone is
    a. prolactin.
    b. adrenalin.
    c. thyroxine.
    d. ACTH.
*   e. somatotropin.

E 43. Which of the following hormones is different from the others based upon the range of its target cells?
    a. corticotropin
    b. luteinizing hormone
*   c. somatotropin
    d. thyrotropin
    e. follicle-stimulating hormone

D 44. The secretion of each of the hormones from the anterior pituitary requires
    a. stimulation from the posterior pituitary.
    b. that they first be secreted from the neurons of the hypothalamus.
    c. two capillary beds.
    d. the action of minute amounts of releasing hormones.
*   e. two capillary beds and the action of minute amounts of releasing hormones.

FOCUS ON HEALTH: ABNORMAL PITUITARY OUTPUTS

E 45. Dwarfism may be due to insufficient production of
    a. mineralocorticoid.
    b. glucocorticoid.
    c. calcitonin.
*   d. somatotropin.
    e. the parathyroid hormone.

E 46. Acromegaly is the result of excessive secretion of which of the following by adults?
    a. mineralocorticoid
    b. glucocorticoid
    c. thyroxine
    d. testosterone
*   e. somatotropin

SOURCES AND EFFECTS OF OTHER HORMONES

E 47. Which hormone is produced by the liver?
    a. calcitonin
    b. norepinephrine
*   c. somatomedin
    d. erythropoietin
    e. angiotensin

E 48. Angiotensin is produced in the
    a. bloodstream.
    b. adrenal cortex.
    c. adrenal medulla.
*   d. kidneys.
    e. heart.

D 49. You have just moved from Norfolk, Virginia (sea level), to Taos, New Mexico (high in the mountains), and you find yourself out of breath climbing a small hill. Three months later, climbing the same hill, you have no difficulty. In the interim you have not altered your level of activity or diet. Which hormone has been at work?
    a. angiotensin
*   b. erythropoietin
    c. aldosterone
    d. estrogen
    e. none of these

M 50. Which gland promotes the body's immune response as its primary function?
    a. pineal
*   b. thymus
    c. thyroid
    d. gonads
    e. adrenal

M 51. A group of hormones that are believed to affect the membrane surface receptors of lymphocytes are
*   a. thymosins.
    b. prostaglandins.
    c. erythropoietins.
    d. secretins.
    e. none of these

M 52. Which gland is involved in the maturation of lymphocytes?
    a. thyroid
    b. adrenal
    c. kidney
*   d. thymus
    e. parathyroid

FEEDBACK CONTROL OF HORMONAL SECRETIONS

M 53. Glucocorticoids
    a. are secreted by the adrenal cortex.
    b. influence carbohydrate, fat, and protein metabolism.
    c. function during infection and injury as part of the defense response.
    d. are exemplified by cortisol.
*   e. all of these

D **54.** The first hormone produced by the body in response to an attack of hypoglycemia is
   a. adrenocorticotropin.
   b. glucocorticoid.
   * c. corticotropin releasing hormone.
   d. insulin.
   e. thyroxine.

D **55.** A friend tells you that her husband has been feeling guilty and stressed for the past month. During the same time interval he has felt fatigued most of the time, and many foods now seem to upset his stomach. Doctors have already checked for ulcers, cancer, blood pressure changes, and other blood irregularities, but these apparently are normal. You are an endocrinologist, so you suggest that he be tested for the most likely endocrine malfunction, which would be
   a. androgen/estrogen levels in the bloodstream.
   * b. glucocorticoid levels in the bloodstream.
   c. calcitonin level in the bloodstream.
   d. melatonin level in the bloodstream.

E **56.** The adrenal medulla produces
   a. mineralocorticoids.
   * b. epinephrine.
   c. cortisol.
   d. testosterone.
   e. glucocorticoids.

D **57.** Blood glucose levels are regulated by
   a. insulin.
   b. glucagon.
   c. cortisol.
   d. insulin and glucagon only.
   * e. insulin, glucagon, and cortisol.

M **58.** The hormone whose levels remain high when the body is suffering from inflammation and stress is
   * a. cortisol.
   b. somatotropin.
   c. thymosin.
   d. prolactin.
   e. parathyroid hormone.

D **59.** The only endocrine gland whose secretory function is under direct control by sympathetic nerves is the
   a. pancreas.
   b. thyroid.
   * c. adrenal medulla.
   d. thymus.
   e. testis.

E **60.** A goiter is an enlarged form of which gland?
   a. adrenal
   b. pancreas
   * c. thyroid
   d. parathyroid
   e. thymus

D **61.** A goiter is caused by a deficiency in
   a. thyroxine.
   b. triiodothyronine.
   c. calcium.
   * d. iodine.
   e. both thyroxine and triiodothyronine.

E **62.** Synthetic thyroxine taken orally in the form of pills is the recommended treatment for
   * a. hypothyroidism.
   b. goiter.
   c. hyperthyroidism.
   d. Grave's disease.
   e. acromegaly.

M **63.** Which hormone prepares and maintains the uterine lining for pregnancy?
   a. estrogen
   b. progesterone
   c. follicle-stimulating hormone
   d. luteinizing hormone
   * e. both estrogen and progesterone

E **64.** Which gland secretes sex hormones?
   * a. testis
   b. adrenal medulla
   c. thyroid
   d. kidney
   e. pancreas

E **65.** The gonads are another name for the
   a. parathyroid and thyroid.
   * b. ovary and testis.
   c. adrenal cortex and medulla.
   d. anterior and posterior pituitary.
   e. none of these

D **66.** Which of the following is NOT produced by the gonads?
   a. testosterone
   b. progesterone
   * c. follicle-stimulating hormone
   d. androgens
   e. All are produced by the gonads.

M **67.** A grab-bag of local hormones present in tissues throughout the body (lungs, gut, liver, and the prostate gland in males) that may act as mediators between membrane receptors and the enzymes that activate cAMP are
   a. thymosins.
   * b. prostaglandins.
   c. erythropoietins.
   d. secretins.
   e. all of these

M **68.** Prostaglandins
   a. affect blood flow by acting on smooth muscles in the blood cells.
   b. cause menstrual cramps.
   c. may produce strong allergic reactions.
   d. are produced by the corpus luteum if pregnancy does not follow ovulation.
   * e. all of these

D 69. Allergic reactions to airborne dust and pollen may be aggravated by what hormone?
* a. prostaglandin
  b. somatostatin
  c. insulin
  d. growth hormone
  e. nerve growth factor

DIRECT RESPONSES TO CHEMICAL CHANGES

M 70. Calcitonin acts in opposition to
* a. the parathyroid hormone.
  b. thyroxine.
  c. glucagon.
  d. the adrenal medulla.
  e. all of these

M 71. If you eliminated all sources of calcium (dairy products, some vegetables) from your diet, the level of which of the following would rise in an attempt to supply calcium stored in your body to the tissues that need it?
  a. aldosterone
  b. calcitonin
  c. mineralocorticoids
* d. parathyroid hormone
  e. all of these

M 72. Which of the following glands produces only one type of hormone?
  a. adrenal medulla
  b. adrenal cortex
  c. pancreas
* d. parathyroid

M 73. The removal of the _____ gland will result in tetany (muscular spasms).
  a. thymus
  b. thyroid
  c. pituitary
* d. parathyroid

E 74. The normal human individual has how many parathyroid glands?
  a. 2
  b. 3
* c. 4
  d. 5
  e. 6

M 75. The actions of insulin and glucagon could be described as
  a. synergistic.
* b. antagonistic.
  c. cooperative.
  d. permissive.
  e. mutualistic.

D 76. The pancreatic secretions governing glucose levels are precisely controlled by
  a. neural connections to the pancreas.
  b. the blood-brain barrier.
  c. cooperative interactions.
* d. feedback mechanisms.
  e. releasing factors.

M 77. The hormone that is antagonistic in action to glucagon is
  a. norepinephrine.
* b. insulin.
  c. thyroxine.
  d. epinephrine.
  e. mineralocorticoids.

M 78. Insulin directly affects the
  a. secretion of saliva.
  b. storage of proteins.
  c. secretion of pancreatic juices.
* d. metabolism of sugar.
  e. utilization of fat reserves.

D 79. Which of the following does NOT affect blood sugar levels?
  a. glucagon
  b. epinephrine
* c. parathyroid hormones
  d. glucocorticoids
  e. insulin

E 80. Glucagon is produced by the
  a. adrenal cortex.
  b. adrenal medulla.
  c. thyroid.
  d. kidneys.
* e. pancreas.

M 81. Which gland is both an exocrine and endocrine gland?
* a. pancreas
  b. adrenal
  c. ovary
  d. thyroid
  e. pituitary

E 82. Excess glucose is converted into glycogen in the
  a. pancreas.
* b. liver.
  c. thymus.
  d. thyroid.
  e. none of these

E 83. Specialized islet cells that secrete hormones are found scattered throughout the
  a. adrenal cortex.
  b. liver.
  c. thymus.
  d. adrenal medulla.
* e. pancreas.

D 84. If you skip a meal, which of the following conditions
   would prevail?
   a. Insulin levels would rise.
   b. Glucagon levels would rise.
   c. Glycogen would be converted to glucose.
   d. Insulin levels would rise; and Glycogen would be
      converted to glucose.
   * e. Glucagon levels would rise; and Glycogen would
      be converted to glucose.

D 85. Which of the following is true of "type 1 diabetes"?
   a. Insulin levels are near normal.
   b. Target cells do not respond to insulin.
   c. It is the more common form of diabetes.
   * d. It is thought to be an autoimmune disease.
   e. It usually occurs in middle-aged people.

M 86. Which of the following hormones is different from the
   others based upon its chemical structure?
   * a. glucagon
   b. cortisol
   c. estrogen
   d. testosterone
   e. mineralocorticoids

HORMONES AND THE EXTERNAL ENVIRONMENT

M 87. Which gland is associated with biological clocks or
   biorhythms?
   * a. pineal
   b. parathyroid
   c. hypothalamus
   d. pituitary
   e. thymus

E 88. Which gland is the remnant of the "third eye?"
   * a. pineal
   b. pituitary
   c. thyroid
   d. parathyroid
   e. thymus

E 89. The gland that functions in controlling the
   reproductive cycle is the
   a. thyroid.
   * b. pineal.
   c. thymus.
   d. pancreas.
   e. kidney.

Matching Questions

D 90. Matching. Choose the one most appropriate answer
   for each.
   1. ___ adrenal cortex
   2. ___ adrenal medulla
   3. ___ anterior lobe of pituitary
   4. ___ exocrine glands
   5. ___ glandular epithelium in gastrointestinal
      tract
   6. ___ gonad
   7. ___ hypothalamus
   8. ___ intermediate lobe of pituitary
   9. ___ kidneys
   10. ___ pancreatic islets
   11. ___ parathyroid gland
   12. ___ pineal gland
   13. ___ posterior lobe of pituitary
   14. ___ thymus gland
   15. ___ thyroid gland

   A. secretes one hormone that increases the
      metabolic rate and another that inhibits
      calcium release from bone storage sites
   B. secrete insulin and glucagon
   C. secretes hormones that prepare accessory
      reproductive structures for reproduction
   D. involved in lymphocyte maturation
   E. secretes tropic hormones, growth hormone,
      and prolactin
   F. secretes sex hormones, mineralocorticoids,
      and glucocorticoids
   G. in many vertebrates, helps to determine the
      amount and distribution of dark pigments in
      the skin
   H. secrete enzymes that help to form
      angiotensin and erythropoietin
   I. participates in reproductive physiology and
      senses photoperiods
   J. secretes (releases into bloodstream) oxytocin
      and antidiuretic hormone
   K. secretes a hormone that promotes calcium
      release from bone storage sites
   L. produces oxytocin and antidiuretic hormone
   M. secretes cholecystokinin, secretin, and
      gastrin
   N. secretes epinephrine and norepinephrine
   O. secrete pheromones, milk, tears, sweat, and
      mucus

   Answers: 1. F   2. N   3. E   4. O

                 5. M   6. C   7. L   8. G

9. H   10. B   11. K   12. I

13. J   14. D   15. A

Classification Questions

Answer questions 91–95 in reference to the five endocrine glands listed below:

    a. pituitary
    b. adrenal
    c. pancreas
    d. thyroid
    e. thymus

M **91.** This gland is the target for corticotropin (ACTH).

E **92.** Oxytocin is produced in this gland.

M **93.** Antidiuretic hormone is produced in this gland.

M **94.** This gland produces a hormone that controls growth and development.

E **95.** Insulin is produced in this gland.

Answers   91. b   92. a   93. a

              94. d   95. c

Answer questions 96–100 in reference to the five pituitary hormones listed below:

    a. estrogen
    b. luteinizing hormone
    c. somatotropin
    d. oxytocin
    e. antidiuretic hormone

M **96.** This hormone controls water retention and loss.

M **97.** The mammary glands are the target for this hormone.

D **98.** This hormone induces protein synthesis and cell division in young animals.

D **99.** The kidneys are the target for this hormone.

M **100.** Uterine contractions are induced by this hormone.

Answers   96. e   97. d   98. c

              99. e   100. d

Answer questions 101–105 in reference to the five endocrine glands listed below:

    a. adrenal cortex
    b. ovary
    c. pineal
    d. thyroid
    e. thymus

D **101.** This gland controls circadian rhythms.

D **102.** This gland plays a central role in the immune response.

D **103.** This gland secretes a hormone that prepares and maintains the uterus for pregnancy.

M **104.** Progesterone is produced by this gland.

M **105.** Calcium concentration in the blood is controlled by this gland.

Answers   101. c   102. e   103. b

              104. b   105. d

Selecting the Exception

E **106.** Four of the five answers listed below are endocrine glands. Select the exception.
      a. thymus gland
*   b. salivary gland
      c. parathyroid gland
      d. thyroid gland
      e. pituitary gland

D **107.** Four of the five answers listed below are produced by the same lobe of the pituitary. Select the exception.
*   a. antidiuretic hormone
      b. prolactin
      c. corticotropin
      d. somatotropin
      e. luteinizing hormone

M **108.** Four of the five answers listed below are related by a common source. Select the exception.
      a. aldosterone
      b. glucocorticoid
      c. cortisol
*   d. adrenalin
      e. mineralocorticoid

M **109.** Four of the five answers listed below affect blood glucose level. Select the exception.
*   a. calcitonin
      b. glucagon
      c. glucocorticoid
      d. insulin
      e. epinephrine

D 110. Four of the five answers listed below directly affect another endocrine gland. Select the exception.
* a. cortisol
b. corticotropin
c. luteinizing hormone
d. follicle-stimulating hormone
e. angiotensin

D 111. Four of the five answers listed below are characteristic of hyperthyroidism. Select the exception.
a. excessive weight loss
* b. excessive water loss through urination
c. intolerance of heat
d. increased heart rate and blood pressure
e. excessive sweating

M 112. Four of the five answers listed below are related by a similar source. Select the exception.
* a. prolactin
b. progesterone
c. androgen
d. estrogen
e. testosterone

D 113. Four of the five answers listed below are related by a similar gland. Select the exception.
a. goiter
b. deficiency of iodine in the diet
c. hypothyroidism
* d. rickets
e. excessive stimulation of the thyroid gland

D 114. Four of the five answers listed below are related by the same action. Select the exception.
a. activates vitamin D
b. induces reabsorption of calcium by the kidney
c. removes calcium and phosphate from bones
* d. regulates blood volume
e. involved in the biofeedback control of extracellular calcium

D 115. Four of the five answers listed below are characteristic actions of prostaglandins. Select the exception.
a. act on smooth muscles in airways
b. may produce allergic responses to dust and pollen
c. may produce excessive bleeding and cramping during menstrual cycle
* d. generate the fight or flight response
e. destroy the corpus luteum if pregnancy does not occur

CHAPTER 37
PROTECTION, SUPPORT, AND MOVEMENT

Multiple-Choice Questions

EVOLUTION OF VERTEBRATE SKIN

E   1.   The word *integument* is derived from the word for
         a.   protection.
         b.   support.
     *   c.   covering.
         d.   contraction.
         e.   resistance.

E   2.   The integumentary system is responsible for all but
         which of the following?
         a.   protection against bacterial attack
         b.   protection against abrasion
         c.   synthesis of certain vitamins
     *   d.   blood cell formation
         e.   control of temperature and prevention of
              desiccation

E   3.   The body covering of arthropods is
         a.   a secreted cuticle.
         b.   made of hardened cells.
         c.   also its skeleton.
     *   d.   a secreted cuticle and also its skeleton.
         e.   a secreted cuticle; made of hardened cells, and is
              also its skeleton.

E   4.   Beaks, hooves, horns, claws, nails, and quills are
         outgrowths of
     *   a.   epidermis.
         b.   hypodermis.
         c.   dermis.
         d.   gastrodermis.
         e.   all of these

E   5.   The largest organ of the vertebrate body is which of
         the following?
         a.   lungs
         b.   liver
         c.   stomach
     *   d.   skin
         e.   small intestines

M   6.   All but which of the following are functions of the
         skin?
         a.   protection from bacterial invasion
         b.   regulation of body temperature
     *   c.   production of tanning hormones
         d.   sensing of the external world
         e.   production of vitamin D

E   7.   Vitamin D is required for _____ metabolism.
         a.   sulfur
         b.   phosphorus
     *   c.   calcium
         d.   potassium
         e.   zinc

M   8.   Beaks, hooves, horns, claws, and nails all contain
         a.   collagen.
     *   b.   keratin.
         c.   myosin fibers.
         d.   cutin.
         e.   all of these

M   9.   Which of the following is NOT found in the
         epidermis?
         a.   stratified epithelium
     *   b.   blood vessels
         c.   tight cell junctions
         d.   keratin
         e.   melanin

M   10. Which of the following is NOT characteristic of the
         epidermis?
         a.   stratified epithelium
     *   b.   fat for insulation and capillaries
         c.   keratinocytes
         d.   stratum corneum
         e.   melanin pigments

E   11. Melanin protects the skin from
         a.   desiccation.
         b.   abrasion.
     *   c.   ultraviolet radiation.
         d.   infrared damage.
         e.   invasion by bacteria.

M   12. Which of the following statements is false?
     *   a.   Differences in human skin color are the result of
              differences in quantities of melanocytes.
         b.   Skin is about the thickness of a piece of paper.
         c.   In a blister, the epidermis is separated from the
              dermis.
         d.   Hair is composed of layers of dead cells.
         e.   Nails, hooves, horns, and hair contain keratin.

E   13. Which of the following statements is false concerning
         the outermost layer of the epidermis?
         a.   It is the first to feel any abrasion.
         b.   Keratin provides waterproofing.
         c.   Millions of cells are worn off daily.
     *   d.   Its cells are undergoing rapid cell division.
         e.   It is called the stratum corneum.

M   14. Which of the following components of the dermis is
         incorrectly matched with its usual function?
         a.   blood vessels: nutrient supply
     *   b.   sweat glands: hormone secretion
         c.   oil glands: lubrication of hair and skin
         d.   hairs: insulation
         e.   receptors: pain

TYPES OF SKELETONS

M 15. Organisms with external skeletons are exemplified by
 a. octopuses and earthworms.
 b. mollusks.
 c. sea anemones.
 * d. insects and crabs.
 e. vertebrates.

E 16. Which organisms have a hydrostatic skeleton with a soft body wall?
 * a. earthworms
 b. spiders
 c. sponges
 d. crabs
 e. vertebrates

E 17. In which of the following types is the skeleton substance NOT technically a part of the animal?
 a. exoskeleton
 b. endoskeleton
 c. musculoskeleton
 d. articuloskeleton
 * e. hydrostatic

M 18. For an arthropod, an exoskeleton has which serious disadvantage?
 * a. inability to grow
 b. too much weight for flying
 c. poor placement of muscles for leverage
 d. lack of flexible appendages
 e. poor water retention

E 19. Which organisms have a somewhat rigid internal skeleton and many muscles?
 a. octopuses
 b. earthworms
 c. sea anemones
 d. insects
 * e. vertebrates

E 20. The mineral stored in greatest quantity in bones is
 a. phosphorus.
 b. iron.
 c. magnesium.
 * d. calcium.
 e. sulfur.

HUMAN SKELETAL SYSTEM

M 21. The human axial skeleton includes all but which of the following?
 a. skull
 b. ribs
 * c. pectoral girdle
 d. sternum
 e. vertebral column

E 22. Which of the following is NOT part of the appendicular skeleton?
 a. clavicle
 b. scapula
 c. fibula
 * d. ribs
 e. patella

E 23. The bone in the upper arm is the
 a. radius.
 b. ulna.
 c. tibia.
 * d. humerus.
 e. femur.

E 24. Bones in fingers or toes are called
 a. hyoid.
 b. patella.
 c. scapula.
 d. clavicle.
 * e. phalanges.

E 25. The kneecap is the
 a. hyoid.
 * b. patella.
 c. scapula.
 d. clavicle.
 e. phalanx.

E 26. The collarbone is the
 a. hyoid.
 b. patella.
 c. scapula.
 * d. clavicle.
 e. phalanx.

E 27. The shoulder blade is the
 a. hyoid.
 b. patella.
 * c. scapula.
 d. clavicle.
 e. phalanx.

M 28. Which of the following joins two bones
 a. fontanels
 * b. ligaments
 c. keratinocytes
 d. tendons
 e. sarcomeres

M 29. Bones of the cranium portion of the skull are examples of which kind of bones?
 a. long
 b. short
 * c. flat
 d. irregular
 e. all of these

M 30. Bones of the face and vertebrae are examples of which kind of bones?
 a. long
 b. short
 c. flat
 * d. irregular
 e. all of these

E 31. Bones such as the humerus and femur are examples of which kind of bones?
*   a. long
     b. short
     c. flat
     d. irregular
     e. all of these

A CLOSER LOOK AT BONES AND JOINTS

E 32. In spongy bone tissue, the spaces are filled with
     a. air.
     b. blood.
     c. cartilage.
*   d. marrow.
     e. lymph.

M 33. Which tissue has Haversian canals?
     a. adipose
*   b. bone
     c. cartilage
     d. epithelial
     e. muscular

D 34. Growth of long bones
     a. follows the cartilage model.
     b. occurs in the middle at first, then at both ends.
     c. is characterized by bone tissue replacing calcified cartilage.
     d. is characterized by the persistence of cartilage at both ends of the shaft at the epiphyseal plates until growth stops.
*   e. all of these

D 35. Which of the following statements is false?
     a. Calcium is the most important mineral involved with bone tissue turnover.
     b. Osteocytes and osteoclasts are involved with the reabsorption and repair of bones.
     c. Bone mass decreases with age.
*   d. Males have greater problems with loss of bone tissue than females.
     e. Marrow fills the cavities in the spaces of the spongy bone and in the center of the shaft of the bone almost as quickly as the spaces are formed.

D 36. If some bleached bones found lying in the desert were carefully examined, which of the following would NOT be present?
*   a. osteocytes
     b. Haversian canals
     c. calcium
     d. marrow cavity
     e. compact bone tissue

D 37. All but which of the following are associated with bone formation?
     a. osteoblasts
     b. cartilage
*   c. osteoporosis
     d. marrow cavity formation
     e. calcium

M 38. The nonmoving joints between skull bones are examples of what kind of joints?
     a. synovial
*   b. fibrous
     c. cartilaginous
     d. hinge
     e. none of these

M 39. The vertebral discs with small amounts of movement are examples of what kind of joints?
     a. synovial
     b. fibrous
*   c. cartilaginous
     d. hinge
     e. none of these

M 40. What kind of joints are freely movable and the bones are separated by a fluid-filled cavity?
*   a. synovial
     b. fibrous
     c. cartilaginous
     d. hinge
     e. none of these

SKELETAL-MUSCULAR SYSTEMS

M 41. Smooth muscle
*   a. is involuntary and nonstriated.
     b. is responsible for movement of the skeleton.
     c. is involved in contraction of the heart.
     d. is connected to bones by tendons.
     e. is involuntary and nonstriated; plus it is involved in contraction of the heart.

M 42. The ability to extend a leg originates from
     a. contraction of ligaments and tendons.
*   b. contraction of a muscle.
     c. lengthening of a muscle.
     d. combination of push and pull by antagonistic muscle pairs.

E 43. Muscles are attached to bones by means of
     a. sarcomeres.
     b. ligaments.
     c. cross-bridges.
     d. cuticle.
*   e. tendons.

E 44. Each muscle fiber is also called a
     a. muscle.
*   b. muscle cell.
     c. myofibril.
     d. sarcomere.
     e. all of these

M 45. The gastrocnemius muscle is located
     a. in the forelimb.
     b. on the back.
     c. in the hip area.
*   d. in the lower leg.
     e. in the neck.

E 46. The pectoralis major muscle is located
* a. in the chest.
b. on the back.
c. near the hips.
d. in the upper leg.
e. in the lower leg.

D 47. Reciprocal innervation of reflexes between antagonistic muscle pairs
* a. is the usual basis of coordinated contractions.
b. is the means by which rods prevent cones from being stimulated.
c. refers to the lens adjustments that bring about precise focusing onto the retina.
d. explains the mechanism for the operation of the calcium pump.
e. all of these

HOW DOES SKELETAL MUSCLE CONTRACT?

D 48. Which of the following includes all the others?
a. actin
b. myofibril
c. myosin
d. myofilament
* e. muscle fiber

D 49. When a sarcomere shortens,
a. the actin filaments shorten.
b. the myosin filaments shorten.
c. both actin and myosin shorten.
* d. neither actin nor myosin shortens.

D 50. During muscle contractions,
a. the myofibrils shorten.
b. the actin and myosin filaments slide over each other.
c. the filaments move toward the middle of the sarcomere during contraction and away on relaxation.
d. the muscle fibers thicken.
* e. all of these

D 51. During contraction,
a. cross-bridges of muscle filaments are broken and reformed.
b. ATP is used to form cross-bridges.
c. muscle cells use glycogen as their energy source.
d. if there is a poor supply of oxygen, glycogen depletion by glycolysis will lead to fatigue.
* e. all of these

D 52. In their action, muscles would be most like
* a. ropes.
b. levers.
c. push rods.
d. screws.
e. hammers.

WHAT CONTROLS CONTRACTION?

E 53. Functionally, the plasma membrane of a muscle cell is most like that of a
a. bone cell.
* b. nerve cell.
c. cartilage cell.
d. pancreatic islet cell.
e. epidermal cell.

E 54. The element specifically associated with muscle contraction is
a. phosphorus.
b. potassium.
* c. calcium.
d. sodium.
e. chlorine.

D 55. Which of the following statements does NOT describe normal activity in a motor system?
a. All motor systems require the presence of some medium or structural element against which force can be applied.
b. In a skeletal muscle system, coordinated contraction depends on reciprocal innervation of motor neurons to antagonistic muscle pairs.
c. In vertebrates, only skeletal muscle acts to move the body through the environment.
* d. In a resting muscle, energy is stored in the form of tropomyosin.
e. all of these

M 56. Which substance is released by motor neurons to initiate a muscle contraction?
* a. acetylcholine
b. dopamine
c. serotonin
d. noradrenalin
e. all of these

M 57. Which of the following statements is false?
a. Calcium ions are released as an action potential is propagated along a skeletal muscle cell.
* b. Acetylcholine provides energy to propel actin filaments past myosin filaments during muscle cell activity.
c. Calcium ions are actively collected and stored in the sarcoplasmic reticulum as the muscle returns to the resting state.
d. The interaction of acetylcholine with receptors on the sarcolemma may produce graded potentials.
e. Tetanus is the normal mode of contraction in human skeletal muscle.

ENERGY FOR CONTRACTION

E 58. The most immediate, but necessarily limited, source of energy for reformation of ATP in muscle cells is
a. aerobic respiration.
b. mitochondrial pathways.
c. electron transport phosphorylation.
* d. creatine phosphate.
e. anaerobic fermentation.

M 59. Which of these occurs as a result of rigorous muscular exercise?
   a. ATP accumulation
   b. actin depletion
   * c. oxygen debt
   d. glycogen buildup
   e. sarcomere formation

PROPERTIES OF WHOLE MUSCLES

M 60. An active, nonfatiguing muscle would be expected to have
   a. aerobic respiration.
   b. numerous mitochondria.
   c. moderate rates of contraction.
   d. aerobic respiration and moderate rates of contraction.
   * e. aerobic respiration, moderate rates of contraction, and numerous mitochondria.

E 61. Muscle fatigue is a result of
   * a. accumulation of lactic acid.
   b. exhaustion of available ATP.
   c. reduction in lactic acid and oxygen debt.
   d. failure of calcium channels to open after prolonged use.

M 62. A motor neuron and all the muscles under its control is called what kind of unit?
   a. end
   b. movement
   c. muscle
   * d. motor
   e. coordination

M 63. The mechanical force that resists gravity in the lifting of an object is
   a. muscle fatigue.
   b. a motor unit.
   * c. muscle tension.
   d. a muscle twitch.
   e. tetanus.

Classification Questions

Answer questions 64–68 in reference to the five bones listed below:
   a. clavicle
   b. lumbar vertebra
   c. tibia
   d. metatarsal
   e. metacarpal

E 64. This bone is not part of the appendicular skeleton.

M 65. This bone is part of the wishbone of birds.

M 66. If one had a slipped disk, that disk might be next to this bone.

D 67. This bone is a toe bone in birds.

M 68. This bone connects to the femur.

Answers   64. b   65. a   66. b
            67. d   68. c

Answer questions 69–73 in reference to the five muscles listed below:
   a. pectoralis major
   b. deltoid
   c. rectus femoris
   d. triceps
   e. gastrocnemius

D 69. This muscle is a principal muscle of the upper leg.

M 70. This muscle is located on the upper shoulder.

M 71. This muscle is antagonistic to the action of the biceps.

D 72. The Achilles' tendon attaches this muscle to the heel bones.

D 73. This muscle is the principal flight muscle of birds.

Answers   69. c   70. b   71. d
            72. e   73. a

Selecting the Exception

M 74. Four of the five answers listed below are located in the same layer. Select the exception.
   a. sebaceous gland
   b. hair follicle
   c. sweat gland
   d. nerve and sensory cells
   * e. adipose (fat) cells

D 75. Four of the five answers listed below are found in bone. Select the exception.
   a. lacunae
   * b. collagen fibers
   c. Haversian system
   d. lamellae
   e. osteocyte

E   76.   Four of the five answers listed below possess the same type of skeleton. Select the exception.
*   a.   beetle
    b.   snake
    c.   bird
    d.   human
    e.   frog

M   77.   Four of the five answers listed below possess the same type of skeleton. Select the exception.
    a.   butterfly
    b.   fly
*   c.   earthworm
    d.   crab
    e.   grasshopper

M   78.   Four of the five answers listed below are parts of the same anatomical area. Select the exception.
    a.   humerus
*   b.   fibula
    c.   radius
    d.   clavicle
    e.   scapula

M   79.   Four of the five answers listed below are parts of the same skeletal division. Select the exception.
    a.   cranium
    b.   ribs
    c.   sternum
    d.   vertebrae
*   e.   phalanges

M   80.   Four of the five answers listed below are types of bones. Select the exception.
*   a.   immovable
    b.   long
    c.   short
    d.   flat
    e.   irregular

M   81.   Four of the five answers listed below are muscles. Select the exception.
    a.   pectoralis
*   b.   patella
    c.   gastrocnemius
    d.   deltoid
    e.   sartorius

D   82.   Four of the five answers listed below are molecules that participate in muscle contraction. Select the exception.
*   a.   sarcolemma
    b.   troponin
    c.   tropomyosin
    d.   actin
    e.   myosin

CHAPTER 38
CIRCULATION

Multiple-Choice Questions

E   1.   The first electrocardiogram was performed on a
  - a. parrot.
  - * b. bulldog.
  - c. cat.
  - d. monkey.
  - e. human.

D   2.   Which of the following systems is the only one to have direct interactions with the other three?
  - a. digestive
  - b. urinary
  - * c. circulatory
  - d. respiratory

EVOLUTION OF CIRCULATORY SYSTEMS

M   3.   Which of the following is usually NOT present in an open circulation system?
  - * a. veins
  - b. the heart
  - c. arteries
  - d. blood
  - e. arterioles

E   4.   Which animal has a closed circulatory system?
  - a. clam
  - * b. earthworm
  - c. spider
  - d. snail
  - e. insect

M   5.   Which of the following statements is false?
  - a. The systemic circuit carries oxygenated blood.
  - * b. Humans have an open circulatory system.
  - c. The function of the heart is to generate pressure to make the blood flow through the circulatory system.
  - d. The rate of blood flow varies throughout the circulatory system.
  - e. The interstitial fluid is returned to the circulatory system in the lymphatic system.

M   6.   Which of the following statements is false?
  - * a. Blood circulates faster through a fish than through a human.
  - b. Fish have only one heart pump, but humans have a heart divided into two pumps.
  - c. Humans have one major capillary bed, whereas fish have two capillary beds.
  - d. Blood pressure is lower in the capillary beds than in the major blood vessels.
  - e. The circulation of blood in humans is more efficient than in fish.

M   7.   The pulmonary circuit
  - a. involves the hepatic portal vein.
  - b. moves oxygen-rich blood to the lungs.
  - c. includes the coronary arteries.
  - * d. leads to, through, and from the lungs.
  - e. all of these

M   8.   In the human systemic circuit, blood will pass through all but which of the following?
  - a. liver
  - b. limbs
  - * c. lungs
  - d. digestive organs
  - e. brain

E   9.   Which of the following is NOT a function of the lymph system?
  - a. fighting infection
  - * b. transporting dissolved gases
  - c. reclaiming fluids
  - d. harboring white blood cells
  - e. All of these are functions of the lymph system.

CHARACTERISTICS OF BLOOD

E   10.   All but which of the following can occur in the blood?
  - * a. digestion of nutrients
  - b. combining of oxygen with hemoglobin
  - c. transport of phagocytic cells
  - d. stabilization of pH
  - e. equalization of internal temperatures

D   11.   Which cell does NOT belong with the others?
  - * a. erythrocytes
  - b. neutrophils
  - c. lymphocytes
  - d. eosinophils
  - e. monocytes

E   12.   Which white blood cells are most abundant?
  - * a. neutrophils
  - b. lymphocytes
  - c. monocytes
  - d. eosinophils
  - e. basophils

M   13.   Which cell is NOT involved with the immune response?
  - * a. erythrocytes
  - b. neutrophils
  - c. lymphocytes
  - d. eosinophils
  - e. monocytes

266

M 14. Which cell is the most abundant in the human body?
   a. lymphocytes
   b. basophils
* c. erythrocytes
   d. neutrophils
   e. platelets

M 15. Which cell produces the fibrin used in blood clots?
   a. lymphocytes
   b. basophils
   c. erythrocytes
   d. neutrophils
* e. platelets

E 16. In humans, which cell does NOT have a nucleus?
* a. erythrocytes
   b. lymphocytes
   c. neutrophils
   d. eosinophils
   e. monocytes

E 17. Human red blood cells
* a. have no nucleus.
   b. are the primary carriers of carbon dioxide in the blood.
   c. are phagocytes.
   d. release clotting factors when they are ruptured.
   e. are produced in lymphoid organs.

E 18. Most of the oxygen in the blood is transported by
   a. plasma.
   b. serum.
   c. platelets.
* d. hemoglobin.
   e. leukocytes.

E 19. Red blood cells originate in the
   a. liver.
   b. spleen.
   c. yellow bone marrow.
* d. red bone marrow.
   e. thymus gland.

M 20. Stem cells
* a. retain the ability to divide and give rise to groups of cells.
   b. are phagocytic.
   c. are the most common type of blood cells.
   d. transport oxygen and carbon dioxide.
   e. are more numerous in women than in men.

D 21. A normal red blood cell count would be in the range of __?__ per microliter.
   a. 3,000-6,750
   b. 250,000-300,000
* c. 4.8-5.4 million
   d. 1.6-3.2 million
   e. 20,000-100,000

M 22. How long does the average red blood cell live?
   a. 4 days
   b. 4 weeks
* c. 4 months
   d. 1 year
   e. 4 years

D 23. Stem cells are found in the
   a. arteries.
* b. bone marrow.
   c. liver
   d. spleen
   e. pancreas

E 24. Stem cells give rise to
   a. red blood cells.
   b. megakaryocytes.
   c. macrophages.
   d. lymphocytes.
* e. all of these

E 25. About how many quarts of blood does a normal, 150-pound, human male have?
   a. 2-3
   b. 3-4
* c. 4-5
   d. 5-6
   e. 6-7

E 26. What percent of the total blood volume does plasma normally amount to?
   a. 15 to 25
   b. 33 to 40
* c. 50 to 60
   d. 66 to 75
   e. about 80

M 27. Proteins constitute what percentage of the human plasma?
   a. 1-2
   b. 91-92
   c. 12-15
* d. 7-8
   e. 50-60

E 28. Which of the following makes up the greatest percentage of human plasma?
   a. albumin
   b. red blood cells
   c. white blood cells
* d. water
   e. dissolved ions, sugars, hormones, etc.

E 29. Hemoglobin contains which element?
   a. chlorine
   b. sodium
* c. iron
   d. copper
   e. magnesium

E 30. Megakaryocytes fragment to produce
   a. red blood cells.
   b. lymphocytes.
 * c. platelets.
   d. eosinophils.
   e. neutrophils.

E 31. Megakaryocytes
 * a. produce platelets by fragmentation.
   b. produce leukocytes.
   c. are wandering phagocytes.
   d. are disc-shaped cells that transport gases.
   e. produce antibodies.

M 32. Blood rich in oxygen is what color?
   a. yellow
   b. pink
 * c. bright red
   d. blue
   e. purple

E 33. If a test tube of whole blood is subjected to centrifugation, the cells will be packed in the bottom of the tube and the fluid above it will be designated
   a. water.
   b. serum.
   c. lymph.
   d. interstitial fluid.
 * e. plasma.

M 34. When they are mature and circulating in the blood, which of the following cells have no nuclei?
   a. platelets
   b. leukocytes
   c. erythrocytes
 * d. platelets and erythrocytes
   e. leukocytes and erythrocytes

BLOOD TRANSFUSION AND TYPING

M 35. Type A blood will NOT agglutinate when mixed with
   a. type B blood.
   b. type A blood.
   c. type AB blood.
   d. type O blood.
 * e. types A and AB, but will clump with types B and O.

D 36. If you are blood type A,
 * a. you carry antibodies for type B blood.
   b. you carry markers for type B blood.
   c. you can donate blood to a person with type O blood.
   d. you can receive blood from a person with type AB blood.
   e. none of these

E 37. Which blood type is the universal donor?
   a. A+
   b. B
   c. AB+
   d. AB
 * e. O

E 38. Which blood type is the universal recipient?
   a. A
   b. B+
   c. AB+
 * d. AB
   e. O+

D 39. In Rh disease, the mother
   a. must be positive and her first and second children positive.
 * b. must be negative and her first and second children positive.
   c. must be negative and her first and second children negative.
   d. must be positive and her first and second children negative.
   e. and the father must both be negative and the child positive.

D 40. For erythroblastosis fetalis to occur,
   a. the mother must be positive and the father negative.
   b. the mother must be negative and the father negative.
 * c. the mother must be negative and the child positive.
   d. the mother must be negative and the father positive.
   e. the mother must be positive and the child negative.

HUMAN CARDIOVASCULAR SYSTEM

E 41. In its travel through the human body, blood usually continues on from capillaries to enter
   a. arterioles.
 * b. venules.
   c. arteries.
   d. veins.
   e. other capillaries.

D 42. Which of the following statements is true?
   a. Arteries carry only oxygenated blood.
 * b. The systemic circuit leaves the heart from the left ventricle.
   c. Blood passes through only one capillary bed on its trip through the systemic circuit.
   d. Platelets survive a longer time than erythrocytes.
   e. The heart is able to pick up the oxygen it needs as the blood flows through it.

M 43. Blood in arteries
 *   a. always travels away from the heart.
      b. travels away from the heart only if it is oxygen-rich.
      c. always travels toward the heart.
      d. travels from the lungs.
      e. is always oxygen-rich.

THE HEART IS A LONELY PUMPER

M 44. The receiving zone of a vertebrate heart is
      a. a plaque.
      b. the aorta.
 *   c. an atrium.
      d. a capillary bed.
      e. all of these

M 45. Atria differ from ventricles in that they
      a. are larger.
      b. have thicker walls with more muscles.
 *   c. receive blood from veins.
      d. have a higher blood pressure.
      e. empty through the semilunar valves.

E 46. The aorta leaves the
      a. left atrium.
      b. right atrium.
 *   c. left ventricle.
      d. right ventricle.

E 47. The pulmonary artery carries blood away from the
      a. aorta.
      b. right atrium.
 *   c. right ventricle.
      d. left atrium.
      e. left ventricle.

E 48. Blood from the body is first received by the heart in the
      a. coronary vein.
      b. left atrium.
      c. right ventricle.
 *   d. right atrium.
      e. left ventricle.

M 49. The human heart
 *   a. will contract as a result of stimuli from the sinoatrial node.
      b. contracts only as a result of nerve stimulation from the central nervous system.
      c. is activated primarily through the autonomic nervous system.
      d. pulse is primarily under the control of the atrioventricular node.
      e. is independent of all nervous control.

M 50. The pacemaker is which of the following nodes?
 *   a. sinoatrial
      b. semilunar
      c. atrioventricular
      d. inferior vena cava
      e. superior vena cava

M 51. Heart excitation originates in the
      a. atrioventricular node.
      b. intercalated disk.
 *   c. sinoatrial node.
      d. pericardium.
      e. all of these

E 52. Which of the following has the highest blood pressure?
      a. right ventricle
      b. right atrium
 *   c. left ventricle
      d. left atrium
      e. pulmonary circulation

M 53. What occurs during systole?
      a. Oxygen-rich blood is pumped to the lungs.
 *   b. The heart muscle tissues contract.
      c. The atrioventricular valves suddenly open.
      d. Oxygen-poor blood from all body regions except the lungs flows into the right atrium.
      e. all of these

D 54. If a physician hears two "lub" sounds instead of one, then which of the following conditions is true?
      a. The semilunar valves are not closing simultaneously.
      b. The atrial blood is flowing backward and causing the extra sound.
 *   c. The atrioventricular valves are not closing at the same time.
      d. The AV and semilunar valves are not closing at the same time.
      e. No such double sound has ever been heard.

M 55. The coronary vessels
 *   a. supply and drain the heart muscle.
      b. bypass the heart ventricles.
      c. send blood directly to the lungs.
      d. are not really necessary because the heart can get its blood supply from the "inside."
      e. lead directly from the atria to the ventricles.

D 56. An artificial pacemaker supplements the actions of
      a. sympathetic nerves.
      b. the atrioventricular node.
      c. the medulla oblongata.
 *   d. the sinoatrial node.
      e. the heart muscle itself.

M 57. Which of the following statements is false?
 *   a. A heart will stop beating when the nerves to the heart are severed.
      b. Some cardiac muscle cells are self-excitatory.
      c. The pacemaker of the heart is the sinoatrial node.
      d. Cardiac muscles join end to end to allow rapid communication.
      e. Cardiac muscles contract essentially in unison.

BLOOD PRESSURE IN THE CARDIOVASCULAR SYSTEM

E 58. Blood pressure is highest in the
* a. aorta.
  b. pulmonary artery.
  c. capillary bed.
  d. subclavian vein.
  e. inferior vena cava.

D 59. What portion of the brain is sensitive to changes in blood pressure and send messages to adjust heart beat and vessel diameters?
* a. medulla oblongata
  b. cerebrum
  c. thalamus
  d. hypothalamus
  e. cerebellum

E 60. The part of the brain responsible for blood pressure is the
* a. medulla oblongata.
  b. cerebellum.
  c. cerebrum.
  d. corpus callosum.
  e. pons.

M 61. The blood pressure and flow to the biceps in the arm may be decreased by
  a. the action of the medulla oblongata.
  b. changes in diameter of the arterioles.
  c. changes in pressure and blood flow.
  d. the action of certain hormones.
* e. all of these

D 62. Which of the following is NOT found in an arteriole?
  a. elastic layer
  b. basement membrane
  c. circular smooth muscle
* d. valve
  e. endothelium

M 63. The diastolic pressure for a normal young adult would be
  a. 60 mm Hg.
* b. 80 mm Hg.
  c. 100 mm Hg.
  d. 120 mm Hg.
  e. 140 mm Hg.

D 64. Which of the following statements is (are) true?
  a. The systolic pressure is determined when the first sound is heard after pumping up the pressure cuff.
  b. The diastolic pressure is the smaller of the two pressure values.
  c. The difference between the systolic and diastolic pressure is the pulse pressure.
  d. Diastole is at the end of the cardiac cycle.
* e. All of these are true.

M 65. The greatest drop in blood pressure occurs in the
  a. arteries.
* b. arterioles.
  c. capillaries.
  d. venules.
  e. veins.

D 66. A normal pulse pressure would be
  a. 20 mm Hg.
* b. 40 mm Hg.
  c. 60 mm Hg.
  d. 80 mm Hg.
  e. 100 mm Hg.

E 67. The hormone that affects blood pressure is
  a. insulin.
  b. thyroxin.
* c. angiotensin.
  d. somatotropin.
  e. glucagon.

D 68. Which of the following statements is false?
* a. Angiotensin is a hormone that triggers vasodilation.
  b. Parasympathetic nervous system stimulation decreases heart rate.
  c. Adjustments to blood flow can come from stimuli from the nervous and endocrine systems and from changes in local chemicals.
  d. Thrombin is an enzyme that acts on fibrinogen.
  e. Hemostasis stops bleeding.

FROM CAPILLARY BEDS BACK TO THE HEART

M 69. The interstitial fluid is
  a. a reservoir.
  b. the extracellular fluid.
  c. supplied by the blood.
  d. similar to sea water.
* e. all of these

M 70. Extracellular fluid contains all but which of the following?
* a. erythrocytes
  b. ions
  c. white blood cells
  d. lymph
  e. water

M 71. At the arteriole end of the capillary, more fluid leaves the capillary than enters as a result of
  a. osmotic pressure.
* b. hydrostatic force.
  c. gap junctions.
  d. vasodilation.
  e. all of these

M   72. Reabsorption
         a. is the movement of materials through capillaries.
         b. is the movement of components of the interstitial
             fluid into a capillary bed.
         c. occurs at the beginning of the capillary bed.
         d. occurs at the end of the capillary bed.
    *   e. is the movement of components of the interstitial
             fluid into a capillary bed and occurs at the end of
             the capillary bed.

E   73. By controlling their musculature, which of the
         following can vary the resistance to blood flow?
         a. arteries
         b. veins
         c. capillaries
    *   d. arterioles
         e. all of these

M   74. Because of their great elasticity, which of the
         following can function as blood volume reservoirs
         during times of low metabolic output?
    *   a. veins and venules
         b. arteries
         c. arterioles
         d. capillaries
         e. all of these

E   75. Which of the following controls the distribution of
         blood?
         a. arteries
    *   b. arterioles
         c. capillaries
         d. venules
         e. veins

E   76. Which of the following are pressure reservoirs with
         low resistance to flow?
    *   a. arteries
         b. arterioles
         c. capillaries
         d. venules
         e. veins

E   77. Which of the following are highly distensible
         reservoirs for blood volume?
         a. arteries
         b. arterioles
         c. capillaries
         d. venules
    *   e. veins

E   78. The greatest volume of blood is found in the
         a. aorta and arteries.
         b. capillaries.
    *   c. veins.
         d. lungs.
         e. heart.

FOCUS ON HEALTH: CARDIOVASCULAR DISORDERS

M   79. The most common vascular disease is
         a. phlebitis.
    *   b. hypertension.
         c. leukemia.
         d. sickle-cell anemia.
         e. a stroke.

D   80. Which of the following statements is false?
         a. Of the nine risk factors, four are beyond a person's
             individual control.
         b. Until age 50, males have a greater risk of a heart
             attack than females.
         c. Hypertension is called the silent killer.
         d. In atherosclerosis, the diameter of the lumen of a
             blood vessel decreases.
    *   e. If a blood clot becomes dislodged and travels in
             the bloodstream, it is called a thrombus.

M   81. In "arteriosclerosis,"
         a. there is a buildup of calcium salts in arterial walls.
         b. there is a buildup of fibrous tissue in arterial walls.
         c. the arteries lose their elasticity.
         d. blood pressure increases.
    *   e. all of these

E   82. A stroke is a rupture of a blood vessel in the
         a. leg.
    *   b. brain.
         c. heart.
         d. lung.
         e. internal organs.

M   83. In atherosclerosis,
         a. abnormal multiplication of smooth muscle cells in
             blood vessels occurs.
         b. the arterial walls fill with connective tissue.
         c. the lipids in the bloodstream become embedded in
             the walls of the endothelial lining.
         d. a fibrous net covers the entire abnormal area.
    *   e. all of these

M   84. The mineral associated with arteriosclerosis is
         a. iron.
         b. magnesium.
         c. cobalt.
    *   d. calcium.
         e. iodine.

M   85. Cholesterol is believed to be carried by
         a. albumin.
         b. high-density lipoproteins.
         c. low-density lipoproteins.
         d. triglycerides.
    *   e. both high-density and low-density lipoproteins.

HEMOSTASIS

M   **86.** Which of the following is NOT involved in the formation of a blood clot?
    *   a. plasma cells
       b. fibrinogen
       c. thrombin
       d. fibrin
       e. All of these are involved.

D   **87.** Hemostasis in vertebrates includes all but which of the following?
       a. blood clot formation
       b. vasoconstriction
    *   c. release of iron to aid in the clumping of platelets
       d. vascular spasms
       e. spiny platelets releasing substances that cause them to attract each other

M   **88.** Which of the following is the proper sequence in clotting?
       a. prothrombin, fibrinogen, fibrin, thrombin, clot
       b. prothrombin, fibrin, fibrinogen, thrombin, clot
    *   c. prothrombin, thrombin, fibrinogen, fibrin, clot
       d. thrombin, prothrombin, fibrin, fibrinogen, clot

M   **89.** Which of the following is an enzyme?
       a. fibrinogen
       b. fibrin
       c. prothrombin
    *   d. thrombin
       e. plasminogen

LYMPHATIC SYSTEM

M   **90.** Which of the following is transported in greater quantities in the lymphatic system than in the blood?
       a. red blood cells
       b. wastes
    *   c. fats
       d. amino acids
       e. white blood cells

M   **91.** Which of the following statements is NOT true of the lymph vascular system? The lymph vascular system
       a. transports lipids absorbed from the small intestine to the bloodstream.
       b. recovers and transports interstitial fluid back to the bloodstream.
    *   c. absorbs glucose from the small intestine and transports it to the brain.
       d. serves the body's system of defenses against bacteria and other infectious agents.
       e. performs all of these functions.

M   **92.** The lymphoid organs include all but the
       a. spleen.
    *   b. stomach.
       c. thymus.
       d. tonsils and adenoids.
       e. appendix.

Classification Questions

Answer questions 93–97 in reference to the five components of mammalian blood listed below:
       a. red blood cells
       b. basophils
       c. platelets
       d. serum albumin
       e. sodium and potassium chloride

E   **93.** This blood component plays a central role in clotting blood following a wound.

E   **94.** This blood component contains hemoglobin.

E   **95.** This blood component helps to maintain proper osmolarity.

E   **96.** This blood protein plays a role in maintaining the ionic balance of the body.

E   **97.** Oxygen is transported throughout the body by this blood component.

Answers   93. c   94. a   95. d

              96. e   97. a

Answer questions 98–102 in reference to the four structures of the heart listed below:
       a. right atrium
       b. left atrium
       c. left ventricle
       d. right ventricle

M   **98.** Blood from the superior and inferior venae cavae enters the heart via this structure.

M   **99.** Blood passes to the lungs from this structure.

M **100.** Deoxygenated blood exits the heart from this structure.

M **101.** Oxygenated blood enters the heart via this structure.

M **102.** Blood is pumped to the majority of the body by this structure.

Answers   98. a   99. d   100. d

              101. b   102. c

Selecting the Exception

D 103. Four of the five answers listed below designate organisms with open circulations. Select the exception.
    a. insects
    b. snails
    c. spiders
    d. clams
  * e. frogs

M 104. Four of the five answers listed below are related by a common property. Select the exception.
    a. neutrophil
  * b. erythrocyte
    c. lymphocytes
    d. monocyte
    e. basophil

M 105. Four of the five answers listed below are blood proteins. Select the exception.
  * a. epinephrine
    b. globulin
    c. hemoglobin
    d. fibrinogen
    e. albumin

D 106. Four of the five answers listed below are related by the "type" of blood they carry. Select the exception.
    a. pulmonary artery
  * b. aorta
    c. hepatic portal vein
    d. inferior vena cava
    e. jugular vein

M 107. Four of the five answers listed below are characteristics of most veins. Select the exception.
    a. blood volume reservoirs
    b. contain valves
    c. low resistance-transport tubes
  * d. transport oxygen
    e. low blood pressure

D 108. Four of the five answers listed below are related by a common feature. Select the exception.
    a. A
    b. B
    c. AB
  * d. Rh+
    e. O

D 109. Four of the five answers listed below are related by a common function. Select the exception.
  * a. heart
    b. spleen
    c. thymus
    d. tonsils
    e. lymph node

CHAPTER 39
IMMUNITY

Multiple-Choice Questions

D   1.   Successful inoculation against smallpox used
   a.   scabs from smallpox sores.
   b.   pus and exudates from open smallpox sores.
   c.   blood from a person who had become immune to smallpox.
 * d.   material from a cowpox sore.
   e.   all of these

M   2.   The first disease that was demonstrated to be caused by a specific microorganism was
 * a.   anthrax.
   b.   rabies.
   c.   cowpox.
   d.   smallpox.
   e.   influenza.

E   3.   The first disease for which a successful vaccination was developed was
   a.   the plague.
 * b.   smallpox.
   c.   rabies.
   d.   chicken pox.
   e.   diphtheria.

E   4.   The person who developed and demonstrated the first successful vaccine was
   a.   Pasteur.
   b.   Koch.
   c.   Lister.
 * d.   Jenner.
   e.   Erhlich.

E   5.   The word *vaccination* comes from the Latin word for
   a.   germ.
 * b.   cow.
   c.   chicken.
   d.   rabbit.
   e.   rat.

M   6.   All but which of the following can be called a pathogen?
   a.   virus
   b.   bacterium
   c.   fungus
 * d.   cancer
   e.   protozoan

THREE LINES OF DEFENSE

M   7.   The barrier to invasion by microbes involves
   a.   urine.
   b.   the symbiotic microorganisms already in the body.
   c.   ciliated mucous membranes.
   d.   lysozyme and other enzymes.
 * e.   all of these

E   8.   All but which of the following are good barriers to invasion by microbes?
   a.   mucous membranes
   b.   eye secretions
 * c.   broken skin
   d.   urine
   e.   gut bacteria

M   9.   Lysozyme
   a.   is secreted by endocrine glands in the skin.
 * b.   destroys the cell wall of invading bacteria.
   c.   is produced in the lymph nodes and actively disables bacteria.
   d.   has proved to be a very effective defense against viruses.
   e.   is active within the circulatory system.

D   10.   Normal bacterial inhabitants of the human body
   a.   are naturally resistant to antibiotics.
 * b.   are able to outcompete some invading pathogens and thus are one of the body's defense mechanisms.
   c.   can be transformed into pathogenic forms if a person's resistance to disease is low.
   d.   are unable to survive the human body's defense mechanisms.
   e.   none of these

COMPLEMENT PROTEINS

M   11.   Which system involves plasma proteins activated when they contact a bacterial cell?
   a.   infection
 * b.   complement
   c.   bodyguard
   d.   enhancer
   e.   defender

D   12.   Which of the following would NOT be the result of the action of the complement system?
   a.   lysis of a pathogen's membrane
 * b.   trapping of pathogens in tangled protein threads
   c.   marking of pathogens for destruction by macrophages
   d.   attraction of phagocytes to scene of pathogen invasion

M **13.** The complement system
    a. includes a group of about 20 plasma proteins.
    b. induces a cascade of proteins that counteract invasion by coating the invading cells.
    c. attracts phagocytic leukocytes to attack invading cells.
    d. causes the lysis of the plasma membranes of invading cells.
    * e. all of these

INFLAMMATION

M **14.** All but which of the following types of cells can be called "phagocytes"?
    a. monocytes
    * b. erythrocytes
    c. neutrophils
    d. eosinophils
    e. macrophages

M **15.** Phagocytes perform their services in
    a. the blood.
    b. tissue spaces.
    c. the lymph system.
    d. the blood and tissue spaces, only.
    * e. the blood, tissue spaces, and lymph system.

M **16.** Phagocytes are derived from stem cells in the
    a. spleen.
    b. thymus.
    * c. bone marrow.
    d. blood.
    e. liver.

M **17.** Histamine causes
    a. blood vessels to contract.
    b. capillaries to lose their permeability.
    * c. an outward flow of fluids from the capillaries.
    d. a destruction of mast cells.
    e. an opening of the area of infection through which the body's defense system can enter.

E **18.** The accumulation of fluid at the site of a wound is the result of the secretion of
    a. kinins.
    * b. histamines.
    c. neutrophils.
    d. interferons.
    e. leukocytes.

M **19.** Which event does NOT occur in the inflammatory response?
    a. Tissue swells because of outflow from capillary beds.
    * b. Blocking antibodies inactivate the resident mast cells.
    c. White blood cells are attracted to the area by chemotaxis.
    d. Complement proteins help identify invading material.
    e. The foreign invaders are engulfed and destroyed by phagocytosis.

M **20.** Inflammation
    * a. leads to the release of histamine, which causes capillaries to become "leaky."
    b. is increased by use of antihistamine drugs.
    c. does not occur during allergic reactions.
    d. is initiated by the buildup of dead cells and bacteria.
    e. is not affected by the action of the complement system.

D **21.** An antihistamine drug would have as its SPECIFIC action which of the following?
    * a. constriction of the capillaries
    b. decreased redness
    c. reduced warmth
    d. promotion of clotting
    e. attraction of phagocytes

D **22.** Interleukins
    a. are secreted by macrophages.
    b. trigger any B cell that has become sensitive to the specific antigen (the one inducing interleukin production) to divide.
    c. are the chemical triggers that cause tissue to release antihistamine.
    d. are effective only on pathogens that have invaded body cells.
    * e. are secreted by macrophages and trigger any B cell that has become sensitive to the specific antigen (the one inducing interleukin production) to divide.

OVERVIEW OF THE IMMUNE SYSTEM

M **23.** Terms that describe the immune response include all but which of the following?
    a. specific
    b. rapid
    c. memory
    * d. general
    e. effective

E **24.** Which cells are divided into two groups: T cells and B cells?
    a. macrophages
    * b. lymphocytes
    c. complement cells
    d. platelets
    e. all of these

M **25.** Which cells produce and secrete antibodies that set up bacterial invaders for subsequent destruction by macrophages?
    a. phagocytes
    b. macrophages
    * c. B cells
    d. T cells
    e. all of these

M 26. Which of the following are NOT generally targets of T cells?
   a. transplants of foreign tissue
   b. cancer
   c. infections caused by viruses
 * d. infections caused by bacteria
   e. all of these

M 27. Which cells produce antibodies?
   a. helper T
   b. natural killer cells
   c. cytotoxic T
   d. memory
 * e. B

M 28. Which cells cause rapid division of the lymphocytes?
 * a. helper T
   b. natural killer cells
   c. cytotoxic T
   d. memory
   e. B

D 29. Which of the following statements is false?
   a. Cytotoxic T cells kill cancer cells only if the cause is viral.
   b. MHC markers of grafted cells are identified as foreign in organ transplants unless the donor is a twin.
 * c. The function of helper T cells is to phagocytize invading organisms.
   d. Each pathogen has its own unique antigen.
   e. The clonal selection theory holds that an activated B cell or T cell divides rapidly to produce a clone of immunologically identical cells that are specific for the antigen that selected them.

M 30. Which cells are held in reserve to be used for a rapid response to subsequent intruders of the same type?
   a. helper T
   b. natural killer cells
   c. cytotoxic T
 * d. memory
   e. B

M 31. Which cells are the longest lasting in the body?
   a. helper T
   b. natural killer cells
   c. cytotoxic T
 * d. memory
   e. B

M 32. Which cells directly destroy body cells infected by viral or fungal parasites?
   a. helper T
   b. natural killer cells
 * c. cytotoxic T
   d. memory
   e. B

M 33. Mutant and cancerous cells are destroyed by which cells?
   a. helper T
   b. natural killer cells
 * c. cytotoxic T
   d. memory
   e. B

E 34. All of the cells involved in the immune response are
   a. leukocytes.
   b. erythrocytes.
   c. white blood cells.
 * d. leukocytes, also called white blood cells.
   e. erythrocytes, also called white blood cells.

M 35. Body cells have self-markers located
   a. in their nuclei.
   b. in the endoplasmic reticulum.
   c. in the mitochondria.
 * d. on the plasma membrane.
   e. inside the Golgi bodies.

M 36. Which of the following would be ignored in most instances by lymphocytes?
   a. cells coated with complement proteins
   b. cells with antigens on their surface
 * c. "self" cells with MHC markers
   d. cells with both antigen and self-MHC markers
   e. cells with damaged or mutant self-MHC markers

M 37. The markers for each cell in a body are referred to by the letters
 * a. MHC.
   b. HTC.
   c. ADS.
   d. RSW.
   e. AKA.

E 38. The markers that identify "self" are actually
   a. genes.
 * b. proteins.
   c. lipids.
   d. small surface bumps.
   e. three letters of the alphabet.

HOW LYMPHOCYTES FORM AND DO BATTLE

D 39. After a primary immune response,
   a. a clone of sensitive lymphocytes is ready for any subsequent invasion of the same antigen.
   b. some of the clone cells will remain alive for decades.
   c. clone cells may be modified to attack new invaders.
   d. clone cells are continually reproduced to confer immunity against subsequent invasion.
 * e. a clone of sensitive lymphocytes is ready for any subsequent invasion of the same antigen and some of the clone cells will remain alive for decades.

M   40.   Clones of B or T cells are
          a.   being produced continually.
          b.   interchangeable.
     *   c.   produced only when their surface proteins
               recognize specific protein.
          d.   known as memory cells.
          e.   produced and mature in the bone marrow.

D   41.   The infinite variety of antibodies that can be generated
          by B cells is due to
          a.   the infinite variety of genes in these cells.
     *   b.   the shuffling of genes to produce an infinite
               variety of proteins.
          c.   the recombination of genes due to crossing over.
          d.   the infinite variety of genes in these cells and the
               recombination of genes due to crossing over.
          e.   the infinite variety of genes in these cells, the
               recombination of genes due to crossing over, and
               the shuffling of genes to produce an infinite
               variety of proteins.

M   42.   The primary immune response
          a.   is shorter in duration than a secondary response.
          b.   is quicker than a secondary response.
          c.   depends on random construction of appropriate
               antibodies.
          d.   is the result of a reproduction of an appropriate
               lymphocyte resulting in a sensitive clone.
     *   e.   depends on random construction of appropriate
               antibodies and is the result of a reproduction of an
               appropriate lymphocyte resulting in a sensitive
               clone.

M   43.   Which of the following statements is false?
          a.   Only B cells and their progeny make antibodies.
     *   b.   The primary immune response is faster and more
               complete than a secondary immune response.
          c.   Virgin B cells already have antibodies but have
               not yet encountered an antigen.
          d.   Macrophages will digest invading bacterial cells
               but do not destroy the antigens that eventually
               become mounted on the surface of the
               macrophages.
          e.   Some B cell progeny differentiate into memory
               cells.

M   44.   Which of the following is NOT a lymphoid organ?
          a.   tonsils
          b.   nodules
     *   c.   thyroid
          d.   spleen
          e.   thymus

M   45.   Which of the following is mostly likely to happen in a
          lymph node?
          a.   oxygenation of the interstitial fluid
          b.   production of B and T lymphocytes
     *   c.   phagocytosis of organisms foreign to the body
          d.   attachment of MHC markers to self cells
          e.   red blood cells are destroyed and their contents
               recycled

ANTIBODY-MEDIATED RESPONSES

E   46.   Antibodies are shaped like the letter
          a.   C.
          b.   E.
          c.   H.
          d.   K.
     *   e.   Y.

E   47.   The antibody molecule consists of how many
          polypeptide chains, including light and heavy chains?
          a.   2
          b.   3
     *   c.   4
          d.   5
          e.   6

E   48.   Antibodies are
     *   a.   proteins.
          b.   steroids.
          c.   polysaccharides.
          d.   lipoproteins.
          e.   all of these

E   49.   Antibodies belong to a group of compounds known as
          a.   self-recognizing compounds.
     *   b.   immunoglobulins.
          c.   histosaccharides.
          d.   antisteroids.
          e.   virulent bases.

M   50.   The antigen binds to the _____ region of an
          antibody.
          a.   constant
          b.   curved
     *   c.   variable
          d.   Z
          e.   Q

D   51.   The base, heavy-chain portion of an antibody
          a.   can activate the complement system.
          b.   can be split into new sites that bind antigens.
          c.   may bind to receptors on phagocytic cells.
          d.   may break off and form the basis for immune
               memory.
     *   e.   can activate the complement system and may bind
               to receptors on phagocytic cells.

D   52.   Which of the following is false regarding an antigen?
          a.   It can lead to the generation of an antibody.
          b.   It identifies a pathogen as "foreign" to the body.
          c.   It can be an oligosaccharide.
     *   d.   It passes directly between the plasma membranes
               of the pathogen and macrophage.
          e.   It forms complexes with the MHC markers.

D   53. Which statement is NOT true?
    a. When an invading bacterium is destroyed by a macrophage, its antigens are preserved.
 * b. Antibodies attack and destroy invading antigens.
    c. Helper T cells recognize the major histocompatibility complex and antigens on the surface of macrophages.
    d. Self cells have major histocompatibility complex markers or antigens.
    e. Helper T cells secrete interleukins, which help the cells of the immune system communicate with each other.

M   54. Which immunoglobulin is able to pass the placenta to protect the fetus from pathogens?
 * a. IgG
    b. IgA
    c. IgD
    d. IgM
    e. IgE

M   55. Which immunoglobulin is the first to be secreted and initiates the complement cascade?
    a. IgG
 * b. IgA
    c. IgD
    d. IgM
    e. IgE

CELL-MEDIATED RESPONSES

D   56. Which of the following statements is false?
    a. Cytotoxic T cells kill body cells that have been invaded by pathogens.
 * b. The cell-mediated response is ineffective against a pathogen that has already entered the cytoplasm of a body cell.
    c. Cytotoxic T cells are produced by the bone marrow but mature in the thymus gland.
    d. Cytotoxic T cells are unable to destroy free-floating viruses they encounter in the bloodstream.
    e. Cytotoxic T cells secrete perforins that are able to punch holes in infected cells.

M   57. Effector cells
    a. are fully differentiated lymphocytes.
    b. manufacture and secrete antibodies.
    c. can develop from either T or B cells.
    d. secrete antibodies or interleukins depending on their origin.
 * e. all of these

M   58. Cell-mediated response
 * a. involves helper T cells.
    b. involves the action of antibodies to destroy invaders.
    c. acts only on extracellular clues.
    d. results in the production of clones of plasma cells.
    e. all of these

M   59. Most organ transplants fail because
    a. of poor vascular connection between host and donor tissue.
    b. the migrating leukocytes attack the tissue adjacent to the transplant.
 * c. cytotoxic T cells enter the transplant through the connecting blood vessels and kill the individual transplant tissue.
    d. introduced tissues produce antibodies that cause a massive reaction.
    e. all of these

M   60. The leading cause of death among transplant patients is
    a. loss of a vital organ when the transplant fails.
 * b. pneumonia.
    c. a transplant reaction similar to blood transfusion reactions.
    d. an excessive number of antigens released into the bloodstream.
    e. a blockage of the major histocompatibility complex in the plasma cells.

E   61. Organ transplants are safest between
    a. two brothers.
    b. father and daughter.
    c. fraternal twins.
 * d. identical twins.
    e. nonrelated individuals.

D   62. What is the cell that fights tumor cells even though they are not cancerous due to a virus?
    a. cytotoxic T cells
 * b. natural killer cells
    c. helper T cells
    d. macrophages
    e. MHC-guided cells

DEFENSES ENHANCED, MISDIRECTED, OR COMPROMISED

M   63. A vaccine contains
    a. killed pathogen.
    b. weakened pathogen.
    c. noninfective fragments of a pathogen.
    d. full-strength pathogen.
 * e. all except "full-strength pathogen" may be used

M   64. Passive immunity can be obtained by
    a. having the disease.
    b. receiving a vaccination against the disease.
    c. receiving antibodies by injection.
    d. receiving antibodies from mother at birth.
 * e. receiving antibodies by injection or receiving antibodies from mother at birth.

D 65. The purpose of a vaccine is to
    a. produce a mild case of the disease.
    b. stimulate the immune response.
    c. cause memory cells to be formed.
    d. stimulate the immune response and cause memory cells to be formed.
*   e. produce a mild case of the disease, stimulate the immune response, and cause memory cells to be formed.

M 66. Whenever the body is reexposed to a sensitizing agent, the IgE antibodies cause the
*   a. production of prostaglandins and histamine.
    b. release of antihistamines.
    c. suppression of the inflammatory response.
    d. production of clonal cells.
    e. all of these

M 67. Which of the following statements is false?
    a. Individuals are injected with antibodies in passive immunity.
    b. A genetically engineered virus is not as potentially dangerous as a weakened but intact pathogen.
    c. Allergies occur when the body makes a secondary immune response to a normally harmless substance.
*   d. Allergies are a nuisance but are never dangerous or life-threatening.
    e. Allergies cause the secretion of mucus, prostaglandins, and histamines.

M 68. A person sensitive to bee stings may die minutes after a sting due to
    a. a collapse of the immune system.
    b. a clogging of the capillaries.
*   c. a release of excessive fluids from the capillary beds.
    d. respiratory distress caused by excessive mucus.
    e. the extremely sharp rise in blood pressure.

M 69. When the body's defenses turn against its own cells, the disorder is called
*   a. an autoimmune response.
    b. anaphylactic shock.
    c. acquired immune deficiency syndrome.
    d. passive immunity.
    e. an inflammatory response.

FOCUS ON HEALTH: AIDS–THE IMMUNE SYSTEM COMPROMISED

E 70. The reason AIDS is so serious is that
    a. the excessive immune reaction leads to death.
    b. it is so highly contagious.
*   c. it is fatal.
    d. it is caused by a retrovirus.
    e. many natural reservoirs may spread the disease at any time.

E 71. Kaposi's sarcoma is characteristic of people who have
*   a. AIDS.
    b. allergic reactions.
    c. a hypersensitive immune system.
    d. ancestors who come from Cyprus.
    e. herpes.

M 72. Which of the following statements is false?
    a. The virus that causes AIDS is the human immunodeficiency virus.
    b. The AIDS virus is a retrovirus.
    c. The AIDS virus attacks macrophages and helper T cells.
    d. Even though the AIDS virus does not have its own DNA, it causes the host to produce DNA that will become part of host chromosomes.
*   e. Antibodies to the AIDS virus can be detected immediately after infection occurs.

E 73. Of the following, AIDS is usually transferred by
    a. casual contact.
    b. food.
    c. water.
*   d. sexual intercourse.
    e. insect bites.

E 74. The human immunodeficiency virus (HIV-1) primarily destroys which cells?
    a. B
    b. M
    c. T1
*   d. T4
    e. natural killer cells

M 75. Interferon is a chemical produced by
    a. helper T cells.
    b. plasma cells.
    c. B cells.
    d. macrophages.
*   e. cells that have been invaded by a virus.

M 76. Monoclonal antibodies are the fusion of
*   a. cancer cells and B cells.
    b. spleen cells and T cells.
    c. embryonic cells and plasma cells.
    d. thymus cells and helper T cells.
    e. marrow cells and B cells.

M 77. Monoclonal antibodies
    a. are formed by hybrid cells.
    b. are produced by cancer cells.
    c. are derived from spleen cells.
    d. produce identical antibodies and are all derived from the same parental cells.
*   e. all of these

E **78.** Which of the following statements is false?

    a. There is evidence that antibodies do not neutralize the HIV virus.

    b. HIV has the highest mutation rate of any known virus.

*   c. The HIV virus can be transferred by means of saliva, breast milk, tears, vaginal secretions, semen, blood, amniotic fluid, cerebrospinal fluid, and urine.

    d. It will be very difficult to form a vaccine against all the mutated forms of HIV.

    e. Currently, prevention of the spread of HIV depends upon implementing behavioral controls through education.

Matching Questions

D   **79.** Matching. Include the most appropriate letter in each blank at the left.

    1. ___ antigens

    2. ___ B lymphocytes

    3. ___ perforin

    4. ___ clone

    5. ___ complement proteins

    6. ___ cytotoxic T lymphocytes

    7. ___ interleukins

    8. ___ macrophages

    9. ___ memory cells

    10. ___ plasma cells

    11. ___ retroviruses

    12. ___ stem cells

    13. ___ natural killer cells

    14. ___ vaccine

A. cells that do not divide, die in less than a week, and secrete of antibodies

B. cells that directly destroy body cells already infected by viral or fungal parasites, as well as mutant and cancerous cells

C. lymphocytes that are held in reserve, circulate in the bloodstream, and enable a rapid response to subsequent encounters with the same invader

D. able to lyse cells by forming pore complexes

E. cells that are produced in the bone marrow and are never changed by the thymus; these cells produce antibodies

F. able to destroy cells but not dependent on recognition of antigen-MHC complexes

G. a class of proteins that help cells of the immune system communicate

H. "big eaters" that alert other lymphocytes to the invasion of specific antigens

I. immature cells that may or may not be committed to develop into one of several mature cell types

J. a group of cells that are all produced asexually from one original parent cell

K. surface patterns of nonself molecules or particles

L. proteins released by cytotoxic T cells to destroy target cell membranes

M. preparation injected into the body to elicit a primary immune response

N. one of this group has been identified as the causative agent of AIDS

Answers:

1. K	2. E	3. L	4. J
5. D	6. B	7. G	8. H
9. C	10. A	11. N	12. I
13. F	14. M		

Classification Questions

Answer questions 80–84 in reference to the five types of white cells listed below:

    a. macrophages
    b. helper T cells
    c. B cells
    d. cytotoxic T cells
    e. natural killer cells

D   **80.** These cells kill tumor cells but are not B or T lymphocytes.

M   **81.** These cells scavenge dead cells and attack bacteria directly.

D   **82.** These cells destroy cells infected by viruses.

D   **83.** These cells recognize cell surface antigens and initiate the proliferation of lymphocytes.

M   **84.** Antibody production occurs in these cells.

Answers   80. e   81. a   82. d

               83. b   84. c

Answer questions 85–89 in reference to the five items listed below:

    a. antigens
    b. antibodies
    c. helper T cells
    d. cytotoxic T cells
    e. memory B cells

E   **85.** These bind, as in a lock-and-key mechanism, to foreign proteins.

D   **86.** These produce immunoglobulins in response to the reinvasion by a virus.

D   **87.** These directly attack the foreign cells of an incompatible skin graft.

M   **88.** An Rh+ molecule in the body of an Rh woman is an example of these.

D   **89.** Bacteria and viruses in the blood are attacked by proteins produced by these.

Answers   85. b   86. e   87. d

               88. a   89. e

Selecting the Exception

M   **90.** Four of the five answers listed below are barriers to invasion. Select the exception.
    a. intact skin
    b. mucous membrane
    c. urine
  * d. blood plasma
    e. lysozyme

D   **91.** Four of the five answers listed below are characteristic reactions of the complement system to invaders. Select the exception.
    a. causes an amplifying cascade of reactions to invaders
  * b. triggers the secretion of histamines
    c. causes invading cells to lyse
    d. enhances the recognition of invaders by phagocytes
    e. creates gradients that attract phagocytes

D   **92.** Four of the five answers listed below are events of the inflammatory response. Select the exception.
    a. increase in capillary permeability
    b. release of histamine
    c. dilation of blood vessels
  * d. decrease in temperature of the affected areas
    e. migration of phagocytes toward the affected area

M   **93.** Four of the five answers listed below are targets of the immune system. Select the exception.
    a. viruses
  * b. normal cells
    c. cancer cells
    d. bacteria
    e. debris and dead cells

E   **94.** Four of the five answers listed below are treatments for cancer. Select the exception.
    a. surgery
  * b. vaccination
    c. radiation
    d. interferon
    e. monoclonal antibodies

CHAPTER 40
RESPIRATION

Multiple-Choice Questions

M 1. Which of the following statements is false?
    a. At high altitudes, one out of every five atoms is an oxygen atom.
    b. Oxygen deficit can produce altitude sickness.
    c. Edema is a common response to high altitude.
   * d. At high altitudes, the concentrations of hemoglobin and myoglobin decline.
    e. Mountain climbers stay at high-level camps to become acclimated to the high altitude before attempting the climb.

E 2. Which vertebrate body system is most closely associated functionally with respiration?
    a. urinary
    b. digestive
    c. endocrine
   * d. circulatory
    e. integumentary

THE NATURE OF RESPIRATION

E 3. The most abundant gas in the earth's atmosphere is
    a. oxygen.
    b. water vapor.
    c. argon.
   * d. nitrogen.
    e. carbon dioxide.

E 4. The concentration of nitrogen in the earth's atmosphere is approximately
   * a. 78 percent.
    b. 66 percent.
    c. 50 percent.
    d. 33 percent.
    e. 20 percent.

E 5. The concentration of carbon dioxide in the earth's atmosphere is
    a. 0.004 percent.
   * b. 0.04 percent.
    c. 0.4 percent.
    d. 4.0 percent.
    e. 40 percent.

D 6. The concentration of carbon dioxide in the atmosphere is 4 parts for each _____ molecules.
    a. 100
    b. 1,000
   * c. 10,000
    d. 100,000
    e. 1,000,000

E 7. The atmospheric pressure of air at sea level is
    a. 1,000 mm Hg.
   * b. 760 mm Hg.
    c. 540 mm Hg.
    d. 400 mm Hg.
    e. 320 mm Hg.

M 8. Exchange across a membrane requires
    a. moisture.
    b. transport proteins.
    c. pressure gradients.
   * d. moisture and pressure gradients, only.
    e. moisture, pressure gradients, and transport proteins.

M 9. According to Fick's Law, the degree of diffusion of gases is dependent on
    a. surface area available.
    b. differences in partial pressure.
    c. composition of the membrane.
   * d. surface area available and differences in partial pressure.
    e. surface area available, differences in partial pressure, and composition of the membrane.

M 10. The movement of both oxygen and carbon dioxide in the body is accomplished by
    a. exocytosis and endocytosis.
    b. bulk flow.
    c. osmosis.
   * d. diffusion.
    e. facilitated diffusion.

D 11. As an animal grows larger, the surface area increases by the _____ of its dimensions.
    a. cube
   * b. square
    c. square root
    d. doubling
    e. quotient

M 12. Which of the following is false?
    a. All respiratory surfaces must be kept moist.
    b. The amount of gas diffusing across a respiratory membrane is dependent upon the surface area and the partial pressure of each gas.
   * c. The surface area of an expanding balloon increases at the same rate as its volume.
    d. The movement of the flap over a fish's gill is known as ventilation.
    e. A hemoglobin molecule binds to four oxygen molecules.

M **13.** Ventilation could be defined as
   a. bailing water over the gills.
   b. movement of water past cells by using flagella.
   c. moving air in and out of lungs.
   d. tracheal exchanges.
   * e. all of these

D **14.** All but which of the following increase the amount of oxygen in a given volume of water?
   a. cold temperature
   * b. increased salt
   c. sunlight
   d. circulation
   e. All of these increase the oxygen content.

INVERTEBRATE RESPIRATION

M **15.** Which of the following do NOT use integumentary exchange in respiration?
   a. sea hares (gastropod)
   b. some amphibians
   c. earthworms
   d. flatworms
   * e. fish

E **16.** For the surface of an animal to function in the integumentary exchange of gases, it must
   a. be thin and soft.
   b. have a high number of blood vessels.
   c. have mucus or a moist covering.
   * d. all of these

M **17.** Adult insects exchange respiratory gases by
   a. spiracles.
   * b. tracheas.
   c. lungs.
   d. gills.
   e. body surface.

D **18.** Which of the following facts concerning insect tracheas is false?
   a. The fine tubules extend to individual muscle cells.
   b. The opening to the trachea can be closed.
   * c. Gases in the trachea are exchanged with the circulatory system.
   d. The tubes are reinforced by rings of chitin to prevent collapse.

M **19.** A spiracle is
   * a. an opening to a trachea of insects.
   b. one of the individual branches of a gill system.
   c. an opening to an alveolus.
   d. the opening to the swim bladder.
   e. the opening to the air sacs of birds.

VERTEBRATE RESPIRATION

D **20.** Countercurrent flow, in conjunction with respiratory systems, is a mechanism that explains how
   * a. oxygen uptake by blood capillaries in the lamellae of fish gills occurs.
   b. ventilation occurs.
   c. sounds originating in the vocal cords of the larynx are formed.
   d. intrapleural pressure is established.
   e. all of these

E **21.** External gills are characteristic of
   a. some invertebrates.
   b. larval amphibians.
   c. fish larvae.
   * d. all of these

M **22.** Swim bladders
   * a. keep a fish from sinking.
   b. are organs that prevent osmotic difficulties.
   c. are accessory excretory organs.
   d. are outgrowths of the digestive tract.
   e. are pockets found on the external surface of some fish.

D **23.** Which of the following statements is false?
   a. Aquatic animals work harder to obtain oxygen than terrestrial animals.
   * b. Aquatic environments hold only 0.5 percent of the oxygen found in the air.
   c. Aquatic environments are more dense and viscous than air.
   d. Cold water holds more oxygen than warm water.

E **24.** The group of animals with the most efficient respiratory system is the
   a. amphibians.
   * b. birds.
   c. mammals.
   d. reptiles.
   e. fish.

M **25.** Birds
   a. exchange gases through air sacs.
   b. exchange gases with their lungs as they breathe in or out.
   c. have exceptionally large and flexible lungs.
   d. have four air sacs for each lung that behave like bellows.
   * e. exchange gases with their lungs as they breathe in or out and have four air sacs for each lung that behave like bellows.

HUMAN RESPIRATORY SYSTEM

M **26.** What is the proper sequence in the flow of air in mammals?
   a. nasal cavities, larynx, pharynx, bronchi, trachea
   b. nasal cavities, pharynx, bronchi, larynx, trachea
   * c. nasal cavities, pharynx, larynx, trachea, bronchi
   d. nasal cavities, larynx, pharynx, trachea, bronchi
   e. nasal cavities, bronchi, larynx, trachea, pharynx

M 27. The last mammalian structure that air moves through before the alveoli is the
    a. larynx.
    b. glottis.
*   c. bronchioles.
    d. trachea.
    e. pharynx.

D 28. When humans breathe using only the mouth, which of the following is most diminished?
*   a. filtering
    b. warming
    c. moisturizing
    d. texturizing

M 29. Food and drink are prevented from entering the respiratory passageways during swallowing by means of the
    a. glottis.
    b. pharynx.
*   c. epiglottis.
    d. larynx.
    e. trachea.

M 30. When you swallow, the epiglottis covers the opening to the
    a. pharynx.
    b. esophagus.
*   c. larynx.
    d. bronchus.
    e. alveoli.

M 31. In pleurisy,
    a. some of the alveoli fill with fluid.
*   b. the pleural membrane becomes inflamed and swollen and causes painful breathing.
    c. the diaphragm develops muscular cramps.
    d. the vagus nerve is irritated.
    e. the intercostal muscles become inflamed and cause pain during deep breathing.

E 32. Actual exchange of gases in the lungs occurs in the
    a. bronchi.
*   b. alveoli.
    c. bronchioles.
    d. tracheas.
    e. glottis.

M 33. Which of the following is NOT found in lung tissue?
    a. blood capillaries
    b. alveolar sacs
    c. interstitial fluid
    d. connective tissue
*   e. muscle

E 34. The human vocal cords are located in the
    a. glottis.
    b. pharynx.
    c. trachea.
*   d. larynx.
    e. bronchus.

CYCLIC REVERSALS IN AIR PRESSURE GRADIENTS

M 35. During inhalation,
    a. the pressure in the thoracic cavity is greater than the pressure within the lungs.
*   b. the pressure in the thoracic cavity is less than the pressure within the lungs.
    c. the diaphragm moves upward and becomes more curved.
    d. the chest cavity volume decreases.
    e. all of these

E 36. The maximum amount of air that can be taken into the lungs in a single deep breath is the
*   a. vital capacity.
    b. tidal volume.
    c. pleural volume.
    d. alveolar volume.
    e. inspirational capacity.

GAS EXCHANGE AND TRANSPORT

M 37. Oxygen moves from alveoli to the bloodstream
*   a. because the concentration of oxygen is greater in alveoli than in the blood.
    b. mainly due to the activity of carbonic anhydrase in the red blood cells.
    c. by using the assistance of carbaminohemoglobin.
    d. through active transport.
    e. all of these

M 38. Hemoglobin
    a. tends to give up oxygen in regions where partial pressure of oxygen exceeds that in the lungs.
    b. tends to hold onto oxygen when the pH of the blood drops.
    c. tends to release oxygen where the temperature is lower.
*   d. releases oxygen more readily in highly active tissues.
    e. all of these

M 39. Which of the following statements is false?
    a. Carbon dioxide is more soluble in fluid than is oxygen.
    b. Carbon dioxide diffuses more rapidly across the respiratory surface than does oxygen.
    c. The major muscle involved in breathing is the diaphragm.
*   d. Oxygen is carried mainly by blood plasma.
    e. Carbon dioxide is carried by blood plasma.

M 40. Oxyhemoglobin gives up O_2 when
*   a. carbon dioxide concentrations are high.
    b. body temperature is lowered.
    c. pH values are high.
    d. CO_2 concentrations are low.
    e. all of these

D   41. Hemoglobin
        a. tends to release oxygen under warmer
            temperatures.
        b. picks up more oxygen the higher its partial
            pressure.
        c. picks up more oxygen when it is saturated.
        d. will give up oxygen when the partial pressure of
            oxygen is higher than it is in the lungs.
    *   e. tends to release oxygen under warmer
            temperatures and picks up more oxygen the higher
            its partial pressure.

D   42. Which of the following statements is false?
        a. Hemoglobin functions as a buffer.
        b. Bicarbonate ions tend to diffuse out of red blood
            cells into the blood plasma.
        c. The movement of molecules is in different
            directions in the metabolically active tissues and
            the alveoli.
    *   d. Carbonic anhydrase is an enzyme that promotes
            the formation of oxyhemoglobin.

M   43. Carbonic anhydrase
        a. combines with water to form carbonic acid.
        b. dissociates into bicarbonate and hydrogen ions.
    *   c. is normally found in red blood cells.
        d. is responsible for maintaining the high levels of
            carbon dioxide in the lungs and the low levels of
            carbon dioxide in the body tissues.
        e. all of these

M   44. Most of the carbon dioxide produced by the body is
        transported to the lungs in
        a. a gaseous form.
        b. blood plasma.
        c. carbaminohemoglobin.
    *   d. bicarbonate ions.
        e. carbonic acid.

M   45. The enzyme responsible for converting free carbon
        dioxide in the blood into forms in which it can be
        transported in the blood is
    *   a. carbonic anhydrase.
        b. carboxypeptidase.
        c. carbonase.
        d. decarboxylase.
        e. dehydrogenase.

M   46. The rate and depth of breathing are governed by
        a. chemoreceptors in arterial walls.
        b. baroreceptors in the diaphragm.
        c. the partial pressure of O_2 in the atmosphere.
        d. a respiratory center in the brainstem.
    *   e. all of these except "baroreceptors in the
            diaphragm."

M   47. Which of the following statements is true?
        a. Breathing rate and depth are completely under
            voluntary control.
        b. A person can commit suicide by holding his or her
            breath.
        c. The contraction of the diaphragm and muscles of
            the rib cage are under the control of the reticular
            formation.
        d. There are chemoreceptors in the medulla
            oblongata that monitor the blood pH and control
            breathing.
    *   e. The contraction of the diaphragm and muscles of
            the rib cage are under the control of the reticular
            formation; and There are chemoreceptors in the
            medulla oblongata that monitor the blood pH and
            control breathing.

M   48. Exhaling into a paper bag and rebreathing the exhaled
        air would be expected to
        a. alert the brain.
        b. increase the breathing rate.
        c. stimulate the carotid bodies.
        d. increase the breathing rate and stimulate the
            carotid bodies.
    *   e. increase the breathing rate, stimulate the carotid
            bodies, and alert the brain.

FOCUS ON HEALTH: WHEN THE LUNGS BREAK DOWN

E   49. Carbon monoxide
        a. has a very low affinity or attraction to
            hemoglobin.
        b. is unlikely to be transported by the circulatory
            system.
        c. is not the cause of death of people who breathe
            excessive amounts of automobile exhaust.
    *   d. can arise from cigarette smoke.
        e. is not the cause of death of people who breathe
            excessive amounts of automobile exhaust and can
            arise from cigarette smoke.

E   50. The cessation of smoking
        a. can reduce the risk of stillbirth.
        b. reduces the chances of cancer.
        c. reduces the chances of coronary heart disease.
        d. improves lung functioning.
    *   e. all of these

E   51. Smoking has been shown to cause
        a. bronchitis.
        b. emphysema.
        c. lung cancer.
        d. coronary heart disease.
    *   e. all of these

Matching Questions

M   **52.**   Hypoxia
  a.   causes hyperventilation.
  b.   may cause headaches, nausea, and lethargy.
  c.   can lead to loss of consciousness and death.
  d.   may be the result of changes in altitude.
  *   e.   all of these

M   **53.**   The oxygen-binding pigment found in the muscles of whales is
  a.   hemoglobin
  *   b.   myoglobin.
  c.   oxyhemoglobin.
  d.   carbaminohemoglobin.
  e.   carbonic anhydrase.

D   **54.**   Although carbon dioxide is normally carried by hemoglobin, the fact that carbon monoxide reduces hemoglobin's oxygen-carrying capacity would indicate that
  a.   different hemoglobins carry different gases.
  *   b.   carbon monoxide competes with oxygen for the same binding sites on hemoglobin.
  c.   binding of different gases is directed by a variety of enzymes.
  d.   carbon dioxide is an abnormal gas.

E   **55.**   Decompression sickness is caused by
  a.   a rapid rise of carbon dioxide in the blood.
  b.   lack of oxygen in the tissues.
  *   c.   bubbles of nitrogen in the blood.
  d.   glucose deficiency.
  e.   descending too rapidly into deep water.

D   **56.**   Matching. Choose the one most appropriate answer for each.
  1.   ___   alveoli
  2.   ___   bronchi
  3.   ___   diaphragm
  4.   ___   epiglottis
  5.   ___   rib muscles
  6.   ___   larynx
  7.   ___   medulla oblongata
  8.   ___   oxyhemoglobin
  9.   ___   pharynx
  10.   ___   pleural sac
  11.   ___   trachea
  12.   ___   ventilation

  A.   flexible windpipe reinforced with cartilage
  B.   surrounds each lung
  C.   oxygen-rich form of respiratory protein
  D.   contains two true vocal cords
  E.   alter chest cavity volume
  F.   part of the brainstem; controls breathing
  G.   throat cavity behind the mouth
  H.   inhalation and exhalation
  I.   connect trachea to lungs
  J.   flaplike structure that points upward and allows air to enter trachea; closed during swallowing
  K.   contraction moves it downward
  L.   microscopically small pockets lined with moist epithelium

Answers: 1. L   2. I   3. K   4. J
  5. E   6. D   7. F   8. C
  9. G   10. B   11. A   12. H

Classification Questions

Answer questions 57–61 in reference to the five components of respiratory systems listed below:

a. pharynx
b. larynx
c. trachea
d. bronchiole
e. alveolus

E **57.** The voice box is located here.

M **58.** This is the last component of the human lung that air flows into.

M **59.** Gas exchange between the air in the lungs and their blood supply occurs here.

E **60.** Air moves from the nasal cavity into this component.

M **61.** Spent air moves from the bronchial tubes back to this component.

Answers   57. b   58. e   59. e

              60. a   61. c

Selecting the Exception

E **62.** Four of the five answers listed below are parts of the same body system. Select the exception.
   a. trachea
 * b. swim bladder
   c. alveoli
   d. bronchiole
   e. glottis

M **63.** Four of the five answers listed below are components of the human respiratory system. Select the exception.
   a. thoracic cavity
   b. pleural sac
   c. diaphragm
 * d. spiracle
   e. larynx

D **64.** Four of the five answers listed below are related by the same function. Select the exception.
   a. blood plasma
   b. carbaminohemoglobin
 * c. oxyhemoglobin
   d. carbonic acid
   e. bicarbonate ions

D **65.** Four of the five answers listed below are related by a similar function. Select the exception.
 * a. intercostal muscles
   b. medulla oblongata
   c. aortic bodies
   d. reticular formation
   e. carotid bodies

CHAPTER 41
DIGESTION AND HUMAN NUTRITION

Multiple-Choice Questions

D   **1.**   The respiratory system interacts with the digestive system in the role of
  - a. supplying oxygen for metabolism of nutrients.
  - b. carrying away carbon dioxide.
  - c. providing nitrogen for protein synthesis.
  - *   d. supplying oxygen for metabolism of nutrients and carrying away carbon dioxide.
  - e. supplying oxygen for metabolism of nutrients, carrying away carbon dioxide, and providing nitrogen for protein synthesis.

THE NATURE OF DIGESTIVE SYSTEMS

M   **2.**   Which of the following possess an incomplete digestive system?
  - a. annelids
  - *   b. flatworms
  - c. mollusks
  - d. arthropods
  - e. echinoderms

E   **3.**   Ruminants need special enzymes to digest
  - a. starch.
  - b. proteins.
  - *   c. cellulose.
  - d. lignin.
  - e. catin.

M   **4.**   Which of the following statements about pronghorn antelopes is false?
  - a. They are ruminant animals.
  - b. Their eye sockets are positioned far back in their skulls.
  - *   c. They do not require as much food as predators.
  - d. They spend more of their time eating than predators.
  - e. Their cheek teeth (molars) have much larger crowns than human teeth.

D   **5.**   Which of the following statements about digestion is false?
  - a. Ruminant animals have symbiotic bacteria to aid in the digestion of their food.
  - b. It takes longer to digest plant material than meat.
  - c. Chewing results in mechanically breaking down food and exposing more cellulose to digestive enzymes.
  - d. Humans have a greater range of foods in their diet than most other species.
  - *   e. Pronghorn antelopes and other herbivores are characterized by a single but disproportionately large stomach.

E   **6.**   The muscular digestive organ in which food is ground into small bits is the
  - a. lumen.
  - *   b. gizzard.
  - c. crop.
  - d. stomach.
  - e. cloaca.

E   **7.**   Chewing
  - a. breaks food down into smaller pieces.
  - b. physically and mechanically breaks up the food.
  - c. increases the surface area of food exposed to digestive enzymes.
  - d. actually mixes some enzymes with the food.
  - *   e. all of these

M   **8.**   The process that moves nutrients into the blood or lymph is
  - *   a. absorption.
  - b. assimilation.
  - c. digestion.
  - d. ingestion.
  - e. all of these

M   **9.**   Animals without teeth, such as earthworms and birds, have an organ that accomplishes the same action as teeth. What is it?
  - a. beak
  - b. pharynx
  - *   c. gizzard
  - d. cloaca
  - e. dentine

D   **10.**   Which of the following groups of animals has a digestive system most unlike the others?
  - a. mollusks
  - b. arthropods
  - *   c. cnidarians
  - d. annelids
  - e. echinoderms

E   **11.**   Earthworms and birds have a crop that is modified for
  - a. digestion of cellulose.
  - *   b. food storage.
  - c. mechanical breakdown of food.
  - d. digestion of fats.
  - e. storage and elimination of undigested food.

M 12. Which of the following statements is false?
* a. The digestive system acts alone to meet the body's metabolic needs.
   b. Food does not really enter the body until it has been digested.
   c. Animals with only one opening to the digestive system are said to have an incomplete digestive system.
   d. Specialized regions of a complete digestive system can be correlated with feeding habits.
   e. Predators and scavengers exhibit discontinuous feeding habits.

VISUAL OVERVIEW OF HUMAN DIGESTIVE SYSTEM

D 13. Which of the following is NOT an active participant in the digestive process?
   a. small intestine
* b. esophagus
   c. pancreas
   d. mouth
   e. liver

M 14. Which of the following organs of the digestive system is different from the other four because it does NOT produce any secretions that aid in the digestive process?
   a. stomach
   b. liver
* c. esophagus
   d. pancreas
   e. salivary gland

INTO THE MOUTH, DOWN THE TUBE

E 15. Sphincters
   a. are circular muscles.
   b. prevent backflow.
   c. are smooth muscles.
   d. are found at the entrance and exit of the stomach.
* e. all of these

M 16. Sphincters are
   a. areas of the gastrointestinal tract where food is stored.
* b. rings of circular muscles that subdivide the gut.
   c. outpouchings of the gut that provide fluids for solubilizing food.
   d. specialized glands that secrete digestive juices.
   e. a double layer of muscles that envelop digestive organs such as the stomach or small intestine.

E 17. A bolus is formed in the
* a. mouth.
   b. esophagus.
   c. stomach.
   d. small intestine.
   e. large intestine.

E 18. The digestion of which class of foods begins in the mouth?
* a. carbohydrates
   b. proteins
   c. lipids
   d. amino acids
   e. nucleic acids

M 19. During the process of swallowing, the
   a. esophagus is temporarily closed by the glottis.
* b. epiglottis closes the trachea leading to the lungs.
   c. pharynx restricts food entry to the esophagus.
   d. epiglottis seals the esophagus.
   e. none of these

DIGESTION IN THE STOMACH AND SMALL INTESTINE

M 20. High stomach acidity
   a. creates ideal conditions for carbohydrate digestion.
   b. promotes emulsification of fats.
* c. favors protein digestion.
   d. blocks the release of histamine, thereby favoring production of peptic ulcers.
   e. converts lipases into their active forms.

M 21. Stomach motility
   a. decreases following a heavy meal.
* b. controls the amount of material leaving the pyloric sphincter.
   c. is unaffected by emotional state or external environmental factors.
   d. may be retarded when stretch receptors on the stomach wall are activated.
   e. is increased by hormones released in response to high stomach acidity.

E 22. Chyme is formed in the
   a. mouth.
   b. esophagus.
* c. stomach.
   d. small intestine.
   e. large intestine.

E 23. Which process propels the food down the esophagus into the stomach?
   a. glycolysis
   b. plasmolysis
   c. emulsion
* d. peristalsis
   e. all of these

M 24. Peristalsis
   a. is an adverse reaction to improper food.
* b. occurs in the digestive tract from the esophagus to the large intestine.
   c. occurs only in humans.
   d. is a defensive mechanism that reduces the bacterial invasion of the digestive tract.
   e. is an inflammation of the intestinal mucosa.

E 25. The digestion of proteins begins in the
*   a. stomach.
         b. pancreas.
         c. small intestine.
         d. large intestine.
         e. esophagus.

M 26. Which of the following is NOT a secretion of the
         stomach?
         a. pepsinogen
         b. mucus
         c. gastrin
         d. hydrochloric acid
*   e. lipase

D 27. Which of the following components of a hamburger
         would leave the stomach chemically undigested?
         a. protein
         b. starch
         c. sugar (in the catsup)
         d. lipid
*   e. both sugar (in the catsup) and lipid

M 28. Which of the following does NOT digest proteins?
         a. trypsin
         b. chymotrypsin
         c. aminopeptidase
         d. pepsin
*   e. lipase

E 29. Fats are digested by which of the following?
         a. aminopeptidase
         b. disaccharidases
         c. amylase
*   d. lipase
         e. trypsin

D 30. All but which of the following are in some way
         involved with protein digestion?
         a. chymotrypsin
*   b. amylase
         c. aminopeptidase
         d. pepsin
         e. trypsin

E 31. The acid released in the stomach is
         a. carbonic acid.
*   b. hydrochloric acid.
         c. nitric acid.
         d. sulfuric acid.
         e. phosphoric acid.

D 32. Which of the following is NOT an active form of an
         enzyme?
         a. trypsin
         b. amylase
         c. pepsin
*   d. pepsinogen
         e. chymotrypsin

M 33. Which of the following speeds up the passage of food
         through the pyloric sphincter?
*   a. the larger number of mechanoreceptors in the
             stomach wall that are activated
         b. the presence of acid in the duodenum
         c. hormones such as cholecystokinin
         d. emotional conditions (depression or fear)
         e. the presence of fat in the duodenum

E 34. The first part of the small intestine is the
*   a. duodenum.
         b. ileum.
         c. colon.
         d. cecum.
         e. jejunum.

M 35. Ducts from the pancreas and liver enter the
         a. stomach.
         b. colon.
*   c. duodenum.
         d. jejunum.
         e. ileum.

M 36. Which of the following is NOT found in bile?
         a. salts
         b. cholesterol
         c. pigments
*   d. digestive enzymes
         e. lecithin

M 37. Bile
         a. has no effect on digestion.
*   b. helps in the digestion of fats.
         c. helps in the digestion of carbohydrates.
         d. helps in the digestion of proteins.
         e. helps in the digestion of both carbohydrates and
             proteins.

E 38. Bile
         a. is produced by the liver and is stored in the
             gallbladder.
         b. contains cholesterol and lipids.
         c. has no digestive enzymes.
         d. emulsifies fats to increase the surface contact
             between fat and lipases.
*   e. all of these

M 39. Which of the following factors does NOT stimulate the
         stomach to pass on its contents to the small intestine?
*   a. depression and fear
         b. stimulation of mechanoreceptors in the stomach
             wall following a large meal
         c. reduced fat or acid content of chyme in the
             duodenum
         d. elation and relaxation
         e. all of these

E 40. Protein digestion begins in the
         a. esophagus.
*   b. stomach.
         c. mouth.
         d. small intestine.
         e. large intestine.

M **41.** Concerning the role of the pancreas in digestion,
* a. no digestion occurs in the pancreas.
  b. endocrine cells secrete bicarbonate, which helps neutralize highly acidic chyme.
  c. endocrine cells release enzymes that break down carbohydrates, fats, proteins, and nucleic acids in the small intestine.
  d. exocrine tissue produces insulin and glucagon that help regulate the metabolism of sugar.
  e. all of these

D **42.** Digestion of the stomach wall by gastric juice is usually prevented by
  a. secretion of protein-digesting enzymes in inactive form.
  b. a covering of mucus.
  c. histamine.
* d. secretion of protein-digesting enzymes in inactive form and a covering of mucus.
  e. secretion of protein-digesting enzymes in inactive form, a covering of mucus, and histamine.

D **43.** A deficiency in the supply of pancreatic juice to the small intestine could have what result?
  a. lack of insulin
* b. duodenal ulcers
  c. accumulation of large globs of fat
  d. lack of insulin and accumulation of large globs of fat
  e. lack of insulin, accumulation of large globs of fat, and duodenal ulcers

D **44.** Which of the following is NOT a hormone?
  a. gastrin
  b. secretin
* c. mucin
  d. cholecystokinin
  e. All of these are hormones.

M **45.** Which of the following is NOT secreted by the intestinal mucosa?
  a. secretin
  b. cholecystokinin
* c. gastrin
  d. GIP
  e. All are secreted by the intestine.

D **46.** Which of the following chemicals is the first hormone secreted by the intestinal tract in response to the presence of food?
  a. salivary amylase
  b. cholecystokinin
  c. glucose insulinotropic peptide (GIP)
* d. gastrin
  e. secretin

M **47.** Which of the following secretes a hormone that causes its own secretory cells to respond?
  a. small intestine
  b. pancreas
  c. large intestine
* d. stomach
  e. liver

M **48.** Which of the following acts enzymatically rather than hormonally?
  a. cholecystokinin
* b. pepsin
  c. secretin
  d. gastrin
  e. all of these

M **49.** Which of the following stimulates the gallbladder to contract?
  a. salivary amylase
* b. cholecystokinin
  c. glucose insulinotropic peptide (GIP)
  d. gastrin
  e. secretin

ABSORPTION FROM THE SMALL INTESTINE

M **50.** Which of the following layers lies next to the lumen of the intestinal tract?
  a. longitudinal muscles
  b. circular muscle layer
  c. submucosa
* d. mucosa
  e. serosa

E **51.** Which of the following layers forms the outer covering of the gastrointestinal tract?
* a. serosa
  b. mucosa
  c. conjunctiva
  d. muscle layer
  e. submucosa

M **52.** In doing a biopsy on the digestive tract, the second layer of cells encountered would be the
  a. mucosa.
* b. submucosa.
  c. lumen.
  d. muscle layer.
  e. serosa.

D **53.** The function of segmentation is to
  a. move the food through the digestive tract.
  b. churn the food and mix the contents with the digestive tract.
  c. bring the contents to the wall of the tract, where they could be absorbed.
  d. produce a wavelike push of the gut contents through the system.
* e. churn the food and mix the contents with the digestive tract, plus bring the contents to the wall of the tract, where they could be absorbed.

E **54.** The digestion of fats mostly occurs in the
  a. stomach.
  b. pancreas.
* c. small intestine.
  d. lymph vascular system.
  e. liver.

E 55. Of the following, the greatest amount of nutrient absorption takes place in the
   a. stomach.
 * b. small intestine.
   c. colon.
   d. pancreas.
   e. esophagus.

M 56. Which of the following are absorbed by the lymphatic system?
   a. monosaccharides
   b. amino acids
   c. monoglycerides
   d. fatty acids
 * e. both monoglycerides and fatty acids

M 57. Movement of glucose through the membranes of the small intestine is primarily by
   a. osmosis.
   b. bulk flow.
 * c. active transport.
   d. diffusion.
   e. all of these

D 58. Which of the following are tiny projections of the mucosal wall?
   a. microvilli
   b. mucins
 * c. villi
   d. submucosa
   e. jejunum

DISPOSITION OF ABSORBED ORGANIC COMPOUNDS

E 59. The organ that stores and detoxifies different organic compounds is the
   a. pancreas.
   b. small intestine.
 * c. liver.
   d. spleen.
   e. gallbladder.

M 60. The liver is associated with all but which of the following functions?
   a. formation of urea
   b. formation of bile
   c. detoxification of poisons
 * d. secretion of bicarbonate ions
   e. lipid metabolism

M 61. The liver is associated with all but which of the following functions?
   a. inactivation of drugs
   b. assembly and storage of fats
   c. assembly and disassembly of certain proteins
   d. degradation of worn-out blood cells
 * e. formation of glucagon

M 62. The liver is associated with all but which of the following functions?
   a. conversion of glucose into glycogen
   b. conversion of glycogen into glucose
 * c. production of fat-digesting enzymes
   d. transmission of amino acids through the Krebs cycle
   e. conversion of ammonia into urea

M 63. Which organ takes glucose out of the blood and stores it as glycogen?
   a. pancreas
   b. spleen
 * c. liver
   d. skin
   e. kidney

THE LARGE INTESTINE

E 64. The primary function of the large intestine is
   a. storage of feces.
   b. retention of water.
   c. manufacture of vitamin K.
   d. digestion of fats.
 * e. absorption of water.

D 65. What structure is located at the junction of the small and large intestines?
 * a. cecum
   b. rectum
   c. anus
   d. villus
   e. pharynx

M 66. Bulk in the diet
   a. increases the length of time material is in the colon.
   b. increases the chance of cancer.
 * c. prevents diarrhea and irritable colon syndrome.
   d. may increase the incidence of appendicitis in the people who eat too much bulk.
   e. is characteristic of people in urban areas.

HUMAN NUTRITIONAL REQUIREMENTS

M 67. The surgeon general recommends reducing all but which of the following components of our diet?
   a. saturated fat
   b. cholesterol
 * c. complex carbohydrates
   d. salt
   e. sugar

M 68. The ideal diet consists of all but which of the following?
   a. bulk
 * b. few complex carbohydrates
   c. little salt and sugar
   d. little red meat
   e. fish, poultry, and legumes

M   69.   Which of the following should be present in the human
         diet in the highest percentage?
         a. protein
    *   b. carbohydrate
         c. lipid
         d. vitamins
         e. minerals

M   70.   Lipids can serve in all but which of the following
         capacities?
    *   a. enzymes
         b. energy
         c. membrane structure
         d. insulation
         e. It can serve in all of these capacities.

E   71.   Of the 20 amino acids, how many are considered to be
         essential in that the human body cannot synthesize
         them?
         a. 2
         b. 5
    *   c. 8
         d. 10
         e. 12

M   72.   Which of the following represents the best source of
         protein (net protein utilization)?
         a. milk
    *   b. eggs
         c. fish
         d. soybeans
         e. cheese

D   73.   People who do not eat meat (vegetarians) must choose
         their food carefully to get the necessary
         a. vitamins.
         b. minerals.
         c. carbohydrates.
    *   d. amino acids.
         e. fatty acids.

VITAMINS AND MINERALS

M   74.   Which of the following vitamins is fat-soluble and can
         be stored in the body?
    *   a. A
         b. B_1 (thiamine)
         c. C (ascorbic acid)
         d. B_2 (riboflavin)
         e. niacin

M   75.   A deficiency of which vitamin produces rickets in
         children and osteomalcia in adults?
         a. A
         b. B
         c. C
    *   d. D
         e. E

M   76.   Which vitamin functions in forming a blood clot?
         a. A
         b. E
    *   c. K
         d. B
         e. all of these

M   77.   A deficiency of vitamin C may give rise to
         a. beriberi.
    *   b. scurvy.
         c. pellagra.
         d. hypothyroidism.
         e. all of these

M   78.   Beriberi is a deficiency disease related to which of the
         following vitamins?
         a. A
    *   b. B_1 (thiamine)
         c. C (ascorbic acid)
         d. B_2 (riboflavin)
         e. niacin

M   79.   Pellagra is a deficiency disease related to which of the
         following vitamins?
         a. A
         b. B_1 (thiamine)
         c. C (ascorbic acid)
         d. B_2 (riboflavin)
    *   e. niacin

M   80.   Scurvy is a deficiency disease related to which of the
         following vitamins?
         a. A
         b. B_1 (thiamine)
    *   c. C (ascorbic acid)
         d. B_2 (riboflavin)
         e. niacin

M   81.   Which of the following statements is NOT true
         concerning mineral metabolism?
         a. Sodium and potassium are needed for maintaining
             osmotic balances.
    *   b. Zinc is important in building strong bones and
             teeth.
         c. Sodium and potassium are needed for muscle and
             nerve functioning.
         d. Iron is needed for building cytochromes and heme
             groups.
         e. All of these statements are true.

M   82.   Lack of which element can lead to goiter?
         a. iron
    *   b. iodine
         c. calcium
         d. zinc
         e. magnesium

M   83.   The element needed for blood clotting, nerve
         transmission, and bone and tooth formation is
         a. iron.
         b. iodine.
    *   c. calcium.
         d. zinc.
         e. magnesium.

E   84.   The constituent of hemoglobin whose absence leads to anemia is
*   a.   iron.
    b.   iodine.
    c.   calcium.
    d.   zinc.
    e.   magnesium.

FOCUS ON SCIENCE: WEIGHTY QUESTIONS, TANTALIZING ANSWERS

E   85.   Body weight is controlled by
    a.   caloric intake.
    b.   energy utilization.
    c.   activity of the thyroid gland.
    d.   age and sex.
*   e.   all of these

E   86.   Obesity is defined as what percent over the ideal weight?
    a.   10
    b.   15
    c.   20
*   d.   25
    e.   30

E   87.   Obese people have a greater risk of
    a.   diabetes.
    b.   atherosclerosis.
    c.   high blood pressure.
    d.   death at all ages.
*   e.   all of these

E   88.   If caloric intake is balanced with energy output, body
    a.   weight gain will occur.
    b.   weight loss will occur.
*   c.   weight will remain stable.
    d.   fat content will increase.
    e.   protein will decrease.

M   89.   The binge and purge abnormality is
    a.   anorexia.
    b.   characteristic of some women.
    c.   a psychiatric disorder.
    d.   bulimia.
*   e.   all of these except "anorexia."

Matching Questions

D   90.   Matching I. Choose the one most appropriate answer for each.

1. ___ bile salts
2. ___ bolus
3. ___ cholecystokinin
4. ___ chyme
5. ___ GIP
6. ___ mucosa
7. ___ ruminants
8. ___ secretin
9. ___ segmentation
10. ___ serosa

A.   a process that mixes the contents of the lumen and forces it against the absorptive surface of the gut

B.   stimulates pancreatic bicarbonate secretion

C.   thin, outermost layer of gastrointestinal tract

D.   a softened ball of food particles

E.   emulsify fat globules and hydrate lipid particles

F.   have multiple stomachlike chambers, some of which store populations of microorganisms

G.   innermost layer of the gut; contains diverse secretory cells

H.   glucose insulinotropic peptide

I.   stimulates gallbladder and stomach emptying as well as pancreatic enzyme secretions

J.   a mixture of food particles with the texture of a puree

Answers: 1. E   2. D   3. I   4. J

         5. H   6. G   7. F   8. B

         9. A   10. C

D   **91.**   Matching II. Choose the one most appropriate answer for each.

     1. _____ amylase

     2. _____ bile

     3. _____ disaccharidase

     4. _____ gastrin

     5. _____ lipase

     6. _____ monosaccharides

     7. _____ pepsin

     8. _____ amino- and carboxypeptidase

     9. _____ sphincter

     10. _____ trypsin

     A. made in the small intestine and pancreas; act on peptide fragments

     B. glucose, fructose, and galactose

     C. made in the pancreas; acts on fats

     D. made by the pancreas and salivary glands; acts on starch

     E. made by the small intestine; acts on double sugars

     F. made by the pancreas; acts on proteins and polypeptides

     G. contains cholesterol; helps emulsify fats

     H. made in the stomach; acts on proteins

     I. stimulates hydrochloric acid secretion

     J. separates the stomach from the small intestine

Answers: 1. D   2. G   3. E   4. I

           5. C   6. B   7. H   8. A

           9. J   10. F

Classification Questions

Answer questions 92-96 in reference to the five components of the gastrointestinal tract listed below:

     a. stomach
     b. gallbladder
     c. small intestine
     d. appendix
     e. large intestine

D   **92.**   Many organisms, such as birds, have ceca in which bacteria break down difficult-to-digest plant materials. These ceca are homologous to this in humans.

M   **93.**   This organ absorbs about 95 percent of the water that enters the human body, either as fluids or as part of food being eaten.

M   **94.**   Enzymatic digestion of proteins occurs primarily in this organ.

E   **95.**   Bile salts, bile pigments, cholesterol, and lecithin are stored by this organ.

E   **96.**   The digestion of cellulose occurs in this part of the digestive system of the cow.

Answers   92. d   93. e   94. c

              95. b   96. a

Answer questions 97-101 in reference to the four glands or structures of the mammalian gastrointestinal tract listed below:

     a. salivary glands
     b. stomach mucosa
     c. intestinal mucosa
     d. pancreas

M   **97.**   The enzyme pepsin is produced there.

M   **98.**   The enzyme carboxypeptidase is produced there.

D   **99.**   The fat-digesting enzyme, lipase, is formed there.

D   **100.**   The peptide-digesting enzyme, aminopeptidase, is produced there.

M   **101.**   The protein-digesting enzyme, trypsin, is produced there.

Answers: 97. b   98. d   99. d

              100. c   101. d

Answer questions 102–106 in reference to the five vitamins listed below:

    a. Vitamin B_1
    b. Vitamin B_2
    c. Niacin
    d. Vitamin B_6
    e. Vitamin B_{12}

D **102.** This vitamin is a coenzyme involved in amino acid metabolism and is obtained from whole grains.

D **103.** This vitamin is a component of the coenzyme thiamine pyrophosphate.

M **104.** This vitamin is a constituent of the coenzymes NAD^+ and $NADP^+$.

M **105.** A deficiency of this vitamin causes pellagra.

D **106.** A deficiency of this vitamin causes pernicious anemia and neurological disorders.

Answers: 102. d   103. a   104. c

              105. c   106. e

Selecting the Exception

E **107.** Four of the five answers listed below are structures through which ingested foodstuffs travel. Select the exception.
    a. crop
*   b. liver
    c. gizzard
    d. large intestine
    e. small intestine

E **108.** Four of the five answers listed below possess a complete digestive system. Select the exception.
    a. human
    b. bird
    c. earthworm
*   d. planaria
    e. fish

M **109.** Four of the five answers listed below are ruminants. Select the exception.
    a. deer
    b. cattle
    c. antelopes
    d. goats
*   e. bears

M **110.** Four of the five answers listed below are layers of the digestive tract. Select the exception.
*   a. peritoneum
    b. mucosa
    c. serosa
    d. submucosa
    e. muscle layer

M **111.** Four of the five answers listed below are functions of the digestive organs. Select the exception.
*   a. excretion
    b. absorption
    c. motility
    d. secretion
    e. digestion

M **112.** Four of the five answers listed below produce secretions that assist digestion. Select the exception.
    a. salivary gland
*   b. esophagus
    c. pancreas
    d. gallbladder
    e. liver

D **113.** Four of the five answers listed below are hormones associated with digestion. Select the exception.
*   a. bile
    b. gastrin
    c. secretin
    d. cholecystokinin
    e. glucose insulinotropic peptide

M **114.** Four of the five answers listed below increase HCl secretion. Select the exception.
    a. cola drinks
    b. coffee
*   c. beer
    d. chocolate
    e. tea

D **115.** Four of the five answers listed below are end products of digestion ready for intestinal absorption. Select the exception.
    a. monoglyceride
    b. nucleotides
*   c. disaccharides
    d. amino acids
    e. free fatty acids

D **116.** Four of the five answers listed below digest the same class of foods. Select the exception.
    a. aminopeptidase
    b. pepsin
*   c. amylase
    d. trypsin
    e. chymotrypsin

D **117.** Four of the five answers listed below perform their task in the same workplace. Select the exception.
*   a. pepsin
    b. lipase
    c. carboxypeptidase
    d. nuclease
    e. disaccharidase

E **118.** Four of the five answers listed below are conditions related to diet. Select the exception.
    a. colon cancer
    b. kidney stones
    c. cardiovascular disorders
    d. obesity
*   e. Alzheimer's disease

M 119. Four of the five answers listed below are all of the same class of vitamins. Select the exception.
   a. Vitamin A
   b. Vitamin K
   * c. Vitamin C
   d. Vitamin D
   e. Vitamin E

D 120. Four of the five answers listed below are conditions caused by vitamin deficiency. Select the exception.
   a. scurvy
   b. pellagra
   c. rickets
   d. beriberi
   * e. goiter

D 121. Four of the five answers listed below are functions performed by the same organ. Select the exception.
   * a. pH regulation of body fluids
   b. removal of toxic substances from the blood
   c. storage and interconversion of carbohydrates, fats, and proteins
   d. inactivation of hormones
   e. formation of urea from nitrogenous waste

M 122. Four of the five answers listed below are members of the B complex vitamins. Select the exception.
   * a. ascorbic acid
   b. folic acid
   c. pantothenic acid
   d. riboflavin
   e. thiamine

CHAPTER 42
THE INTERNAL ENVIRONMENT

Multiple-Choice Questions

M 1. The kangaroo rat is adapted to living in the dry environment of the southwestern United States because of
   a. behavioral modifications resulting in nocturnal activity patterns and staying in burrows during the heat of the day.
   b. a more efficient kidney capable of conserving water.
   c. the ability to utilize water produced in the metabolism of carbohydrates.
   d. the lack of sweat glands.
 * e. all of these

E 2. Animals began invading land how many million years ago?
   a. 800
   b. 600
 * c. 375
   d. 250
   e. 150

D 3. A by-product of electron transport phosphorylation that is of vital importance to the kangaroo rat is
   a. glucose.
 * b. metabolic water.
   c. phosphate ions.
   d. NADH.
   e. ADP.

E 4. Extracellular fluid includes
   a. interstitial fluid.
   b. blood.
   c. lymph.
   d. blood and lymph, only.
 * e. interstitial fluid, blood, and lymph.

URINARY SYSTEM OF MAMMALS

M 5. All but which of the following are significant routes for water loss from the body?
   a. excretion in urine
 * b. sneezing
   c. sweating
   d. elimination in feces
   e. evaporation from respiratory surfaces

E 6. The process that normally exerts the greatest control over the water balance of an individual is
   a. sweating.
   b. elimination in feces.
 * c. kidney function.
   d. evaporation through the skin.
   e. respiratory loss.

D 7. Which of the following does NOT dispose of a type of waste directly to the environment?
   a. digestive system
   b. respiratory system
   c. integumentary system
 * d. circulatory system
   e. urinary system

D 8. Humans gain the least amounts of water by what route?
 * a. metabolism
   b. ingestion of liquids
   c. ingestion of solids
   d. All of these contribute equal amounts of water.

E 9. The most abundant waste product of metabolism is
 * a. carbon dioxide.
   b. ammonia.
   c. urea.
   d. uric acid.
   e. water.

D 10. Which of the following solutes would NOT leave the vertebrate body under normal conditions?
   a. nutrients
   b. ammonia
   c. urea
   d. carbon dioxide
 * e. hormones

D 11. The most toxic substances routinely found in the blood are metabolites of
   a. carbohydrates.
 * b. proteins.
   c. lipids.
   d. minerals.
   e. vitamins.

E 12. The tube leading from each kidney to the bladder is the
   a. glomerulus.
 * b. ureter.
   c. urethra.
   d. bladder.
   e. rectum.

E 13. Which of the following is the last structure that urine passes through?
   a. distal tubule
 * b. urethra
   c. urinary bladder
   d. ureter
   e. loop of Henle

E 14. About what percent of the fluid removed from the blood is eventually returned to the blood?
   a. 59
   b. 90
   * c. 98
   d. 0.9
   e. 9

M 15. Which of the following processes is under voluntary control?
   a. filtration
   b. reabsorption
   * c. urination
   d. secretion
   e. excretion

E 16. The subunit of a kidney that purifies blood and restores solute and water balance is called a
   a. glomerulus.
   b. loop of Henle.
   * c. nephron.
   d. ureter.
   e. all of these

E 17. The functional unit of the kidney is the
   a. Bowman's capsule.
   * b. nephron.
   c. glomerulus.
   d. urinary bladder.

M 18. In the kidney, the collecting duct leads immediately into the
   a. renal cortex.
   b. renal medulla.
   * c. renal pelvis.
   d. ureter.
   e. urethra.

M 19. Filtration occurs in which section of mammalian nephrons?
   * a. glomerulus
   b. loop of Henle
   c. proximal tubules
   d. distal tubules
   e. peritubular capillaries

E 20. Filtrate that is removed from the blood is collected by the
   a. loop of Henle.
   b. glomerulus.
   c. distal tubule.
   d. proximal tubule.
   * e. Bowman's capsule.

D 21. After the blood leaves the glomerular capillaries, it next goes to the
   a. renal vein.
   b. renal artery.
   * c. peritubular capillaries.
   d. vena cava.
   e. heart.

URINE FORMATION

E 22. The movement of excess H^+ and K^+ ions from peritubular capillaries to the nephron tubules is called
   a. reabsorption.
   * b. secretion.
   c. excretion.
   d. filtration.
   e. osmosis.

M 23. What is the name given to the fluid removed from the blood but not yet processed by the nephron tubules?
   a. urine
   b. water
   c. uretrial fluid
   * d. filtrate
   e. renal plasma

M 24. The process during which potassium and hydrogen ions, penicillin, and some toxic substances are put into the urine by active transport is called
   * a. tubular secretion.
   b. reabsorption.
   c. filtration.
   d. countercurrent multiplication.

E 25. Which of the following substances is NOT filtered from the bloodstream?
   a. water
   * b. plasma proteins
   c. urea
   d. glucose
   e. sodium

M 26. The longer this structure is, the greater is an animal's capacity to conserve water and to concentrate solutes for excretion in the urine.
   a. Bowman's capsule
   * b. loop of Henle
   c. proximal tubule
   d. ureter

D 27. Which of the following features would tend to promote water retention by the kidney?
   a. many nephridia
   * b. a long loop of Henle
   c. a long proximal tubule
   d. a short distal tubule
   e. a high filtration rate

M 28. Reabsorption is the movement of water and solutes from the _____ to the _____.
   a. interstitial fluid; tubules
   b. glomerular capillaries; Bowman's capsule
   c. Bowman's capsule; nephron tubules
   * d. nephron tubules; capillaries
   e. glomerular capillaries; peritubular capillaries

E 29. In reabsorption,
   a. plasma proteins are returned to the blood.
   b. excess hydrogen ions are removed from the blood.
   c. excess water is passed on to the urine.
 * d. nutrients and salts are selectively returned to the blood.
   e. drugs and foreign substances are passed into the urine.

M 30. Which of the following are most permeable to water and small molecules?
 * a. glomerular capillaries.
   b. peritubular capillaries.
   c. proximal tubules.
   d. ureters.
   e. collecting ducts

D 31. The process of filtration in the glomerulus is driven by
   a. active transport.
 * b. hydrostatic pressure.
   c. osmosis.
   d. dialysis.
   e. sodium-potassium pumps.

D 32. Most of the water and sodium is reabsorbed in the
   a. glomerulus.
 * b. proximal tubule.
   c. distal tubule.
   d. loop of Henle.
   e. collecting duct.

D 33. The reabsorption of solutes is the result of active transport of
   a. potassium.
 * b. sodium.
   c. carbonate.
   d. chloride.
   e. all of these

M 34. The hormone that influences sodium reabsorption in the kidney is
   a. antidiuretic hormone.
   b. cortisone.
 * c. aldosterone.
   d. corticotropic hormone.
   e. adrenalin.

M 35. Which of the following processes occurs first in the adjustment of body fluid volume?
   a. An inactive protein is converted into angiotensin.
   b. Distal tubules and collecting ducts reabsorb sodium faster.
   c. Target cells secrete aldosterone.
 * d. Sense receptors in walls of blood vessels and the heart reveal a drop in extracellular fluid level.
   e. Renin is secreted by the juxtaglomerular apparatus.

D 36. When the body has excess sodium, which of the following does NOT happen?
   a. More sodium is excreted.
 * b. More sodium is reabsorbed.
   c. Edema occurs.
   d. Blood pressure rises.
   e. Aldosterone secretion is inhibited.

M 37. Water reabsorption into the capillaries associated with a nephron is achieved principally by
   a. bulk flow.
 * b. active transport and diffusion.
   c. countercurrent multiplication.
   d. phagocytosis.
   e. all of these

M 38. During reabsorption, sodium ions cross the proximal tubule walls into the interstitial fluid principally by means of
   a. bulk flow.
 * b. active transport.
   c. countercurrent multiplication.
   d. phagocytosis.
   e. all of these

D 39. In mammals, which of the following does NOT act to maintain the osmotic gradient necessary for the concentration of urine?
   a. countercurrent multiplication at the loop of Henle
 * b. decreased hypothalamic signals leading to a decrease in ADH production
   c. adjustments in urine concentration at the collecting ducts
   d. countercurrent exchange at the peritubular capillaries
   e. all of these

M 40. The antidiuretic hormone
   a. promotes processes that lead to an increase in the volume of urine.
 * b. promotes processes that lead to a decrease in the volume of urine.
   c. acts on the proximal tubules of nephrons in the kidney.
   d. is produced by the adrenal cortex.
   e. all of these

M 41. Which of the following is a trigger for the other actions described?
   a. Posterior pituitary secretes ADH.
   b. Solute concentration in the extracellular fluid rises above a set point.
   c. Distal tubules of the nephrons and the collecting ducts become more permeable to water.
 * d. Extracellular fluid volume is reduced.
   e. A small amount of concentrated urine is excreted.

M   42. Which of the following is actively transported out of the proximal tubules of the kidney?
     a. bicarbonate ions
   * b. sodium ions
     c. chloride ions
     d. water

E   43. The hormone that controls the concentration of urine is
     a. insulin.
     b. glucagon.
   * c. the antidiuretic hormone.
     d. thyroxine.
     e. epinephrine.

D   44. A rise in sodium levels and extracellular volume leads to a rise in blood pressure. As a result,
     a. renin levels rise, but aldosterone levels fall.
     b. renin levels fall, but angiotensin levels rise.
     c. renin and aldosterone levels all rise.
   * d. renin and aldosterone levels all drop.

M   45. The hormonal control over excretion occurs in the
     a. Bowman's capsule.
     b. proximal tubule.
   * c. distal tubule.
     d. loop of Henle.
     e. urinary bladder.

D   46. Ethanol (drinking alcohol) is an inhibitor of ADH. Therefore, a person consuming a couple of mixed drinks should excrete
     a. less water because ADH promotes reabsorption.
     b. the alcohol because ADH cannot degrade it.
     c. ketone bodies formed from the alcohol.
   * d. more water because ADH normally promotes reabsorption.
     e. more water plus the alcohol due to the ADH inhibition.

E   47. Which of the following does NOT belong with the others?
     a. ADH
     b. aldosterone
     c. renin
   * d. insulin

E   48. In humans, the thirst center is located in the
     a. adrenal cortex.
   * b. hypothalamus.
     c. anterior pituitary.
     d. glomerulus.
     e. stomach.

M   49. In mammals, which of the following governs both the thirst mechanism and the hormonal action that affects the amount of water and solutes excreted in the urine?
     a. adrenal cortex
     b. adrenal medulla
     c. anterior pituitary
   * d. hypothalamus
     e. none of these

FOCUS ON HEALTH: WHEN KIDNEYS BREAK DOWN

D   50. Kidney stones form in the
   * a. renal pelvis.
     b. ureters.
     c. urethra.
     d. urinary bladder.
     e. glomerulus.

E   51. A kidney machine removes solutes from the blood by means of
     a. osmosis.
     b. diffusion.
   * c. dialysis.
     d. active transport.
     e. bulk flow.

THE BODY'S ACID-BASE BALANCE

D   52. The urinary system helps to maintain the extracellular fluid pH by
     a. synthesizing buffers.
     b. retaining carbon dioxide in the filtrate.
   * c. excreting hydrogen ions as water.
     d. combining hydrogen ions with urea.

D   53. Which of the following does NOT influence the pH of the blood and extracellular fluids?
     a. respiration
     b. blood proteins
     c. bicarbonate ions
   * d. filtration by glomerulus
     e. phosphate and ammonia ions

ON FISH, FROGS, AND KANGAROO RATS

M   54. Excess salts of saltwater fish are excreted
     a. by relatively large kidneys.
     b. through the skin.
     c. through the eyes.
     d. through special salt glands located in the tail.
   * e. through the gills.

HOW ARE CORE TEMPERATURES MAINTAINED?

E   55. The usual upper temperature limit before proteins are denatured is
     a. 35°C.
   * b. 40°C.
     c. 45°C.
     d. 50°C.
     e. 55°C.

M   56. The rate of a chemical reaction is cut in half for a drop of every
     a. 5°C.
   * b. 10°C.
     c. 15°C.
     d. 20°C.
     e. 25°C.

E   57. Heat loss by direct exchange of energy between
          molecules is called
     *   a. conduction.
          b. radiation.
          c. convection.
          d. metabolism.
          e. evaporation.

M   58. Which of the following processes is able to move heat
          in one direction only—away from the body?
          a. convection
     *   b. evaporation
          c. conduction
          d. radiation
          e. collection

E   59. The transfer of heat directly from a surface to the body
          by contact is called
          a. radiation.
     *   b. conduction.
          c. convection.
          d. denaturing.
          e. evaporation.

E   60. Endothermic animals
          a. use up more energy than ectotherms.
          b. have more stamina than ectotherms.
          c. have a higher metabolic rate than ectotherms.
          d. have layers of fat to reduce heat loss.
     *   e. all of these

M   61. Which of the following statements is false?
          a. Endotherms have a higher metabolic rate than
              ectotherms.
          b. Endotherms can regulate their temperature
              through behavior.
          c. Ectotherms regulate their temperatures through
              behavior.
          d. Heterotherms may function as either an ectotherm
              or an endotherm.
     *   e. Ectotherms do better in cold climates.

M   62. Ectothermic animals
          a. are more likely to use metabolism for heat.
          b. shun the sun during the daylight hours.
          c. are more adapted to cold.
     *   d. are more likely to use behavioral temperature
              regulation.
          e. all of these

TEMPERATURE REGULATION IN MAMMALS

M   63. Which of the following is NOT a response to low
          temperature that increases the chance for survival?
     *   a. hypothermia
          b. shivering
          c. production of brown fat
          d. pilomotor response
          e. increased metabolism

M   64. Which of the following is NOT involved in
          thermoregulation?
          a. sweat glands
          b. adrenal medulla
          c. thyroid
     *   d. parathyroid
          e. anterior pituitary

M   65. The primary thermostat of the body is located in the
          a. heart.
     *   b. hypothalamus.
          c. medulla oblongata.
          d. cerebellum.
          e. thyroid gland.

M   66. Which of the following is NOT part of the initial
          response to cold temperature?
     *   a. opening of peripheral blood vessels
          b. shivering
          c. increased respiration
          d. shunting of the blood to the core regions of the
              body
          e. increased metabolism

M   67. In mammals, which of the following is the seat of
          temperature control?
          a. adrenal cortex
          b. adrenal medulla
          c. thymus
     *   d. hypothalamus
          e. heart

E   68. Responses to heat stress include
          a. reduction in muscle contraction.
          b. increased sweating.
          c. dilation of peripheral blood vessels.
          d. loss of salts and liquids.
     *   e. all of these

Matching Questions

D   69.   Matching. Choose the one most appropriate answer for each.

1. ___ nephron
2. ___ aldosterone
3. ___ secretion
4. ___ ADH
5. ___ conduction
6. ___ convection
7. ___ pilomotor response
8. ___ ectothermic
9. ___ evaporation
10. ___ glomerular filtration
11. ___ hemodialysis
12. ___ hypothermia
13. ___ heterothermic
14. ___ radiation
15. ___ tubular reabsorption

A. do not maintain the same body temperature at all times; are capable of internal heat production

B. heat energy is released to the air when water escapes from the body surfaces

C. bulk flow of protein-free plasma from capillaries into Bowman's capsule

D. animals with more or less constant body temperature

E. infrared wavelengths released from body surface when environmental temperature is lower

F. movement of ions from peritubular capillaries into nephron tubules

G. loss of too much body heat

H. heat next to the body's surface undergoes mass transport by air or water currents

I. active and passive transport of solutes from peritubular capillaries into the nephron

J. a long, slender tubular unit in the vertebrate kidney that forms urine

K. body temperatures rise and fall with environmental changes

L. secreted by adrenal glands; influences sodium reabsorption

M. passive transport of water; active and passive transport of solutes out of the nephron into peritubular capillaries

N. heat energy is transferred from high to low temperature regions due to collisions between adjacent molecules

O. released from the posterior lobe of the pituitary in response to hypothalamic signals

P. toxic substances are extracted from blood circulating in cellophane tubes suspended in a warm-water bath

Q. erection of hairs and feathers by smooth muscles in the skin

Answers: 1. J   2. L   3. F   4. O
5. N   6. H   7. Q   8. K
9. B   10. C   11. P   12. G
13. A   14. E   15. M

Classification Questions

Answer questions 70–74 in reference to the four regions of a nephron listed below:

a. Bowman's capsule
b. proximal tubule
c. descending portion of loop of Henle
d. distal tubule

M   70.   Sodium ions are actively transported out of the nephron from this region.

E   71.   Filtration of the blood occurs in association with this structure.

D   72.   Antibiotics are secreted from this structure.

M   73.   Permeability to water is regulated by antidiuretic hormone in this structure.

E   74.   The glomerular capillaries are intimately associated with this structure.

Answers   70. b   71. a   72. d
73. d   74. a

Selecting the Exception

E   75.   Four of the five answers listed below are methods by which the body exchanges heat into the environment. Select the exception.
*   a. muscle contraction
       b. radiation
       c. evaporation
       d. convection
       e. conduction

E   76.   Four of the five answers listed below are ectotherms. Select the exception.
- a. snail
- b. snake
- c. spider
- d. frog
- * e. bird

M   77.   Four of the five answers listed below are features of animals that live in cold climates. Select the exception.
- a. thick fur
- b. body fat
- c. large body size
- * d. large surface-to-volume ratio
- e. thick-limbed bodies with small extremities

E   78.   Four of the five answers listed below are habits of desert animals. Select the exception.
- a. spend time in shade
- b. spend daytime hours in underground burrows
- c. are active mainly at night
- d. have low metabolism during day
- * e. spend nighttime sleeping

M   79.   Four of the five answers listed below are responses to cold temperatures. Select the exception.
- a. vasoconstriction of peripheral blood vessels
- b. uncontrolled muscular contraction
- c. thermoreceptors send messages to the hypothalamus
- * d. enhanced secretion of sweat glands
- e. increased metabolic reactions

M   80.   Four of the five answers listed below are responses of the body to heat. Select the exception.
- a. increased sweating
- * b. increased retention of blood on the core region
- c. decreased rate of muscle activity
- d. increased water loss
- e. dilation of peripheral blood vessels

D   81.   Four of the five answers listed below are responses to the loss of body heat. Select the exception.
- * a. ventricular fibrillation
- b. blood routed to deeper tissues
- c. constriction of peripheral blood vessels
- d. increased respiration
- e. increased metabolic rates

D   82.   Four of the five answers listed below are potentially toxic waste products of metabolism. Select the exception.
- a. urea
- * b. water
- c. uric acid
- d. carbon dioxide
- e. ammonia

M   83.   Four of the five answers listed below are parts of the same structure. Select the exception.
- a. distal tubule
- b. loop of Henle
- * c. ureter
- d. proximal tubule
- e. Bowman's capsule

M   84.   Four of the five answers listed below are functions of the nephron. Select the exception.
- a. filtration
- * b. dilution
- c. excretion
- d. reabsorption
- e. secretion

D   85.   Four of the five answers listed below are the result of ADH (antidiuretic hormone) secretion. Select the exception.
- a. Water is reabsorbed in the distal tubule.
- b. Fluid volume of blood increases.
- * c. Solute concentration in blood rises.
- d. Distal tubule and collecting duct becomes more permeable to water.
- e. Solute concentration decreases.

CHAPTER 43
PRINCIPLES OF REPRODUCTION AND DEVELOPMENT

Multiple-Choice Questions

M **1.** In frogs,
   a. reproduction is internal and occurs in a process called copulation.
   b. fertilization occurs within the body of the female.
   * c. eggs and sperm are released simultaneously during a process called amplexus.
   d. males leave sperm in a nest and females lay eggs in the same nest.
   e. females lay eggs in a nest site and males release sperm in the same general area.

THE BEGINNING: REPRODUCTIVE MODES

M **2.** Which of the following is NOT true of asexual reproduction?
   a. It is more suitable for reproduction in animals in stable environments.
   b. It results in offspring that are identical to each other.
   * c. It promotes genetic variation in each successive generation.
   d. Budding is one type of asexual reproduction.
   e. The offspring are genetically identical to the parents.

M **3.** Which of the following statements is NOT an advantage of asexual reproduction?
   a. Asexual reproduction is more efficient than sexual reproduction.
   b. An individual organism can reproduce asexually by itself.
   * c. Asexual reproduction promotes variation.
   d. Asexual reproduction produces fewer offspring than sexual reproduction.

D **4.** Which of the following is NOT one of the factors contributing to the high cost of sexual reproduction?
   a. specialized reproductive structures such as the male penis
   b. production of excessive numbers of gametes
   c. development of elaborate courtship rituals
   * d. production of the cytoplasm for millions of reproductive buds
   e. nourishment of offspring

D **5.** Which of the following animals would fit this description: "Eggs fertilized outside the body, minimum of yolk, rapid development?"
   a. bird
   * b. sea urchin
   c. bony fish
   d. reptile
   e. human

E **6.** Some animals, such as birds, lay eggs with large yolk reserves; embryonic development occurs within the egg covering outside the mother's body. Such a developmental strategy is called
   * a. oviparity.
   b. viviparity.
   c. ovoviviparity.
   d. parthenogenesis.

D **7.** Which of the following statements is false?
   a. A copperhead snake bears her young alive.
   * b. Some fishes, lizards, snakes, and mammals are ovoviviparous.
   c. Birds and monotremes are oviparous.
   d. Marsupials and placental mammals are viviparous.
   e. Oviparous forms hatch outside their mother's body.

STAGES OF DEVELOPMENT—AN OVERVIEW

M **8.** Gastrulation, produces
   a. hollow balls of cells.
   * b. embryos with germinal layers.
   c. solid balls of cells.
   d. maternal messages.
   e. all of these

E **9.** The heart, muscles, bones, and blood develop primarily from
   a. ectoderm.
   * b. mesoderm.
   c. endoderm.
   d. the placenta.
   e. the gray crescent.

M **10.** Which embryonic tissue is incorrectly associated with its derivative?
   * a. skin from mesoderm
   b. nervous system from ectoderm
   c. liver from endoderm
   d. circulatory system from mesoderm

E **11.** Muscles differentiate from which tissue?
   a. ectoderm
   b. endoderm
   * c. mesoderm
   d. all of these

M **12.** The mesoderm is responsible for the formation of all but which of the following adult tissues?
   a. reproductive system
   b. circulatory system
   * c. nervous system
   d. muscle system
   e. excretory system

M 13. If an experimenter interferes with the mesoderm in an egg, which of the following systems would NOT be affected by the experimenter?
    a. circulatory system
    b. muscular system
    c. reproductive system
*   d integumentary system
    e. excretory system

D 14. Select the correct sequence of animal developmental events.
    a. fertilization——> cleavage ——> gastrula ——> blastula
*   b. fertilization ——> cleavage ——> blastula ——> gastrula
    c. fertilization ——> blastula ——> cleavage ——> gastrula
    d fertilization ——> gastrula ——> blastula ——> cleavage

E 15. In the following list of developmental events, which occurs last?
*   a. tissue specialization
    b. gamete formation
    c. gastrulation
    d cleavage
    e. organ formation

D 16. In the human, which of the following events would occur over the longest period of time?
    a. sperm production
    b. cleavage
    c. fertilization
    d gastrulation
*   e. growth and tissue specialization

E 17. Which of the following statements is NOT true?
    a. It is an advantage for eggs to complete their development as quickly as possible to avoid predation.
    b. The amount of yolk in an egg varies from one species to another.
*   c. Bird egg shells are present before fertilization occurs.
    d Human eggs have almost no yolk.
    e. Yolk is composed of fats and proteins and is high in nutritive value.

EARLY MARCHING ORDERS

M 18. Maternal control elements in the oocyte's cytoplasm consist largely of
    a. DNA.
*   b. RNA.
    c. HeLa cells.
    d puffs.
    e. all of these

D 19. Although the genetic contributions of egg and sperm nuclei are equal, the egg contributes more than the sperm to cell differentiation because of its
    a. larger size.
    b. cytoplasmic determinants.
    c. proteins.
    d cytoplasmic determinants and proteins, only.
*   e. cytoplasmic determinants, proteins, and larger size.

D 20. The significance of polarization is that
    a. cell systems near the anterior (head) end of an organism are aligned differently from cell systems at the posterior end.
    b. controlled cell death occurs in a gradient along the body axis in most organisms.
    c. malignant cells metastasize more readily in polarized regions.
*   d cytoplasmic substances located at one end of the zygote differ from cytoplasmic substances located at the other end.
    e. all of these

D 21. Before gastrulation, the future developmental fate of cell lineages is largely established by which of the following acquired during cleavage?
    a. the genotype
*   b. the portion of egg cytoplasm
    c. surface recognition factors on the plasma membrane
    d the number and type of organelles
    e. all of these

M 22. Which of the following affects the developmental pathways that different embryonic cells eventually will follow?
    a. sperm nucleus
    b. egg nucleus
    c. sperm cytoplasm
*   d egg cytoplasm

D 23. Which of the following statements is false?
    a. Most of the genes of the nucleus are inactive during cleavage.
    b. The particular sector of the egg cytoplasm helps control the differences among cells.
    c. The amount of yolk present in the egg influences cleavage patterns.
*   d The cells of the animal pole are larger than the cells of the vegetal pole.
    e. There is so much yolk in the eggs of reptiles and birds that cleavage is restricted to a very small region of the animal pole.

D 24. Which of the following pairings correctly matches an oocyte component and its function?
    a. microtubules: animal and vegetal poles
    b. yolk: protein synthesis
    c. histones: division planes
*   d nucleus: polarity
    e. RNA: DNA replication

E   25. Which stage in development occurs first?
    a. cleavage
    b. morula
    c. gastrula
  * d. zygote
    e. blastula

M   26. The gray crescent is
    a. formed where the sperm penetrates the egg.
  * b. formed opposite from where the sperm enters the egg.
    c. the portion of the egg where the yolk is found.
    d. located next to the dorsal lip of the blastopore.
    e. the point where the first cleavage occurs.

D   27. The stimulus for the formation of the gray crescent is
    a. provided by the RNA transcripts in the egg.
  * b. the entry of the sperm.
    c. the responsibility of oocyte components.
    d. determined by the polarity of the egg.
    e. determined by all of these except "the entry of the sperm."

D   28. Which of the following statements is false?
    a. The cells in the animal pole are smaller than those in the vegetal pole.
  * b. The gray crescent is formed where the sperm enters the egg.
    c. The archenteron is formed by the process of invagination.
    d. In most mammals, the blastula has a group of cells that will eventually develop into the placenta.
    e. In mutant *Drosophila* embryos, if the polar granules do not migrate properly, the adult produced will be sterile.

M   29. The amount of yolk in a zygote plays a major role in
    a. stimulating morphogenic movements and bringing about controlled cell death.
    b. embryonic induction.
  * c. determining whether cleavage will be complete or incomplete.
    d. determining when metamorphosis will occur.
    e. the fertility of the egg.

E   30. Which of the following is a single-layered, hollow ball of cells?
    a. cleavage
    b. morula
    c. gastrula
    d. zygote
  * e. blastula

E   31. The process of cleavage most commonly produces a
    a. zygote.
  * b. blastula.
    c. gastrula.
    d. puff.
    e. third germ layer.

E   32. Shortly after fertilization, successive cell divisions convert the zygote into a multicellular embryo during a process known as
    a. meiosis.
    b. parthenogenesis.
    c. embryonic induction.
  * d. cleavage.
    e. invagination.

E   33. Which of the following structures is a hollow ball composed of a single layer of cells?
    a. zygote
    b. morula
    c. gastrula
  * d. blastula
    e. yolk sac

D   34. In the process of blastula formation,
    a. the size of individual cells decreases.
    b. the number of cells increases.
    c. the total amount of cytoplasm remains about the same.
    d. the size of individual cells decreases and the number of cells increases.
  * e. the size of individual cells decreases, the number of cells increases, but the total amount of cytoplasm remains about the same..

E   35. Which of the following is the space inside the blastula?
    a. blastocyst
    b. blastofurrow
    c. blastocell
  * d. blastocoel
    e. blastodisk

E   36. The germ layers are formed in which of the following stages?
    a. cleavage
    b. morula
  * c. gastrula
    d. zygote
    e. blastula

E   37. Which of the following is the primitive gut and forms the digestive tract?
    a. ectoderm
    b. blastopore
  * c. archenteron
    d. yolk plug
    e. blastocoel

D   38. Which of the following events is NOT included in what embryologists refer to as gastrulation?
    a. cell rearrangements
    b. formation of the archenteron
  * c. organ formation
    d. formation of germ layers
    e. establishment of the body axis

HOW DO SPECIALIZED TISSUES AND ORGANS FORM?

D 39. Which of the following statements is false?
  a. Cell migration during embryonic development is an example of chemotaxis.
  b. Schwann cells follow adhesive cells as they migrate along the axons of neurons.
  * c. Cells continue migrating throughout the entire embryonic process.
  d. Morphogenesis depends upon local growth.
  e. Controlled cell death leads to morphogenesis.

M 40. During which of the following stages do cells of identical genetic makeup become structurally and functionally different from one another according to the genetically controlled developmental program of the species?
  a. cleavage
  * b. differentiation
  c. morphogenesis
  d. metamorphosis
  e. ovulation

M 41. Which of the following is NOT true of identical twins?
  a. They are appropriately called monozygotic twins.
  b. They always are the same sex.
  * c. They occur more frequently than fraternal twins.
  d. They have exactly the same genotypes and could appropriately be called clones.

M 42. In the process of differentiation,
  a. some daughter cells usually receive varying assortments of genes.
  * b. cells with identical assortments of genes come to have different individual genes expressed.
  c. cells become specialized as a result of meiosis.
  d. daughter cells acquire different characteristics as a result of mutations that have occurred.
  e. all of these

D 43. The explanation for the differences between a cell from the human liver and a cell from the skin is the
  a. maternal and paternal origins of the cell types.
  b. gene content of the two cells.
  * c. expression of the genes in the two cells.
  d. fact that they are in different parts of the body.

M 44. Types of morphogenic movements exclude
  a. movement of organs.
  b. active cellular migration using pseudopods.
  * c. cleavage.
  d. the folding of sheets of cells.

PATTERN FORMATION

M 45. Cells migrate during morphogenesis in response to
  a. chemical gradients.
  b. recognition proteins.
  c. adhesive cues.
  d. chemical gradients and recognition proteins.
  * e. chemical gradients, recognition proteins, and adhesive cues.

D 46. Complex maneuvers such as the folding involved in formation of the neural tube are accomplished primarily by
  a. adhesive cues.
  b. chemical gradients.
  * c. microtubules and microfilaments.
  d. controlled cell death.
  e. chemotaxis.

M 47. Patterns that involve controlled cell death include
  a. formation and hollowing out of tubes.
  b. opening of the eyes and mouth.
  c. formation of fingers and toes.
  d. destruction of certain specific cells.
  * e. all of these

M 48. The differentiation of a body part in response to signals from an adjacent body part is
  a. contact inhibition.
  b. ooplasmic localization.
  * c. embryonic induction.
  d. pattern formation.
  e. all of these

M 49. The mechanism of embryonic induction involves
  * a. chemicals.
  b. electrical signals.
  c. touch.
  d. chemicals and touch.
  e. electrical signals and touch.

M 50. The process in which the fate of a group of cells is controlled by substances produced by other embryonic cells is known as
  * a. embryonic induction.
  b. cytoplasmic localization.
  c. cellular differentiation.
  d. morphogenesis.
  e. formation of the gray crescent.

M 51. If an optic cup is transplanted to an area where ectoderm is available,
  a. the optic cup will be reabsorbed.
  b. the optic cup will develop into a fully functional eye.
  * c. the epidermis will be induced to form a lens.
  d. the eye fails to differentiate any further.

M 52. Homeotic genes
    a. cause lethal mutations.
*   b. control blocks of genes necessary for pattern formation.
    c. are found only in fruit flies where they are responsible for odd placement of appendages.
    d. are also known as "fate maps."
    e. operate only in individuals with two genes of the same kind.

M 53. A homeotic mutation
    a. may cause a leg to develop on the head where an antenna should grow.
    b. affects the expression of imaginal disks.
    c. affects morphogenesis.
    d. may alter the pathway of development.
*   e. all of these

M 54. Signaling molecules responsible for embryonic induction are called
    a. crystallins.
*   b. morphogens
    c. mutagens.
    d. inducagens.
    e. homeoboxes.

E 55. The transformation of a tadpole into a frog is an example of
    a. organogenesis.
*   b. metamorphosis.
    c. gametogenesis.
    d. differentiation.
    e. segmentation.

D 56. An increase in insect larval body size but without a change in form is called
*   a. molting.
    b. metamorphosis.
    c. aging.
    d. homeobox.
    e. gastrulation.

M 57. Which of the following animals undergoes indirect development?
*   a. frogs
    b. snakes
    c. whales
    d. horses
    e. hawks

D 58. Both beetles and frogs undergo a process of metamorphosis; however, only beetles
    a. change their body form.
*   b. molt.
    c. become sexually mature as adults.
    d. feed in the larval stages.
    e. can live on land.

WHY DO ANIMALS AGE?

D 59. Which of the following is NOT currently a possible explanation of the process of aging?
    a. limited number of mitosis cycles
    b. autoimmune attack
*   c. increased mutation rate
    d. gene deterioration
    e. limited division potential

Matching Questions

60. Matching. Choose the one best answer for each numbered item.

1. ___ animal pole
2. ___ archenteron
3. ___ budding
4. ___ chemotaxis
5. ___ cleavage
6. ___ controlled cell death
7. ___ differentiation
8. ___ embryonic induction
9. ___ fertilization
10. ___ fission
11. ___ gastrula
12. ___ gastrulation
13. ___ gray crescent
14. ___ larva
15. ___ metamorphosis
16. ___ molt
17. ___ morphogenesis
18. ___ organogenesis
19. ___ regeneration
20. ___ viviparous

A. visible marker of the site where an amphibian's body axis will be established and where gastrulation will begin

B. larva increases in size but remains a juvenile

C. a developmental stage that generally does not resemble the adult form and feeds separately from the adult

D. the formation of two or three embryonic tissue layers

E. the union of male and female gametes

F. the entire body divides transversely; each half grows and regenerates the missing part

G. rudimentary gut formed by surface cells migrating to interior of embryo

H. change from larva to adult

I. selective gene expression results in different cell types

J. mother retains fertilized eggs, nourishes and protects developing offspring, and gives birth

K. subdividing of the zygote by mitosis; no growth occurs

L. region of zygote that has less yolk and is near the nucleus

M. certain cells begin differentiating and growing outward from the parent body; eventually they break away from the parent and develop into a new individual

N. movement in response to chemical gradients

O. an embryonic stage of development that has three embryonic tissue layers before organogenesis begins

P. replacement of body parts

Q. the formation of organs

R. one body part develops in response to signals from an adjacent part

S. the growth, shaping, and spatial coordination of tissues and organs so that a predefined pattern of the whole organism results

T. occurs in the formation of the human hand and eyelids

Answers:

1. L	2. G	3. M	4. N
5. K	6. T	7. I	8. R
9. E	10. F	11. O	12. D
13. A	14. C	15. H	16. B
17. S	18. Q	19. P	20. J

Classification Questions

Answer questions 61–65 in reference to the five terms below:

    a. asexual
    b. oviparous
    c. ovoviviparous
    d. viviparous
    e. external fertilization

E   **61.** This term describes the reproductive strategy in birds.

E   **62.** This term describes the process that produces identical offspring.

M   **63.** This term describes the strategy that most mammals follow.

M   **64.** This term describes the process by which several snakes and lizards produce live young still enclosed in egg sacs.

E   **65.** This term describes the process of union requiring large numbers of gametes.

Answers

61. b	62. a	63. d
64. c	65. e	

Answer questions 66–70 in reference to the five stages of development listed below:

    a. zygote
    b. blastula
    c. morula
    d. gastrula
    e. embryo

M   **66.** This stage appears as a multicellular, hollow ball.

E   **67.** This is the fertilized egg.

D   **68.** This stage might contain only 16 cells.

D   **69.** The gut cavity of an animal forms during this stage.

D   **70.** The major germ layers are formed during this stage.

Answers   66.b   67. a   68. c

               69. d   70. d

Selecting the Exception

M   **71.** Four of the five answers listed below are oviparous. Select the exception.
    a. duck-billed platypus
    b. snail
*   c. kangaroo
    d. robin
    e. penguin

M   **72.** Four of the five answers listed below are events occurring after fertilization. Select the exception.
    a. cleavage
*   b. gametogenesis
    c. blastula
    d. gastrulation
    e. organogenesis

E   **73.** Four of the five answers listed below possess large amounts of yolk. Select the exception.
*   a. mammalian egg
    b. snake egg
    c. bird egg
    d. turtle egg
    e. fish egg

M   **74.** Four of the five answers listed below are produced by the same germ layer. Select the exception.
*   a. nervous system
    b. muscle system
    c. circulatory system
    d. reproductive system
    e. excretory system

D   **75.** Four of the five answers listed below are examples of controlled cell death. Select the exception.
    a. separation of eyelids
    b. formation of fingers
    c. hollowing of tubes
    d. opening of nostrils, mouth, and ears
*   e. formation of anus

D   **76.** Four of the five answers listed below do NOT undergo metamorphosis. Select the exception.
*   a. frog
    b. turtle
    c. cat
    d. bird
    e. human

D   **77.** Four of the five answers listed below are events associated with the aging process. Select the exception.
    a. skin wrinkling
*   b. increased metabolism
    c. decreased muscle mass
    d. altered collagen
    e. increased fat deposition

CHAPTER 44
HUMAN REPRODUCTION AND DEVELOPMENT

Multiple-Choice Questions

M 1. The male and female sex organs begin to differentiate during which week of gestation?
   a. fourth week
 * b. seventh week
   c. twelfth week
   d. twentieth week
   e. twenty-eighth week

REPRODUCTIVE SYSTEM OF HUMAN MALES

M 2. The major difference between the male and female reproductive systems is the
 * a. provision of a site for fertilization and development in the female.
   b. production of haploid gametes by the male only.
   c. diploid polar bodies of the female.
   d. generation of millions of eggs but only thousands of sperm each month.

E 3. In the human male, several hundred million sperm are produced in the
   a. interstitial cells.
   b. prostate.
 * c. seminiferous tubules.
   d. vas deferens.
   e. epididymis.

E 4. Sperm are produced in the
 * a. testes.
   b. vas deferens.
   c. epididymis.
   d. prostate gland.
   e. penis.

M 5. Seminal fluid is produced by the
   a. prostate gland.
   b. seminal vesicle.
   c. bulbourethral gland.
   d. urinary bladder.
 * e. all except "urinary bladder"

E 6. Which of the following is NOT found in the seminal fluid?
 * a. glucose
   b. buffers
   c. prostaglandins
   d. mucus
   e. fructose

M 7. Occasionally the testes do not descend into the scrotum as they should in a newborn. If this is not corrected surgically,
 * a. sperm production will be affected.
   b. achieving an erection will not be possible.
   c. the child will look like a girl.
   d. growth will be stunted.
   e. the child will not live.

D 8. The seminal vesicles ("sperm vessels") are misnamed. Sperm are actually stored in the
   a. vas deferens.
 * b. epididymis.
   c. prostate.
   d. scrotum.
   e. urethra.

D 9. Which of the following is the site where sperm are stored?
   a. ureter
   b. urethra
   c. vas deferens
   d. vas efferens
 * e. epididymis

D 10. If the vas deferens tubes are cut and tied (vasectomy), the semen will not contain
   a. fructose.
   b. buffers.
   c. mucus.
 * d. sperm.
   e. any of the above

M 11. Which of the following is the last structure that a sperm travels through as it leaves the body?
   a. ureter
 * b. urethra
   c. vas deferens
   d. vas efferens
   e. epididymis

M 12. Which of the following is part of the urinary system, not the reproductive system?
 * a. ureter
   b. urethra
   c. vas deferens
   d. vas efferens
   e. epididymis

MALE REPRODUCTIVE FUNCTION

M 13. Which of the following cells are diploid?
   a. spermatids
   b. primary spermatocytes
   c. secondary spermatocytes
   d. spermatogonia
 * e. both primary spermatocytes and spermatogonia

M   14.   Which cells are produced during meiosis I?
           a.   spermatogonia
           b.   primary spermatocytes
       *   c.   secondary spermatocytes
           d.   spermatids
           e.   sperm

M   15.   Sperm become fully motile in the
           a.   vas deferens.
           b.   epididymis.
           c.   seminiferous tubules.
       *   d.   vagina.
           e.   seminal fluid.

D   16.   The secretions of the interstitial cells (Leydig cells) eventually pass into the
           a.   semen.
           b.   vagina.
       *   c.   blood.
           d.   semen and vagina, only.
           e.   semen, vagina, and blood.

M   17.   All but which of the following hormones are in some way responsible for the production of sperm?
           a.   luteinizing hormone
           b.   follicle-stimulating hormone
           c.   gonadotropic releasing hormone
           d.   testosterone
       *   e.   human chorionic gonadotropin

D   18.   All but which of the following are the products of meiosis?
           a.   male gametes
           b.   spermatids
           c.   sperm
           d.   secondary spermatocytes
       *   e.   spermatogonia

M   19.   Meiosis I results directly in the production of
           a.   spermatids.
           b.   spermatogonial cells.
           c.   primary spermatocytes.
       *   d.   secondary spermatocytes.
           e.   sperm.

M   20.   Testosterone
           a.   stimulates spermatogenesis.
           b.   promotes the normal development and maintenance of sexual behavior.
           c.   is responsible for secondary sexual characteristics.
           d.   is responsible for the development of the male genitalia.
       *   e.   all of these

D   21.   Which of the following is NOT involved in a feedback loop in the male reproductive system?
           a.   anterior pituitary
           b.   hypothalamus
       *   c.   adrenal gland
           d.   Sertoli cells
           e.   interstitial cells

D   22.   The release of testosterone requires
           a.   luteinizing hormone.
           b.   GnRH.
           c.   Sertoli cells.
       *   d.   luteinizing hormone and GnRH.
           e.   luteinizing hormone, GnRH, and Sertoli cells.

D   23.   Based on their response to a particular hormone from the anterior pituitary, Sertoli cells of the male are most like _____ of the female.
           a.   uterine cells
           b.   oviducts
       *   c.   ovarian follicles
           d.   cervix cells
           e.   corpus luteum

D   24.   Which of the following structures is NOT found in mature sperm?
           a.   DNA molecules
           b.   acrosome with enzymes
           c.   mitochondria
           d.   microtubules in the tail
       *   e.   ribosomes

REPRODUCTIVE SYSTEM OF HUMAN FEMALES

E   25.   The female reproductive system includes all but which of the following?
           a.   clitoris
           b.   vagina
           c.   oviduct
           d.   ovary
       *   e.   mammary gland

E   26.   The primary reproductive organ in the human female is the
           a.   uterus.
       *   b.   ovary.
           c.   vagina.
           d.   clitoris.
           e.   vulva.

M   27.   The passageway that channels ova from the ovary into the uterus is known as
           a.   a vagina.
           b.   a uterus.
       *   c.   an oviduct.
           d.   an endometrium.
           e.   all of these

M   28.   The surface of which of the following is covered with ciliated, fingerlike projections that produce a sweeping action?
           a.   ovary
           b.   uterus
           c.   vagina
       *   d.   oviduct
           e.   follicle

M 29. Which of the following statements is false?
   a. A female has more oocytes before she is born than at any time during her life.
   b. Meiosis II will not occur in an oocyte unless it is fertilized.
*   c. Fertilization occurs in the vagina.
   d. Implantation occurs in the uterus.
   e. The vagina serves as the birth canal.

E 30. The cervix is part of the
   a. vulva.
   b. ovary.
*   c. uterus.
   d. oviduct.
   e. vagina.

M 31. Which of the following hormones is exclusively female?
   a. follicle-stimulating hormone
   b. luteinizing hormone
*   c. progesterone
   d. follicle-stimulating hormone and progesterone
   e. follicle-stimulating hormone, progesterone, and luteinizing hormone

M 32. Which of the following statements is false?
*   a. Because males do not have a follicle, the follicle-stimulating hormone has no function in males.
   b. The gonads begin differentiation into an ovary or a testis by the seventh week after fertilization.
   c. The testes descend into the scrotal sac before birth.
   d. For sperm to develop properly they must be in an environment that is below body temperature.
   e. The scrotal sac is equipped with muscles that may raise or lower the testes.

D 33. Which of the following is NOT essential to the reproductive process?
   a. ovary
   b. oviduct
*   c. clitoris
   d. vagina
   e. uterus

M 34. Which mammals do NOT exhibit seasonal sexual activities?
   a. whales
   b. cats
*   c. primates
   d. horses
   e. dogs

E 35. In most mammals, a predictably recurring time when the female becomes sexually receptive to the male is called
*   a. estrus.
   b. endometrium.
   c. menstruation.
   d. coitus.
   e. parturition.

M 36. Which of the following is false?
   a. All mammals have either an estrous or a menstrual cycle.
   b. All primates have a menstrual cycle.
   c. All female primates can be physically and behaviorally receptive to sexual activity at any time.
   d. Eggs released by older women have a greater chance of producing a Down syndrome child.
*   e. All menstrual cycles last from 26 to 30 days.

D 37. Animals with a menstrual cycle do NOT
*   a. have an estrous cycle.
   b. ovulate spontaneously.
   c. display periods of sexual interest.
   d. produce estrogen.

FEMALE REPRODUCTIVE FUNCTION

M 38. Which of the following statements is NOT true of the human female?
   a. She produces all the eggs that she ever will before she is born.
   b. The process of meiosis may take 30 to 50 years to complete.
   c. The primary oocytes lay dormant until puberty.
*   d. She will normally produce more gametes than her male counterpart.
   e. It is possible that more than one egg will be released at ovulation.

M 39. FSH and LH are secreted by the
   a. hypothalamus.
   b. ovaries.
*   c. anterior pituitary.
   d. testes.
   e. uterus.

M 40. Ovulation is triggered by
*   a. high levels of LH.
   b. low levels of LH.
   c. high levels of chorionic gonadotropin.
   d. high levels of estrogen.
   e. high levels of progesterone.

E 41. Menstrual flow results in the discharge of
   a. the follicle.
   b. the corpus luteum.
*   c. the endometrial lining.
   d. surface cells from the vagina.
   e. blood from the blood vessels on the outer surface of the uterus.

M 42. Ovulation is triggered primarily by
*   a. a surge of LH that occurs halfway through the menstrual cycle.
   b. the falling levels of estrogen and progesterone.
   c. the rising levels of progesterone.
   d. both a surge of LH that occurs halfway through the menstrual cycle, and the rising levels of progesterone.

M 43. Ovulation involves the
       a. production of the first polar body.
*   b. release of a secondary oocyte.
       c. beginning of the follicular phase of the menstrual cycle.
       d. suspension of the meiotic process.
       e. deterioration of the corpus luteum.

M 44. Ovulation is triggered by a surge in the level of _____ in the circulatory system.
       a. estrogen
       b. follicle-stimulating hormone
*   c. luteinizing hormone
       d. progesterone
       e. human chorionic gonadotropin

M 45. Destruction of the corpus luteum, if pregnancy does NOT occur, results from the action of
       a. chorionic gonadotropin.
       b. luteinizing hormone.
       c. progesterone.
*   d. prostaglandins.
       e. estrogen.

E 46. Menstruation begins in response to
       a. rising levels of FSH and LH.
       b. falling levels of estrogen.
       c. falling levels of progesterone.
*   d. falling levels of estrogen and progesterone.

D 47. Which of the following serves to end the menstrual cycle?
       a. a surge in luteinizing hormone
       b. the secretion of human chorionic gonadotropin
*   c. the secretion of prostaglandins by the corpus luteum that lead to its self-destruction
       d. a rise in the level of progesterone
       e. a drop in the level of gonadotropic hormones in the blood

D 48. Using your knowledge of the feedback loops of human female hormones, which of the following would you predict is the result of high levels of estrogen and progesterone in the blood?
       a. lack of growth of the corpus luteum
*   b. absence of monthly ovulation
       c. increased secretion of FSH
       d. increased levels of LH
       e. all of these

D 49. The menstrual flow is the result of
       a. no implantation of a zygote.
       b. decreased levels of progesterone.
       c. discarded uterine linings.
       d. no implantation of a zygote and discarded uterine linings.
*   e. no implantation of a zygote, discarded uterine linings, and decreased levels of progesterone.

PREGNANCY HAPPENS

M 50. Orgasm is necessary for
*   a. ejaculation of semen.
       b. pregnancy.
       c. erection.
       d. sexual arousal.
       e. all of these

E 51. Fertilization in mammals occurs in the
       a. ovary.
       b. uterus.
       c. vagina.
*   d. oviduct.
       e. follicle.

E 52. The average number of sperm that enter the vagina during an ejaculation is between
       a. 150,000 and 350,000.
       b. 1.5 and 3.5 million.
       c. 15 and 35 million.
*   d. 150 and 350 million.
       e. 1.5 and 3.5 billion.

FORMATION OF THE EARLY EMBRYO

E 53. The embryo is recognizable as human and is called a fetus by which week of pregnancy?
*   a. eighth
       b. twelfth
       c. sixteenth
       d. twentieth
       e. twenty-fourth

M 54. During a human pregnancy, implantation occurs at which stage?
       a. zygote
       b. early cleavage
*   c. blastocyst
       d. gastrula
       e. morula

E 55. Implantation occurs in the
       a. ovary.
*   b. uterus.
       c. vagina.
       d. oviduct.
       e. follicle.

E 56. During human development, which of the following gives rise to the embryo?
       a. trophoblast
       b. amnion
*   c. embryonic disk
       d. chorion
       e. placenta

M 57. The first several cleavages after fertilization occur in the
       a. uterus.
       b. ovary.
       c. vagina.
*   d. oviduct.
       e. any of the above except vagina

M 58. Which of the following statements is false?
   a. Ovulation occurs when the follicle ruptures and releases an egg.
   b. Cleavage occurs when the zygote divides.
   c. Fertilization occurs in the upper regions of the oviduct.
   d. The blastocyst implants in the endometrial lining of the uterus.
 * e. Implantation occurs about 36 hours after fertilization.

M 59. The presence of which hormone in a mother's urine indicates that she is pregnant?
   a. luteinizing hormone
   b. follicle-stimulating hormone
 * c. chorionic gonadotropin
   d. progesterone
   e. estrogen

M 60. Which of the following hormones is produced only when a woman is pregnant?
   a. testosterone
   b. gonadotropic-releasing hormone
 * c. human chorionic gonadotropin
   d. estrogen
   e. progesterone

M 61. The fact that a blastocyst has been implanted on the uterine wall can be demonstrated by the presence of
 * a. human chorionic gonadotropin.
   b. progesterone.
   c. estrogen.
   d. testosterone.
   e. second polar body.

M 62. In the eggs of birds and reptiles, the waste products are stored in the
 * a. allantois.
   b. placenta.
   c. chorion.
   d. amnion.
   e. yolk sac.

M 63. Which of the following membranes is associated with waste storage?
   a. amnion
   b. yolk sac
   c. chorion
 * d. allantois
   e. none of these

M 64. Which of the following membranes is associated with the formation of the placenta?
   a. amnion
   b. yolk sac
 * c. chorion
   d. allantois
   e. none of these

M 65. In humans, the fluid immediately surrounding the embryo is contained in the
   a. allantois.
   b. placenta.
   c. chorion.
 * d. amnion.
   e. yolk sac.

EMERGENCE OF THE VERTEBRATE BODY PLAN

M 66. Which of the following systems is the first of those listed to begin development in the human embryo?
 * a. nervous system
   b. excretory system
   c. reproductive system
   d. skeletal system
   e. endocrine system

WHY IS THE PLACENTA SO IMPORTANT?

M 67. The membrane that forms the majority of the placenta is the
   a. amnion.
   b. allantois.
 * c. chorion.
   d. yolk sac.
   e. umbilical cord.

M 68. Which of the following would be expected to diffuse in greater amounts from the fetal blood to the mother's blood?
   a. oxygen
 * b. urea
   c. hormones
   d. antibodies
   e. nutrients

EMERGENCE OF DISTINCTLY HUMAN FEATURES

D 69. Which of the following does NOT occur in the first trimester?
   a. formation of a heart
   b. disappearance of the tail
   c. formation of internal organs
 * d. detection of movement of the fetus
   e. segmentation and development of somites

E 70. In humans, the embryonic development of a four-chambered heart and the nerve cord is present by which week?
   a. third
 * b. fourth
   c. fifth
   d. sixth
   e. seventh

E **71.** Which drug, if taken during pregnancy, results in the production of infants without arms or legs?
   a. tetracycline
 * b. thalidomide
   c. streptomycin
   d. salicylic acid
   e. codeine

M **72.** Which disease may produce a malformed embryo if the mother develops the disease early in pregnancy?
 * a. German measles
   b. chicken pox
   c. red measles
   d. hepatitis
   e. mumps

FROM BIRTH ONWARD

M **73.** Which of the following statements is false?
   a. Birth usually occurs within an hour of full dilation of the cervix.
 * b. It is not possible for a women to become pregnant after engaging in intercourse if the male does not ejaculate.
   c. The rupture of the amniotic sac with the release of its fluid is one of the events that usually precedes birth.
   d. After the baby is born, uterine contractions continue so that the placenta is expelled.
   e. Just as females should examine their breasts each month for possible lumps, males should also self-examine their testes for lumps that possibly indicate cancer.

M **74.** The female hormones that participate in milk production for the newborn are
 * a. prolactin and oxytocin.
   b. prolactin and estrogen.
   c. prolactin and progesterone.
   d. oxytocin and estrogen.
   e. oxytocin and progesterone.

M **75.** Milk production in women is stimulated by
   a. estrogen.
 * b. prolactin.
   c. oxytocin.
   d. prostaglandin.
   e. progesterone.

E **76.** Postnatal growth is most rapid in a human child
   a. during the first two weeks.
   b. from two weeks to fifteen months.
   c. from infancy to ten years.
 * d. from ages thirteen to nineteen.
   e. during adulthood.

BIRTH CONTROL OPTIONS

E **77.** Which of the following is the most effective in helping prevent venereal disease?
 * a. condoms
   b. the Pill
   c. douching
   d. the IUD
   e. rhythm

D **78.** Which of the following is the most effective contraceptive approach of those listed?
   a. withdrawal
 * b. diaphragm
   c. cheap condoms
   d. douche
   e. rhythm method

E **79.** The type of contraception that functions by preventing implantation (even after successful fertilization) is
   a. tubal ligation.
   b. spermicidal jelly.
   c. birth control pills.
 * d. RU-486.
   e. diaphragm.

E **80.** The type of contraception that works because ovulation is prevented is
   a. rhythm.
   b. tubal ligation.
 * c. birth control pills.
   d. diaphragm.
   e. condom.

M **81.** Which of the following is NOT an effective temporary method of contraception?
   a. birth-control pills
 * b. vasectomy
   c. condoms
   d. IUD plus spermicide
   e. spermicidal jelly or foam

E **82.** Of the following, which is the least successful method of birth control?
   a. early withdrawal
   b. a condom alone
   c. a spermicidal jelly or foam alone
 * d. douching
   e. the Pill

M **83.** A contraceptive pill contains
   a. estrogen.
   b. progesterone.
   c. the follicle-stimulating hormone.
   d. the luteinizing hormone.
 * e. both estrogen and progesterone.

5. G   6. E   7. A   8. B
9. J   10. D   11. K   12. F
13. M   14. N

FOCUS ON BIOETHICS: **TO SEEK OR END PREGNANCY**

D   **84.**   In *in vitro* fertilization, it is possible to tell that an ovum has been fertilized by the presence of
     a. human chorionic gonadotropin.
     b. progesterone.
     c. estrogen.
     d. testosterone.
*   e. the second polar body.

Matching Questions

D   **85.**   Matching I. Choose the one most appropriate answer for each.

     1. ___ abortion
     2. ___ abstention
     3. ___ coitus
     4. ___ douching
     5. ___ ejaculation
     6. ___ implantation
     7. ___ lactation
     8. ___ menopause
     9. ___ menstruation
     10. ___ miscarriage
     11. ___ orgasm
     12. ___ ovulation
     13. ___ tubal ligation
     14. ___ vasectomy

     A. the production and secretion of milk
     B. sloughing off of endometrium stops permanently
     C. birth control exercised after development begins
     D. an abortion that occurs spontaneously
     E. the burrowing of the blastocyst into the uterus
     F. the release of an egg from the ovary
     G. the release of seminal fluid from the male reproductive tract
     H. a 100-percent-effective method of preventing conception
     I. a highly unreliable form of birth control
     J. the periodic elimination of the uterine lining
     K. characterized by involuntary muscle contractions, release of tension, and warmth
     L. sexual intercourse
     M. sperm and egg cannot meet because a section of oviduct is missing
     N. cutting and tying of vas deferens

Answers: 1. C   2. H   3. L   4. I

D   **86.**   Matching II. Choose the one most appropriate answer for each.

     1. ___ acrosome
     2. ___ allantois
     3. ___ blastocyst
     4. ___ cervix
     5. ___ clitoris
     6. ___ endometrium
     7. ___ epididymis
     8. ___ FSH
     9. ___ interstitial cells
     10. ___ LH
     11. ___ placenta
     12. ___ prostaglandins
     13. ___ seminal vesicles
     14. ___ thalidomide
     15. ___ vas deferens

     A. in females, acts on ruptured follicle to produce corpus luteum
     B. structures that secrete mucus and nutrients absorbable by sperm; open into the ejaculatory duct
     C. forms as an outgrowth of the embryonic gut; becomes part of umbilical cord and placenta
     D. a drug that causes severely deformed arms and legs in developing embryos
     E. two of these connect seminiferous tubules with vasa deferentia
     F. opening between uterus and vagina
     G. organ that supplies the embryo/fetus with nutrients and removes wastes
     H. connects epididymis with ejaculatory duct
     I. hormones that stimulate uterine contractions in the female
     J. cap over the head of a sperm; contains lytic enzymes to penetrate egg
     K. inner cell mass plus trophoblast; attaches to uterine wall
     L. testosterone produced here
     M. part of vulva; develops from same embryonic tissues as does the penis in males
     N. the uterine lining
     O. acts on gonad to help mature gametes; released from anterior lobe of pituitary

Answers: 1. J   2. C   3. K   4. F
               5. M   6. N   7. E   8. O
               9. L   10. A   11. G   12. I

13. B   14. D   15. H

Classification Questions

Answer questions 87–91 in reference to the five stages of sperm development listed below:

    a. spermatogonium
    b. secondary spermatocyte
    c. primary spermatocyte
    d. spermatid
    e. sperm

D   **87.** At this stage of development, the male sex cell is first in the haploid condition.

M   **88.** This continues to undergo mitosis throughout the reproductive life of the male.

D   **89.** This represents the product of the first meiotic division.

D   **90.** This is a mitotic product that then undergoes meiosis.

M   **91.** At this stage of development, the male sex cell is fully motile.

Answers: 87. b   88. a   89. b
               90. c   91. e

Answer questions 92–96 in reference to the five stages and structures involved in the development of the human egg:

    a. oogonium
    b. primary oocyte
    c. secondary oocyte
    d. polar body
    e. secondary follicle

M   **92.** This structure becomes the mature egg only after fertilization is begun.

D   **93.** This structure contains the first sex cell stage to be in the haploid state.

M   **94.** This structure contains a full haploid set of chromosomes but will never be fertilized.

M   **95.** This structure divides by mitosis during the fetal stages of development until all of the approximately 2 million potential eggs have been formed.

D   **96.** This stage lies dormant between birth and puberty.

Answers: 92. c   93. c   94. d
               95. a   96. b

Selecting the Exception

M   **97.** Three of the four answers listed below produce portions of the seminal fluid. Select the exception.
    *   a. epididymis
        b. prostate
        c. seminal vesicle
        d. bulbourethral gland

M   **98.** Three of the four answers listed below are related by the number of chromosomes present. Select the exception.
        a. sperm
    *   b. spermatogonia
        c. secondary spermatocyte
        d. spermatids

E   **99.** Three of the four answers listed below are all parts of a sperm. Select the exception.
        a. flagella
        b. midpiece
        c. acrosome
    *   d. polar body

D   **100.** Four of the five answers listed below are related by a common quantity. Select the exception.
    *   a. urethra
        b. testis
        c. ejaculatory duct
        d. vas deferens
        e. epididymis

D   **101.** Four of the five answers listed below are true of testosterone. Select the exception.
        a. promotes secondary sex characteristics
        b. controls sexual behavior
        c. necessary for growth and function of male reproductive tract
        d. stimulates spermatogenesis
    *   e. produced by spermatogonia cells

E   **102.** Four of the five answers listed below are related by gender. Select the exception.
    *   a. Sertoli cells
        b. cervix
        c. clitoris
        d. myometrium
        e. vulva

M   **103.** Four of the five answers listed below are related by a common location. Select the exception.
        a. follicle
        b. corpus luteum
    *   c. cervix
        d. oogonium
        e. antrum

D   **104.** Four of the five answers listed below are related by a matching feature. Select the exception.
    *   a. blastocyst
        b. amnion
        c. allantois
        d. yolk sac
        e. chorion

M 105. Four of the five answers listed below are related by a
         common theme. Select the exception.
         a. alcohol
         b. thalidomide
         c. German measles
    *   d. vitamins
         e. antibiotics

M 106. Four of the five answers listed below are related by a
         similar effectiveness. Select the exception.
         a. the Pill
         b. tubal ligation
         c. vasectomy
    *   d. douching
         e. IUD

CHAPTER 45
POPULATION ECOLOGY

Multiple-Choice Questions

E   1.   Which of the following includes all the others?
         a. ecosystem
      * b. biosphere
         c. community
         d. individual
         e. population

M   2.   By definition, which of the following is NOT a part of a community?
         a. bacteria
         b. populations
         c. animals
      * d. soil
         e. plants

M   3.   A class project designed to study a pond ecosystem would make careful records of
         a. animal life.
         b. plant life.
         c. abiotic factors.
         d. animal and plant life only.
      * e. animal and plant life, abiotic factors plus bacteria, fungi, and protistans

CHARACTERISTICS OF POPULATIONS

E   4.   The total number of individuals of the same species that occupy a given area at a given time is the
         a. population distribution.
         b. population growth.
         c. population birth rate.
      * d. population size.
         e. carrying capacity.

M   5.   The average number of individuals of the same species per unit of surface area at a given time is the
      * a. population density.
         b. population growth.
         c. population birth rate.
         d. population size.
         e. carrying capacity.

M   6.   To a person studying utilization of classroom space on campus, the most useful data concerning students in a classroom would be expressed by the number of
         a. total individuals.
      * b. individuals per square yard.
         c. individuals per room.
         d. rooms per building.
         e. students of each age.

D   7.   Which of the following is NOT one of the factors that control the dispersion of organisms in nature?
      * a. Most environmental resources are randomly distributed.
         b. Biological conditions tend to be patchy.
         c. Dispersal of seeds and young organisms is often limited or controlled by environmental factors.
         d. The development of societies in some populations controls distribution.
         e. Physical features in the environment are not generally uniform.

D   8.   Which of the following would provide a chicken rancher using a noncaged arrangement for his flock the data necessary to ensure maximum survival of his hens?
      * a. distribution
         b. number of individuals
         c. individuals per square foot
         d. size of room
         e. age structure

M   9.   The distribution of the human population in the United States is
      * a. clumped.
         b. random.
         c. uniform.
         d. constant.

M   10. What distribution pattern is the most common in the natural world?
         a. random
         b. uniform
      * c. clumped
         d. stratified or layered
         e. bimodal

M   11. Uniform distribution of human habitats would likely be the result of _____ , whereas habitats of other animals would be due to _____ .
         a. competition; social interaction
      * b. law; competition
         c. social interaction; chemical avoidance
         d. limited mobility; contact inhibition

E   12. Seasonal bird migrations could be cited as an example of
         a. clumped dispersion.
         b. uniform distribution.
         c. random dispersion.
      * d. distribution over time.
         e. distribution based on age structure.

M   13. Population size depends upon
         a. deaths.
         b. births.
         c. migration.
         d. immigration.
    *   e. all of these

M   14. The size of a population is controlled by all but which
         of the following?
         a. biotic potential
    *   b. feeding level
         c. carrying capacity of the environment
         d. death rate
         e. birth rate

POPULATION SIZE AND EXPONENTIAL GROWTH

M   15. Populations of most species
    *   a. are relatively constant over time.
         b. gradually decrease over time.
         c. gradually increase over time.
         d. vary rapidly, depending upon environmental
             conditions.

M   16. A population
         a. is the unit of evolution.
         b. consists of interbreeding members of the same
             species.
         c. shares the same gene pool.
         d. grows at an exponential rate when the birth rate
             exceeds the death rate at a constant differential, no
             matter how slight the difference.
    *   e. all of these

M   17. Zero population growth is achieved when
         a. a population reaches the carrying capacity of the
             environment.
    *   b. the population size has been stabilized for a long
             time.
         c. births exceed deaths.
         d. deaths exceed births.
         e. migration is prevented.

D   18. If the effects of death are imposed on the birth rate of a
         population,
         a. the growth rate will slow down.
         b. the time scale of population growth changes.
         c. eventually—as the environment is
             overexploited—deaths will exceed births.
         d. an exponential growth curve will be produced if
             births exceed deaths at a constant level.
    *   e. all of these

D   19. The biotic potential
         a. varies from one species to another.
         b. is controlled by the timing of the first
             reproduction.
         c. is controlled by the frequency of reproduction.
         d. is controlled by the number of offspring produced.
    *   e. all of these

M   20. A situation in which the birth rate plus immigration
         equals the death rate plus emigration is called
         a. an intrinsic limiting factor.
         b. exponential growth.
         c. saturation.
    *   d. zero population growth.
         e. geometric growth.

D   21. The rate of increase for a population (r) refers to what
         kind of relationship between birth rate and
         death rate?
         a. their sum
         b. their product
         c. the doubling time between them
    *   d. the difference between them
         e. reduction in each of them

M   22. Which characteristic of a population is a convenient
         way to express the rate of change within a population?
         a. size
    *   b. growth
         c. density
         d. carrying capacity
         e. age

M   23. A population that is growing exponentially in the
         absence of limiting factors can be illustrated by which
         curve?
         a. S-shaped
    *   b. J-shaped
         c. one that terminates in a plateau phase
         d. bimodal
         e. binomial

M   24. Which concept is a way to express the growth rate of a
         given population?
    *   a. doubling time
         b. population density
         c. population size
         d. carrying capacity
         e. all of these

D   25. A population of 1,000 individuals with an $r = 1$ in an
         unlimited environment will number _____ four
         years later.
         a. 1,000
         b. 1,004
         c. 4,000
    *   d. 16,000

D   26. If K for a population is 1,200 and $r = 0.1$, which of the
         following populations will show the greatest increase
         over the course of one year?
         a. $N = 100$
         b. $N = 200$
         c. $N = 300$
    *   d. $N = 700$
         e. $N = 900$

D 27. If K for a population is 1,200 and $r = 0.9$, which of the following populations will show the greatest increase over the course of one year?
   a. $N = 100$
   b. $N = 200$
   c. $N = 300$
 * d. $N = 700$
   e. $N = 900$

M 28. For a population in a limited environment, _____ is a variable function that depends on the relationship between _____ and _____.
   a. K, r, N
   b. N, K, r
 * c. r, K, N

M 29. If a population has an $r = 0.02$, which of the following statements must be true?
   a. Two of every 100 individuals will give birth over the course of a year.
   b. Two individuals will be born for every 100 individuals in the population over the course of a year.
   c. Births will exceed deaths by 2% over the course of a year.
   d. The number of individuals added to the population will be 2% greater than the number of individuals removed from the population over the course of a year.
 * e. none of these

D 30. In a population growing exponentially,
   a. the number of individuals added to the population next year is greater than the number added this year.
   b. the population growth rate increases year after year.
   c. net reproduction per individual increases year after year.
 * d. the number of individuals added to the population next year is greater than the number added this year and the population growth rate increases year after year.
   e. the number of individuals added to the population next year is greater than the number added this year, the population growth rate increases year after year, and net reproduction per individual increases year after year.

M 31. A population will exhibit a negative growth rate if
   a. predation continues indefinitely.
   b. N is greater than $1/2 K$.
   c. number of births + number of immigrants equals number of deaths + number of emigrants.
 * d. r is less than 0.

LIMITS ON THE GROWTH OF POPULATIONS

M 32. Populations
   a. are limited by only one factor at a time.
   b. increase arithmetically.
   c. increase indefinitely.
 * d. are limited by the carrying capacity.
   e. are represented by a minimum of two different sizes.

D 33. In natural communities, feedback mechanisms called _____ operate when the size of a population changes.
   a. density-dependent controls
   b. density-independent factors
   c. biotic factors
   d. physical factors
 * e. density-dependent controls and biotic factors

M 34. Interaction between resource availability and a population's tolerance to prevailing environmental conditions defines
 * a. the carrying capacity of the environment.
   b. exponential growth.
   c. the doubling time of a population.
   d. density-independent factors.
   e. all of these

D 35. Limiting factors
   a. produce more pronounced effects as a population grows.
   b. prevent a population from producing a J-shaped curve.
   c. can be either density-dependent or density-independent.
   d. act together in concert to form the environmental resistance to population growth.
 * e. all of these

D 36. A J-shaped growth curve is converted to an S-shaped one
   a. when the parents are past reproductive age.
   b. if the data are plotted in reverse.
 * c. when the carrying capacity is reached.
   d. if reproduction stops.
   e. only for fast-growing populations such as bacteria.

D 37. The carrying capacity of an environment is determined by
   a. the net rate of reproduction of the female members.
   b. an S-shaped curve.
   c. the predation rate on the females.
   d. diseases suffered by both sexes.
 * e. the sustainable supply of resources it provides.

M 38. Carrying capacity of an environment is increased by
   a. pollution.
   b. predation.
   c. disease.
   d. population growth.
 * e. none of these

D 39. In natural communities, some feedback mechanisms operate whenever populations change in size; they are
*   a. density-dependent factors.
  b. density-independent factors.
  c. always intrinsic to the individuals of the community.
  d. always extrinsic to the individuals of the community.
  e. none of these

E 40. A change in a population that is NOT related strictly to the size of the population is best described as
  a. density-dependent.
*   b. density-independent.
  c. intrinsic.
  d. an S-shaped curve.
  e. a J-shaped curve.

M 41. In itself, a flood that washes away an entire population of rabbits is
  a. a density-dependent factor.
  b. an intrinsic limiting factor.
  c. a consequence of exponential growth.
*   d. density-independent.
  e. all of these

E 42. Density-independent controls over population growth include
  a. parasites.
*   b. temperature.
  c. disease.
  d. competition.
  e. all of these

M 43. Which density-dependent factor controls the size of a population?
  a. wind velocity
  b. light intensity
*   c. nutrient supply
  d. rainfall
  e. wave action in an intertidal zone

E 44. In ecosystems, the factors that tend to reduce the size of some populations, regardless of how large the population is, are called
  a. density-dependent factors.
*   b. density-independent factors.
  c. ecological factors.
  d. abiotic factors.

E 45. Which is NOT a density-dependent, growth-limiting factor?
  a. predation
*   b. drought
  c. parasitism
  d. competition

D 46. A density-dependent factor is one that
  a. increases in intensity as r increases.
  b. increases in intensity as N increases.
*   c. increases in intensity as the ratio N/K increases.
  d. increases in intensity as the ratio K/N increases.

M 47. As population density increases, the chance of _____ also increases.
  a. parasitism
  b. pathogens
  c. predation
  d. competition
*   e. all of these

LIFE HISTORY PATTERNS

M 48. A cohort is
*   a. a group of newborn individuals of the same species.
  b. any member of the same species.
  c. any member of the same species and sex within a population.
  d. a sexual mate.
  e. a litter mate or sibling within a large population.

M 49. Two populations of the same species have equal immigration, emigration, and death rates, and the females in each population produce four offspring on average during their reproductive years. If the two populations have different net reproductive rates, it is because
  a. one population has more food than the other.
  b. one population has less disease than the other.
*   c. one population breeds at later ages than does the other.
  d. one population has more food than the other and one population has less disease than the other.
  e. one population has more food than the other, one population has less disease than the other, and one population breeds at later ages than does the other.

E 50. Life tables provide data concerning
  a. expected life span.
  b. reproductive age.
  c. death rate.
  d. birth rate.
*   e. all of these

D 51. Type II survivorship curves
  a. are characteristic of humans and elephants.
*   b. typify a population in which all ages have an equal chance of surviving.
  c. indicate a high mortality rate in the very young.
  d. show that very few young are produced, that each is given parental support, and that most individuals live a relatively long life and die of old age.
  e. are typical of annual plants.

M 52. A study of a cohort of 1,000 newborn animals showed a death rate per individual in year one of 60% and a death rate per individual in year two of 20%. Quantity of survivors after two years is
  a. 120.
  b. 200.
*   c. 320.
  d. 400.

M 53. A type III survivorship curve is characteristic of
    a. monkeys.
    b. horses.
    c. eagles.
    * d. sea urchins.

M 54. Organisms that demonstrate a type I survivorship curve are characterized by
    a. high r, small offspring.
    b. low r, small offspring.
    * c. low r, large offspring.
    d. high r, large offspring.

M 55. As elephants have become more crowded in African game reserves, their average gestation period has increased from 22 months to as long as 25 months. This observation indicates that
    a. elephants are regulated by density-dependent factors.
    b. r is not a constant.
    c. the elephant population must be decreasing.
    * d. elephants are regulated by density-dependent factors and r is not a constant.
    e. elephants are regulated by density-dependent factors, r is not a constant, and the elephant population must be decreasing.

M 56. A type III survivorship curve (mortality high at birth and decreasing with age) is characteristic of all but which species?
    a. flies
    * b. humans
    c. frogs
    d. reptiles
    e. fish

NATURAL SELECTION AND THE GUPPIES OF TRINIDAD

M 57. The work of Reznick and Endler with guppies has shown that
    a. the r of a population is determined by natural selection.
    b. the average age at which individuals attain sexual maturity is determined by natural selection.
    c. the r of a population has a genetic basis.
    d. the r of a population is determined by natural selection and the average age at which individuals attain sexual maturity is determined by natural selection.
    * e. the r of a population is determined by natural selection, the average age at which individuals attain sexual maturity is determined by natural selection, and the r of a population has a genetic basis.

D 58. Killifish and pike-cichlids raised in natural conditions will
    a. control the size of the guppies that live with them.
    b. function as predators of guppies.
    c. determine the growth rate of guppies.
    d. control the evolution of size and color of the guppies.
    * e. all of these

HUMAN POPULATION GROWTH

E 59. The leading cause of human deaths is
    a. heart disease.
    b. cancer.
    * c. malnutrition and starvation.
    d. war.
    e. accidents.

D 60. All but which one of the following are the reasons for the rapid population explosion of humans?
    a. increases in carrying capacity
    b. expansion into new habitats
    c. removal of limiting factors
    d. reproduction occurring earlier in the life cycle
    * e. longer generation times

M 61. The tremendous increase in the number of human beings over the course of the past 100 years is attributable to
    a. immunization and vaccination programs.
    b. colonization of previously underutilized habitat.
    c. more equal distribution of patchy resources.
    d. immunization and vaccination programs plus colonization of previously underutilized habitat.
    * e. immunization and vaccination programs plus colonization of previously underutilized habitat, and more equal distribution of patchy resources.

M 62. Which of the following is NOT a factor that has led to the dramatic increase in the human population?
    a. increase of carrying capacity
    b. removal of several limiting factors
    c. human invasion of new habitats and climatic zones
    * d. an increase in the levels of pollution in the world
    e. the development of public health and the germ theory of disease

M 63. The earliest human populations were found in
    a. tropical rain forests.
    b. deserts.
    c. the taiga.
    * d. the savanna.
    e. temperate deciduous forests.

M 64. Which of the following groups of plants formed the basis for the development of agriculture and the spread of civilization?
    * a. grasses
    b. legumes
    c. potato-tomato family
    d. sunflower family

D 65. Which of the following is NOT subject to the limits imposed by the principles of logistic growth?
    a. bacteria
    b. fungi
    c. small animals
    d. humans
   * e. All of these are subject to such limits.

M 66. If all disease is eradicated and food supply exceeds demand indefinitely, the human population on the planet earth will NOT continue to grow at an exponential rate indefinitely because
    a. a new disease organism will evolve.
    b. density-independent factors will always remove individuals.
   * c. space will become a limiting factor.
    d. all of these

E 67. The greatest reduction of human population in recorded history was the result of
    a. a global ice age.
    b. two world wars.
   * c. bubonic plague.
    d. family planning.
    e. ozone depletion.

CONTROL THROUGH FAMILY PLANNING

M 68. The most reasonable method of limiting human population growth is
    a. increasing carrying capacity.
   * b. decreasing birth rate.
    c. decreasing competition.
    d. increasing death rate.
    e. exploiting outer space.

M 69. If the reproductive rate drops to the maintenance level (zero population growth), how many year(s) would it take for world population to stop growing?
    a. 1
    b. 20
    c. 50
   * d. 60
    e. 150

E 70. Which of the following countries has established the most extensive family-planning program?
    a. the United States
    b. Brazil
   * c. China
    d. Japan
    e. Pakistan

E 71. When the human population growth of the world is calculated, the doubling time is
    a. about the same as it was 20 years ago.
   * b. decreasing at an accelerated pace.
    c. increasing slowly.
    d. in a gradual decline.
    e. about 1.8%.

M 72. The age-structure diagram for rapidly growing populations
    a. is in the form of a pyramid.
    b. is characterized by a large percentage of the population in the postreproductive years.
    c. has a very broad base showing a large number of young.
    d. has about equal distribution among all age groups.
   * e. is in the form of a pyramid and has a very broad base showing a large number of young.

D 73. If reproduction occurs early in the life cycle, what occurs?
   * a. Population growth rate increases.
    b. Population size declines.
    c. Population size is not affected.
    d. Generation time increases.
    e. Growth rate remains unchanged.

POPULATION GROWTH AND ECONOMIC DEVELOPMENT

M 74. As the twenty-first century approaches, the continent with the highest potential for human population growth rate is _____ , and that with the lowest is _____ .
    a. North America; Asia
    b. Asia; North America
   * c. Africa; Europe
    d. Africa; Asia

D 75. In which demographic model is population growth the fastest?
    a. preindustrial
   * b. transitional
    c. industrial
    d. postindustrial

E 76. Which of the following countries has a population that is farthest from zero population growth?
    a. Sweden
   * b. Mexico
    c. United Kingdom
    d. Germany
    e. Hungary

Matching Questions

D **77.** Matching. Choose the one most appropriate answer for each.

    1. ___ age structure

    2. ___ population growth rate

    3. ___ J-shaped curve

    4. ___ limiting factor

       A. describes a population that is experiencing unrestrained growth

       B. the birth rate minus the death rate plus any inward migration or minus any outward migration

       C. how individuals are distributed at each age level for a population

       D. the amount of glucose in a culture flask containing bacteria, for example

Answers: 1. C   2. B   3. A   4. D

Classification Questions

Answer questions 78–82 in reference to the four levels of organization listed below:

    a. population
    b. community
    c. ecosystem
    d. biosphere

E **78.** This is composed of producers, consumers, decomposers, and the abiotic environment.

E **79.** All of the individuals of a single species living in a region constitute this.

M **80.** A group of different species living together in a single habitat is this.

M **81.** This is the basic functional unit of ecology.

E **82.** This contains all of the others.

Answers: 78. c   79. a   80. b

            81. c   82. d

Answer questions 83–87 in reference to the five terms listed below that are used by ecologists:

    a. carrying capacity
    b. net reproductive rate
    c. age structure
    d. survivorship
    e. growth rate

D **83.** The average number of offspring born to each female over her reproductive lifetime is known as this.

M **84.** The number of individuals in each of several age categories is known as this.

M **85.** The maximum number of individuals that a given habitat can support is known as this.

D **86.** A change in the available food supply in a habitat will affect all of these except this.

E **87.** This term is equal to the birth rate minus the death rate of a species.

Answers   83.b   84. c   85. a

            86. c   87. e

Selecting the Exception

E **88.** Four of the five answers listed below are parts of the ecosystem. Select the exception.

   * a. energy
      b. raw materials and nutrients
      c. decomposers
      d. producers
      e. consumers

D **89.** Four of the five answers below are limits to achieving a population's full biotic potential. Select the exception.

      a. lack of nutrients
      b. predation
   * c. exponential growth
      d. competition for space
      e. waste buildup

E **90.** Four of the five answers listed below are components of the abiotic environment. Select the exception.

      a. soil
      b. rainfall
   * c. competitors
      d. temperature
      e. sunlight

E **91.** Four of the five answers listed below are factors that affect population size. Select the exception.

      a. births
   * b. distribution
      c. emigration
      d. immigration
      e. deaths

D   92.   Four of the five answers listed below follow a type II survivorship curve. Select the exception.
          a.   songbirds
      *   b.   large mammals with extended parental care
          c.   small mammals
          d.   lizards
          e.   seeds prior to germination

D   93.   Four of the five answers listed below follow a type III survivorship curve. Select the exception.
          a.   most insects
          b.   most reptiles
          c.   many fishes
      *   d.   humans
          e.   most marine invertebrates

M   94.   Four of the five answers listed below are density-independent factors. Select the exception.
      *   a.   nutrient supply
          b.   temperature drop
          c.   drought
          d.   volcanic eruption
          e.   hard freeze

CHAPTER 46
SOCIAL INTERACTIONS

Multiple-Choice Questions

E   1.   After starlings build a nest, they add branches with living leaves
    a.   as a form of camouflage against predators.
    b.   as a form of insulation.
  * c.   to repel parasites.
    d.   to prevent other birds from using the nest.
    e.   for reasons that are currently unknown.

D   2.   Which of the following statements is false?
    a.   Behavior patterns are inherited.
    b.   Instinctive behavior involves a complete response to a key stimulus the first time it is encountered.
    c.   Behavior evolved as a result of natural selection.
    d.   Reproductive success is responsible for perpetuating behavior patterns.
  * e.   The mechanisms underlying instinctive and learned behavior are the same.

BEHAVIOR'S HERITABLE BASIS

M   3.   Which of the following statements is false?
    a.   Behavior is controlled by the environmental stimuli an organism receives.
    b.   Behavior is partially genetic so that it undergoes natural selection and evolution.
  * c.   Behavior refers only to responses to external stimuli.
    d.   Behavior sometimes is nonadaptive.
    e.   Behavior patterns can be learned.

M   4.   All but which of the following statements concerning behavior are true?
    a.   The knee-jerk reflex is a behavior.
  * b.   A behavior such as a complex courtship ritual is encoded by a single gene.
    c.   Behaviors are products of natural selection.
    d.   Behaviors are adaptive.

M   5.   Recent studies in humans have shown there is a close relationship between poor nutrition and poor learning ability. These studies suggest that
    a.   there is only a minor genetic component to learned behavior.
  * b.   behavior is modified by the environment.
    c.   learning is adaptive.
    d.   learning is instinctive.

M   6.   Of the following, which is NOT a behavior?
    a.   contraction of muscle
  * b.   enzymatic breakdown of food
    c.   salivation
    d.   breathing

M   7.   Behavior is the result of
    a.   neural networks.
    b.   hormonal interactions.
    c.   genetic predisposition.
    d.   environmental cues.
  * e.   all of these

M   8.   The pineal gland responds to
    a.   light intensity.
  * b.   light duration or photoperiod.
    c.   flashes of light.
    d.   red light.
    e.   different colors of light.

D   9.   Melatonin specifically controls or interacts to control
    a.   the growth of the gonads of birds.
    b.   migration.
    c.   sexual behavior patterns.
    d.   singing and territorial behavior.
  * e.   all of these

M   10.   Motor activity and metabolic rates associated with biological clocks are coordinated by
    a.   thyroxin secreted by the thyroid gland.
  * b.   melatonin secreted by the pineal gland.
    c.   a magnetic sense that is attuned to variations in Earth's magnetic field.
    d.   pheromones released by the dominant animal of the group.
    e.   all of these

M   11.   Which hormone activates the song system when a bird sings?
    a.   melatonin
  * b.   testosterone
    c.   estrogen
    d.   calcitonin
    e.   epinephrine

M   12.   Birds sing
    a.   because they are inherently happy.
    b.   only for species recognition.
  * c.   as a way to declare territory.
    d.   only during courtship.

D   13.   A deficiency of estrogen in a young songbird will
    a.   cause a female to begin singing.
    b.   result in a female becoming a male.
  * c.   disrupt the development of the song system.
    d.   allow more melatonin to be secreted.

M 14. Which of the following statements about white-throated sparrows is false?
   a. There is a region of a bird's brain called the song system.
   b. In young males, the level of estrogen is higher than in young females.
   c. The syrinx is the vocal organ of songbirds.
   d. The two female hormones, estrogen and progesterone, induce the differences in males and females.
   * e. All that is necessary for a bird to sing is the masculinization of the brain.

M 15. Which of the following is true?
   a. Estrogen both organizes the song system and activates it.
   * b. Estrogen organizes the song system, testosterone activates it.
   c. Progesterone organizes the song system, testosterone activates it.
   d. Progesterone organizes the song system, estrogen activates it.
   e. Testosterone activates the song system, estrogen activates it.

M 16. The cells surrounding milk-producing cells in the female mammary gland contract shortly after the female hears the cry of an infant. This is an example of
   a. a response that is not a behavior.
   * b. instinctive behavior.
   c. imprinting behavior.
   d. learned behavior.

M 17. Instinctive behavior is
   a. stereotyped.
   b. unlearned.
   c. induced each and every time the stimulus is presented.
   d. triggered by limited sets of clues.
   * e. all of these

E 18. To get a young baby to smile, simply present a
   a. parent's smiling face.
   b. parent's nonsmiling face.
   c. person's face or a mask.
   d. picture of a face.
   * e. representation of a face, so long as it has two recognizable eyes.

D 19. Which of the following concerning instinctive behavior is false?
   a. Instinctive behavior does not have to be learned.
   b. Behavior in newborn animals is mainly instinctive.
   * c. Instinct is genetically determined but environment controls learning.
   d. Instinct is recognized by its stereotyped nature.

LEARNED BEHAVIOR

D 20. Learned behavior is recognizable by the _____ the animal makes in its responses.
   a. fixed patterns
   * b. changes
   c. stereotyping
   d. repetitions
   e. false starts

M 21. In classical conditioning,
   * a. two different stimuli elicit the same response.
   b. two different stimuli elicit two different responses.
   c. one stimulus elicits one response.
   d. one stimulus elicits two different responses.

M 22. The principal difference between classical Pavlovian conditioning and operant conditioning is
   a. that one uses a reinforcing stimulus and the other does not.
   * b. that one presents the reinforcing stimulus before the response and the other one after.
   c. that one uses a bell as a reinforcing stimulus and the other one uses an instrument.
   d. that a satiety center is involved in one and an aggression center in the other.
   e. all of these

E 23. A cat explores all the rooms of a new home even though such exploration is NOT rewarded. Later, when the cat begins to feel chilled, it goes directly to the warmest room. This is an example of
   a. classical conditioning.
   b. echolocation.
   * c. latent learning.
   d. imprinting.
   e. all of these

M 24. A child grabs a dog's ear, and the dog responds by biting the child. Both behaviors are repeated once again the next day, and again a day later. The child never grabs a dog's ear again. This sequence of events is an example of
   a. insight learning.
   b. latent learning.
   * c. operant conditioning.
   d. imprinting.

E 25. The ability of a rat to solve a maze to obtain a reward is increased if it has the chance to explore the maze before the test begins. This is an example of
   a. insight learning.
   * b. latent learning.
   c. associative learning.
   d. conditioning.
   e. extinction.

D 26. Horticulturists use periodic discharges of loud sounds to scare birds away from their fruit trees. After several days birds can be seen ignoring the sounds due to
  * a. habituation.
  b. imprinting.
  c. conditioning.
  d. insight learning.
  e. instinct.

E 27. If a dog stops responding to the loud noise produced by its master when he bangs his pipe against an ashtray, the dog is exhibiting a behavior pattern known as
  a. imprinting.
  b. insight learning.
  * c. habituation.
  d. trail-and-error learning.

D 28. Humans, and other primates , differ from most animals in their ability to learn by
  a. conditioning.
  b. imprinting.
  c. habituation.
  * d. insight.
  e. latent learning.

E 29. Konrad Lorenz is noted for his studies on
  a. prenatal marking.
  b. mating behavior.
  * c. imprinting.
  d. habituation.
  e. insight learning.

E 30. Imprinting is a
  a. response to a stimulus.
  * b. learned behavior that occurs during a critical time period.
  c. fixed action potential.
  d. decline in the level of a response to a nonthreatening stimulus.

E 31. Newly hatched goslings follow any large moving objects to which they are exposed shortly after hatching. This is an example of
  a. homing behavior.
  * b. imprinting.
  c. piloting.
  d. migration.
  e. none of these

E 32. Which of the following is initiated before birth or hatching?
  a. imprinting
  b. habituation
  c. classic conditioning
  d. operant conditioning
  * e. none of these

D 33. Studies of _____ in young animals could lend support for arguments that human parents and babies need to spend as much time together as possible.
  a. conditioning
  * b. imprinting
  c. habituation
  d. insight learning
  e. latent learning

D 34. Which of the following is false?
  a. Imprinting can be learned only during a limited time span.
  b. Bird song can be learned only during a limited time span.
  c. For a bird to be able to sing the song of its species, it must have heard it.
  d. Instinctive behavior has adaptive value.
  * e. In explaining a behavioral trait, it is better to use an approach based upon a species benefiting rather than an individual benefiting.

M 35. Bird song
  a. has to be heard before a bird can sing it.
  b. is learned during early life.
  c. is specific for each bird species.
  d. has a genetic component.
  * e. all of these

THE ADAPTIVE VALUE OF BEHAVIOR

D 36. Which of the following statements is false?
  a. Territorial pairs of ravens feed silently.
  b. Single nonterritorial ravens proclaim the discovery of a food source.
  c. Sexual selection through competition for mates leads to evolutionary change.
  * d. Reproductive success is based upon the same criteria for both sexes.
  e. Males that do not have territorial or sexual status sometimes employ strategies that allow them to mate.

D 37. During aggressive encounters between members of the same species,
  a. the strong members are always victorious.
  b. the invader into a territory is able to replace the current resident of the territory unless he has already mated.
  * c. opponents usually settle the dispute without bloodshed.
  d. a fight to the death occurs, with the one higher in the pecking order being successful more often.

E 38. Altruistic behavior is
  a. selfish.
  b. sexually directed behavior.
  * c. self-sacrificing behavior.
  d. aggressive behavior.
  e. nonreactive, such as freezing at the sign of danger.

E 39. Which of the following behavior patterns is limited to the most highly evolved forms?
    a. imprinting
*   b. insight learning
    c. habituation
    d. operant conditioning
    e. classical conditioning

M 40. The example used to demonstrate that Darwinian natural selection explains some behavioral traits better than does group selection is
    a. the dilution effect in wildebeest and zebra populations.
    b. siblicide among egrets.
    c. courtship behavior in albatrosses.
*   d. the dispersal of Norwegian lemmings when population densities became extremely high.
    e. all of these

D 41. Altruism in animals other than humans is
*   a. probably a perception by human observers.
    b. gene-based.
    c. a conscious effort to preserve the species.
    d. just lucky behavior.

COMMUNICATION SIGNALS

E 42. Pheromones are
*   a. used in nonverbal communication.
    b. found only in the invertebrates.
    c. signals to members of other species.
    d. types of internal hormones that control maturation.

E 43. Pheromones are advantageous because
    a. they work in the dark.
    b. they are often unique to individual species.
    c. only small amounts are needed.
    d. they do not trigger a response in other species.
*   e. all of these

E 44. Social behavior among insects depends on
    a. genetic similarity.
    b. bonding early in youth.
*   c. communication.
    d. diversity.
    e. polymorphism.

E 45. Social behavior is most obviously the result of
    a. genetics.
*   b. communication signals.
    c. environmental influences.
    d. parental upbringing.
    e. learning.

M 46. Even though the termite can detect the scent of an invading ant, this is not considered a form of communication between termite and ant for which of the following reasons?
    a. The scent is not sufficient to cause a response in the termite.
*   b. Communication must benefit both the signaler and the receiver.
    c. The ant does realize it is giving off a scent.
    d. The scent is not sufficient to cause a response in the termite; and Communication must benefit both the signaler and the receiver.
    e. The scent is not sufficient to cause a response in the termite; Communication must benefit both the signaler and the receiver; and The ant does realize it is giving off a scent.

E 47. A termite that intercepts the scent of an ant is called
*   a. an illegitimate receiver.
    b. an exploiter.
    c. an illegitimate signaler.
    d. smart.

E 48. Which scientist won the Nobel Prize for his research on the behavior of bees and the discovery of the way bees communicated the location of a food source?
*   a. Karl von Frish
    b. Nicholas Tinbergen
    c. Konrad Lorenz
    d. Skinner
    e. Pavlov

E 49. Bees learn the direction to a distant source of food by
    a. following the foraging scout.
    b. following a trail pheromone.
*   c. observing the tail-wagging dance.
    d. observing the round dance.
    e. observing the tail-wagging dance and the round dance.

M 50. Bees use which information for locating food and the hive?
    a. local topographic features
    b. odors
    c. magnetism
*   d. the angle of the sun
    e. distance between plants

D 51. Which of the following communication signals is mismatched?
    a. tactile—honeybees
    b. acoustical—frogs
    c. visual—baboons
    d. chemical or olfactory—termites and honeyflies
*   e. chemical or olfactory—albatrosses

M 52. Communication by means of visual signals has a minimum requirement of
    a. daylight.
    b. short distance.
*   c. a clear line of sight.
    d. keen eyesight.
    e. sharp hearing.

M 53. Which of the following is false?
   a. Yawning by a baboon is a threat signal.
   b. Threat displays evolve through natural selection.
   c. Threat displays benefit both the sender and the receiver.
 * d. Of necessity, visual displays are brief, direct, and obvious.
   e. Some predatory fireflies use light flashes to attract a male firefly for predation.

E 54. The communication signal requiring the most minimal distance between the sender and receiver animals is
   a. visual.
   b. chemical.
   c. acoustical.
 * d. tactile.

MATES, PARENTS, AND INDIVIDUAL REPRODUCTIVE SUCCESS

M 55. Many zoos have reported cases of animals attempting to mate with individuals of different species. It appears that the animals have imprinted on an inappropriate species. These cases indicate that
   a. imprinting has a genetic basis.
   b. insight learning is necessary for species recognition.
 * c. a behavior that is adaptive in one environment may be maladaptive in another.
   d. conditioned reflexes can cause extinction of imprinted behaviors.

M 56. In many bird and mammal species, males compete for females, but females do NOT compete for males because
   a. males are larger than females.
   b. females are larger than males.
 * c. females produce fewer gametes than males do.
   d. females compete for territory.

COSTS AND BENEFITS OF LIVING IN SOCIAL GROUPS

M 57. When researchers attempt to answer the question of why various animals exist in such a diversity of social units from solitary to complex societies, they use
   a. genetic analysis.
   b. habitat data.
 * c. cost-benefit analysis.
   d. environmental studies.
   e. time-density data.

D 58. All but which of the following are disadvantages to sociality?
 * a. predator avoidance
   b. cannibalism
   c. food depletion
   d. contagious diseases
   e. parasite infestation

D 59. The presence of the strongest competitors in the center of a group of animals may qualify the group for status as a(n)
   a. altruistic society.
 * b. selfish herd.
   c. kin group.
   d. dominance hierarchy.

D 60. Which of the following features of territoriality is NOT an advantage?
   a. Territorial behavior enables a male to attract a mate.
 * b. Territoriality requires a male to place himself at risk.
   c. Territoriality ensures an adequate food supply.
   d. Territoriality limits the size of a population and its impact upon its environment.

M 61. In the selfish herd, there is an advantage to
   a. being on the outside.
   b. being near the front.
 * c. being in the middle.
   d. being isolated.
   e. Position is of no advantage.

M 62. Which of the following statements concerning subordinate behavior as exemplified by interactions among members of wolf packs is true?
   a. It is gradually being removed by natural selection.
 * b. It is adaptive.
   c. It is self-sacrificing.
   d. It is inexplicable in terms of reproductive success.

M 63. The example used to demonstrate that competitive interactions lead to the formation of dominance hierarchies involved
   a. albatrosses.
   b. a honeybee colony.
 * c. baboon troops.
   d. greylag geese.
   e. all of these

M 64. Which behavior is exhibited when one animal meets or interacts with a superior member of its group?
   a. aggressive
   b. neutral
   c. sexual
 * d. appeasement
   e. all of these, at certain times

EVOLUTION OF ALTRUISM

D 65. Whatever the motivation of self-sacrificing behavior on the part of nonhuman animals is, we know it is NOT
   a. genetic.
   b. the result of selection.
 * c. derived from conscious reasoning.
   d. a result of dominance hierarchy.

D 66. Which of the following statements is false?
  a. A communication signal has benefits for both the sender and the receiver.
  b. Under some circumstances, solitary individuals may leave more descendants than social ones do.
  * c. Social animals must exhibit altruism.
  d. Not every environment favors the evolution of social life.
  e. Altruism means helping others, which may mean sacrificing personal reproductive success.

E 67. Parental support of offspring is an example of
  a. artificial selection.
  * b. kin selection.
  c. natural selection.
  d. negative selection.
  e. stabilizing selection.

M 68. A bird in a forest sees a falcon and issues an alarm call. As a result of this communication, the falcon is able to orient toward the caller and subsequently capture it. However, calling behavior does NOT disappear in the prey species because
  a. the behavior is not acted on by natural selection.
  * b. of the advantage of kin selection.
  c. calling behavior is genetically based, and mutations constantly occur to produce it.
  d. some of the time, predatory birds such as falcons do not capture the caller.

D 69. Researchers attempt to explain the persistence of altruism by the theory of
  a. self-sacrificing behavior.
  b. dominance hierarchy.
  c. social behavior.
  * d. indirect selection.

M 70. Indirect selection refers to
  a. predators.
  b. dominance hierarchy.
  * c. altruistic behavior.
  d. the development of harems.
  e. symbiotic organisms.

D 71. If an individual for whatever reason cannot pass on its genes to offspring, the best alternative is to show altruism to
  * a. relatives.
  b. strangers.
  c. neighbors.
  d. other species.

FOCUS ON SCIENCE: WHY SACRIFICE YOURSELF?

D 72. Which of the following statements is false?
  a. Humans may exhibit altruistic behavior.
  b. Social life may increase the risk for disease and competition.
  * c. Social species are more highly evolved.
  d. In some social communities sterility is an advantage, so natural selection can act to favor sterility.
  e. Indirect selection is based upon altruism, which in its extreme expression may lead to sterility.

M 73. In highly integrated insect societies,
  a. natural selection favors individual behaviors that lead to greater diversity among members of the society.
  b. there is scarcely any division of labor.
  * c. cooperative behavior predominates.
  d. patterns of behavior are flexible, and learned behavior predominates.
  e. all of these

M 74. Drones in a bee hive are able to do which activity?
  a. search for food
  b. defend the hive
  * c. reproduce
  d. clean and care for the developing larvae
  e. build the honeycomb

M 75. Naked mole-rat colonies of 25 to 300 individuals
  a. are characterized by only one fertile female and two to four fertile males.
  b. show a high level of inbreeding.
  c. demonstrate a high degree of genetic diversity among different colonies
  d. can be genetically characterized by comparing samples of DNA molecules of various individuals by genetic fingerprinting.
  * e. all of these

AN EVOLUTIONARY VIEW OF HUMAN SOCIAL BEHAVIOR

D 76. Only in judging human behaviors does the concept of "_____" supplant "adaptation."
  a. self-sacrifice
  b. altruism
  c. judgment
  * d. morality

Matching Questions

D **77.** Matching. Choose the one most appropriate answer for each. Some letters may not be used.

1. ___ altruism
2. ___ insight
3. ___ instinctive behavior
4. ___ imprinting
5. ___ lek
6. ___ learning
7. ___ Lorenz
8. ___ Pavlov
9. ___ Heinrich

   A. studied territorial feeding in ravens
   B. imprintings in goslings
   C. capacity of an animal to complete complex, stereotyped responses to first-time encounters to key stimuli
   D. problem solving without trial-and-error
   E. an adaptive change in behavior
   F. conditioned reflexes and associative learning
   G. communal display ground
   H. occurs during a sensitive period in which a following response or social attachment becomes fixed on a particular moving object
   I. self-sacrificing behavior

Answers: 1. I   2. D   3. C
              4. H   5. G   6. E
              7. B   8. F   9. A

Classification Questions

Answer questions 78-82 in reference to the four processes listed below associated with learning:

   a. conditioning
   b. latent learning
   c. insight learning
   d. habituation

M **78.** This process is a synthesis of previous experiences to provide novel solutions to a problem.

M **79.** The process whereby an individual's performance on some task or activity improves following a period of inactivity or involvement in some other activity is known as:

M **80.** Trial-and-error learning is a subcategory of this.

M **81.** The ability of an animal to connect a novel experience with one that is familiar is known as this.

E **82.** A person ignores a repetitive noise. This is an example of:

Answers: 78. c   79. b   80. a
           81. a   82. d

Answer questions 83-87 in reference to the five kinds of behavior listed below:

   a. imprinting
   b. sexual selection
   c. antipredator behavior
   d. female-defense behavior
   e. altruism

M **83.** The extreme variation observed among the males of various species of ducks is thought to be due to this kind of behavior.

E **84.** Many organisms increase their apparent size when startled by another. This is an example of:

E **85.** If the young of precocial birds (e.g., chickens or ducks) are continually shown a large moving object during the first few days of their lives, they will follow that object. This is an example of:

M **86.** The adult male who jumps overboard to save a drowning niece is exhibiting:

M **87.** Two male bison butting one another during the breeding season are probably exhibiting:

Answers: 83. b   84. c   85. a
           86. e   87. d

Answer questions 88-92 in reference to the four kinds of reception listed below that are used by social animals:

   a. tactile
   b. auditory
   c. visual
   d. chemical

M **88.** This sensory modality is used by honeybees during the waggle dance.

E **89.** The sex pheromone emitted by a female gypsy moth relies upon this sense in the male.

E **90.** The elaborate posturing displays of male birds-of-paradise utilize this sense in the female.

D **91.** The primary signal sent out by receptive female primates is likely to be this.

D **92.** The alarm signal one snail sends to another is most likely to be this.

Answers: 88. a   89. d   90. c
           91. d   92. d

Answer questions 93-97 in reference to the four kinds of social behavior listed below:

    a. altruism
    b. cooperation
    c. self-sacrifice
    d. kin selection

D   **93.** When the offspring of one brood of Florida scrubjays helps their parents in taking care of their siblings in the next brood, this is an example of:

M   **94.** When a bluejay gives an alarm call at the intrusion of a crow into a woodlot, this is an example of:

E   **95.** When two or more female lions attack a wildebeest together, this is an example of:

M   **96.** When a female woodcock flutters off her nest exhibiting a cripple-wing display to distract a predator, this is an example of:

M   **97.** When a woman raises her brother's children, this is an example of:

Answers: 93. d   94. a   95. b

              96. c   97. d

Selecting the Exception

E   **98.** Four of the five answers listed below are characteristics of behaviors that are inborn. Select the exception.
    * a. modified by the environment
       b. stereotyped
       c. performed the first time stimulus presented
       d. innate
       e. automatic

M   **99.** Four of the five answers listed below are involved in associative learning. Select the exception.
       a. reward
       b. punishment
       c. extinction
       d. selection
    * e. disregard of stimulus

M   **100.** Four of the five answers listed below are species in which the females cluster and the males fight. Select the exception.
    * a. dogs
       b. lions
       c. elk
       d. bison
       e. bighorn sheep

M   **101.** Four of the five answers listed below are castes of termites. Select the exception.
    * a. drone
       b. king
       c. queen
       d. soldier
       e. worker

M   **102.** Four of the five answers listed below are pheromone signals. Select the exception.
       a. sex
       b. alarm or attack
       c. territory
    * d. threat
       e. trail

M   **103.** Four of the five answers listed below are activities of the same type of bee. Select the exception.
    * a. lay eggs
       b. feed larvae
       c. guard hive
       d. clean and maintain nest
       e. forage for food

CHAPTER 47
COMMUNITY INTERACTIONS

Multiple-Choice Questions

WHICH FACTORS SHAPE COMMUNITY STRUCTURE?

E   1.   All of the populations of different species that occupy and are adapted to a given area are referred to by which term?
   a.   biosphere
 * b.   community
   c.   ecosystem
   d.   niche
   e.   ecotone

M   2.   Which of the following would be more likely to affect an animal's habitat than its niche?
 * a.   rainfall
   b.   prey abundance
   c.   predators
   d.   defense mechanisms

E   3.   The term *species richness* refers specifically to the
   a.   greater numbers of each individual species present.
   b.   ability of larger animals to enrich themselves by successfully preying on smaller ones.
 * c.   number of different species in the habitat.
   d.   feeding levels at which the animals are located.

M   4.   What term denotes the range of all factors that influence whether a species can obtain resources essential for survival and reproduction?
   a.   habitat
 * b.   niche
   c.   carrying capacity
   d.   ecosystem
   e.   community

M   5.   When Shakespeare wrote about the world as a stage and each of us being players, he was unknowingly referring to the biological concept of
   a.   succession.
 * b.   the niche.
   c.   different habitats.
   d.   feeding levels.
   e.   interspecific competition.

E   6.   Niche refers to the
   a.   home range of an animal.
   b.   preferred habitat for an organism.
 * c.   functional role of a species in a community.
   d.   territory occupied by a species.

E   7.   A relationship in which two species are dependent on each other for survival is
   a.   neutral relationship.
   b.   commensalism.
   c.   competitive exclusion.
 * d.   mutualism.
   e.   parasitism.

E   8.   A one-way relationship in which one species benefits at the expense of another is called
   a.   commensalism.
   b.   competitive exclusion.
 * c.   parasitism.
   d.   obligate mutualism.
   e.   neutral relationship.

D   9.   Which of the following is NOT characteristic of parasites?
   a.   They are specialists and usually are able to affect only one variety of hosts.
 * b.   They inflict serious injury and kill their hosts.
   c.   Some reside inside their hosts, whereas others live outside their hosts.
   d.   Their host may be a plant as well as an animal.

M   10.   The weakest symbiotic attachment, in which one species simply lives better in the presence of another species, is
 * a.   commensalism.
   b.   competitive exclusion.
   c.   mutualism.
   d.   facultative obligate mutualism.
   e.   parasitism.

E   11.   Species interactions differ in
   a.   the extent to which one species is helped or harmed by the presence of another.
   b.   degree of dependence.
   c.   how exclusive the attachments are.
 * d.   all of these

M   12.   Fruit flies probably have what type of relationship with humans?
   a.   parasitic
   b.   mutualistic
   c.   obligate
 * d.   commensal
   e.   saprobic

E   13.   In the food chain, grass ——> rabbit ——> eagle, the relationship between the grass and eagle is
   a.   predation.
   b.   commensalism.
   c.   competition.
 * d.   neutral.
   e.   mutualism.

D   14. Which of the following is NOT usual as a result of
          predation?
          a. The level of the predator population is maintained
             near or below the carrying capacity.
          b. Both predator and prey undergo selection leading
             to coevolution.
     *   c. The predator or prey becomes extinct.
          d. The level of the prey population is maintained
             near or below the carrying capacity of the
             environment.

E   15. The interaction in which one species benefits and the
          second species is neither harmed nor benefited is
          a. mutualism.
          b. parasitism.
     *   c. commensalism.
          d. competition.
          e. predation.

E   16. The interaction between two species in which one
          species benefits and the other species is harmed is
          a. mutualism.
          b. commensalism.
          c. competition.
     *   d. predation.
          e. none of these

MUTUALISM

M   17. The relationship between an insect and the plants it
          pollinates is best described as
     *   a. mutualism.
          b. competitive exclusion.
          c. parasitism.
          d. commensalism.
          e. all of these

E   18. The relationship between the yucca plant and the yucca
          moth that pollinates it is best described as
          a. camouflage.
          b. commensalism.
          c. competitive exclusion.
     *   d. obligate mutualism.
          e. all of these

E   19. An interaction between two species in which both
          species benefit is known as
     *   a. mutualism.
          b. parasitism.
          c. commensalism.
          d. competition.
          e. predation.

COMPETITIVE INTERACTIONS

M   20. The interaction between two species in which both
          species may be harmed is known as
          a. mutualism.
          b. parasitism.
          c. commensalism.
     *   d. competition.
          e. predation.

M   21. A male wolf who is courting a female bares his teeth
          when a second male approaches the same female. The
          second male retreats. This series of events provides an
          example of
          a. a neutral interaction.
          b. exploitation competition.
     *   c. interference competition.
          d. competitive exclusion.

M   22. The construction of a fence around your yard would
          establish a relationship with the neighbor's dog that
          would be described as
          a. succession.
     *   b. interference competition.
          c. commensalism.
          d. mutualism.
          e. niche.

M   23. Niche overlap initially leads to
          a. mutualism.
          b. commensalism.
     *   c. competition.
          d. predation.
          e. parasitism.

M   24. Competitive exclusion is the result of
          a. mutualism.
          b. commensalism.
     *   c. competition.
          d. predation.
          e. parasitism.

D   25. In most cases of interspecific interference competition,
          the inferior competitor displaced from an area of niche
          overlap is
          a. smaller.
          b. slower.
          c. more specialized in its niche requirements.
     *   d. less specialized in its niche requirements.

M   26. In Gause's experiments with *Paramecium* growing in
          test tubes, he demonstrated that
          a. organisms with similar niches will evolve enough
             to survive in different niches.
          b. organisms with slightly different feeding habits
             will change to become exclusive competitors.
     *   c. organisms with similar feeding habits may
             compete to the point of extinction.
          d. organisms with slightly different feeding habits
             will change to become exclusive competitors, and
             organisms with similar feeding habits may
             compete to the point of extinction.
          e. organisms with similar niches will evolve enough
             to survive in different niches, and organisms with
             similar feeding habits may compete to the point of
             extinction.

M 27. Gause's exclusion principle refers to
    a. isolation.
*   b. competition.
    c. habitat preference.
    d. physiological adaptation.

M 28. Competitive exclusion is based upon the idea that
    a. one species will hold some sort of advantage over the other one.
    b. no two species can completely occupy the same niche.
*   c. both of these
    d. neither of these

M 29. The "final result" of community interaction when viewed by an ecologist observer is
    a. competition.
    b. social parasitism.
    c. predation.
    d. mimicry.
*   e. resource partitioning.

M 30. Which one of the following is the final consequence of the others?
*   a. resource partitioning
    b. competition
    c. predation
    d. parasitism
    e. parasitoidism

PREDATOR-PREY INTERACTIONS

E 31. A goat eating by pulling a plant out of the ground is an example of
    a. parasitism.
*   b. predation.
    c. competition.
    d. commensalism.
    e. mutualism.

M 32. In general, a predator is _____ than its _____.
    a. smaller; host
    b. larger; host
    c. smaller; prey
*   d. larger; prey

D 33. In contrast to a predator, a parasite usually
*   a. does not kill the animal on which or in which it lives.
    b. kills its host.
    c. is a short-term visitor.
    d. is larger than its host.
    e. does not kill the animal on which or in which it lives and is larger than its host.

D 34. Conditions of stable coexistence between predator and prey include
    a. high predator reproductive rate relative to that of the prey.
    b. a carrying capacity for prey which is not high.
    c. large predator size relative to that of the prey.
*   d. high predator reproductive rate relative to that of the prey and a carrying capacity for prey which is not high.
    e. high predator reproductive rate relative to that of the prey, a carrying capacity for prey which is not high, and large predator size relative to that of the prey.

D 35. Humans hunt the black rhinoceros, which is rapidly approaching extinction as a result of this predation. What accounts for the absence of stable coexistence between the two species?
    a. Predator and prey have not coevolved.
    b. Human predation is not necessarily density-dependent.
    c. The prey reproductive rate is greater than that of the predator.
*   d. Predator and prey have not coevolved; and Human predation is not necessarily density-dependent.
    e. Predator and prey have not coevolved; Human predation is not necessarily density-dependent; The prey reproductive rate is greater than that of the predator.

D 36. Ladybugs are effective natural control agents against pest insects, but as gardeners soon find out, they do not reduce pest populations to zero because
    a. they can't fly to find pests on nearby plants.
    b. of their very selective feeding habits.
*   c. to do so would jeopardize their own existence.
    d. they don't live long enough.
    e. their reproductive capacity is nonexistent.

D 37. Without intervention by humans, cockroaches will overrun a kitchen until
    a. the carrying capacity is reached.
    b. predators attack.
    c. parasites invade the roaches' bodies.
    d. density-independent factors such as cold intervene.
*   e. all of these

M 38. Populations are held in check by
    a. resource partitioning.
    b. predation.
    c. social parasitism.
    d. competition.
*   e. all of these

M 39. Which of the following statements about predation is true?
a. It can result in an increase in species diversity within a community.
b. It can cause extinction of a prey species within a community.
c. It can prevent extinction of a prey species within a community.
d. It can result in an increase in species diversity within a community; and It can cause extinction of a prey species within a community.
* e. It can result in an increase in species diversity within a community; It can cause extinction of a prey species within a community; and It can prevent extinction of a prey species within a community.

AN EVOLUTIONARY ARMS RACE

D 40. Which is NOT an example of coevolution?
a. insect and flower
b. predator and prey
c. host and parasite
d. model and mimic
* e. sharks and dolphins

M 41. Which of the following is an adaptation against predation?
a. thorns
b. social behavior
c. mimicry
d. thorns and social behavior
* e. thorns, social behavior, and mimicry

D 42. In fireflies, females attract males of the same species by means of a species-specific flashing pattern. Females of the genus *Photuris* are capable of producing flashing patterns that resemble those produced by fireflies of the genus *Photinus*. When a *Photinus* male approaches a *Photuris* female, she kills and eats him. This is an example of
a. Mullerian mimicry.
b. parasitism.
* c. aggressive mimicry.
d. commensalism.

M 43. Chemicals in both plants and animals serve as which of the following to predators?
a. warnings
b. repellents
c. toxins
d. bad tastes
* e. all of these

D 44. Hover flies like to drop in at outdoor picnics to sample the sweets, but the reaction of the humans is to flee the scene because of the flies' uncanny resemblance to bees. Thus, the survival of the hover fly is enhanced by
* a. mimicry.
b. display behavior.
c. warning coloration.
d. chemical defenses.
e. camouflage.

PARASITE-HOST INTERACTIONS

M 45. Parasitoids
a. are an alternative to pesticides.
b. will kill rather than damage those that they infect.
c. are biotic or natural controls.
d. are better than pesticides in that they are target-specific (they affect a limited number and type of organisms).
* e. all of these

M 46. Which of the following statements about parasites is true?
a. Parasites usually do not kill their hosts.
b. The parasite species that infects a particular host species becomes less virulent over evolutionary time.
c. Warm-blooded animals are frequently infected by parasites.
d. Parasites usually do not kill their hosts; and The parasite species that infects a particular host species becomes less virulent over evolutionary time.
* e. Parasites usually do not kill their hosts; The parasite species that infects a particular host species becomes less virulent over evolutionary time; and Warm-blooded animals are frequently infected by parasites.

D 47. The activities of a parasitoid wasp on jackpine sawflies tend to favor the sawflies that
a. are buried deeply.
b. are buried shallowly.
c. hatch early.
d. hatch later.
* e. are buried deeply and hatch later.

E 48. Which bird is a social parasite and lays its eggs in the nests of other birds?
a. catbird
* b. cowbird
c. magpie
d. Kirtland warbler
e. bluejay

D **49.** Which of the following does NOT apply to parasitoids?
  a. insects
  b. kill animals on which they feed
  * c. host usually survives
  d. smaller in size than prey
  e. effective biocontrol agents

D **50.** Actual physical contact between interactants does not necessarily occur
  a. between parasitoid and prey.
  * b. in social parasitism.
  c. in a predator-prey reaction.
  d. when a parasite feeds on a host.
  e. in any of the above.

M **51.** All of the following are desirable attributes of an effective parasitoid control agent except:
  a. They are well adapted to the host.
  * b. They have limited search capability.
  c. The reproductive rate is high.
  d. They are mobile.
  e. They are capable of quick in their responses to host population change.

FORCES CONTRIBUTING TO COMMUNITY STABILITY

D **52.** During the process of community succession,
  a. the total biomass remains constant.
  * b. there are increasing possibilities for resource partitioning.
  c. the pioneer community gives way quickly to the climax community, followed by a succession of more diverse arrays of organisms.
  d. nutrients cycle more rapidly with time.
  e. all of these

M **53.** Most dominant plant species in a climax community
  a. become quickly reestablished in a cleared area because they are adapted specifically to that geographic region.
  * b. cannot grow or develop fully except as part of a certain integrated community structure.
  c. grow faster in areas exposed to sunlight by clear-cutting.
  d. become quickly reestablished in a cleared area because they are adapted specifically to that geographic region, and grow faster in areas exposed to sunlight by clear-cutting.

M **54.** Which of the following statements is false?
  a. Succession is highly predictable.
  b. Pioneer species have wide ranges of tolerances.
  c. Pioneer plant species are usually small annuals with an abundance of easily dispersed seeds.
  * d. The succession that occurs after a large fire is primary succession.
  e. Climax species are those that are best adapted to the specific climate where the succession occurs.

M **55.** Secondary succession is likely to occur in
  a. a deciduous forest.
  b. a shallow lake.
  c. an abandoned field.
  d. a deciduous forest and a shallow lake.
  * e. a deciduous forest; a shallow lake; and an abandoned field.

M **56.** Pioneer plant species are usually characterized by
  a. small size.
  b. efficient dispersal mechanisms.
  c. slow maturation.
  * d. small size and efficient dispersal mechanisms.
  e. small size, efficient dispersal mechanisms, and slow maturation.

M **57.** Which of the following represent an early stage in primary succession?
  a. pine trees
  * b. moss and lichens on bare rock
  c. weedy annual plants in an open field
  d. climax species in succession

D **58.** Which of the following statements concerning climax communities is true?
  a. A climax community is always a result of primary succession.
  * b. When compared to early successional communities, climax communities usually possess more species.
  c. The species of the climax community require long periods of environmental stability to ensure continued survival in the community.
  d. A climax community is always a result of primary succession; and When compared to early successional communities, climax communities usually possess more species.
  e. A climax community is always a result of primary succession; When compared to early successional communities, climax communities usually possess more species; and The species of the climax community require long periods of environmental stability to ensure continued survival in the community.

M **59.** Secondary succession occurs
  * a. after a fire.
  b. on a new sand dune.
  c. on bare rock.
  d. immediately after the formation of a man-made lake.

M **60.** The plants and animals now present on acreage from which the trees were removed ten years earlier represent
  a. primary succession.
  b. a climax forest.
  c. pioneer species.
  * d. secondary succession.
  e. species introductions.

D 61. Farmland that is under regular and continued tillage will not
    a. undergo succession.
  * b. produce a climax community.
    c. experience competition.
    d. suffer from the effects of disturbance.
    e. develop species diversity.

M 62. The climax community
    a. is formed by species with the greatest range of environmental tolerance.
    b. is the most common community found in an area.
    c. changes over time.
  * d. is well adapted to the climate and persists until the climate changes.

M 63. In 1882, the tropical volcanic island Krakatoa exploded and was reduced to an abiotic island covered by a thick layer of volcanic ash. By 1933, populations of all of the following organisms were present. Which population was probably established after the others?
    a. ferns
    b. bacteria
    c. insects
  * d. rodents

FORCES CONTRIBUTING TO COMMUNITY INSTABILITY

E 64. A keystone species is
    a. a single dominant species.
    b. in control of the prey species.
    c. exemplified by the sea star.
    d. a single dominant species and is exemplified by the sea star.
  * e. a single dominant species; is exemplified by the sea star; and is in control of the prey species.

D 65. Which exotic was NOT intentionally introduced to this country?
  * a. Japanese beetle
    b. English house sparrow
    c. carp
    d. water hyacinth
    e. starling

M 66. Many introduced species have had deleterious effects on communities and ecosystems because
  * a. coevolved parasites and competitors are absent.
    b. the introduced species are long-lived.
    c. predators prefer the introduced species, and the local prey therefore proliferate to dangerously high levels.
    d. the communities from which they came lost an important predator, competitor, or parasite.

PATTERNS OF BIODIVERSITY

E 67. Of the following four islands at the same latitude, the one possessing the fewest species is
    a. 1,000 square kilometers and 300 km from the mainland.
    b. 3,000 square kilometers and 100 km from the mainland.
  * c. 100 square kilometers and 3,000 km from the mainland.
    d. 300 square kilometers and 1,000 km from the mainland.

M 68. In the United States, the number of breeding bird species increases from
  * a. Minnesota to Texas.
    b. mainland Florida to the Florida Keys.
    c. low mountain altitudes to high mountain altitudes.
    d. Minnesota to Texas and from mainland Florida to the Florida Keys.
    e. Minnesota to Texas, from mainland Florida to the Florida Keys, and from low mountain altitudes to high mountain altitudes.

M 69. Stable coexistence between predator and prey is least likely to occur on an island that is
  * a. small and distant from the mainland.
    b. small and close to the mainland.
    c. large and close to the mainland.
    d. large and distant from the mainland.

M 70. There are more insect species per square kilometer in a Brazilian rainforest than there are in a redwood forest of the Pacific Northwest of the United States. According to contemporary ecological hypotheses, an explanation for this finding is that
    a. the tropics have been climatically stable for a longer period of time than have temperate areas.
    b. niches in the tropics are smaller than those in temperate areas.
    c. on average, insects are smaller in the tropics than they are in temperate areas.
  * d. the tropics have been climatically stable for a longer period of time than have temperate areas, and niches in the tropics are smaller than those in temperate areas.
    e. the tropics have been climatically stable for a longer period of time than have temperate areas, niches in the tropics are smaller than those in temperate areas, and on average, insects are smaller in the tropics than they are in temperate areas.

M 71. An equilibrium population of 5 individuals on an island is more likely to go extinct than an equilibrium population of 50 individuals because
    a. intraspecific competition is more intense in smaller groups.
  * b. density-independent factors are more likely to eliminate smaller rather than larger groups.
    c. there is more ecological space for predators if there are fewer prey.
    d. predation pressure increases as prey populations decrease.

Matching Questions

D 72. Matching. Choose the one most appropriate answer for each.
    1. ___ camouflage
    2. ___ commensalism
    3. ___ competitive exclusion
    4. ___ habitat
    5. ___ mimicry
    6. ___ mutualism
    7. ___ parasitism
    8. ___ primary succession
    9. ___ climax community
    10. ___ secondary succession
    11. ___ succession

    A. blending in and being hidden by the background
    B. where an organism is generally located in an environment
    C. one organism benefits at another organism's expense
    D. a self-sustaining array of interacting organisms that is best suited for a particular environment
    E. lichens on newly hardened, newly cooled lava
    F. robins and human populations
    G. the yucca moth and the yucca
    H. one species is forced from an area of niche overlap
    I. repugnant species resemble tasty one
    J. the process that converts a pioneer community to a climax community
    K. natural reforestation of burned-over forest

Answers: 1. A   2. F   3. H   4. B
       5. I   6. G   7. C   8. E
       9. D   10. K   11. J

Classification Questions

Answer questions 73–77 in reference to the five kinds of species interactions listed below:
    a. competition
    b. predation
    c. mutualism
    d. commensalism
    e. parasitism

E 73. In this interaction, one species benefits while the other is neither harmed nor benefited.

M 74. In this interaction between two species, both species are harmed in some way.

M 75. In this interaction, both species benefit.

E 76. In this interaction, one individual or species is usually killed while the other benefits by eating the first.

M 77. In this interaction, one species is harmed, but usually not killed, to the benefit of the other that lives on or in the first.

Answers   73. d   74. a   75. c
       76. b   77. e

Answer questions 78–82 in reference to the five kinds of species interactions listed below:
    a. competition
    b. parasitoidism
    c. mutualism
    d. commensalism
    e. parasitism

E 78. The relationship between a dog and a wood tick is this kind of relationship.

M 79. The interaction between a human and the intestinal bacterium *E. coli* is usually this kind of relationship.

M 80. The interaction between two closely related species of woodpeckers that live in a temperate forest is likely to be this.

M 81. If a wasp lays its eggs inside the larva of a fly, the interaction is this.

M 82. When a tropical bird places its nest in association with a wasp nest on the same tree, the interaction is this.

Answers: 78. e   79. c   80. a
        81. b   82. d

Selecting the Exception

M **83.** Four of the five answers listed below are relationships in which at least one of the interactants benefits. Select the exception.
* a. competition
   b. parasitism
   c. mutualism
   d. commensalism
   e. predation

D **84.** Four of the five answers listed below are examples of mutualism. Select the exception.
   a. plants and pollinators
   b. plants and seed dispersal by seed-eating animals
   c. mycorrhizae
* d. antibiotics
   e. lichen

E **85.** Four of the five answers listed below are examples of defense coloration. Select the exception.
   a. industrial melanism
   b. warning coloration
   c. camouflage
* d. albinism
   e. mimicry

E **86.** Four of the five answers listed below are defense chemicals. Select the exception.
* a. perfume
   b. warning odors
   c. poisons
   d. alarm substances
   e. repellents

M **87.** Four of the five answers listed below are exotic or introduced species. Select the exception.
   a. Argentine fire ant
* b. cockroach
   c. starling
   d. water hyacinth
   e. chestnut blight

M **88.** Four of the five answers below are related by role. Select the exception.
   a. scavenger
* b. intestinal tract
   c. saprophyte
   d. producer
   e. decomposer

M **89.** Four of the five answers listed below are events that lead to secondary succession. Select the exception.
   a. opening the canopy in a tropical rain forest
   b. abandoning a cotton field
* c. retreat of a glacier in Alaska
   d. the finish of a fire
   e. growth of weeds in a lawn that is not mowed

CHAPTER 48
ECOSYSTEMS

Multiple-Choice Questions

M   1.   In the Antarctic, blue whales feed mainly on
     a.   petrels.
   * b.   krill.
     c.   seals.
     d.   fish and small squid.
     e.   penguins.

THE NATURE OF ECOSYSTEMS

E   2.   In a natural community, the primary consumers are
   * a.   herbivores.
     b.   carnivores.
     c.   scavengers.
     d.   decomposers.
     e.   all of these

E   3.   Which of the following is usually a primary carnivore?
     a.   chicken
     b.   cow
     c.   rabbit
   * d.   wolf
     e.   squirrel

M   4.   Which of the following is a primary consumer?
   * a.   cow
     b.   dog
     c.   hawk
     d.   fox
     e.   snake

M   5.   All living organisms are dependent upon plants because
     a.   plants produce oxygen as a by-product of photosynthesis.
   * b.   as producers, they form the base of food chains.
     c.   they function to prevent erosion and reduce desertification.
     d.   as they remove carbon dioxide from the atmosphere, they reduce the problems generated by the greenhouse effect.

D   6.   Which of the following combinations of organisms could be expected to survive in isolation from other forms of life available?
   * a.   producers and decomposers
     b.   producers and carnivores
     c.   carnivores and decomposers
     d.   herbivores, carnivores, and decomposers

M   7.   Wastes would accumulate and most nutrients would stop cycling if the _____ in the ecosystem died.
     a.   protozoans and protistans
   * b.   bacteria and fungi
     c.   flatworms, roundworms, and earthworms
     d.   insects

E   8.   Herbivores represent the
   * a.   primary consumers.
     b.   secondary consumers.
     c.   tertiary consumers.
     d.   primary producers.
     e.   secondary producers.

D   9.   Chemosynthetic organisms are
     a.   primary consumers.
     b.   secondary consumers.
     c.   tertiary consumers.
   * d.   primary producers.
     e.   secondary producers.

M   10.   Detritivores are
     a.   bacteria.
     b.   plants.
     c.   fungi.
   * d.   animals.
     e.   both bacteria and fungi

E   11.   A network of interactions that involve the cycling of materials and the flow of energy between a community and its physical environment is which of the following?
     a.   population
     b.   community
   * c.   ecosystem
     d.   biosphere
     e.   species

M   12.   A community differs from an ecosystem in that the former does NOT include
     a.   unicellular organisms.
     b.   decomposers.
   * c.   abiotic factors.
     d.   unicellular organisms and decomposers.
     e.   unicellular organisms, decomposers, and abiotic factors.

M   13.   Which of the following are NOT heterotrophs?
     a.   primary carnivores
     b.   herbivores
     c.   detritivores
     d.   decomposers
   * e.   All of these are heterotrophs.

D 14. Which of the following is NOT dependent on the others as a food supply?
   a. carnivores
   b. herbivores
 * c. producers
   d. detritivores
   e. decomposers

E 15. Which of the following is the correct word meaning "to feed"?
   a. tropic
 * b. trophic
   c. topic
   d. tophic
   e. tropical

D 16. Most of the energy available to a primary consumer
 * a. will be used up in various biological activities.
   b. will be converted into biomass.
   c. is obtained directly from solar energy.
   d. will be passed on to the animal that feeds upon it.

THE NATURE OF FOOD WEBS

M 17. Which of the following is NOT true of ecosystems?
   a. Although they may include many different species, many features of ecosystem structure and function are alike.
   b. Autotrophs secure energy and nutrients that are then used by heterotrophs.
 * c. Energy cycles and minerals flow through ecosystems.
   d. Many different niches are represented in most ecosystems.
   e. Ecosystems are characterized by relatively few trophic levels.

D 18. Which of the following statements is true?
   a. A population cannot exceed the carrying capacity even temporarily.
 * b. An organism can occupy more than one trophic level, depending upon the feeding habits of the organism.
   c. Once populations of organisms become isolated, they remain so by various types of isolation mechanisms.
   d. The limits of a population are all traced to climatic or physical factors.
   e. Organisms with different evolutionary backgrounds can occupy the same niche at the same time.

M 19. The primary consumer is also
   a. the second link in a food chain.
   b. a herbivore.
   c. an animal.
   d. a herbivore and an animal.
 * e. the second link in a food chain, a herbivore, and an animal.

D 20. A secondary consumer could eat
   a. only herbivores.
   b. only primary producers.
   c. primary carnivores.
 * d. anything "below" it in the food web.

D 21. Food chains rarely have more than three levels of consumers because
   a. the animals are too large to search for prey.
   b. the growing season of plants is not long enough.
   c. pyramids do not go that high.
 * d. the amount of energy still available is too small.

D 22. After a shipwreck you are alone on a deserted island with a pair of pigs and a large supply of corn. Your best strategy would be to
   a. feed the corn to the pigs and feed upon their offspring.
 * b. kill the pigs immediately and then eat the corn.
   c. share the corn with the pigs and then eat the pigs when the corn is gone.
   d. eat only the pigs.

M 23. In the food webs of Antarctica, the top consumer is the
   a. krill.
 * b. killer whale.
   c. penguin.
   d. blue whale.
   e. leopard seal.

M 24. Which of the following statements about ecosystems is false?
   a. The rate of energy flow depends on the ratio of producers to consumers.
   b. The requirements of an ecosystem change with age.
   c. The larger the ecosystem, the more flexible it is.
 * d. The smaller the ecosystem, the more stable it is.
   e. The more efficient the producers are, the more energy must be put in and the more energy is available for the next trophic level.

D 25. Stability of an ecosystem can usually be increased by increasing the
   a. length of a food chain.
   b. number of individuals in the ecosystem.
 * c. number of species in the ecosystem.
   d. biomass contained in the first trophic level.

M 26. Detritus specifically includes
   a. organic wastes.
   b. toxic materials.
   c. dead and partially decayed material.
   d. living bacteria and fungi.
 * e. both organic wastes plus dead and partially decayed material.

D 27. The amount of energy that flows through a detrital food web is _____ that which flows through a grazing web.
a. the same as
* b. greater than
c. less than
d. the sum of
e. the difference of

M 28. Which of the following statements is false?
a. Heat loss represents a one-way loss of energy from an ecosystem.
* b. Organisms in the food chain use all the energy contained in the food that they eat.
c. In some ecosystems, the majority of the energy stored in plants does not become available until the plants die.
d. Heat and energy are lost by each organism in the ecosystem.
e. The two food webs are classified as grazing and detrital.

M 29. Decomposers perform their recycling efforts on organisms
a. at the end of a food chain.
b. on the top of a pyramid.
c. that are producers.
d. that are consumers.
* e. all of these

E 30. Decomposers
a. are able to enter a food chain at any trophic level.
b. are the most numerous organisms in an ecosystem.
c. include bacteria and fungi.
* d. all of these

M 31. Primary carnivores are
a. tertiary consumers in the third trophic level.
* b. secondary consumers in the third trophic level.
c. secondary consumers in the second trophic level.
d. tertiary consumers in the fourth trophic level.

M 32. Which of the following cannot be placed in a single trophic level?
a. oak tree
b. zebra
* c. mushroom
d. rabbit

FOCUS ON SCIENCE: BIOLOGICAL MAGNIFICATION IN FOOD WEBS

M 33. Biological magnification refers to the
a. increase in size of animals as they progress through a food chain.
b. increase in size of organisms as they progress through ecological succession.
c. increase in the efficiency of energy utilization as organisms progress through a food chain.
* d. accumulation of toxic pollutants as animals pass through a food chain.

E 34. In biological magnification,
* a. poisons build up in food chains and webs so that the concentration is highest at the high end of the food chain.
b. there is a tendency for an environment to change when organisms first invade.
c. more highly evolved forms are able to build large populations under favorable conditions.
d. parasites spread rapidly through congested populations.
e. sediments fill in aquatic environments so that succession will occur if organisms disturb the aquatic habitat.

M 35. Which substance is magnified during transfers in ecosystems?
* a. fat-soluble pesticides
b. carbohydrates
c. inorganic phosphates
d. fat-soluble pesticides and carbohydrates
e. fat-soluble pesticides, carbohydrates, and inorganic phosphates

M 36. The release of DDT into the environment to control some insect pests will result in the highest detectable concentrations
a. at the bottom of the food chain.
b. in the targeted insect pest.
c. in the middle of the food chain.
* d. at the end of the food chain.

M 37. Long-lasting pesticides such as DDT
a. are target-specific.
b. are the most effective control over pests.
* c. build up in concentration as they pass through a food chain.
d. break down after the organism that receives the pesticide dies.

STUDYING ENERGY FLOW THROUGH ECOSYSTEMS

D 38. Net primary productivity is the
a. rate of photosynthesis.
b. rate of energy flow.
c. amount of energy stored in the ecosystem.
d. amount of energy utilized.
* e. amount of energy stored in the plant tissue in excess of that used by autotrophs in respiration.

M 39. Gross primary productivity refers to the
a. total energy reaching the ecosystem in a given period of time.
b. total energy reaching the ecosystem in a given area.
* c. total rate of photosynthesis for the entire ecosystem for a given time period.
d. total energy used by the heterotrophic part of the ecosystem in a given period of time.

E   40. The ultimate source of all energy in a terrestrial ecosystem is
       a. the organic matter in all the organisms of the ecosystem.
       b. water.
     * c. sunlight.
       d. carbon dioxide.

D   41. The difference between gross primary productivity and net primary productivity is
       a. the amount of sunlight reflected by plants.
       b. the rate of photosynthesis of autotrophs.
     * c. the rate of respiration of autotrophs.
       d. the rate of herbivorous consumption of autotrophs.

M   42. Consumption of _____ is _____ in plants than in animals.
     * a. oxygen; less
       b. carbon dioxide; less
       c. oxygen; greater
       d. carbohydrate; greater
       e. carbon monoxide; greater

E   43. Most of the energy within an ecosystem is lost
       a. when organisms disperse.
       b. when organisms die.
     * c. as a result of metabolism.
       d. by organisms at the top of the food web.

M   44. About what percent of the solar energy reaching the earth's surface is stored as organic material?
     * a. 1–2
       b. 5–6
       c. 10–12
       d. 15–18
       e. 25

E   45. At the bottom or base of a pyramid of energy are the
     * a. primary producers.
       b. secondary producers.
       c. primary consumers.
       d. secondary consumers.
       e. tertiary consumers.

M   46. The pyramid
       a. of biomass may be upside-down.
       b. of numbers may be upside-down.
       c. of energy may be upside-down.
       d. is a way to represent trophic structures of ecosystems.
     * e. All but "of energy may be upside-down" are correct.

E   47. At the top of a pyramid of biomass are the
       a. primary producers.
       b. secondary producers.
       c. primary consumers.
       d. secondary consumers.
     * e. tertiary consumers.

M   48. The biomass of a community is the weight of the
       a. material decomposed in a year.
       b. producers.
     * c. living organisms.
       d. consumers.
       e. decomposers.

D   49. The pyramid of energy is
       a. a demonstration of the first law of thermodynamics.
     * b. a result of the decline in the energy available as energy travels through the trophic levels.
       c. fundamentally different from the pyramid of biomass and the pyramid of numbers.
       d. just one of the manifestations of competition.

M   50. Of the following, which must always have a base larger than the other components?
       a. pyramid of numbers
     * b. pyramid of energy
       c. pyramid of biomass
       d. pyramids of numbers and energy
       e. all pyramids

D   51. Energy pyramids are characteristic of ecosystems because
       a. not all of what is eaten is absorbed by a consumer.
       b. not all of what is killed is eaten by a predator.
       c. not all of what is produced in one trophic level is consumed by organisms in the next highest trophic level.
       d. not all of what is eaten is absorbed by a consumer and not all of what is killed is eaten by a predator.
     * e. not all of what is eaten is absorbed by a consumer, not all of what is killed is eaten by a predator, and not all of what is produced in one trophic level is consumed by organisms in the next highest trophic level.

M   52. The simple food chain, grass ——> zebra ——> lion, provides a good example of a pyramid of
       a. energy.
       b. heat.
       c. biomass.
     * d. both energy and biomass.
       e. energy, heat, and biomass.

E   53. Energy flow in an ecosystem is
       a. cyclical.
     * b. one-way.
       c. two-way.
       d. reversible under different conditions.

FOCUS ON SCIENCE: ENERGY FLOW AT SILVER SPRINGS

E   54. Of the energy that enters one trophic level, approximately what percent becomes available for the next trophic level?
       a. 100
     * b. 10
       c. 1
       d. 0.1
       e. 0.01

D 55. Assume that an energy pyramid has four levels (producers plus three consumers), and also assume that the energy in the producer level is set at 100%. What percent of the energy in the producers will be obtained by the tertiary consumers?
   a. 100
   b. 10
   c. 1
 * d. 0.1
   e. 0.01

BIOGEOCHEMICAL CYCLES—AN OVERVIEW

E 56. Materials in sedimentary cycles
   a. pass through both a solid and a gaseous phase.
 * b. are never present as gases in the ecosystem.
   c. are present as liquids in the earth but as gases in the atmosphere.
   d. pass through both a solid and a gaseous phase, and are present as liquids in the earth but as gases in the atmosphere.

E 57. Which of the following does NOT cycle through an ecosystem?
   a. water
   b. carbon
 * c. energy
   d. phosphorus
   e. nitrogen

M 58. The chemical elements that are available to producers are usually in what form?
 * a. ions
   b. gases
   c. solids
   d. compounds
   e. hydrocarbons

D 59. Which of the following statements is false?
   a. Ecologists use models to represent relationships between biogeochemical cycles and most ecosystems.
 * b. The physical environment has virtually no reservoir for most elements.
   c. Inputs from the physical environment and recycling made possible by decomposers and detritivores maintain the nutrient reserves in an ecosystem.
   d. In most major ecosystems, the amount of nutrients that is cycled within the ecosystem is greater than the amount entering or leaving the ecosystem in a given year.
   e. Once elements are in the biological parts of the biogeochemical cycles, they are unlikely to leave until the organism dies.

HYDROLOGIC CYCLE

M 60. The Hubbard Brook watershed studies revealed the importance of tree roots in preventing loss of calcium from an ecosystem. Calculation of calcium loss is performed by sampling
   a. the roots of the trees.
   b. the soil of the watershed.
 * c. the stream exiting the watershed.
   d. the roots of the trees and the soil of the watershed.
   e. the roots of the trees, the soil of the watershed, and the stream exiting the watershed.

M 61. Water molecules reside for the longest time in which phase of the hydrologic cycle?
 * a. detention
   b. evaporation
   c. precipitation
   d. transportation

M 62. Most of the water vapor in the earth's atmosphere comes from evaporation from
   a. lakes.
   b. rivers.
   c. land.
 * d. oceans.
   e. plants.

CARBON CYCLE

M 63. Which gas is increasing in the atmosphere and threatening the world with the greenhouse effect?
 * a. carbon dioxide
   b. carbon monoxide
   c. ozone
   d. fluorocarbons
   e. oxygen

E 64. Carbon is stored in what form?
   a. biomass
   b. fossil fuels
   c. limestone rocks
   d. shells of animals
 * e. all of these

M 65. Carbon is introduced into the atmosphere by all but which of the following means?
   a. respiration
   b. volcanic eruptions
   c. burning of fossil fuels
 * d. wind erosion

M 66. A significant fraction of the earth's carbon is found in all but which of the following?
   a. carbonate
   b. carbon dioxide
   c. cellulose
 * d. carbon monoxide

M 67. The concentration of carbon dioxide in the atmosphere in recent years is approximately how many parts per million?
   a. 3.4
   b. 34
 * c. 346
   d. 3,400
   e. 34,000

D 68. Carbon enters the biomass of animal bodies in the form of
   a. carbon dioxide.
   b. carbon monoxide.
 * c. carbohydrates.
   d. fossil fuels.
   e. calcium carbonate.

M 69. Most of the carbon now present in the earth's atmosphere will eventually end up in what two "holding stations"?
   a. plants and animals
   b. plants and decomposers
   c. plants and soil
 * d. plants and oceans
   e. plants and fossil fuels

M 70. In which of the following locations does carbon remain for the shortest time?
   a. peat bogs
 * b. tropical forests
   c. marshes
   d. sea shells
   e. fossil fuels

NITROGEN CYCLE

M 71. Which of the following is NOT part of the nitrogen cycle?
   a. denitrification
 * b. deammonification
   c. nitrogen fixation
   d. ammonification
   e. production of amino acids

D 72. Nitrification
 * a. converts ammonia into nitrates.
   b. reduces nitrates to nitrites.
   c. converts nitrogenous compounds into free nitrogen.
   d. is a synonym for nitrogen fixation.

M 73. A process in which nitrogenous waste products or organic remains of organisms are decomposed by soil bacteria and fungi that use the amino acids being released for their own growth and release the excess as NH_3 or NH_4^+ is
   a. nitrification.
 * b. ammonification.
   c. denitrification.
   d. nitrogen fixation.
   e. hydrogenation.

E 74. The greatest concentration of nitrogen on earth is found in
   a. living organisms, including bacteria.
 * b. the atmosphere.
   c. soil minerals.
   d. fossil fuels.
   e. oceans.

E 75. Nitrogen is released into the atmosphere by
   a. nitrogen fixation.
 * b. denitrification.
   c. nitrification.
   d. ammonification.
   e. decomposition.

E 76. Which plants are planted to increase the amount of nitrogen in the soil?
   a. watermelon and cantaloupe vines
 * b. legumes
   c. mints
   d. grasses
   e. heaths

M 77. Plant cells assimilate nitrogen in the form of
   a. ammonia and N_2.
   b. N_2 and nitrite.
 * c. nitrate and ammonia.
   d. urea and nitrate.

M 78. Nitrifying bacteria convert
 * a. NH_4^+ to NO_2^- and NO_3^-.
   b. NO_3^- to NO_2^- to N_2.
   c. NO_3^- to NH_3.
   d. urea to NH_3.

E 79. If agricultural soil has been depleted of nitrates, a good crop to plant and subsequently plow under is
   a. wheat.
   b. corn.
 * c. clover.
   d. sugar beets.

D 80. Humans incorporate nitrogen into their bodies
   a. by nitrification.
   b. through ammonification.
 * c. by assimilation and biosynthesis.
   d. via dinitrification.
   e. by the process of decomposition.

SEDIMENTARY CYCLES

D 81. Animals obtain minerals such as phosphorus
   a. primarily dissolved in drinking water.
   b. by inhalation.
   c. in meats.
   d. by eating plants.
 * e. in meats and by eating plants.

Matching Questions

D **82.** Matching. Choose the one most appropriate answer for each.

    1. ____ biological magnification

    2. ____ detritus

    3. ____ legumes

    4. ____ net primary production

    5. ____ primary productivity

    6. ____ ruminants

    7. ____ gross primary production

    A. rate at which energy becomes stored in organic compounds through photosynthesis; generally expressed as $kcal/m^2/yr$

    B. total amount of solar energy stored in organic compounds during photosynthesis

    C. convert low-grade plant protein into high-grade meat protein by harboring cellulose-degrading microbes in their gut

    D. the potential chemical energy remaining (after aerobic respiration by autotrophs) that can still be passed on to other trophic levels

    E. DDT spraying program in Borneo

    F. a kind of plant that often harbors symbiotic nitrogen fixers in its roots

    G. particles of organic waste products, dead or partly decomposed tissues

Answers: 1. E   2. G   3. F   4. D

               5. A   6. C   7. B

Classification Questions

Answer questions 83–87 in reference to the five trophic categories of an ecosystem listed below:

    a. producer

    b. herbivore

    c. primary carnivore

    d. secondary carnivore

    e. decomposer

M **83.** A primary consumer is this.

M **84.** A Venus flytrap obtains its nitrogen when it functions as this.

M **85.** Most mushrooms function as this.

M **86.** A bear feeding on a salmon is functioning as this.

E **87.** A bear eating blueberries is functioning as this.

Answers   83. b   84. c   85. e

               86. d   87. b

Answer questions 88–92 in reference to the four steps of the nitrogen cycles listed below:

    a. nitrogen fixation

    b. nitrification

    c. denitrification

    d. ammonification

M **88.** The action of bacteria on urea occurs during this process.

M **89.** The action of bacteria on ammonia, ultimately converting it to nitrate, occurs during this process.

E **90.** The action of bacteria on nitrates, converting them to gaseous nitrogen, occurs during this process.

E **91.** The process whereby gaseous nitrogen is first converted to ammonia and then to other nitrogenous compounds is this.

M **92.** The process whereby nitrite is converted to nitrate is an important part of this process.

Answers: 88. d   89. b   90. c

               91. a   92. b

Selecting the Exception

M **93.** Four of the five answers listed below are heterotrophic. Select the exception.

    a. consumers

    b. carnivores

    c. herbivores

    d. parasites

  * e. producers

M **94.** Three of the four answers listed below are related by a common theme. Select the exception.

    a. numbers

  * b. nutrients

    c. biomass

    d. energy

M **95.** Four of the five answers listed below are related by a common action. Select the exception.

    a. volcanic eruption

  * b. photosynthesis

    c. respiration

    d. fire

    e. decomposition

CHAPTER 49
THE BIOSPHERE

Multiple-Choice Questions

D   **1.** The most likely explanation for two closely related plants being located in different areas of the world is that
     a. humans transported the seeds from one location to the other.
     b. they are remnants of once widely dispersed forms that are now restricted in distribution.
     c. their isolation allowed the evolution of distinct but related forms.
*   d. their ancestors were found close together on Pangea, but the related populations separated as the continents drifted apart.
     e. dispersal mechanisms allowed these two forms to invade new locations and become widely separated.

E   **2.** The portion of the biosphere that is composed entirely of water is the
     a. atmosphere.
     b. lithosphere.
     c. geosphere.
*   d. hydrosphere.
     e. thermosphere.

M   **3.** To be a part of the biosphere, any particular region must
     a. be close to the earth's surface.
     b. include plenty of water.
*   c. support life.
     d. include oxygen.
     e. be terrestrial.

M   **4.** All but which of the following are affected by climate?
     a. land surface
     b. lakes
     c. oceans
     d. atmosphere
*   e. deep oceans

AIR CIRCULATION PATTERNS AND REGIONAL CLIMATES

E   **5.** The amount of ultraviolet radiation hitting the earth's surface is greatly reduced by which gas in the atmosphere?
*   a. ozone
     b. oxygen
     c. water vapor
     d. carbon dioxide
     e. nitrogen

E   **6.** Of all the radiation that penetrates the atmosphere, what percent actually reaches the surface?
     a. 10
     b. 25
     c. 32
     d. 40
*   e. 50

E   **7.** An important gas in the absorption of ultraviolet radiation is
     a. N_2.
*   b. O_3.
     c. CO_2.
     d. SO_2.

M   **8.** The amount of solar energy that any spot on the surface of the earth receives is controlled by
     a. the photoperiod or duration of light.
     b. the angle at which the sun strikes the earth.
     c. the amount of atmosphere above the spot.
     d. the particulate matter and pollution in the atmosphere.
*   e. all of these

M   **9.** At how many degrees north and south of the equator does air rise as a result of differential heating and cooling?
     a. 10
     b. 30
     c. 40
*   d. 60
     e. 75

M   **10.** The tradewinds in the zone from 0 to 30 degrees north latitude are generally from the
     a. north.
     b. northwest.
*   c. northeast.
     d. southeast.
     e. southwest.

M   **11.** Major air masses rise from the earth's surface at
     a. the equator and 30 degree latitudes.
     b. 30 degree and 60 degree latitudes.
*   c. the equator and 60 degree latitudes.
     d. 30 degree latitudes and the poles.

M   **12.** Which factor has the least affect on the amount of incoming light that strikes an area?
     a. latitude
*   b. temperature
     c. the degree that a slope is exposed to the incoming light
     d. the amount of recurring cloud cover
     e. all of these

D 13. The primary reason for climatic differences from one part of the world to another is
   a. differences in atmospheric pressures.
   * b. differential absorption of solar energy.
   c. prevailing wind currents.
   d. differences in humidity.
   e. the amount and type of pollution present.

D 14. Which of the following statements is false?
   a. The length of day and night are equal at any place on the earth when the sun crosses the equator.
   b. In June, if you wanted to get in a round of golf after 7 P.M., you would have longer to play in Minneapolis than in Atlanta.
   * c. The southern end of the earth's axis points toward the sun in the northern hemisphere's summer.
   d. The organisms living in most parts of the world are adapted to seasonal variations in environmental conditions.
   e. Seasonal changes become more pronounced the greater the latitude.

THE OCEAN, LANDFORMS, AND REGIONAL CLIMATES

E 15. What portion of the earth's surface is covered by oceans?
   a. less than 10%
   b. more than 80%
   c. about 50%
   * d. approximately 70%
   e. barely 20%

M 16. Water in the oceans tends to move in great currents from
   a. north pole to south pole
   b. equator to poles
   * c. poles to equator
   d. south pole to north pole
   e. poles to equator and back again

M 17. A mountain rain shadow is the
   a. arid area on the windward slope.
   b. wet area on the windward slope.
   * c. arid area on the leeward slope.
   d. wet area on the leeward slope.

M 18. Mountains produce
   a. rain shadows on the windward sides.
   b. precipitation on the leeward sides.
   * c. deserts on the leeward sides.
   d. extensive grasslands on the windward sides.
   e. all of these

M 19. The formation of mountains affects the climate and vegetation of the surrounding areas to the greatest extent by influencing
   a. temperature.
   * b. moisture relationships.
   c. light regimens.
   d. wind.

M 20. The windward side of a mountain range
   a. supports arid types of vegetation typical of a desert.
   * b. is subjected to high precipitation levels.
   c. is located in a rain shadow.
   d. is protected from the effects of the wind.
   e. has essentially identical climates and vegetation as the leeward side.

M 21. Temperature variations during the course of a year tend to increase with
   * a. increasing distance from the equator and increasing distance from the oceans.
   b. increasing distance from the equator and decreasing distance from the oceans.
   c. decreasing distance from the equator and decreasing distance from the oceans.
   d. decreasing distance from the equator and increasing distance from the oceans.

M 22. Many biological rhythms are correlated with the abiotic factors that are most _____ in a region. For example, the leafing out of maple trees in New England is closely correlated to _____.
   a. constant; daylength
   * b. variable; daylength
   c. variable; rainfall
   d. constant; rainfall

REALMS OF BIODIVERSITY

M 23. In general, which of the following lists places the terms in order of increasing size?
   a. ecosystem, biogeographical realm, biome, biosphere
   b. ecosystem, biome, biosphere, biogeographical realm
   c. biome, ecosystem, biogeographical realm, biosphere
   * d. ecosystem, biome, biogeographical realm, biosphere

E 24. Productivity of a biome increases as
   a. water availability increases and elevation increases.
   b. water availability decreases and elevation increases.
   * c. water availability increases and elevation decreases.
   d. water availability decreases and elevation decreases.

D 25. Which is NOT a biogeographical realm?
   a. Palearctic
   b. Ethiopian
   * c. Pantropical
   d. Neotropical
   e. Nearctic

D 26. The first two scientists to divide the world into biogeographical realms were
   a. Lamarck and Cuvier.
   b. Linnaeus and Ray.
   c. Darwin and Huxley.
   d. Elowitz and Whipple.
 * e. Sclater and Wallace.

M 27. Biogeographical realms
   a. are composed of different biomes.
   b. were first proposed by W. Sclater and then Alfred Wallace, the codiscoverer of evolution.
   c. are primarily based upon geography rather than climate.
   d. would be entirely different if continental drift had not occurred.
 * e. all of these

E 28. The first widely accepted attempt at an analysis of biogeographical distribution of life used six
   a. biomes.
 * b. realms.
   c. ecosystems.
   d. biotas.
   e. life zones.

M 29. Distribution of biomes tends to be influenced by all but which one of the following?
   a. topography
   b. soil
   c. latitude
 * d. longitude
   e. climate

M 30. Which of the following factors is most important in determining the type of biomes found in a particular region?
   a. soil type
   b. light intensity
 * c. temperature
   d. type of animals in the region

M 31. A particular biome is characterized by
   a. climate.
   b. vegetation.
   c. animals.
   d. vegetation and animals, only.
 * e. vegetation, animals, and climate.

D 32. Similarity of one biome to another may be due to
   a. altitude.
   b. latitude.
   c. longitude.
 * d. altitude and latitude, only.
   e. altitude, latitude, and longitude.

SOILS OF MAJOR BIOMES

E 33. The most productive soil is
   a. humus.
   b. sand.
   c. soil.
 * d. loam.
   e. silt.

M 34. Which of the following would be the least suitable for conversion to agriculture?
   a. grassland
 * b. tropical forests
   c. deciduous forest
   d. prairie
   e. silted in lake

DESERTS

E 35. Most desert biomes are in close proximity to what other biome?
   a. tundra
 * b. grasslands
   c. deciduous forests
   d. evergreen forests

M 36. At which latitudes are deserts usually found?
   a. 0–15
   b. 15–25
 * c. 25–40
   d. 40–60
   e. 60–90

M 37. The biome with the greatest range of daily temperature extremes is the
   a. tundra.
   b. taiga.
   c. tropical rain forest.
 * d. desert.
   e. grassland.

M 38. The biome that currently is increasing in size most rapidly is
   a. tundra.
   b. taiga.
   c. tropical rain forest.
 * d. desert.
   e. grassland.

M 39. The only one of the following characteristics that all deserts have in common is
 * a. low rainfall amounts.
   b. heat.
   c. sand.
   d. lack of vegetation.
   e. cacti.

D 40. The biome most in danger of desertification is
   a. desert.
 * b. grassland.
   c. deciduous forest.
   d. tropical rain forest.
   e. taiga.

DRY SHRUBLANDS, DRY WOODLANDS, AND GRASSLANDS

M **41.** In shrublands,
 *   a. cool winters are followed by prolonged drought.
       b. primary production is abundant throughout the year.
       c. there are constant cool temperatures throughout the year.
       d. winters are mild and summers are wet.
       e. precipitation occurs evenly year round.

D **42.** Which of the following areas would NOT be characterized by chaparral vegetation?
       a. California coast
       b. Central Chile
 *   c. Cuba
       d. southern tip of Africa
       e. land near the Mediterranean Sea

M **43.** The biome most closely associated with fire (and later, mudslides) is the
       a. desert.
       b. tropical rain forest.
 *   c. chaparral (shrublands).
       d. temperate deciduous forest.
       e. taiga.

D **44.** Fire in the dry shrublands does not kill the small bushy plants most probably because
       a. the plants have a tough protective bark.
       b. the leaves are very heavy and wet.
 *   c. there is not much to "feed" the fire and thus it moves rapidly through the area.
       d. humans live close by and have fire-fighting equipment.

E **45.** The biome with the greatest amount of topsoil and the richest, most fertile soil is
       a. tundra.
       b. taiga.
       c. tropical rain forest.
       d. desert.
 *   e. grassland.

M **46.** The Dust Bowl of the 1930s was the result of destruction of
       a. desert
       b. chaparral.
       c. tallgrass prairie.
 *   d. shortgrass prairie.
       e. temperate deciduous forest.

M **47.** Which of the following biomes would support and be characterized by the greatest number and diversity of herbivores?
       a. tundra
       b. taiga
 *   c. grassland
       d. chaparral
       e. desert

M **48.** A biome with grasses as primary producers and scattered trees adapted to prolonged dry spells is known as a
       a. warm desert.
 *   b. savanna.
       c. tundra.
       d. taiga.
       e. chaparral.

M **49.** A wind system that influences large climatic regions and reverses direction seasonally, producing dry and wet seasons, is referred to as
       a. a geothermal ecosystem.
       b. an upwelling.
       c. a taiga.
 *   d. a monsoon.
       e. a hurricane.

D **50.** Grassland biomes around the earth vary in several ways, but the chief factor causing the variation is
 *   a. rainfall amounts.
       b. vegetation.
       c. soil type.
       d. the animals present.
       e. prevailing winds.

TROPICAL RAIN FORESTS AND OTHER BROADLEAF FORESTS

E **51.** The biome with the greatest diversity of life is
       a. tundra.
       b. taiga.
 *   c. tropical rain forest.
       d. desert.
       e. grassland.

M **52.** In tropical rain forests,
 *   a. competition for available sunlight is intense.
       b. diversity is limited because the tall forest canopy shuts out most of the incoming light.
       c. conditions are extremely favorable for growing luxuriant food crops.
       d. there is little competition for resources.
       e. habitat partitioning is minimal.

M **53.** Which of the following is mismatched?
       a. elm, maple, beech, oak, hickory—temperate deciduous forest
       b. permafrost, mosquito, lichens, caribous—tundra
       c. chaparral, firestorms—dry shrubland
 *   d. conifers—tropical rain forests
       e. short life cycles, erosion, wide daily temperature fluctuations—deserts

E **54.** Which biome is best described as highly stratified?
       a. tundra
       b. taiga
 *   c. tropical rain forest
       d. desert
       e. grassland

M 55. The removal of trees from tropical rain forest for the purpose of large-scale food crop agriculture is not recommended because
    a. the soil is poor in organic nutrients.
    b. erosion rates accelerate when trees are removed.
    c. the soil has few decomposers.
*   d. the soil is poor in organic nutrients and erosion rates accelerate when trees are removed.
    e. the soil is poor in organic nutrients, erosion rates accelerate when trees are removed, and the soil has few decomposers.

E 56. Which biome is characterized by plants whose leaves drop off in the wintertime?
    a. coniferous forest
    b. tundra
*   c. temperate deciduous forest
    d. tropical rain forest
    e. all of these

M 57. Concerning biomes where maple and beech trees are the dominant vegetation, which of the following statements is true?
    a. Winters are warm.
    b. Rainfall is low.
    c. Rate of evaporation is low.
*   d. Soil nutrient concentration is high.

CONIFEROUS FORESTS

E 58. The largest biome in North America is the
*   a. taiga (evergreen coniferous).
    b. tundra.
    c. temperate grassland.
    d. temperate deciduous forest.
    e. chaparral (shrublands).

E 59. The taiga could best be described as what type of forest?
    a. deciduous
    b. thorn
*   c. evergreen coniferous
    d. broad-leafed
    e. shrub

D 60. Which is NOT true of a mature temperate deciduous forest?
    a. Larger predators and herbivores use the forest more for shelter than for food; they tend to feed in clearings.
    b. Extensive tree roots prevent a great deal of soil erosion.
*   c. The principal producers are the bushes and low-lying grasses.
    d. The mature trees are the primary energy foundation for the entire community and play a key role in recycling nutrients.
    e. All of these are not true.

D 61. Evergreen trees are found in the
    a. tropics.
    b. temperate zones.
    c. taiga.
    d. temperate zones and taiga, only.
*   e. tropics, temperate zones, and taiga.

M 62. The biome at the top of a very high mountain at the equator would be
*   a. tundra.
    b. taiga (boreal forest).
    c. tropical rain forest.
    d. temperate deciduous forest.
    e. chaparral (shrublands).

ARCTIC AND ALPINE TUNDRA

E 63. Which biome is a treeless plain that occurs around the Arctic Circle?
    a. chaparral
    b. taiga
    c. desert
    d. grassland
*   e. tundra

M 64. Permafrost and low rainfall are characteristic of which biome?
    a. boreal forest
    b. montane coniferous forest
*   c. tundra
    d. evergreen coniferous forest

M 65. Low temperature, short growing seasons, limited rainfall, dwarf trees, and herbaceous plants characterize the
*   a. tundra.
    b. taiga.
    c. temperate deciduous forest.
    d. grassland.
    e. tropical montane forests.

E 66. The word *permafrost* is associated with which biome?
*   a. tundra
    b. taiga
    c. temperate deciduous forest
    d. grassland
    e. montane forest

D 67. Arctic and alpine tundras are alike in all but which of the following ways?
    a. low moisture
*   b. permafrost
    c. minimal plant life
    d. cold temperatures
    e. nutrient-poor soils

E 68. If you were to travel to the equator and then to the top of Mount Kilimanjaro, the changes in vegetation you would observe would mimic the changes you would experience if you traveled
   *   a. from the equator toward the poles.
        b. from the poles toward the equator.
        c. from wet to dry areas.
        d. from east to west.

E 69. If you were in Central Africa and you decided to climb Mount Kilimanjaro, which biome would you expect to find at the top?
        a. tropical rain forest
        b. taiga
   *   c. tundra
        d. grassland

FRESHWATER PROVINCES

M 70. The greatest diversity of organisms in lake ecosystems is found in what zone?
        a. profundal
        b. limnetic
        c. thermocline
   *   d. littoral

E 71. Freshwater lakes will turn over in the
        a. fall.
        b. winter.
        c. spring.
        d. summer.
   *   e. both fall and spring.

M 72. In a lake, the open sunlit water with its suspended phytoplankton is referred to as which zone?
        a. epipelagic
   *   b. limnetic
        c. littoral
        d. profundal
        e. benthic

M 73. The profundal zone is characterized by
        a. plankton.
        b. algae.
        c. plants and animals.
   *   d. decomposers.
        e. all of these

M 74. Thorough mixing of oxygen and nutrients within a lake occurs in
        a. winter and summer.
        b. winter and spring.
        c. spring and summer.
   *   d. spring and autumn.
        e. summer and autumn.

E 75. The upper and lower levels of a lake are separated by the
        a. limnetic zone.
   *   b. thermocline.
        c. littoral zone.
        d. lentic zone.
        e. eutrophic zone.

E 76. A lake in which minerals are scarce is
        a. profundal.
   *   b. oligotrophic.
        c. eutrophic.
        d. benthic.
        e. pelagic.

M 77. Oligotrophic lakes are characterized by all but which of the following?
        a. deep water
        b. steep banks
        c. abundant oxygen
        d. low nutrients
   *   e. high production of fish

D 78. Which of the following is mismatched?
   *   a. oligotrophic lake—high productivity
        b. cool water—high gas content
        c. eutrophic lake—pollution
        d. eutrophic lake—succession
        e. eutrophic lake—oxygen depletion

M 79. Eutrophication refers to which change in a lake?
        a. decrease in depth
   *   b. increase in dissolved nitrogen and phosphorus
        c. increase in species diversity
        d. decrease in nutrient concentrations

E 80. Riffles, pools, and runs are words used to describe
        a. estuaries.
        b. sandy shores.
        c. coral reefs.
   *   d. streams.
        e. lake ecosystems.

M 81. Which of the following would be expected to have the LEAST effect on the materials suspended in the waters of a stream?
        a. agricultural wastes
        b. microorganisms
   *   c. vertebrate animals
        d. trees along the banks
        e. rocks and sand in streambed

THE OCEAN PROVINCES

M 82. Because thermal stratification is _____ prevalent in tropical oceans, they exhibit _____ productivity when compared to oceans in temperate regions.
        a. more; higher
   *   b. more; lower
        c. less; higher
        d. less; lower

D 83. The Galápagos Rift is a geothermal ecosystem 2,500 meters beneath the ocean's surface that has which of the following as its primary producers?
        a. blue-green algae
        b. protistans
        c. nitrogen-fixing organisms
   *   d. chemosynthetic organisms
        e. vascular plants

M 84. Which of the following factors would be likely to be limiting in the open ocean?
* a. nutrients
b. temperature
c. oxygen
d. light
e. wind

M 85. The ocean zone that exhibits the greatest degree of species diversity is
a. estuary.
b. rocky intertidal.
* c. neritic.
d. continental shelf.

M 86. Which zone of the ocean is found above the continental shelf?
a. abyssal
b. benthic
c. pelagic
* d. neritic
e. oceanic

M 87. The organisms that occupy the first trophic level near hydrothermal vents are
a. detritivores.
* b. chemosynthetic bacteria.
c. decomposers.
d. photosynthetic bacteria.

WETLANDS AND THE INTERTIDAL ZONE

M 88. Estuaries often exhibit a great degree of species diversity because
a. saltwater and freshwater species are present.
b. many species of the open ocean spend a portion of their life cycles in estuarine waters.
c. there is a continued upwelling of nutrients.
* d. saltwater and freshwater species are present, plus many species of the open ocean spend a portion of their life cycles in estuarine waters.
e. saltwater and freshwater species are present, plus many species of the open ocean spend a portion of their life cycles in estuarine waters, and there is a continued upwelling of nutrients

M 89. Water draining from the land mixes with seawater carried in on tides in which of the following?
a. abyssal zone
b. rift zone
c. upwelling
* d. estuary
e. pelagic zone

M 90. Differences in which factor determine the distribution of producer organisms in marine ecosystems?
a. the intensity of incoming solar radiation
b. the salinity of surface waters
c. the availability of nutrients
* d. all of these

D 91. Which are nursery grounds for shrimp and many marine forms?
a. photic zones
b. benthic zones
* c. estuaries
d. pelagic zone
e. limnetic areas

E 92. The region where freshwater and saltwater mix is the
a. neritic zone.
* b. estuary.
c. lotic zone.
d. littoral region.
e. pelagic zone.

EL NINO AND THE BIOSPHERE

D 93. Upwelling
* a. increases productivity by bringing nutrient-rich cool water to the surface of the ocean.
b. occurs in freshwater lakes when the thermocline is destroyed by changing temperatures.
c. refers to the accumulation of pollution in certain estuaries.
d. occurs when warm ocean currents approach the edge of continents.
e. generates the major climatic changes in the Pacific Ocean known as El Niño.

Matching Questions

D **94.** Matching. Choose the one most appropriate answer for each.

1. ___ benthic province
2. ___ biome
3. ___ cold deserts
4. ___ hydrothermal ecosystem
5. ___ estuary
6. ___ savanna
7. ___ shortgrass prairie
8. ___ taiga
9. ___ tallgrass prairie
10. ___ deciduous forest
11. ___ littoral zone
12. ___ tropical rain forest
13. ___ tundra
14. ___ upwellings
15. ___ warm deserts

   A. northern coniferous forest
   B. strong vertical currents
   C. Steinbeck and Michener lamented their disruption
   D. mosaics of tall, coarse grasses, shrubs, and low trees, even humid forests; high rainfall
   E. commonly called the intertidal zone
   F. buffalo, Indians, and future fields of corn and wheat
   G. includes sediments and rocks on ocean bottom
   H. sagebrush communities of the western United States; frost and arid conditions
   I. stratified communities with vines, orchids, and monkeys
   J. Galápagos Rift with its bacteria, tubeworms, and mollusks
   K. large temperature fluctuations, prickly pear cacti, ocotillo
   L. dwarf willows, mosses, lichens, caribou, and lemmings
   M. *Spartina*, eelgrass, and diatoms
   N. a large region characterized by its large array of dominant primary producers
   O. Southern Appalachian mountains; moderate rain, cold snowy winters; deer kept in check by hunters

Answers:

1. G	2. N	3. H	4. J
5. M	6. D	7. C	8. A
9. F	10. O	11. E	12. I
13. L	14. B	15. K	

Classification Questions

Answer questions 95–99 in reference to the five biomes listed below:

   a. tundra
   b. grassland
   c. desert
   d. taiga (boreal forest)
   e. savanna

M **95.** A plant community composed primarily of shrubby trees widely spaced and surrounded by grasses is this biome.

M **96.** A community composed of herbaceous plants, no trees, a very short growing season, and relatively few animal species is likely to be this biome.

E **97.** This biome is characterized by variable daily temperatures and plants that are highly resistant to desiccation.

M **98.** This biome has the richest soils.

E **99.** Conifers are most likely to be found in this biome.

Answers: 95. e   96. a   97. c
            98. b   99. d

Answer questions 100–104 in reference to the five biomes listed below:

   a. tundra
   b. chaparral
   c. desert
   d. taiga (coniferous forest)
   e. deciduous forest

M **100.** In this biome you could find a black spruce.

E **101.** In this biome you are most likely to find sagebrush.

M **102.** In this biome you would expect to find a lemming.

D **103.** This biome would be most likely to have a black oak.

M **104.** This biome is most likely to have a population of moose.

Answers: 100. d   101. b   102. a
            103. e   104. d

Selecting the Exception

D **105.** Four of the five answers below are related by inclusion in the same type of biome. Select the exception.
   a. shortgrass prairie
   b. monsoon grassland
   c. savanna
   * d. chaparral
   e. tallgrass prairie

M 106. Four of the five answers listed below are characteristics of the tropical rain forest. Select the exception.
    a. slash and burn
    b. great diversity
    c. highly stratified
    d. lack of nutrients
*   e. large herds of herbivores

E 107. Four of the five answers listed below are related by a common biome. Select the exception.
    a. no trees
    b. permafrost
    c. short growing seasons
*   d. found in the rain shadows
    e. may be found above Arctic Circle or at top of mountains

D 108. Four of the five answers listed below are related by a similar habitat. Select the exception.
    a. neritic zone
*   b. littoral zone
    c. benthic zone
    d. pelagic zone
    e. abyssal zone

CHAPTER 50
PERSPECTIVE ON HUMANS AND THE BIOSPHERE

Multiple-Choice Questions

M   1.   Human populations began to increase dramatically about 10,000 years ago due to
*   a.   more intensive agriculture.
     b.   advances in medicine.
     c.   the Industrial Revolution.
     d.   the use of fossil fuels.
     e.   all of these

M   2.   The critical environmental problems of today can ultimately be traced to
*   a.   the demands of a rapidly increasing human population.
     b.   the greenhouse effect.
     c.   air pollution.
     d.   lack of water.
     e.   the erosion of tillable soil.

E   3.   The most effective way to reduce pollution in the world today would be through
     a.   awareness due to education.
     b.   passage of appropriate laws governing pollution.
*   c.   reduction in the size of the human population.
     d.   exhaustion of all fossil fuels.
     e.   development of appropriate landfills.

AIR POLLUTION—PRIME EXAMPLES

E   4.   Air pollution
     a.   reduces visibility.
     b.   corrodes buildings.
     c.   causes various human diseases.
     d.   damages plants.
*   e.   all of these

E   5.   Air pollution may cause
     a.   lung cancer.
     b.   emphysema.
     c.   bronchitis.
     d.   burning eyes.
*   e.   all of these

M   6.   Carbon dioxide is a pollutant because it
     a.   is absorbed by the ocean and converted into insoluble carbonates.
     b.   is liberated when fossil fuel is burned.
     c.   is a waste product of respiration.
*   d.   cannot be recycled at a rate equal to its present production.

M   7.   In the United States, how many metric tons of pollutants are discharged into the atmosphere each day?
     a.   1,000
     b.   100,000
*   c.   700,000
     d.   5 million
     e.   15 to 30 million

E   8.   Transportation-produced smog causes air to turn
     a.   gray.
     b.   black.
*   c.   brown.
     d.   red.
     e.   blue.

M   9.   A thermal inversion refers to
     a.   an abnormal occurrence not predicted by meteorologists.
     b.   an Indian summer.
     c.   an unusually quick change in weather patterns.
     d.   the process of cool air drainage at night.
*   e.   a layer of cool air trapped underneath a warm-air blanket.

D   10.   A thermal inversion
     a.   occurs when rising air is blocked from rising further.
     b.   is characteristic of stable air masses.
     c.   occurs when a warm front rises over a stationary cold air mass.
     d.   occurs only at night.
*   e.   occurs when rising air is blocked from rising further and is characteristic of stable air masses.

E   11.   When fossil fuel burning gives off particulates and sulfur oxides, we have
     a.   photochemical smog.
*   b.   industrial smog.
     c.   a thermal inversion.
     d.   both a and c
     e.   all of these

E   12.   Industrial smog causes air to turn
*   a.   gray.
     b.   black.
     c.   brown.
     d.   red.
     e.   blue.

M   13.   Which city has brown fog?
     a.   London
*   b.   Los Angeles
     c.   Chicago
     d.   New York
     e.   Pittsburgh

M 14. When fossil fuel burning gives off particulates and sulfur oxides, what results?
   a. photochemical smog
 * b. industrial smog
   c. a thermal inversion
   d. both a and c, but not b
   e. all of these

M 15. Which of the following factors is NOT characteristic of a city primarily plagued by industrial smog?
   a. high concentration of sulfur oxides
   b. dependence on fossil fuel for manufacturing
   c. cold, wet winters
 * d. high concentration of nitrogen oxides

M 16. Which of the following factors is NOT characteristic of a city primarily plagued by photochemical smog?
 * a. high concentration of sulfur oxides
   b. high concentration of nitrogen oxides
   c. significant amounts of PANs
   d. large numbers of internal combustion engines

M 17. In brown air fog, which substance combines with nitrogen dioxide in the sunlight to form photochemical smog?
   a. carbon monoxide
   b. water vapor
 * c. hydrocarbons
   d. sulfuric acid
   e. all of these

D 18. What results when nitrogen dioxide and hydrocarbons react in the presence of sunlight?
 * a. photochemical smog
   b. industrial smog
   c. a thermal inversion
   d. both a and c
   e. all of these

M 19. Which of the following acids is a severe air pollutant?
   a. carbonic acid
 * b. nitric acid
   c. hydrofluoric acid
   d. hydrochloric acid
   e. boric acid

M 20. Acid rain occurs when
   a. carbon dioxide combines with water in the atmosphere.
   b. phosphorus-rich water in lakes evaporates to form phosphoric acid.
 * c. sulfur released in burning fossil fuels combines with water in the atmosphere.
   d. excess hydrogen is released into the atmosphere where ozone is formed.

E 21. Acid rain
   a. attacks nylons.
   b. attacks marble statues.
   c. causes toxic metals to become motile in the ecosystem.
   d. can be reduced in the local area by tall smokestacks.
 * e. all of these

M 22. Acid rain
   a. increases the mobility of toxic heavy metals.
   b. is the major reason for the production of sterile lakes around the world.
   c. is rainwater with a pH above 7.
   d. is primarily the result of industrial pollution.
 * e. All but choice "is rainwater with a pH above 7" are correct.

M 23. All but which of the following substances contribute to wet acid deposition?
 * a. ozone
   b. waste products from the burning of coal
   c. nitrogen fertilizers
   d. waste products from the burning of gasoline

M 24. Acid rain is NOT a serious problem in some areas because of the presence of which substance in the soil?
   a. granite
 * b. carbonate
   c. clay
   d. sand

M 25. The unequal distribution of acid rain over the United States is closely correlated with
   a. per capita energy use.
   b. fertilizer use.
 * c. combustion of fossil fuels.
   d. average summer temperatures.

M 26. The region of the United States most affected by acid rain is the
   a. Northwest.
   b. Southwest.
 * c. Northeast.
   d. Southeast.

M 27. The two chemical elements associated with acid deposition are
   a. nitrogen and oxygen.
   b. sulfur and oxygen.
 * c. nitrogen and sulfur.
   d. carbon and oxygen.
   e. nitrogen and carbon.

OZONE THINNING—GLOBAL LEGACY OF AIR POLLUTION

M 28. Chlorofluorocarbons (CFCs) are pollutants because
 * a. biogeochemical mechanisms for their removal have not yet appeared in the biosphere.
   b. they combine with water to form hydrochloric and hydrofluoric acids.
   c. they are found in smog.
   d. they are photochemical oxidants.

M 29. The atmosphere above which region is known to have a hole in the ozone layer?
 * a. Antarctica
   b. eastern North America
   c. northern Europe
   d. the western Pacific

M 30. All but which of the following factors appear to be correlated with a decrease in atmospheric ozone?
   a. suppression of the immune system
   b. decreased rates of photosynthesis
   c. increased incidence of skin cancers
 * d. decreased levels of atmospheric carbon dioxide

M 31. Uses of chlorofluorocarbons include all but which of the following?
 * a. gasoline additives
   b. aerosol propellants
   c. refrigeration coolants
   d. plastic packaging

D 32. At the present time, there are alternatives to the use of CFCs (chlorofluorocarbons) in all the applications listed below except
   a. drink and hamburger containers.
   b. propellants in spray cans.
   c. solvents.
 * d. refrigerators.

WHERE TO PUT SOLID WASTES? WHERE TO PRODUCE FOOD?

E 33. About how many beverage containers sold in the United States each year are nonreturnable cans and bottles, many of which are discarded in public places?
   a. 25 million
   b. 25 billion
   c. 50 million
 * d. 50 billion
   e. 100 million

E 34. What percentage of urban wastes are paper products?
   a. 10
   b. 20
 * c. 50
   d. 75
   e. more than 90

E 35. About how many trees are used to print the United States' Sunday newspapers?
   a. 20,000
   b. 100,000
   c. 200,000
 * d. 500,000
   e. nearly 1,000,000

E 36. Landfills should contain
   a. all garbage.
   b. nonbiodegradable wastes.
 * c. nonrecycled solid wastes.
   d. glass and metallic debris.
   e. organic litter.

M 37. Approximately 50 percent of the billions of tons of solid wastes produced in the United States is
   a. glass.
 * b. paper.
   c. aluminum.
   d. plastic.

E 38. Which substance cannot be recycled after being extracted from wastes in a recovery system?
   a. plastic
   b. metals
   c. glass
 * d. residue
   e. none of these

D 39. More consumers might recycle their solid wastes if
   a. the technology were available to do so.
 * b. it were more convenient.
   c. there were mandatory laws.
   d. it cost more to do it.

M 40. Of the earth's land, what is the maximum percentage now being used for agriculture?
   a. 10
 * b. 21
   c. 35
   d. 50
   e. 75

M 41. The new high-yield crops require which of the following that cannot be supplied by subsistence agriculture?
   a. irrigation
   b. pesticides
   c. fertilizers
   d. fossil fuel energy
 * e. all of these

M 42. For a given crop yield, modern agricultural practices require how many times more energy and mineral resources than is required by subsistence agricultural practices?
   a. 0.01
   b. 0.25
   c. 4
   d. 25
 * e. 100

D 43. Subsistence agriculture does not utilize
   a. human labor.
   b. sunlight.
   c. available soil.
 * d. synthetic fertilizers.
   e. water.

M 44. Approximately what percentage of the earth's land is not usable, or even potentially usable, for agriculture?
   a. 25
 * b. 50
   c. 15
   d. 75
   e. 0; all is potentially usable

DEFORESTATION—AN ASSAULT ON FINITE RESOURCES

M 45. Tropical plants or their products have provided humans with all but which of the following?
   a. medicines
* b. grain
   c. spices
   d. fuel

M 46. Deforestation results in
   a. increased air temperatures.
   b. decreased soil fertility.
   c. altered rainfall patterns.
   d. increased air temperatures and decreased soil fertility.
* e. increased air temperatures, decreased soil fertility, and altered rainfall patterns.

M 47. At present rates of clearing and degradation, the disappearance of the tropical rain forest biome will be complete by the year
* a. 2035.
   b. 2100.
   c. 2150.
   d. 2200.

D 48. The soils in the tropical rain forest are nutrient-poor because
   a. they are located near the equator.
   b. the trees remove most of the good things.
* c. decomposition of organic matter is very rapid.
   d. leaching occurs even before tree cutting.
   e. of shifting cultivation.

WHO TRADES GRASSLANDS FOR DESERTS?

M 49. The primary cause of desertification in the world today is
   a. increased salinity resulting from irrigation practices.
* b. overgrazing of marginal lands.
   c. clearing and degradation of tropical forests.
   d. herbicide and fertilizer runoff.

A GLOBAL WATER CRISIS

M 50. For every million liters of water in the world, only about _____ liters are in a form that can be used for human consumption or agriculture.
* a. 6
   b. 60
   c. 600
   d. 6,000

D 51. Of all the water on the earth's surface, most of it is NOT fit for human consumption because it contains
   a. microbial pollutants.
* b. salt.
   c. heavy metals.
   d. pesticides.
   e. CFCs.

M 52. Large-scale agriculture accounts for about what percent of freshwater use?
   a. 5
   b. 10
   c. 35
   d. 50
* e. 65

M 53. Which of the following is NOT a result or effect of irrigation?
   a. increased food production
   b. waterlogging of soil
   c. raised water tables
* d. alteration of soil type

M 54. Which of the following elements released in compound form can cause conditions that lead to an exhaustion of oxygen from aquatic ecosystems?
* a. phosphorus
   b. sulfur
   c. calcium
   d. zinc

M 55. Which of the following elements released from sewage would be most likely to cause conditions that lead to an exhaustion of oxygen from an aquatic ecosystem?
* a. nitrogen
   b. sulfur
   c. calcium
   d. potassium

E 56. Primary treatment of sewage involves
* a. filtration and sedimentation, which physically treat water.
   b. the biological degradation of the organic material.
   c. the most expensive sewage-treatment process.
   d. the chemical treatment of the water to neutralize its effects.
   e. chlorination or ultrasonic vibration, removal of nitrogen from ammonia, and precipitation of phosphate compounds.

M 57. After secondary sewage treatment, the water may contain all but which of the following?
   a. viruses
   b. oxygen-demanding wastes
   c. nitrates and phosphates
* d. large suspended solids
   e. pesticides and industrial chemicals

M 58. Which of the following processes is NOT generally considered a component of tertiary wastewater treatment?
* a. microbial action
   b. precipitation of suspended solids
   c. reverse osmosis
   d. absorption of dissolved organic compounds

M 59. Primary treatment of wastewater does NOT involve using which of the following?
   a. sedimentation tanks
* b. aeration with pure oxygen
   c. mechanical screens
   d. chemicals such as aluminum sulfate

D   60. Which of the following is a reliable indicator of water quality?
        a. color
        b. scent
        c. viscosity (resistance to flow)
        d. location
    *   e. none of these

D   61. Of the following, which would probably be the safest source of drinking water?
        a. municipal water supply
        b. clear mountain stream
    *   c. deep well
        d. shallow well
        e. rainwater

A QUESTION OF ENERGY INPUTS

M   62. The most harmful element in coal that causes serious pollution problems is
        a. nitrogen.
        b. silver.
        c. carbon.
    *   d. sulfur.
        e. chlorine.

E   63. Fossil fuels
        a. are renewable natural resources.
    *   b. will be commercially depleted within the next 100 years.
        c. can be utilized without any environmental degradation.
        d. are essentially pure carbon deposits.

E   64. Carbon dioxide in the atmosphere
        a. is destroying the ozone layer.
    *   b. has dramatically increased in the last few decades.
        c. is one of the prime reasons for acid rain.
        d. is a waste gas produced by respiration and has no biological use.

M   65. As the earth warms from the greenhouse effect, which transformation of biomes could most likely occur?
        a. taiga to tropical rain forest
        b. temperate deciduous forest to taiga
        c. tundra to temperate deciduous forest
    *   d. tundra to taiga

M   66. Problems associated with the extraction or use of coal as a large-scale source of energy include all but which of the following?
        a. production of sulfur oxides
        b. stripmining in fragile semiarid environments
    *   c. limited reserves
        d. amplification of the general warming trend of the earth

M   67. Which of the following is the most reliable source of energy for the next few hundred or thousands of years?
        a. oil
        b. coal
    *   c. sun
        d. natural gas
        e. nuclear

M   68. The wastes from a nuclear power reactor must be contained for how many years before they are safe?
        a. 25
        b. 250
    *   c. 250,000
        d. 1 million
        e. 250 million

M   69. Which of the following statements about nuclear power plants is true?
    *   a. Their net energy production is relatively low.
        b. Their waste products lead to the production of acid rain.
        c. Their waste products are not radioactive.
        d. Their net energy production is relatively low; and Their waste products lead to the production of acid rain.
        e. Their net energy production is relatively low; Their waste products lead to the production of acid rain; and Their waste products are not radioactive.

ALTERNATIVE SOURCES OF ENERGY

E   70. What is the main drawback to the use of wind energy?
        a. It is too costly.
    *   b. Winds don't blow on a regular schedule.
        c. The technology is not yet available.
        d. Windmills are unsightly.
        e. The energy is not as good as that produced by other means.

M   71. To produce power from fusion,
        a. breeder reactors must convert uranium to plutonium.
        b. hydrogen and oxygen are combined to yield water.
    *   c. hydrogen atoms are joined to form helium.
        d. breeder reactors must convert uranium to plutonium, plus hydrogen and oxygen are combined to yield water.
        e. breeder reactors must convert uranium to plutonium, plus hydrogen atoms are joined to form helium.

M   72. Which of the following accurately describes the concept of solar-hydrogen energy?
        a. Hydrogen gas is trapped by solar cells.
        b. Solar energy is used to fuse hydrogen atoms into helium atoms.
        c. Electricity is produced by the splitting of hydrogen atoms using sunlight power.
    *   d. Sunlight produces electricity which is used to produce hydrogen fuel.
        e. Solar power is tapped for use in hydrogen-breeder reactors.

Matching Questions

D   **73.** Matching. Choose the one most appropriate answer for each.

1. ___ breeder reactor
2. ___ dry acid depositions
3. ___ fossil fuels
4. ___ salination
5. ___ fusion power
6. ___ chlorofluorocarbons
7. ___ meltdown
8. ___ shifting cultivation
9. ___ primary treatment
10. ___ PANS
11. ___ reverse osmosis
12. ___ thermal inversion
13. ___ secondary treatment

A. a process that is part of tertiary wastewater treatment

B. could happen in a conventional nuclear fission reactor

C. coal, oil, gas

D. photochemical smog component, like tear gas

E. dense air trapped beneath a layer of warm air

F. its reactions resemble those occurring in the sun

G. depends on microbial action

H. slash and burn

I. forms sludge from coarse, suspended solids

J. generates plutonium, the most toxic substance known

K. can cause depletion of ozone

L. tiny particles that attack marble and cause crop damage

M. salt deposition that results from irrigating arid-zone soils

Answers:
1. J	2. L	3. C	4. M
5. F	6. K	7. B	8. H
9. I	10. D	11. A	12. E
13. G			

Selecting the Exception

E   **74.** Four of the five answers listed below are particulate wastes. Select the exception.
   a. smoke
   b. soot
   c. asbestos
   d. dust
  * e. ozone

E   **75.** Four of the five answers listed below are nonrenewable resources. Select the exception.
  * a. biomass
   b. coal
   c. natural gas
   d. oil
   e. nuclear

M   **76.** Four of the five answers listed below are effects of acid rain. Select the exception.
   a. attacks marble, metals, mortar, nylons
  * b. causes air inversion and pollution events
   c. makes toxic heavy metals more mobile
   d. has different effects in different watersheds
   e. produces sterile lakes

M   **77.** Four of the five answers listed below are human efforts to improve the carrying capacity of the earth for humans. Select the exception.
  * a. desertification
   b. recycling
   c. green revolution
   d. irrigation
   e. conservation